INTRODUCTION TO
ELECTROMAGNETIC
FIELDS AND WAVES

A SERIES OF
BOOKS IN PHYSICS

Editors: HENRY M. FOLEY AND
MALVIN A. RUDERMAN

INTRODUCTION TO ELECTROMAGNETIC FIELDS AND WAVES

Dale R. Corson CORNELL UNIVERSITY

Paul Lorrain UNIVERSITY OF MONTREAL

W. H. FREEMAN AND COMPANY

SAN FRANCISCO AND LONDON

PREFACE

This introduction to electromagnetic theory is intended for students having a good background in elementary electricity and in differential and integral calculus. It should also be useful for scientists and engineers who wish to review the basic concepts and methods of the subject. It has been taught for many years by the authors both at Cornell University and at the University of Montreal at the advanced undergraduate level.

To reduce the mathematical requirements, we have included discussions of various topics in mathematics which are essential to a proper understanding of the text. For example, the first chapter deals with vector analysis in Cartesian and in other coordinate systems. There is also an appendix on the technique which involves replacing $\cos \omega t$ by $\exp(j\omega t)$ for dealing with periodic phenomena, and another on wave propagation. The solution of partial differential equations by the separation of variables and the solution of the Legendre differential equation are discussed in Chapter 4. The mathematical level may be adjusted to a considerable extent either by delaying or omitting various sections, as indicated in footnotes.

Our aim has been to give the student a good grasp of the basic concepts and methods. This meant covering fewer subjects more thoroughly. For example, we have dealt with the solution of Laplace's equation in rectangular and spherical coordinates, but not in cylindrical coordinates. For the same reason, the discussion of electromagnetic waves in the second half of the book is concerned with only three types of media: dielectrics, good conductors, and low-pressure ionized gases.

The discussion has been kept as systematic and as thorough as possible, and hazy "physical" arguments have been avoided. We have also stressed the internal logic of the subject, and we have clearly stated all assumptions. This approach should accelerate the learning process and help the student gain self-confidence. In most cases we have illustrated the theory by means of examples which are accompanied by figures showing the main characteristics of the fields.

v

The illustrations have all been designed and executed with exceptional care, in the hope that they would give the student a much better grasp of the subject than would the usual blackboard-type sketch. Wherever possible, the illustrations are *quantitative*, and three-dimensional objects or phenomena are represented as such. In particular, fields such as those shown in Figures 4-9 and 13-10 are quantitative.

Short summaries are provided at the end of each chapter to give a general view of the subject matter, and, throughout the book, new results are tied in with previously acquired results so as to consolidate, as well as to extend, the reader's knowledge.

The problems form an essential part of the book. Many are designed to help the student extend the theory expounded in the text. They should be done with care.

A few words are in order concerning the units and the notation used in this book. As to the units, we have used exclusively the rationalized m.k.s., or meter-kilogram-second system. A table is provided in Appendix C for converting these units into the various c.g.s. systems. The notation used is that suggested by the Commission on Symbols, Units, and Nomenclature of the International Union of Pure and Applied Physics, with the following three exceptions. We have used the term "dielectric coefficient" and the symbol K_e, instead of the relative permittivity ϵ/ϵ_0. We have also used K_m instead of μ/μ_0, but have called it the *relative* permeability, as suggested by the Commission. Thus ϵ has been replaced by $K_e\epsilon_0$ and μ by $K_m\mu_0$, which has the advantage of stressing the effects of the properties of the medium. In the latter part of the book, however, from Chapter 10 on, this consideration is pedagogically less important and we have used ϵ and μ so as to simplify the notation. Finally, we have used the operators ∇, $\nabla\cdot$, and $\nabla\times$ instead of grad, div, and curl, respectively. The ∇ notation is pedagogically much preferable to the other for Cartesian coordinates. For example, a student recognizes immediately that $\nabla\cdot\nabla V = \nabla^2 V$ and that $\nabla\cdot\nabla\times\mathbf{A} = 0$ (the two top rows of the determinant are identical), whereas div grad V and div curl $\mathbf{A}$ seem quite meaningless. The student is made to realize clearly that the operator ∇ can be defined only in Cartesian coordinates.

The exponential function for periodic phenomena can be chosen to be either exp $(j\omega t)$ or exp $(-j\omega t)$, since the real part of both of these functions is cos ωt. We have chosen the positive exponent. This, we believe, is essential at this level; otherwise, in circuit theory, an impedance Z becomes equal to $R - jX$ instead of the conventional $R + jX$.

We have also used extensively the radian length $\lambda = \lambda/2\pi$ instead of the wave length λ. This considerably simplifies the calculations. The situation here is similar to that with respect to the frequency f. In both cases, the quantity which has an intuitively obvious meaning, namely, frequency and wave length, is *not* the one which enters into the calculations, but rather $2\pi f = \omega$ and $\lambda/2\pi = \lambda$.

The book starts with Coulomb's law and ends with the electromagnetic field of a moving charge. As indicated below, there are many possible ways of utilizing only part of this material. The first chapter deals with vector analysis in Cartesian, orthogonal curvilinear, cylindrical, and spherical coordinates. The following three chapters then cover electrostatic fields, first in a vacuum, and then in dielectrics. These are investigated at length from the "molecular" point of view. Chapters 5 and 6 deal, respectively, with the magnetic fields associated with constant and with variable currents. The first is based on the force between two current-carrying circuits, whereas the second is based on the Lorentz force on a charged particle moving in a magnetic field.

Chapter 7 contains a discussion of magnetic materials which parallels to a certain extent that of Chapter 3 on dielectrics. At this point, all four of Maxwell's equations have been found, and Chapter 8 is devoted to a short discussion of these equations, as well as to some new material which follows directly from them.

Chapters 9 to 14 are all based on the Maxwell equations. The first subject discussed is the propagation of plane electromagnetic waves, in a vacuum, and then in dielectrics, in good conductors, and in low-pressure ionized gases. Chapter 11 then discusses at length the phenomena of reflection and refraction at the interface between two dielectrics and between a dielectric and a good conductor. The reflection in a low-pressure ionized gas such as the ionosphere is also discussed at some length. This chapter should make the student thoroughly familiar with the use of Maxwell's equations. The next chapter is concerned with guided waves. It covers some general considerations and includes a discussion of two relatively simple cases, that of the coaxial line and that of the *TE* wave in a rectangular wave guide.

Finally, the last two chapters deal with the radiation of electromagnetic fields. They are based entirely on the electromagnetic potentials V and $\mathbf{A}$, which, in turn, follow from Maxwell's equations. Chapter 13 covers some general considerations and then discusses electric and magnetic dipole and quadrupole radiation. Chapter 14 contains a simplified discussion of the fields of moving charges using only elementary methods. This chapter should provide a useful background for a course in relativity.

Many will be of the opinion that the book contains more material than can be discussed thoroughly in the time available in class. There are, however, many ways in which parts of the book may be omitted without losing continuity. For example, a relatively elementary course could be limited to the first eight chapters leading up to and including a discussion of Maxwell's equations. Or, for a more advanced course, the first seven chapters could either be omitted or reviewed rapidly by making use of the summaries provided at the end of each one. Chapters 3 and 7, on the molecular approach to dielectrics and magnetic materials, could be omitted if necessary. This would limit the discussion to the macroscopic theory and the Maxwellian point of view. It would not be advisable, however, to omit Chapter 3 and not Chapter 7, since the latter rests rather heavily on Chapter 3. Chapter 11, "Reflection and Refraction," could be treated briefly; it is not essential to Chapter 12, "Guided Waves." Chapter 12 is instructive both because of the insight it provides into electromagnetic wave propagation and because of its engineering implications, but none of its results are required for the following chapters. Chapter 13, "Radiation of Electromagnetic Waves," is of course fundamental, but it should not be studied without having a thorough grasp of Chapters 8 and 9. Chapter 13 is necessary for a proper understanding of Chapter 14, "Electromagnetic Field of a Moving Charge."

It is a pleasure indeed to acknowledge the help of the many persons who cooperated in producing this book. We are indebted to Mr. Gilles Cliche, who was responsible for the numerical calculations required for the many quantitative figures. The $K\lambda$ surface (Figure 13-10) was drawn at his suggestion. Mr. Gaétan Marchand also took part in the calculations and helped in the preparation of the manuscript. All the illustrations were designed and partly executed by Mr. Paul Carrière. The cooperation of Miss Evanell Towne in putting them in their final form was much appreciated. The typing was ably done by Miss Huguette Boileau, Mrs. Judith Barnes, Mrs. Marjorie Kinsman, Mrs. Thérèse Fournier, and Mrs. Yolande LeCavalier. Last but not least, we are indebted to the many students, both at Cornell University and at the University of Montreal, who provided the main incentive and many stimulating discussions.

June 1962   DALE R. CORSON

                                                               PAUL LORRAIN

CONTENTS

CHAPTER 1

Vectors

We shall discuss electric and magnetic phenomena in terms of the *fields* of electric charges and currents. For example, the force between two electric charges will be considered as being due to an interaction between one of the charges and the field of the other.

It is therefore essential that the student acquire at the very outset a thorough understanding of the mathematical methods required to deal with fields. This is the purpose of the present chapter on Vectors. It is important to note that the concept of field and the mathematics of vectors are essential not only to electromagnetic theory but also to most of present-day physics. We shall assume that the student is not familiar with vectors and that a thorough discussion is required.

Mathematically, a field is a function which describes a physical quantity at all points in space. In *scalar fields* this physical quantity is completely specified by a single number for each point. Temperature, density, and electrostatic potential are examples of scalar quantities which can vary from one point to another in space. For *vector fields* both a number and a direction are required. Wind velocity, gravitational force, and electric field intensity are examples of such vector quantities.

Vector quantities will be indicated by **boldface** type; lightface type will indicate either a scalar quantity or the magnitude of a vector quantity.

We shall follow the usual custom of using a *right-hand coordinate system* as in Figure 1-1: the positive z direction is the direction of advance of a right-hand screw rotated in the sense that turns the positive x-axis into the positive y-axis through a 90 degree angle.

1.1. Vector Algebra

A vector can be specified by its *components* along any three mutually perpendicular axes. In the Cartesian coordinate system of Figure 1-1, for example, the vector **A** has components A_x, A_y, and A_z.

1

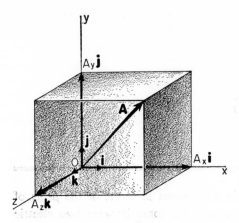

Figure 1-1

A vector **A** *and the three vectors* $A_x\mathbf{i}$,
$A_y\mathbf{j}$, $A_z\mathbf{k}$, *which, when placed end-to-
end, are equivalent to* **A**.

The vector can be uniquely expressed in terms of its components through the
use of *unit vectors* **i**, **j**, and **k**, which are defined as vectors of unit magnitude in
the positive *x*, *y*, and *z* directions, respectively:

$$\mathbf{A} = \mathbf{i}A_x + \mathbf{j}A_y + \mathbf{k}A_z. \tag{1-1}$$

The vector **A** is the sum of three vectors of magnitude A_x, A_y, and A_z, parallel
to the *x*-axis, *y*-axis, and *z*-axis, respectively. It is clear that the magnitude of **A**
is given by

$$A = (A_x^2 + A_y^2 + A_z^2)^{1/2}. \tag{1-2}$$

The sum of two vectors is equal to the sum of their components:

$$\mathbf{A} + \mathbf{B} = \mathbf{i}(A_x + B_x) + \mathbf{j}(A_y + B_y) + \mathbf{k}(A_z + B_z). \tag{1-3}$$

Subtraction is simply addition with one of the vectors changed in sign:

$$\mathbf{A} - \mathbf{B} = \mathbf{A} + (-\mathbf{B}) = \mathbf{i}(A_x - B_x) + \mathbf{j}(A_y - B_y) + \mathbf{k}(A_z - B_z). \tag{1-4}$$

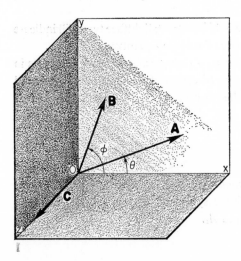

Figure 1-2

Two vectors **A** *and* **B** *in the xy-plane.
The vector* **C** *is their vector product*
A × **B**.

There are two types of multiplication: the scalar, or dot product; and the vector, or cross product. The *scalar*, or *dot product*, is the scalar quantity obtained on multiplying the magnitude of the first vector by the magnitude of the second and by the cosine of the angle between the two vectors. In Figure 1-2, for example,

$$\mathbf{A} \cdot \mathbf{B} = AB \cos (\phi - \theta). \tag{1-5}$$

It follows from this definition that the usual commutative and distributive rules of ordinary arithmetic multiplication hold:

$$\mathbf{A} \cdot \mathbf{B} = \mathbf{B} \cdot \mathbf{A}, \tag{1-6}$$

and

$$\mathbf{A} \cdot (\mathbf{B} + \mathbf{C}) = \mathbf{A} \cdot \mathbf{B} + \mathbf{A} \cdot \mathbf{C}. \tag{1-7}$$

A simple physical example of the scalar product is the work W done by a force $\mathbf{F}$ acting through a displacement $\mathbf{s}$: $W = \mathbf{F} \cdot \mathbf{s}$.

From the definition of the scalar product it follows that

$$\mathbf{i} \cdot \mathbf{i} = 1, \quad \mathbf{j} \cdot \mathbf{j} = 1, \quad \mathbf{k} \cdot \mathbf{k} = 1, \tag{1-8}$$

$$\mathbf{j} \cdot \mathbf{k} = 0, \quad \mathbf{k} \cdot \mathbf{i} = 0, \quad \mathbf{i} \cdot \mathbf{j} = 0. \tag{1-9}$$

Then

$$\mathbf{A} \cdot \mathbf{B} = (\mathbf{i}A_x + \mathbf{j}A_y + \mathbf{k}A_z) \cdot (\mathbf{i}B_x + \mathbf{j}B_y + \mathbf{k}B_z), \tag{1-10}$$
$$= A_x B_x + A_y B_y + A_z B_z. \tag{1-11}$$

We shall use this result frequently.

For two vectors in a plane, as in Figure 1-2, it is easy to see that $\mathbf{A} \cdot \mathbf{B} = A_x B_x + A_y B_y$, since

$$\mathbf{A} \cdot \mathbf{B} = AB \cos (\phi - \theta) = AB \cos \phi \cos \theta + AB \sin \phi \sin \theta \tag{1-12}$$

$$= A_x B_x + A_y B_y. \tag{1-13}$$

The *vector product*, or *cross product*, of two vectors is a vector whose direction is perpendicular to the plane containing the two initial vectors and whose magnitude is the product of the magnitudes of those vectors and the sine of the angle between them. We indicate the vector product thus:

$$\mathbf{A} \times \mathbf{B} = \mathbf{C}, \tag{1-14}$$

where the magnitude of $\mathbf{C}$ is given by

$$C = AB \sin (\phi - \theta), \tag{1-15}$$

with ϕ and θ defined as in Figure 1-2. The direction of $\mathbf{C}$ is given by the right-hand screw rule: it is the direction of advance of a right-hand screw whose axis, held perpendicular to the plane of $\mathbf{A}$ and $\mathbf{B}$, is rotated in the sense that rotates the first-named vector ($\mathbf{A}$) into the second-named ($\mathbf{B}$) through the smaller angle.

The commutative rule is *not* followed for the vector product, since, from Eq. *1-15*,

$$\mathbf{A} \times \mathbf{B} = -(\mathbf{B} \times \mathbf{A}). \tag{1-16}$$

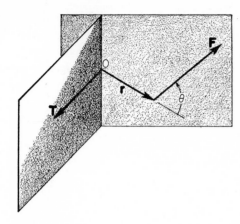

Figure 1-3

*An example of vector multiplication. The torque **T** of the force **F** about the point O is given by **r** × **F**. This vector has a magnitude of rF sin θ and is oriented as shown.*

The distributive rule, however, is followed:

$$\mathbf{A} \times (\mathbf{B} + \mathbf{C}) = (\mathbf{A} \times \mathbf{B}) + (\mathbf{A} \times \mathbf{C}). \tag{1-17}$$

This will be shown in Problem 1-8.

A good physical example of the cross product is the torque **T** produced by a force **F** acting with a moment arm **r** about a point O, as in Figure 1-3, where **T** = **r** × **F**. A second example is the area of a parallelogram, as in Figure 1-4, where the area **S** = **A** × **B**. The area is thus represented by a vector perpendicular to the surface.

From the definition of the vector product it follows that

$$\mathbf{i} \times \mathbf{i} = 0, \quad \mathbf{j} \times \mathbf{j} = 0, \quad \mathbf{k} \times \mathbf{k} = 0, \tag{1-18}$$

$$\mathbf{i} \times \mathbf{j} = \mathbf{k}, \quad \mathbf{j} \times \mathbf{k} = \mathbf{i}, \quad \mathbf{k} \times \mathbf{i} = \mathbf{j}, \quad \mathbf{j} \times \mathbf{i} = -\mathbf{k}, \quad \text{and so on.} \tag{1-19}$$

Writing out the vector product of **A** and **B** in terms of the components gives

$$\mathbf{A} \times \mathbf{B} = (\mathbf{i}A_x + \mathbf{j}A_y + \mathbf{k}A_z) \times (\mathbf{i}B_x + \mathbf{j}B_y + \mathbf{k}B_z), \tag{1-20}$$

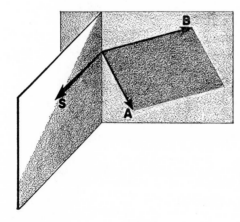

Figure 1-4

*Another example of vector multiplication. The area of the parallelogram is **A** × **B** = **S**. The vector **S** is normal to the parallelogram.*

$$\mathbf{A} \times \mathbf{B} = \mathbf{i}(A_y B_z - A_z B_y) + \mathbf{j}(A_z B_x - A_x B_z) + \mathbf{k}(A_x B_y - A_y B_x), \quad (1\text{-}21)$$

$$= \begin{vmatrix} \mathbf{i} & \mathbf{j} & \mathbf{k} \\ A_x & A_y & A_z \\ B_x & B_y & B_z \end{vmatrix}. \quad (1\text{-}22)$$

Just as for the scalar product, we can arrive at the vector product for the vectors **A** and **B** of Figure 1-2 by expanding $\sin(\phi - \theta)$ and noting that the product vector is in the negative z direction.

Many other multiplication operations could be defined. The scalar and the vector product operations as defined here are unique, however, in that they are useful in describing real physical quantities.

1.2. The Time Derivative

We shall often be concerned with the rates of change of scalar and vector quantities with both time and space coordinates, and thus with the time and space derivatives.

The time derivative of a vector quantity is straightforward. In a time Δt, a vector **A**, as in Figure 1-5, may change by $\Delta\mathbf{A}$, which in general represents a change both in magnitude and in direction. Since $\Delta\mathbf{A}$ has components ΔA_x, ΔA_y, and ΔA_z, it may be written as

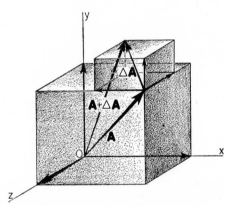

$$\Delta\mathbf{A} = \mathbf{i}\,\Delta A_x + \mathbf{j}\,\Delta A_y + \mathbf{k}\,\Delta A_z. \quad (1\text{-}23)$$

On dividing $\Delta\mathbf{A}$ by Δt and taking the limit in the usual way, we arrive at the definition of $d\mathbf{A}/dt$:

Figure 1-5. *A vector* **A** *and an increment* $\Delta\mathbf{A}$. *The components of* **A** *and of* $\Delta\mathbf{A}$ *are shown.*

$$\frac{d\mathbf{A}}{dt} = \lim_{\Delta t \to 0} \frac{\mathbf{A}(t + \Delta t) - \mathbf{A}(t)}{\Delta t}, \quad (1\text{-}24)$$

$$= \lim_{\Delta t \to 0} \frac{\mathbf{i}(A_x + \Delta A_x) + \mathbf{j}(A_y + \Delta A_y) + \mathbf{k}(A_z + \Delta A_z) - (\mathbf{i}A_x + \mathbf{j}A_y + \mathbf{k}A_z)}{\Delta t}, \quad (1\text{-}25)$$

$$= \lim_{\Delta t \to 0} \frac{\mathbf{i}\,\Delta A_x + \mathbf{j}\,\Delta A_y + \mathbf{k}\,\Delta A_z}{\Delta t}, \quad (1\text{-}26)$$

$$= \mathbf{i}\frac{dA_x}{dt} + \mathbf{j}\frac{dA_y}{dt} + \mathbf{k}\frac{dA_z}{dt}. \quad (1\text{-}27)$$

The time derivative of a vector is thus equal to the vector sum of the time derivatives of its components.

1.3. The Gradient

We shall be interested in one particular function of the space derivatives of a scalar quantity—the gradient—and in two particular functions of the space derivatives of a vector quantity—the divergence and the curl. Again, many other such functions could be defined, but those studied here are unique in that they are useful to describe certain physical quantities.

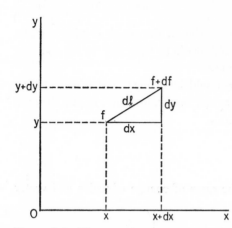

Figure 1-6. *The quantity f, a function of position, changes from f to f + df over the distance dl.*

Let us consider a scalar quantity which is a continuous and differentiable function of the coordinates and has the value f at a certain point, as in Figure 1-6. We wish to know how f changes over the distance $\mathbf{dl}$ measured from that point. We know that

$$df = \frac{\partial f}{\partial x}\, dx + \frac{\partial f}{\partial y}\, dy. \tag{1-28}$$

Now df is the scalar product of two vectors **A** and **B** as follows:

$$\mathbf{A} = \mathbf{i}\frac{\partial f}{\partial x} + \mathbf{j}\frac{\partial f}{\partial y}, \tag{1-29}$$

$$\mathbf{B} = \mathbf{i}\, dx + \mathbf{j}\, dy = \mathbf{dl}. \tag{1-30}$$

The vector **A**, whose components are the rates of change of f with distance along the coordinate axes, is called the *gradient* of the scalar quantity f. Gradient is commonly abbreviated as *grad*, and the operation on the scalar f defined by the term gradient is indicated by the symbol ∇, called *del*. Thus

$$\mathbf{A} = \operatorname{grad} f = \nabla f. \tag{1-31}$$

For the general 3-dimensional case, the operator ∇ is defined as

$$\nabla = \left(\mathbf{i}\frac{\partial}{\partial x} + \mathbf{j}\frac{\partial}{\partial y} + \mathbf{k}\frac{\partial}{\partial z} \right). \tag{1-32}$$

The partial differentiations indicated are to be carried out on whatever scalar quantity stands to the right of the ∇ symbol.

The magnitude of df can thus be written as

$$df = \nabla f \cdot \mathbf{dl} = |\nabla f|\,|\mathbf{dl}|\cos\theta, \tag{1-33}$$

where θ is the angle between the vectors ∇f and $\mathbf{dl}$.

We can now ask what direction we should choose for **dl** in order that *df* should be a maximum. The answer is: the direction in which cos θ = 1 or θ = 0, that is, the direction of ∇*f*. The gradient of *f* is thus a vector whose magnitude and direction are those of the maximum space rate of change of *f*.

In terms of its components, the magnitude of ∇*f* is

$$|\nabla f| = \left[\left(\frac{\partial f}{\partial x}\right)^2 + \left(\frac{\partial f}{\partial y}\right)^2 + \left(\frac{\partial f}{\partial z}\right)^2\right]^{1/2}. \qquad (1\text{-}34)$$

To summarize, the gradient of a scalar function is a vector with the following properties.

(1) Its components at any point are the rates of change of the function along the directions of the coordinate axes at that point.

(2) Its magnitude at the point is the maximum rate of change of the function with distance.

(3) Its direction is that of the maximum rate of change of the function, and it points toward *larger* values of the function.

The gradient is thus a vector point-function derived from a scalar point-function.

As an example of the gradient, consider Figure 1-7, in which the function *E* is the elevation above sea level in the vicinity of a hill. The function *E* is a function of the *x*- and *y*-coordinates measured on a horizontal plane, and points of constant elevation may be joined together by contour lines. The gradient of

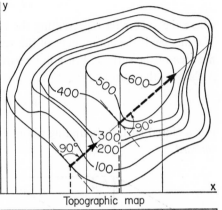

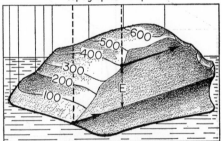

Figure 1-7. *Topographic map of a hill. The quantity E is the elevation. The gradient of E is the slope of the hill at the point considered, and it points toward an increase in elevation:* ∇E = **i**(∂E/∂x) + **j**(∂E/∂y). *The arrows show* ∇E *for two different points.*

the elevation then has the following properties: (a) it is perpendicular to the contour lines; (b) its magnitude is equal to the maximum rate of change of elevation with displacement measured in a horizontal plane; and (c) it points toward an increase in elevation.

The gradient vector, as defined above, is important in physics because certain forces—the electrostatic forces, for example—can be expressed as the negative gradient of a scalar potential function. This property of the electrostatic field will be developed in Chapter 2.

1.4. Flux and Divergence. The Divergence Theorem

It is often necessary to calculate the flux of a vector through a surface. The flux $d\Phi$ of a vector $\mathbf{A}$ through an infinitesimal surface $\mathbf{da}$ is given by

$$d\Phi = \mathbf{A}\cdot\mathbf{da}, \qquad (1\text{-}35)$$

where the vector $\mathbf{da}$ representing the element of area is normal to its surface. The flux $d\Phi$ is the component of the vector normal to the surface multiplied by the area of the surface. For a finite surface, we find the total flux by integrating $\mathbf{A}\cdot\mathbf{da}$ over the entire surface:

$$\Phi = \int_S \mathbf{A}\cdot\mathbf{da}. \qquad (1\text{-}36)$$

For a closed surface bounding a finite volume, the vector $\mathbf{da}$ is taken to point *outward*.

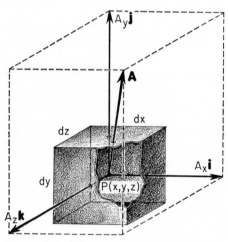

Figure 1-8. *Element of volume dx dy dz around a point P, where the vector* $\mathbf{A}$ *has the value illustrated by the arrow.*

As an example of flux, let us consider fluid flow. Here we can define a vector $\rho\mathbf{v}$, ρ being the fluid density and $\mathbf{v}$ the fluid velocity at a point. The flux through any closed surface is the net rate at which fluid leaves the volume bounded by the surface.

The outward flux of a vector through a closed surface can be calculated either by using Eq. *1-36* or as follows. Let us consider an infinitesimal volume $dx\,dy\,dz$ and a vector $\mathbf{A}$, as in Figure 1-8, whose components A_x, A_y, and A_z are functions of the coordinates x, y, and z. We consider an infinitesimal volume and allow only first-order variations of the vector $\mathbf{A}$.

The value of A_x at the center of the right-hand face can be taken to be the average value over the entire face. Through the right-hand face of the volume element, the outgoing flux is thus

$$d\Phi_R = \left(A_x + \frac{\partial A_x}{\partial x}\frac{dx}{2}\right)dy\,dz, \qquad (1\text{-}37)$$

since the normal component of **A** at the right-hand face is the x-component of **A** at that face.

At the left-hand face, we have

$$d\Phi_L = -\left(A_x - \frac{\partial A_x}{\partial x}\frac{dx}{2}\right) dy\, dz. \qquad (1\text{-}38)$$

The minus sign before the parenthesis is necessary here because, $\mathbf{i}A_x$ being inward at this face and **da** being outward, the cosine of the angle between the two vectors is -1. The net outward flux through the two faces is then

$$d\Phi_R + d\Phi_L = \frac{\partial A_x}{\partial x}\, dx\, dy\, dz = \frac{\partial A_x}{\partial x}\, d\tau, \qquad (1\text{-}39)$$

where $d\tau$ is the volume of the infinitesimal element.

If we calculate the net flux through the other pairs of faces in the same manner, we find the total outward flux for the element of volume $d\tau$ to be

$$d\Phi_{\text{tot}} = \left(\frac{\partial A_x}{\partial x} + \frac{\partial A_y}{\partial y} + \frac{\partial A_z}{\partial z}\right) d\tau. \qquad (1\text{-}40)$$

Suppose now that we have two adjoining infinitesimal volume elements and that we add the flux through the bounding surface of the first volume to the flux through the bounding surface of the second. At the common face, the fluxes are equal in magnitude but opposite in sign, hence they cancel. The result, then, of adding the flux from the first volume to that from the second is the flux through the bounding surface of the combined volumes. The total outward flux is thus

$$d\Phi_{1+2} = \left(\frac{\partial A_x}{\partial x} + \frac{\partial A_y}{\partial y} + \frac{\partial A_z}{\partial z}\right)_1 d\tau_1 + \left(\frac{\partial A_x}{\partial x} + \frac{\partial A_y}{\partial y} + \frac{\partial A_z}{\partial z}\right)_2 d\tau_2. \quad (1\text{-}41)$$

To extend this calculation to a finite volume, we must sum the individual fluxes for each of the infinitesimal volume elements in the finite volume. The total outward flux is then given by

$$\Phi_{\text{tot}} = \int_\tau \left(\frac{\partial A_x}{\partial x} + \frac{\partial A_y}{\partial y} + \frac{\partial A_z}{\partial z}\right) d\tau. \qquad (1\text{-}42)$$

At any given point in the volume, the quantity

$$\left(\frac{\partial A_x}{\partial x} + \frac{\partial A_y}{\partial y} + \frac{\partial A_z}{\partial z}\right) \qquad (1\text{-}43)$$

is thus the *outgoing* flux per unit volume. We call this the *divergence* of the vector **A** at the point.

The divergence of a vector point-function is thus a scalar point-function.

According to the rules for the scalar product, we can write the divergence of **A** as

$$\text{div } \mathbf{A} = \boldsymbol{\nabla} \cdot \mathbf{A} \qquad (1\text{-}44)$$

where the operator $\boldsymbol{\nabla}$ is defined in Eq. *1-32*.

The operator $\nabla\cdot$ has physical meaning, not by itself, but only as it operates on a function standing to the right of it. The symbol ∇ is not a vector, of course, but it is convenient to use the notation of the scalar product to indicate the operation that is to be carried out.

In Eq. *1-42* the total outward flux is also equal to the surface integral of the normal outward component of **A**, thus

$$\int_S \mathbf{A}\cdot\mathbf{da} = \int_\tau \left(\frac{\partial A_x}{\partial x} + \frac{\partial A_y}{\partial y} + \frac{\partial A_z}{\partial z}\right) d\tau, \qquad (1\text{-}45)$$

$$= \int_\tau \nabla\cdot\mathbf{A}\, d\tau. \qquad (1\text{-}46)$$

This is the *divergence theorem*. Note that the left-hand side involves only the values of **A** on the surface S, whereas the right-hand side involves the values of **A** throughout the volume τ enclosed by S. This important theorem will be used frequently.

If the volume τ is allowed to shrink sufficiently, such that $\nabla\cdot\mathbf{A}$ does not vary appreciably over it, then

$$\int_S \mathbf{A}\cdot\mathbf{da} = (\nabla\cdot\mathbf{A})\,\tau, \qquad (1\text{-}47)$$

and the divergence can therefore be defined as

$$\nabla\cdot\mathbf{A} = \lim_{\tau\to 0}\frac{1}{\tau}\int_S \mathbf{A}\cdot\mathbf{da}. \qquad (1\text{-}48)$$

As we have seen, the divergence is the *outward* flux per unit volume as the volume approaches zero.

1.5. Line Integral and Curl

The integrals

$$\int_a^b \mathbf{A}\cdot\mathbf{dl}, \quad \int_a^b \mathbf{A}\times\mathbf{dl}, \quad \text{and} \quad \int_a^b f\,\mathbf{dl},$$

evaluated from the point a to the point b on some specified curve, are examples of line integrals.

In the first one, each element of length **dl** on the curve is multiplied by the local value of **A**, according to the rule for the scalar product. These products are then summed to obtain the value of the integral. Of all the possible line integrals which can be defined, this particular one is especially important in physics. For example, the work W done by a force **F** acting from a to b along some specified path is given by

$$W = \int_a^b \mathbf{F}\cdot\mathbf{dl}, \qquad (1\text{-}49)$$

where both **F** and **dl** must of course be known functions of the coordinates if the integral is to be evaluated analytically.

As an example, let us calculate the work done by a force **F**, which is in the y direction and has a magnitude proportional to y, as it moves around the circular path from a to b in Figure 1-9. Since $F = kr \sin \theta$, $dl = r \, d\theta$, and the scalar product introduces a $\cos \theta$ factor,

$$W = \int_a^b \mathbf{F} \cdot \mathbf{dl} \tag{1-50}$$

$$= \int_0^{\pi/2} (kr \sin \theta)(r \, d\theta) \cos \theta,$$

$$= \frac{kr^2}{2}. \tag{1-51}$$

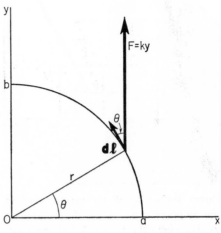

Figure 1-9. *The force* **F** *is proportional to* y, *and its point of application moves from* a *to* b. *The work done is given by the line integral of* **F·dl** *over the curve shown.*

A vector field in which the line integral of **A·dl** around any closed path is zero is said to be *conservative*. Thus, for a conservative field,

$$\oint \mathbf{A} \cdot \mathbf{dl} = 0. \tag{1-52}$$

The circle on the integral sign indicates that the path is closed.

For an infinitesimal element of path **dl** in the xy-plane, and from the definition of the scalar product,

$$\mathbf{A} \cdot \mathbf{dl} = A_x \, dx + A_y \, dy. \tag{1-53}$$

Thus for any closed path in the xy-plane,

$$\oint \mathbf{A} \cdot \mathbf{dl} = \oint A_x \, dx + \oint A_y \, dy. \tag{1-54}$$

For the infinitesimal path of Figure 1-10, there are two contributions to the first integral on the right-hand side of Eq. *1-54*, one at y, and one at $y + dy$:

$$\oint A_x \, dx = \left(A_x - \frac{\partial A_x}{\partial y} \frac{dy}{2} \right) dx - \left(A_x + \frac{\partial A_x}{\partial y} \frac{dy}{2} \right) dx. \tag{1-55}$$

The second term here is negative because the path element at $y + dy$ is in the negative x direction. Therefore

$$\oint A_x \, dx = - \frac{\partial A_x}{\partial y} \, dy \, dx. \tag{1-56}$$

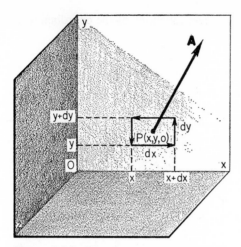

Figure 1-10. *Closed, rectangular path in the xy-plane centered on the point P(x, y, O), where the vector **A** has the value illustrated by the heavy arrow. The integration around the path is performed in the direction of the light arrows.*

Similarly,

$$\oint A_y \, dy = \frac{\partial A_y}{\partial x} \, dx \, dy, \qquad (1\text{-}57)$$

and

$$\oint \mathbf{A} \cdot \mathbf{dl} = \left(\frac{\partial A_y}{\partial x} - \frac{\partial A_x}{\partial y} \right) dx \, dy \qquad (1\text{-}58)$$

for the infinitesimal path of Figure 1-10.

If we set

$$g_3 = \frac{\partial A_y}{\partial x} - \frac{\partial A_x}{\partial y}, \qquad (1\text{-}59)$$

then

$$\mathbf{A} \cdot \mathbf{dl} = g_3 \, da, \qquad (1\text{-}60)$$

where $da = dx \, dy$ is the area enclosed on the xy-plane by the infinitesimal path. Note here that Eq. 1-60 is correct only if the line integral is evaluated in the positive direction in the xy-plane, that is, in the direction in which one would have to turn a right-hand screw to make it advance in the positive direction along the z-axis.

What if the small path is arbitrarily oriented in space? Then $\oint \mathbf{A} \cdot \mathbf{dl}$ is the sum of the projections of **da** on the coordinate planes, multiplied by functions similar to g_3 in Eq. 1-60:

$$\oint \mathbf{A} \cdot \mathbf{dl} = da \cos (n, x) g_1 + da \cos (n, y) g_2 + da \cos (n, z) g_3, \qquad (1\text{-}61)$$

$$= da_x g_1 + da_y g_2 + da_z g_3, \qquad (1\text{-}62)$$

where, for example, $\cos (n, x)$ is the cosine of the angle between the vector **da**, which is normal to the surface and the x-axis, and where

$$g_1 = \frac{\partial A_z}{\partial y} - \frac{\partial A_y}{\partial z}, \qquad (1\text{-}63)$$

$$g_2 = \frac{\partial A_x}{\partial z} - \frac{\partial A_z}{\partial x}, \qquad (1\text{-}64)$$

$$g_3 = \frac{\partial A_y}{\partial x} - \frac{\partial A_x}{\partial y}. \qquad (1\text{-}65)$$

But the right-hand side of Eq. *1-62* is just the scalar product of **da** with a vector **C** such that $C_x = g_1$, $C_y = g_2$, and $C_z = g_3$. The vector **C** is called the *curl*
of **A**:

$$\text{curl } \mathbf{A} = \mathbf{i}\left(\frac{\partial A_z}{\partial y} - \frac{\partial A_y}{\partial z}\right)$$

$$+ \mathbf{j}\left(\frac{\partial A_x}{\partial z} - \frac{\partial A_z}{\partial x}\right) \tag{1-66}$$

$$+ \mathbf{k}\left(\frac{\partial A_y}{\partial x} - \frac{\partial A_x}{\partial y}\right),$$

$$= \begin{vmatrix} \mathbf{i} & \mathbf{j} & \mathbf{k} \\ \dfrac{\partial}{\partial x} & \dfrac{\partial}{\partial y} & \dfrac{\partial}{\partial z} \\ A_x & A_y & A_z \end{vmatrix} = \nabla \times \mathbf{A}, \tag{1-67}$$

where the vector product and the operator ∇ are defined as in Eqs. *1-22* and *1-32*.

The operator ∇ has thus been used for the gradient of a scalar point-function
and for the divergence and curl of a vector point-function. In all three uses, ∇ is
defined by a single expression, and we obtain the gradient, the divergence, or
the curl by performing the appropriate multiplication. This relatively simple
situation is peculiar to the Cartesian coordinate system. As we shall see later
on, other coordinate systems do not permit a single definition for the operator ∇
but lead to more complicated expressions for the gradient, the divergence, and
the curl.

Let us now return to Eq. *1-62*. For the small path of integration,

$$\oint \mathbf{A} \cdot \mathbf{dl} = (\nabla \times \mathbf{A}) \cdot \mathbf{da}. \tag{1-68}$$

Here again, we must be careful about the direction in which the line integral
is evaluated. This direction of integration must be related to the direction in
which the right side of Eq. *1-68* is positive by the right-hand screw rule. The
above equation provides us with a definition of the curl that is the same for all
coordinate systems:

$$(\nabla \times \mathbf{A})_n = \lim_{S \to 0} \frac{1}{S} \oint \mathbf{A} \cdot \mathbf{dl}. \tag{1-69}$$

The component of the curl of a vector normal to a surface S is equal to the line
integral of the vector around the boundary of the surface divided by the area
of the surface for the limiting case in which the surface area approaches zero.

As an example, let us calculate the curl of the gravitational force. We shall
first calculate the components in a formal manner in rectangular coordinates
and then calculate these same components starting with the above definition of
the curl.

For the first method we can choose a coordinate system in which the z-axis is perpendicular to the earth's surface and pointing upward, and in which the x- and y-axes are parallel to the earth's surface. Then the gravitational force $\mathbf{F}$ on a mass m has the following components:

$$F_x = F_y = 0, \quad F_z = -mg. \tag{1-70}$$

Then

$$\nabla \times \mathbf{F} = \begin{vmatrix} \mathbf{i} & \mathbf{j} & \mathbf{k} \\ \dfrac{\partial}{\partial x} & \dfrac{\partial}{\partial y} & \dfrac{\partial}{\partial z} \\ 0 & 0 & -mg \end{vmatrix} = 0. \tag{1-71}$$

If we proceed in the second manner, we can choose small rectangles around which to evaluate $\oint \mathbf{F} \cdot \mathbf{dl}$. To obtain the z-component of the curl, we choose a path in the xy-plane. Since $\mathbf{F}$ is perpendicular to $\mathbf{dl}$ on all parts of the path,

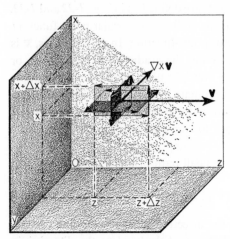

$\mathbf{F} \cdot \mathbf{dl} = 0$ around this path, and so $(\nabla \times \mathbf{F})_z = 0$. To find the y-component of the curl, we choose a path lying in the xz-plane. On the two parts of the path parallel to the z-axis there are contributions to the integral, but they are equal and opposite, thus $(\nabla \times \mathbf{F})_y = 0$. By similar arguments, $(\nabla \times \mathbf{F})_x$ is also zero.

We could, of course, have said from the beginning that the curl of the gravitational force field is zero, for we know that such a force field is conservative. It should also be obvious from Eq. 1-67 that the curl of a vector that is not a function of x, y, or z is zero.

Figure 1-11. *The velocity $\mathbf{v}$ in a viscous fluid is assumed to be in the direction of the z-axis and proportional to the distance x from the bottom. Then $\nabla \times \mathbf{v} = -c\mathbf{j}$.*

As a second example, let us consider the velocity field in a fluid stream in which the velocity $\mathbf{v}$ is proportional to the distance from the bottom of the stream. We choose the z-axis parallel to the direction of flow, and the x-axis perpendicular to the stream bottom, as in Figure 1-11. Then

$$v_x = 0, \quad v_y = 0, \quad v_z = cx. \tag{1-72}$$

We calculate the curl from Eq. 1-69. For $(\nabla \times \mathbf{v})_z$ we choose a path parallel to the yz-plane. In evaluating

$$\oint \mathbf{v} \cdot \mathbf{dl}$$

around such a path we note that the contributions are equal and opposite on the parts parallel to the z-axis, hence $(\nabla \times \mathbf{v})_x = 0$. Likewise, $(\nabla \times \mathbf{v})_z = 0$.

For the y-component we choose a path parallel to the xz-plane and evaluate the integral around it in the sense that would advance a right-hand screw in the positive y direction. On the parts of the path parallel to the x-axis, $\mathbf{v} \cdot \mathbf{dl} = 0$ since $\mathbf{v}$ and $\mathbf{dl}$ are perpendicular. On the bottom part of the path, at a distance x from the yz-plane,

$$\int \mathbf{v} \cdot \mathbf{dl} = cx\,\Delta z, \tag{1-73}$$

whereas at $(x + \Delta x)$

$$\int \mathbf{v} \cdot \mathbf{dl} = -c(x + \Delta x)\,\Delta z. \tag{1-74}$$

For the whole path,

$$\oint \mathbf{v} \cdot \mathbf{dl} = -c\,\Delta x\,\Delta z, \tag{1-75}$$

and the y-component of the curl is

$$(\nabla \times \mathbf{v})_y = \lim_{S \to 0} \frac{\oint \mathbf{v} \cdot \mathbf{dl}}{S} = \frac{-c\,\Delta x\,\Delta z}{\Delta x\,\Delta z} = -c. \tag{1-76}$$

Calculating $\nabla \times \mathbf{v}$ in a formal manner,

$$\nabla \times \mathbf{v} = \begin{vmatrix} \mathbf{i} & \mathbf{j} & \mathbf{k} \\ \dfrac{\partial}{\partial x} & \dfrac{\partial}{\partial y} & \dfrac{\partial}{\partial z} \\ 0 & 0 & cx \end{vmatrix} = -c\mathbf{j}, \tag{1-77}$$

which is the same result as above.

1.6. Stokes's Theorem

Equation *1-68* is true only for a path so small that $\nabla \times \mathbf{A}$ can be considered constant over the surface $\mathbf{da}$ bounded by the path. What if the path is large enough such that this condition is not met? The equation can be extended readily to arbitrary paths. We divide the surface—any surface bounded by the path of integration in question—into elements of area $\mathbf{da}_1$, $\mathbf{da}_2$, and so forth, as in Figure 1-12. For any one of these small areas,

$$\oint \mathbf{A} \cdot \mathbf{dl}_i = (\nabla \times \mathbf{A}) \cdot \mathbf{da}_i. \tag{1-78}$$

We add the left-hand sides of these equations for all the $\mathbf{da}$'s, and then we add all the right-hand sides. The sum of the left-hand sides is the line integral around the external boundary, since there are always two equal and opposite

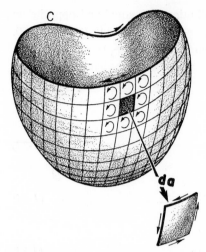

Figure 1-12. *An arbitrary surface bounded by the curve C. The sum of the line integrals around the curvilinear squares shown is equal to the line integral around C.*

contributions to the sum along every common side between adjacent **da**'s. The sum of the right sides is merely the integral of $(\nabla \times \mathbf{A}) \cdot \mathbf{da}$ over the finite surface. Thus, for an *arbitrary* path,

$$\oint \mathbf{A} \cdot \mathbf{dl} = \int_S \nabla \times \mathbf{A} \cdot \mathbf{da}. \quad (1\text{-}79)$$

This is *Stokes's theorem*. It relates a line integral to a surface integral over *any* surface of which the line integral path is a boundary.

Now under what condition is a vector field conservative? From Stokes's theorem, the line integral of $\mathbf{A} \cdot \mathbf{dl}$ around an arbitrary closed path is zero if $\nabla \times \mathbf{A} = 0$ everywhere. This condition can be met if we can write

$$\mathbf{A} = \nabla f, \quad (1\text{-}80)$$

for then

$$A_x = \frac{\partial f}{\partial x}, \quad A_y = \frac{\partial f}{\partial y}, \quad A_z = \frac{\partial f}{\partial z}, \quad (1\text{-}81)$$

and

$$(\nabla \times \mathbf{A})_x = \frac{\partial A_z}{\partial y} - \frac{\partial A_y}{\partial z} = \frac{\partial^2 f}{\partial y \, \partial z} - \frac{\partial^2 f}{\partial z \, \partial y} = 0. \quad (1\text{-}82)$$

and so on for the other components of the curl. Then $\nabla \times \mathbf{A} = 0$, and the function $\mathbf{A}$ is conservative.

We have thus shown that the vector field of $\mathbf{A}$ is conservative if $\mathbf{A}$ can be expressed as the gradient of a scalar point-function f, since the curl of a gradient is always zero:

$$\nabla \times \nabla f = 0. \quad (1\text{-}83)$$

We shall now show that the divergence of the curl is always zero. From Stokes's theorem (*1-79*),

$$\oint \mathbf{A} \cdot \mathbf{dl} = \int_S \nabla \times \mathbf{A} \cdot \mathbf{da},$$

in which $\mathbf{A}$ is any vector point-function. Remembering that Stokes's theorem holds for any surface bounded by the path of integration of the line integral, we consider two different surfaces bounded by the same path. These two surfaces enclose a region of space, and since they have a common boundary,

$$\int_{S_1} \mathbf{\nabla} \times \mathbf{A} \cdot \mathbf{da_1} = \int_{S_2} \mathbf{\nabla} \times \mathbf{A} \cdot \mathbf{da_2}. \qquad (1\text{-}84)$$

Here $\mathbf{da_1}$ and $\mathbf{da_2}$ represent vectors in directions determined by the sense in which the line integral is evaluated. If we reverse the direction of the vector $\mathbf{da_2}$ and call it $\mathbf{da_2'} = -\mathbf{da_2}$, where both $\mathbf{da_1}$ and $\mathbf{da_2'}$ point either inward or outward from the volume enclosed by the two surfaces, then

$$\int_{S_1} \mathbf{\nabla} \times \mathbf{A} \cdot \mathbf{da_1} + \int_{S_2'} \mathbf{\nabla} \times \mathbf{A} \cdot \mathbf{da_2'} = 0. \qquad (1\text{-}85)$$

This expression is just the total flux of $\mathbf{\nabla} \times \mathbf{A}$, either inward or outward, for the volume enclosed by the two surfaces. Then, from the divergence theorem,

$$\int_\tau \mathbf{\nabla} \cdot \mathbf{\nabla} \times \mathbf{A} \, d\tau = 0. \qquad (1\text{-}86)$$

Since this expression must be true for *any* two surfaces bounded by *any* arbitrary closed path in the field, it follows that, everywhere,

$$\mathbf{\nabla} \cdot \mathbf{\nabla} \times \mathbf{A} = 0. \qquad (1\text{-}87)$$

This result becomes obvious if we calculate the divergence of the curl with its components written out in rectangular coordinates.

1.7. The Laplacian

The divergence of the gradient is of great importance in electromagnetic theory, as well as in many other parts of physics. Since

$$\mathbf{\nabla}f = \mathbf{i}\frac{\partial f}{\partial x} + \mathbf{j}\frac{\partial f}{\partial y} + \mathbf{k}\frac{\partial f}{\partial z}, \qquad (1\text{-}88)$$

then

$$\mathbf{\nabla} \cdot \mathbf{\nabla}f = \mathbf{\nabla}^2 f = \frac{\partial^2 f}{\partial x^2} + \frac{\partial^2 f}{\partial y^2} + \frac{\partial^2 f}{\partial z^2}. \qquad (1\text{-}89)$$

The divergence of the gradient is the sum of the second derivatives with respect to the rectangular coordinates. The product $\mathbf{\nabla} \cdot \mathbf{\nabla}f$ is commonly abbreviated to $\mathbf{\nabla}^2 f$, and the operator $\mathbf{\nabla}^2$ is called the *Laplacian*.

We have defined the Laplacian of a scalar point-function f. It is also useful to define the Laplacian of a vector point-function $\mathbf{A}$:

$$\mathbf{\nabla}^2 \mathbf{A} = \mathbf{i} \, \mathbf{\nabla}^2 A_x + \mathbf{j} \, \mathbf{\nabla}^2 A_y + \mathbf{k} \, \mathbf{\nabla}^2 A_z. \qquad (1\text{-}90)$$

1.8. Curvilinear Coordinates*

It is frequently convenient, because of the symmetries that exist in certain fields, to use coordinate systems other than the rectangular one. Of all the other

---

* The material contained in Sections 1.8 to 1.8.6 inclusive is required only for Sections 4.6 to 4.6.3, for Section 5.12.3, and for Chapter 13.

possible coordinate systems, we shall restrict our discussion to cylindrical and spherical polar coordinates, the two most commonly used.

We could calculate the gradient, the divergence, and so on, in both cylindrical and spherical coordinates, but it is somewhat less tedious and much more general to introduce first the idea of orthogonal curvilinear coordinates. Consider the equation

$$f(x, y, z) = q, \qquad (1\text{-}91)$$

in which q is a constant. This equation determines a family of surfaces in space, each member of the family being characterized by a particular value of the parameter q. An obvious example is $x = q$, which determines the surfaces parallel to the yz-plane in Cartesian coordinates.

Consider the three equations

$$f_1(x, y, z) = q_1,$$
$$f_2(x, y, z) = q_2, \qquad (1\text{-}92)$$
$$f_3(x, y, z) = q_3,$$

which are chosen such that the three families of surfaces are mutually perpendicular, or orthogonal. A point in space can then be defined as the intersection of three of these surfaces, one of each family; the point is completely defined if we state the values of q_1, q_2, and q_3 corresponding to these three surfaces. The variables q_1, q_2, and q_3 are called the *curvilinear*

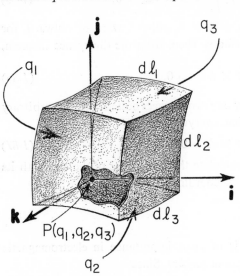

Figure 1-13. *Element of volume in curvilinear coordinates. The unit vectors* **i**, **j**, *and* **k** *are respectively normal to the* q_1, q_2, *and* q_3 *surfaces at the point* $P(q_1, q_2, q_3)$. *They are mutually perpendicular and are oriented in such a way that* **i** $\times$ **j** $=$ **k**.

coordinates of the point, as in Figure 1-13.

Let us call dl_1 an element of length perpendicular to the surface q_1. This element of length is the distance between the surfaces q_1 and $q_1 + dq_1$ in the infinitesimal region considered. The element of length dl_1 is related to dq_1 by the equation

$$dl_1 = h_1 \, dq_1, \qquad (1\text{-}93)$$

in which h_1 is, in general, a function of the coordinates q_1, q_2, and q_3. Similarly,

$$dl_2 = h_2 \, dq_2, \qquad (1\text{-}94)$$

and

$$dl_3 = h_3 \, dq_3. \qquad (1\text{-}95)$$

In the Cartesian system of coordinates, h_1, h_2, and h_3 are all unity.

The *unit vectors* **i**, **j**, and **k** are defined as being of unit length, normal respectively to the q_1, q_2, and q_3 surfaces, and oriented toward increasing values of these coordinates. They are chosen such that $\mathbf{i} \times \mathbf{j} = \mathbf{k}$.

The orientation of the three unit vectors depends, in general, on the point of space considered. Only in rectangular coordinates do they all have fixed directions.

The volume element

$$d\tau = dl_1\, dl_2\, dl_3, \tag{1-96}$$

$$= h_1 h_2 h_3 (dq_1\, dq_2\, dq_3). \tag{1-97}$$

Let us now find the q's, the h's, the elements of length, and the elements of volume for cylindrical and spherical coordinates.

1.8.1. Cylindrical Coordinates. In cylindrical coordinates, as in Figure 1-14, the position of any point P in space is specified by ρ, ϕ, and z. The coordinate ρ
is the perpendicular distance from
the z-axis; ϕ is the azimuth angle of
the plane containing P and the z-axis,
measured from the xz-plane in the
right-hand screw sense; and z is the
distance from the xy-plane. The q's
are thus ρ, ϕ, and z in this case.

At the point P there are three
mutually orthogonal directions specified by three unit vectors: **i** in the
direction of the perpendicular from
the z-axis extended through P; **j** perpendicular to the plane containing
the z-axis and P in the direction corresponding to increasing ϕ; and **k** in
the positive z direction. These unit
vectors do *not* maintain the same

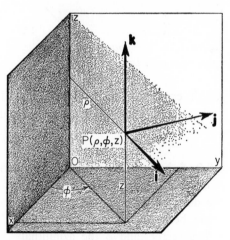

Figure 1-14. *Cylindrical coordinate system.*

directions in space as the point P moves about, but they always remain mutually orthogonal.

The vector **r**, describing the position of P is

$$\mathbf{r} = \mathbf{i}\rho + \mathbf{k}z, \tag{1-98}$$

the **j** component being zero. It will be noticed that this expression does not involve the angle ϕ. It does not therefore determine uniquely a point in space. This is due to the fact that the unit vectors shown in Figure 1-14 do not have a fixed orientation in space but are quite free to move about, the only limitation being that they must have a definite orientation with respect to the axis of the coordinate system.

Elements of length corresponding to infinitesimal changes in the coordinates of a point are important. If the coordinates ϕ and z of the point P are kept constant while ρ is allowed to increase by $d\rho$, P is displaced by an amount $\mathbf{dl} = \mathbf{i} \, d\rho$. On the other hand, if ρ and z are held constant while ϕ is allowed to increase by $d\phi$, then P is displaced by $\mathbf{dl} = \mathbf{j}\rho \, d\phi$. Finally, if ρ and ϕ are held constant while z is allowed to increase by dz, then $\mathbf{dl} = \mathbf{k} \, dz$. For arbitrary increments $d\rho$, $d\phi$, and dz,

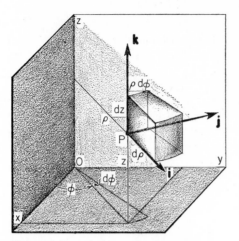

$$\mathbf{dl} = \mathbf{i} \, d\rho + \mathbf{j}\rho \, d\phi + \mathbf{k} \, dz, \quad (1\text{-}99)$$

and

$$dl = [(d\rho)^2 + (\rho \, d\phi)^2 + (dz)^2]^{1/2}. \quad (1\text{-}100)$$

Figure 1-15. *Element of volume in cylindrical coordinates.*

Figure 1-15 shows the volume element whose edges are the elements of length corresponding to infinitesimal increments in the coordinates at the point P of Figure 1-14. The infinitesimal volume is

$$d\tau = \rho \, d\rho \, d\phi \, dz. \quad (1\text{-}101)$$

1.8.2. Spherical Coordinates. In spherical coordinates, the position of a point P is specified by r, θ, and ϕ, r being the distance from the origin, θ the angle between the z-axis and the radius vector, and ϕ the azimuthal angle. At the point P the unit vectors are as shown in Figure 1-16: $\mathbf{i}$ is in the direction of the radius vector extended through P; $\mathbf{j}$ is perpendicular to the radius vector in the plane containing the z axis and the radius vector; and $\mathbf{k}$ is perpendicular to that plane. Again, these unit vectors do *not* maintain the same directions in space as the point P moves about.

The vector $\mathbf{r}$ describing the position of P is now simply $\mathbf{r} = r\mathbf{i}$, and,

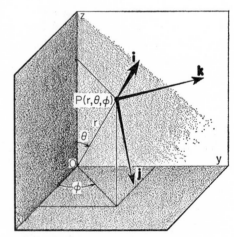

Figure 1-16. *Spherical coordinate system.*

as with cylindrical coordinates, it does *not* determine P uniquely.

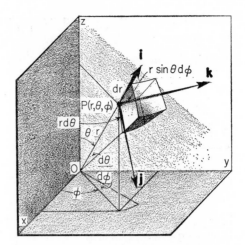

Figure 1-17

Element of volume in spherical coordinates.

The distance element **dl** corresponding to arbitrary increments of the coordinates is

$$\mathbf{dl} = \mathbf{i}\, dr + \mathbf{j}r\, d\theta + \mathbf{k}r \sin\theta\, d\phi, \tag{1-102}$$

$$dl = [(dr)^2 + r^2(d\theta)^2 + r^2 \sin^2\theta(d\phi)^2]^{1/2}. \tag{1-103}$$

The volume element at point P is shown in Figure 1-17, and

$$d\tau = r^2 \sin\theta\, dr\, d\theta\, d\phi. \tag{1-104}$$

The table below shows the correspondence of curvilinear coordinates to Cartesian, cylindrical, and spherical coordinates.

Curvilinear	Cartesian	Cylindrical	Spherical
q_1	x	ρ	r
q_2	y	ϕ	θ
q_3	z	z	ϕ
h_1	1	1	1
h_2	1	ρ	r
h_3	1	1	$r \sin\theta$

We are now in a position to find the gradient, divergence, and curl operators in curvilinear coordinates. Once these are found, it will be a simple matter to find the operators in cylindrical and spherical coordinates, for then we need only substitute the appropriate values of q_1, q_2, q_3, h_1, h_2, and h_3.

1.8.3. The Gradient Operator. To find the form of the gradient operator, we require the rate of change of a scalar function f in each of the coordinate directions:

$$\nabla f = \mathbf{i}\frac{\partial f}{\partial l_1} + \mathbf{j}\frac{\partial f}{\partial l_2} + \mathbf{k}\frac{\partial f}{\partial l_3}, \tag{1-105}$$

$$\nabla f = \mathbf{i}\,\frac{1}{h_1}\frac{\partial f}{\partial q_1} + \mathbf{j}\,\frac{1}{h_2}\frac{\partial f}{\partial q_2} + \mathbf{k}\,\frac{1}{h_3}\frac{\partial f}{\partial q_3}. \tag{1-106}$$

Substitution of the appropriate functions for the h's, and of the appropriate q's gives the gradient for any orthogonal coordinate system. In cylindrical coordinates

$$\nabla f = \mathbf{i}\,\frac{\partial f}{\partial \rho} + \mathbf{j}\,\frac{1}{\rho}\frac{\partial f}{\partial \phi} + \mathbf{k}\,\frac{\partial f}{\partial z}, \tag{1-107}$$

and in spherical coordinates

$$\nabla f = \mathbf{i}\,\frac{\partial f}{\partial r} + \mathbf{j}\,\frac{1}{r}\frac{\partial f}{\partial \theta} + \mathbf{k}\,\frac{1}{r\sin\theta}\frac{\partial f}{\partial \phi}. \tag{1-108}$$

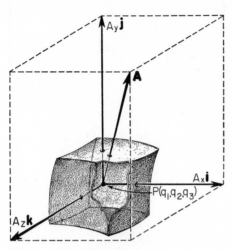

Figure 1-18. *Element of volume in curvilinear coordinates centered on the point* $P(q_1, q_2, q_3)$, *where the vector* **A** *has the value shown by the arrow.*

1.8.4. The Divergence. To find the divergence operator, we consider the volume element of Figure 1-18. The quantity A_1 is the q_1 component of the vector **A** at the center of the volume element; h_1, h_2, and h_3 are the h values at the center. Then the outward flux through the left-hand face is

$$d\Phi_L = -A_{1L}h_{2L}h_{3L}\,dq_2\,dq_3, \tag{1-109}$$

$$= -\left(A_1 - \frac{\partial A_1}{\partial q_1}\frac{dq_1}{2}\right)\left(h_2 - \frac{\partial h_2}{\partial q_1}\frac{dq_1}{2}\right)\left(h_3 - \frac{\partial h_3}{\partial q_1}\frac{dq_1}{2}\right)dq_2\,dq_3. \tag{1-110}$$

It must be remembered that h_2 and h_3 may be functions of q_1, as well as of A_1. If we neglect differentials of order higher than the third, then

$$d\Phi_L = -A_1h_2h_3\,dq_2\,dq_3 + \frac{\partial}{\partial q_1}(A_1h_2h_3)\frac{dq_1}{2}\,dq_2\,dq_3. \tag{1-111}$$

By a similar argument,

$$d\Phi_R = A_1h_2h_3\,dq_2\,dq_3 + \frac{\partial}{\partial q_1}(A_1h_2h_3)\frac{dq_1}{2}\,dq_2\,dq_3 \tag{1-112}$$

for the right-hand face. The net flux through these pairs of faces is then

$$d\Phi_{LR} = \frac{\partial}{\partial q_1}(A_1h_2h_3)\,dq_1\,dq_2\,dq_3. \tag{1-113}$$

The same calculation can be repeated for the other pairs of faces to find the net outward flux through the bounding surface. Dividing by the volume of the element then gives the divergence. Since we have considered only differentials up to the third order, we have already passed to the limit of $\tau \longrightarrow 0$, and

$$\nabla \cdot \mathbf{A} = \frac{1}{h_1 h_2 h_3} \left[\frac{\partial}{\partial q_1} (A_1 h_2 h_3) + \frac{\partial}{\partial q_2} (A_2 h_3 h_1) + \frac{\partial}{\partial q_3} (A_3 h_1 h_2) \right]. \quad (1\text{-}114)$$

Substituting the h's and q's gives the divergence in cylindrical coordinates:

$$\nabla \cdot \mathbf{A} = \frac{1}{\rho} \frac{\partial}{\partial \rho} (\rho A_\rho) + \frac{1}{\rho} \frac{\partial A_\phi}{\partial \phi} + \frac{\partial A_z}{\partial z}, \quad (1\text{-}115)$$

$$= \frac{A_\rho}{\rho} + \frac{\partial A_\rho}{\partial \rho} + \frac{1}{\rho} \frac{\partial A_\phi}{\partial \phi} + \frac{\partial A_z}{\partial z}, \quad (1\text{-}116)$$

and in spherical coordinates,

$$\nabla \cdot \mathbf{A} = \frac{1}{r^2 \sin \theta} \left[\frac{\partial}{\partial r} (r^2 \sin \theta A_r) + \frac{\partial}{\partial \theta} (r \sin \theta A_\theta) + \frac{\partial}{\partial \phi} (r A_\phi) \right], \quad (1\text{-}117)$$

$$= \frac{2}{r} A_r + \frac{\partial A_r}{\partial r} + \frac{A_\theta}{r} \cot \theta + \frac{1}{r} \frac{\partial A_\theta}{\partial \theta} + \frac{1}{r \sin \theta} \frac{\partial A_\phi}{\partial \phi}. \quad (1\text{-}118)$$

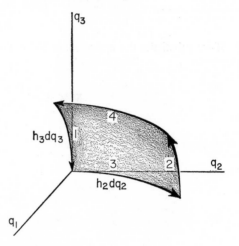

Figure 1-19

Path of integration for the component number 1 of the curl in curvilinear coordinates.

1.8.5. The Curl. From the fundamental definition given in Eq. *1-69,*

$$(\nabla \times A)_1 = \lim_{S \to 0} \frac{1}{S} \oint \mathbf{A} \cdot \mathbf{dl}, \quad (1\text{-}119)$$

where the path of integration must lie in the surface defined by $q_1 = $ constant, and where the direction of integration must be related to the direction of the unit vector **i** by the right-hand screw rule. For the paths labeled (1), (2), (3), and (4) in Figure 1-19, we have the following contributions to the line integral:

(1) $-A_3 h_3 \, dq_3,$

(2) $\left(A_3 + \frac{\partial A_3}{\partial q_2} dq_2 \right) \left(h_3 + \frac{\partial h_3}{\partial q_2} dq_2 \right) dq_3,$

(3) $+A_2 h_2 \, dq_2,$

(4) $-\left(A_2 + \frac{\partial A_2}{\partial q_3} dq_3 \right) \left(h_2 + \frac{\partial h_2}{\partial q_3} dq_3 \right) dq_2.$

The sum of these four terms (neglecting higher-order differentials because we are interested in the limit of $S \longrightarrow 0$) is equal to the right-hand side of Eq. *1-109*. Then

$$(\nabla \times \mathbf{A})_1 = \frac{1}{h_2 h_3 \, dq_2 \, dq_3} \left[\frac{\partial}{\partial q_2} (A_3 h_3) \, dq_2 \, dq_3 - \frac{\partial}{\partial q_3} (A_2 h_2) \, dq_2 \, dq_3 \right], \quad (1\text{-}120)$$

$$= \frac{1}{h_2 h_3} \left[\frac{\partial}{\partial q_2} (A_3 h_3) - \frac{\partial}{\partial q_3} (A_2 h_2) \right]. \quad (1\text{-}121)$$

Corresponding expressions for the other two components of the curl can be found either by proceeding again as above or by proper rotation of the indices. Finally,

$$\nabla \times \mathbf{A} = \frac{1}{h_1 h_2 h_3} \begin{vmatrix} \mathbf{i} h_1 & \mathbf{j} h_2 & \mathbf{k} h_3 \\ \dfrac{\partial}{\partial q_1} & \dfrac{\partial}{\partial q_2} & \dfrac{\partial}{\partial q_3} \\ h_1 A_1 & h_2 A_2 & h_3 A_3 \end{vmatrix}. \quad (1\text{-}222)$$

If we substitute the appropriate h's and q's for cylindrical coordinates, then

$$\nabla \times \mathbf{A} = \frac{1}{\rho} \begin{vmatrix} \mathbf{i} & \mathbf{j}\rho & \mathbf{k} \\ \dfrac{\partial}{\partial \rho} & \dfrac{\partial}{\partial \phi} & \dfrac{\partial}{\partial z} \\ A_\rho & \rho A_\phi & A_z \end{vmatrix}, \quad (1\text{-}123)$$

whereas for spherical coordinates

$$\nabla \times \mathbf{A} = \frac{1}{r^2 \sin \theta} \begin{vmatrix} \mathbf{i} & \mathbf{j}r & \mathbf{k}r \sin \theta \\ \dfrac{\partial}{\partial r} & \dfrac{\partial}{\partial \theta} & \dfrac{\partial}{\partial \phi} \\ A_r & r A_\theta & r A_\phi \sin \theta \end{vmatrix}. \quad (1\text{-}124)$$

1.8.6. The Laplacian.

We calculate the Laplacian in curvilinear coordinates by combining the expressions for the divergence and for the gradient:

$$\nabla^2 f = \nabla \cdot \nabla f. \quad (1\text{-}125)$$

$$= \frac{1}{h_1 h_2 h_3} \left[\frac{\partial}{\partial q_1} \left(\frac{h_2 h_3}{h_1} \frac{\partial f}{\partial q_1} \right) + \frac{\partial}{\partial q_2} \left(\frac{h_3 h_1}{h_2} \frac{\partial f}{\partial q_2} \right) + \frac{\partial}{\partial q_3} \left(\frac{h_1 h_2}{h_3} \frac{\partial f}{\partial q_3} \right) \right]. \quad (1\text{-}126)$$

For cylindrical coordinates,

$$\nabla^2 f = \frac{1}{\rho} \frac{\partial}{\partial \rho} \left(\rho \frac{\partial f}{\partial \rho} \right) + \frac{1}{\rho^2} \left(\frac{\partial^2 f}{\partial \phi^2} \right) + \frac{\partial^2 f}{\partial z^2}, \quad (1\text{-}127)$$

and for spherical coordinates

$$\nabla^2 f = \frac{1}{r^2} \frac{\partial}{\partial r} \left(r^2 \frac{\partial f}{\partial r} \right) + \frac{1}{r^2 \sin \theta} \frac{\partial}{\partial \theta} \left(\sin \theta \frac{\partial f}{\partial \theta} \right) + \frac{1}{r^2 \sin^2 \theta} \frac{\partial^2 f}{\partial \phi^2}, \quad (1\text{-}128)$$

$$= \frac{2}{r} \frac{\partial f}{\partial r} + \frac{\partial^2 f}{\partial r^2} + \frac{\cot \theta}{r^2} \frac{\partial f}{\partial \theta} + \frac{1}{r^2} \frac{\partial^2 f}{\partial \theta^2} + \frac{1}{r^2 \sin^2 \theta} \frac{\partial^2 f}{\partial \phi^2}. \quad (1\text{-}129)$$

We have already seen in Section 1.7 that the Laplacian of a vector **A** in Cartesian coordinates is itself a vector whose components are the Laplacians of A_x, A_y, and A_z. It will be shown in Problem 1-24 that

$$\nabla \times \nabla \times \mathbf{A} = \nabla(\nabla \cdot \mathbf{A}) - \nabla^2\mathbf{A} \qquad (1\text{-}130)$$

is then an identity in Cartesian coordinates. In the more general case of curvilinear coordinates, however, we define $\nabla^2\mathbf{A}$ differently: it is a vector whose components are those of $\nabla(\nabla \cdot \mathbf{A}) - \nabla \times \nabla \times \mathbf{A}$. The Laplacian operator must *not* be applied to the components of a vector, except in Cartesian coordinates.

Upon comparing the expressions for the gradient, the divergence, the curl, and the Laplacian, it will be observed that *there does not exist an expression for the operator* ∇ *in the general case of curvilinear coordinates. Only in Cartesian coordinates does* ∇ *have a meaning in itself as in Eq. 1-32*. This point was mentioned before in Section 1.5.

For a summary of Chapter 1, see Appendix B on Vector Definitions, Identities, and Theorems.

Problems

1-1. Show that the two vectors $\mathbf{A} = 9\mathbf{i} + \mathbf{j} - 6\mathbf{k}$ and $\mathbf{B} = 4\mathbf{i} - 6\mathbf{j} + 5\mathbf{k}$ are perpendicular to each other.

1-2. Find the angle between the two vectors $\mathbf{A} = 2\mathbf{i} + 3\mathbf{j} + \mathbf{k}$ and $\mathbf{B} = \mathbf{i} - 6\mathbf{j} + \mathbf{k}$.

1-3. Using the fundamental definition of the scalar product, prove that $\mathbf{A} \cdot (\mathbf{B} + \mathbf{C}) = (\mathbf{A} \cdot \mathbf{B}) + (\mathbf{A} \cdot \mathbf{C})$ if **A**, **B**, and **C** are three coplanar vectors.

1-4. If $\mathbf{r} \cdot d\mathbf{r} = 0$, show that $r = $ constant.

1-5. If **A** and **B** are the sides of a parallelogram, **C** and **D** are the diagonals, and θ is the angle between **A** and **B**, show that $(C^2 + D^2) = 2(A^2 + B^2)$ and that $(C^2 - D^2) = 4AB \cos \theta$.

1-6. Let **a** and **b** be two unit vectors lying in the xy-plane. Let α be the angle **a** makes with the x-axis, and let β the angle **b** makes with the x-axis, such that $\mathbf{a} = \mathbf{i} \cos \alpha + \mathbf{j} \sin \alpha$ and $\mathbf{b} = \mathbf{i} \cos \beta + \mathbf{j} \sin \beta$. Show that the trigonometric relations for the sine and cosine of the sum and difference of two angles follow from the interpretation of $(\mathbf{a} \cdot \mathbf{b})$ and $(\mathbf{a} \times \mathbf{b})$.

1-7. Show that $(\mathbf{A} \times \mathbf{B}) \cdot \mathbf{C}$ is the volume of a parallelepiped whose edges are **A**, **B**, and **C**, and show that $(\mathbf{A} \times \mathbf{B}) \cdot \mathbf{C} = \mathbf{A} \cdot (\mathbf{B} \times \mathbf{C})$.

1-8. Show that the distributive rule applies to the vector product (Eq. *1-17*).

1-9. Show that $\mathbf{a} \times (\mathbf{b} \times \mathbf{c}) = \mathbf{b}(\mathbf{a} \cdot \mathbf{c}) - \mathbf{c}(\mathbf{a} \cdot \mathbf{b})$.

1-10. Let **r** be the radius vector from the origin of coordinates to any point, and let **A** be a constant vector. Show that $\nabla(\mathbf{A} \cdot \mathbf{r}) = \mathbf{A}$.

1-11. Show that $\nabla \cdot \mathbf{r} = 3$. What is the flux of **r** through a spherical surface of radius r?

1-12. A circular disk rotates with angular velocity ω about its axis of symmetry, which is taken to be the z-axis. The direction of rotation is related to that of the z-axis by the right-hand screw rule. Find the velocity $\mathbf{v}$ of a point on the disk, and show that

$$\nabla \times \mathbf{v} = 2\omega\mathbf{k}.$$

If now the disk is assumed to be nonrigid, such that ω is a function of the radius r, show that $\nabla \times \mathbf{v} = 0$ if $\omega = \text{const}/r^2$.

1-13. A vector field is defined by $\mathbf{A} = f(r)\mathbf{r}$. Show that $f(r) = \text{const}/r^3$ if $\nabla \cdot \mathbf{A} = 0$. Show that $\nabla \times \mathbf{A} = 0$.

1-14. Show that

$$\nabla \cdot (f\mathbf{A}) = f\nabla \cdot \mathbf{A} + \mathbf{A} \cdot \nabla f,$$

where f is a scalar function and $\mathbf{A}$ is a vector function.

1-15. The vector $\mathbf{A} = 3x\mathbf{i} + y\mathbf{j} + 2z\mathbf{k}$, and $f = x^2 + y^2 + z^2$. Show that $\nabla \cdot f\mathbf{A}$ at the point $(2, 2, 2)$ is 120 by finding the vector $f\mathbf{A}$ and taking its divergence.

Make the same calculation by first finding the vector ∇f and using the identity of Problem 1-14 above.

If x, y, and z are measured in centimeters, what are the units of $\nabla \cdot f\mathbf{A}$?

1-16. The components of a vector $\mathbf{A}$ are

$$A_x = y\frac{\partial f}{\partial z} - z\frac{\partial f}{\partial y}, \quad A_y = z\frac{\partial f}{\partial x} - x\frac{\partial f}{\partial z}, \quad A_z = x\frac{\partial f}{\partial y} - y\frac{\partial f}{\partial x},$$

where f is a function of x, y and z. Show that

$$\mathbf{A} = \mathbf{r} \times \nabla f, \quad \mathbf{A} \cdot \mathbf{r} = 0, \quad \text{and} \quad \mathbf{A} \cdot \nabla f = 0.$$

1-17. Show that a field of force is conservative if the force exerted on a body is always directed toward a fixed center and is only a function of r. Such a field is called a central force field. Find the potential energy at a distance r from a center of attraction if the force varies as $1/r^2$. Set the potential energy equal to zero at infinity.

1-18. The azimuthal force exerted on an electron in a certain betatron is proportional to $r^{0.4}$. Find the curl of this force in cylindrical coordinates, and show that the force is nonconservative.

1-19. Show, by differentiating the appropriate expressions for $\mathbf{r}$, that the velocity $\dot{\mathbf{r}}$ is given by

$$\dot{\mathbf{r}} = \dot{\rho}\mathbf{i} + \rho\dot{\phi}\mathbf{j} + \dot{z}\mathbf{k}$$

in cylindrical coordinates and by

$$\dot{\mathbf{r}} = \dot{r}\mathbf{i} + r\dot{\theta}\mathbf{j} + r\sin\theta\,\dot{\phi}\mathbf{k}$$

in spherical coordinates.

1-20. The vector $\mathbf{A}$ is such that it is everywhere perpendicular to, and directed away from, a given straight line; that is, in cylindrical coordinates, $A_z = A_\phi = 0$. Calculate the outgoing flux for a volume element, and show that

$$\nabla \cdot \mathbf{A} = \frac{A_\rho}{\rho} + \frac{\partial A_\rho}{\partial \rho}.$$

1-21. The vector $\mathbf{r}$ is directed from $P'(x', y', z')$ to $P(x, y, z)$. If the point P is fixed and the point P' is allowed to move, show that the gradient of $(1/r)$ under these conditions is given by

$$\nabla'\left(\frac{1}{r}\right) = \frac{\mathbf{r}_1}{r^2},$$

where $\mathbf{r}_1$ is the unit vector along $\mathbf{r}$. Show that the above expression gives the maximum rate of change of $1/r$.

Show similarly that, if P' is fixed and P is allowed to move,

$$\nabla\left(\frac{1}{r}\right) = -\frac{\mathbf{r}_1}{r^2}.$$

1-22. Show that $\nabla \times f\mathbf{A} = f(\nabla \times \mathbf{A}) - \mathbf{A} \times \nabla f$, where f is a scalar function and $\mathbf{A}$ is a vector function.

1-23. Show that $\nabla \cdot (\mathbf{A} \times \mathbf{B}) = \mathbf{B} \cdot (\nabla \times \mathbf{A}) - \mathbf{A} \cdot (\nabla \times \mathbf{B})$, where $\mathbf{A}$ and $\mathbf{B}$ are any two vectors.

1-24. Show that

$$\nabla \times \nabla \times \mathbf{A} = \nabla(\nabla \cdot \mathbf{A}) - \nabla^2 \mathbf{A}$$

in Cartesian coordinates, but not in the general case of curvilinear coordinates if $\nabla^2\mathbf{A}$ is taken to be $\mathbf{i}\,\nabla^2 A_1 + \mathbf{j}\,\nabla^2 A_2 + \mathbf{k}\,\nabla^2 A_3$. Hint: You can solve this problem without having to write out the equations in full.

1-25. Show that

$$\int_\tau (\nabla \times \mathbf{A})\, d\tau = -\int_S \mathbf{A} \times d\mathbf{a},$$

where $\mathbf{A}$ is an arbitrary vector and S is the surface bounding the volume τ.

CHAPTER 2

Electrostatic Fields I

We shall assume that the student is familiar with the qualitative aspects of electric charges and their interactions. For example, there are two kinds of electrostatic charges, one called positive and another called negative. A glass rod rubbed with silk acquires a positive charge, whereas a hard rubber rod rubbed with cat's fur acquires a negative charge. If rods charged in this way are suspended on insulating threads one can show that two bodies carrying like charges repel each other, whereas two bodies carrying unlike charges attract each other. We now know that the basic positive charges are the protons in atomic nuclei and that the basic negative charges are the electrons which surround the atomic nuclei. In uncharged matter electrons and protons are present in equal numbers. Processes which separate the two types of charge, as when glass is rubbed with silk, are processes in which electrons are transferred from one body to another, leaving an electron deficiency (and therefore a net positive charge) on one, and an electron excess (and therefore a net negative charge) on the other.

2.1. Coulomb's Law

It has been found experimentally that the force between two electrostatic charges Q_a and Q_b of the type discussed above (a) acts along the line joining the two charges, (b) is proportional to the product $Q_a Q_b$, and (c) is inversely proportional to the square of the distance r separating the charges.

This is true if the dimensions of the charges are negligible compared to r. If the charges are extended the situation is more complicated in that the "distance between the charges" has no definite meaning. Moreover, the presence of Q_b can modify the charge distribution within Q_a, and inversely, giving to a complicated variation of force with distance.

We thus have Coulomb's law for point charges:

$$\mathbf{F}_{ab} = K \frac{Q_a Q_b}{r^2} \mathbf{r}_1, \qquad (2\text{-}1)$$

where $\mathbf{F}_{ab}$ is the force exerted *by Q_a on Q_b*, K is a constant of proportionality, and $\mathbf{r}_1$ is a unit vector pointing in the direction from Q_a toward Q_b, as in Figure 2-1. The force is repulsive if Q_a and Q_b are of the same sign, and is attractive if they are of different sign.

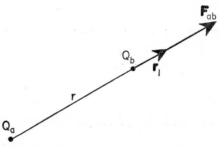

The exact verification of Coulomb's law has been carried out by a somewhat indirect experiment which measures the exactness of the inverse square dependence of the force on distance. The exponent has been found to be correct to better than one part in 10^9.*

The magnitude of the constant of proportionality K depends on the

Figure 2-1. *Charges Q_a and Q_b separated by a distance r. The force exerted on Q_b by Q_a is $\mathbf{F}_{ab}$ and is in the direction $\mathbf{r}_1$ along the line joining the two charges.*

units which are used for the measurement of force, charge, and distance. In the c.g.s. system of units, K is made unity by choosing appropriate units for these quantities. In the *rationalized m.k.s. system*, which we shall use throughout this book, the units are defined from other relationships, which we shall study later on. In these units Coulomb's law is written as

$$\mathbf{F}_{ab} = \frac{1}{4\pi\epsilon_0} \frac{Q_aQ_b}{r^2} \mathbf{r}_1, \qquad (2\text{-}2)$$

where the force $\mathbf{F}$ is measured in newtons; the charges Q_a and Q_b, in coulombs (the magnitude of which will be defined in terms of magnetic interactions in Chapter 5); and the distance r, in meters. The quantity 4π appears in explicit form so as to simplify other equations which are used much more extensively than Coulomb's law. The constant ϵ_0 is called the *permittivity of free space:*

$$\epsilon_0 = 8.85 \times 10^{-12} \text{ farad/meter.}$$

Equation 2-2 applies to a pair of point charges situated in a vacuum. It also applies in dielectrics and conductors if $\mathbf{F}_{ab}$ is taken to be the direct force between Q_a and Q_b, irrespective of the other forces arising from the displacement of charges within the medium. We shall discuss conductors later on in Section 2-6, and then dielectrics in Chapter 3.

2.2. The Electrostatic Field Intensity

We think of the interaction between the point charges Q_a and Q_b in Coulomb's law as being an interaction between Q_a and the field of Q_b, and *vice versa*. We define the *electric field intensity* $\mathbf{E}$ to be the force per unit charge exerted on a

* Plimpton and Lawton, *Phys. Rev.* **50,** 1066 (1936).

test charge in the field. Thus the electric field intensity due to the point charge Q_a is given by

$$\mathbf{E}_a = \frac{\mathbf{F}_{ab}}{Q_b} = \frac{Q_a}{4\pi\epsilon_0 r^2}\mathbf{r}_1. \tag{2-3}$$

The electric field intensity is measured in volts per meter. The electric field due to the point charge Q_a is the same whether the test charge Q_b is in the field or not, even if Q_b is large compared to Q_a.

In the case where the electric field is produced by a charge distribution which might be disturbed by the introduction of a finite test charge Q', we can define $\mathbf{E}$ to be the limiting force per unit charge as the test charge $Q' \longrightarrow 0$:

$$\mathbf{E} = \lim_{Q'\to 0}\frac{\mathbf{F}}{Q'}. \tag{2-4}$$

If the electric field is produced by more than one charge distribution, each one produces its own field, and the resultant field intensity is simply the vector sum of all the individual field intensities. This is called the *principle of super-position*.

2.3. The Electrostatic Potential

Consider a test point charge Q' which can be moved about in an electric field. The work W required to move it from a point P_1 to a point P_2 along a given path is given by the line integral

$$W = -\int_{P_1}^{P_2}\mathbf{E}Q'\cdot\mathbf{dl} \tag{2-5}$$

along the path considered. The negative sign is required here to obtain the work done *against* the field. Here again, we assume that Q' is small, such that the charge distributions are not disturbed by its presence.

If the path is closed, the total work done is

$$W = -\oint\mathbf{E}Q'\cdot\mathbf{dl}. \tag{2-6}$$

Let us evaluate this integral. To simplify matters, we shall first consider the electric field produced by a single point charge Q. Then

$$\oint\mathbf{E}Q'\cdot\mathbf{dl} = \frac{QQ'}{4\pi\epsilon_0}\oint\frac{(\mathbf{r}_1\cdot\mathbf{dl})}{r^2}. \tag{2-7}$$

Now the term under the integral on the right side is simply dr/r^2 or $-d(1/r)$. The sum of the increments of $(1/r)$ over a closed path is zero, since r has the same value at the beginning and at the end of the path. Then the line integral in Eq. 2-7 is zero, and the net work done in moving a point charge Q' around a closed path in the field of another fixed point charge Q is zero.

If the electric field is produced not by a single point charge Q but by some fixed charge distribution in space, the line integrals corresponding to each individual charge of the distribution are all zero. Thus, in general,

$$\oint \mathbf{E} \cdot \mathbf{dl} = 0. \qquad (2\text{-}8)$$

We can now show that the work done in moving a test charge from a point P_1 to a point P_2 is independent of the path. Let a and b be any two different paths leading from P_1 to P_2. Then these two paths together form a closed curve such that the work done in going from P_1 to P_2 along a, and then from P_2 back to P_1 along b is zero. Then the work done in going from P_1 to P_2 is the same along a as it is along b.

An electrostatic field is therefore conservative. Then, from Stokes's theorem (Section 1.6), at all points in space,

$$\mathbf{\nabla} \times \mathbf{E} = 0, \qquad (2\text{-}9)$$

and we can write that

$$\mathbf{E} = -\mathbf{\nabla}V, \qquad (2\text{-}10)$$

where V is a scalar point function, since $\mathbf{\nabla} \times \mathbf{\nabla}V \equiv 0$. We can thus describe the field completely by means of the function $V(x, y, z)$, which is called the *electrostatic potential*. The negative sign is required in Eq. *2-10* in order that the electric field intensity $\mathbf{E}$ can point toward a *decrease* in potential, according to the usual convention. It is important to note that V is not uniquely defined in that we can add to it any constant without affecting $\mathbf{E}$ in any way.

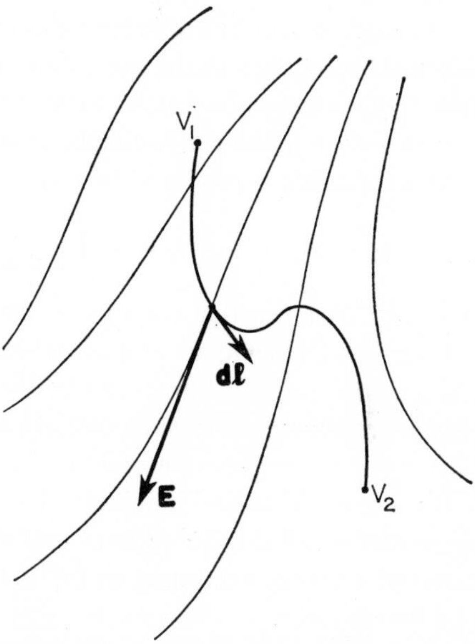

We must remember that we are dealing here with electrostatics. If there were moving charges present, $\mathbf{\nabla} \times \mathbf{E}$ would not be zero and $\mathbf{\nabla}V$ would then describe only part of the electric field intensity $\mathbf{E}$. We shall investigate this more complicated case in Chapter 6.

According to Eq. *2-10*,

Figure 2-2. *The potential difference $V_2 - V_1$ between two points is given by the line integral of $\mathbf{E} \cdot \mathbf{dl}$ from 1 to 2, where $\mathbf{E}$ is the electric field intensity and $\mathbf{dl}$ is an element of the path along which the integral is to be calculated. The light lines represent lines of force.*

$$\mathbf{E} \cdot \mathbf{dl} = -\mathbf{\nabla}V \cdot \mathbf{dl} = -dV. \qquad (2\text{-}11)$$

Then

$$V_2 - V_1 = -\int_1^2 \mathbf{E} \cdot d\mathbf{l} = \int_2^1 \mathbf{E} \cdot d\mathbf{l}, \qquad (2\text{-}12)$$

as in Figure 2-2. Note that the electric field intensity $\mathbf{E}$ determines only *differences* between the potentials at two different points. When we wish to speak of the electrostatic potential at a given point, we must therefore arbitrarily define the potential in a given region of space to be zero. It is usually convenient to choose the potential at infinity to be zero. Then the potential V at the point r is given by

$$V = \int_r^\infty \mathbf{E} \cdot d\mathbf{l}. \qquad (2\text{-}13)$$

The only case in which we cannot set V equal to zero at infinity is that in which charge is assumed to extend to infinity. An example of this will be discussed in Section 2.7.3.

The work W required to bring a charge Q' from a point at which the potential is defined to be zero to the point considered is VQ'. Thus V can be written as $V = W/Q'$ and can be defined to be the work per unit charge. The potential V is expressed in joules per coulomb, or in volts.

When the field is produced by a single point charge Q,

$$V = \int_r^\infty \frac{Q}{4\pi\epsilon_0} \frac{dr}{r^2} = \frac{Q}{4\pi\epsilon_0 r}. \qquad (2\text{-}14)$$

It will be observed that the sign of the potential V is the same as that of Q.

If we join all the points in space which have the same potential, we obtain an *equipotential surface*. For example, the equipotential surfaces about a point charge are concentric spheres. We can see from Eq. *2-10* that the electric field intensity $\mathbf{E}$ is everywhere normal to the equipotential surfaces.

If we join end-to-end infinitesimal vectors representing $\mathbf{E}$, we get a curve in space that is called a *line of force* and which is everywhere normal to the equipotential surfaces, according to Eq. *2-10*. The vector $\mathbf{E}$ is everywhere tangent to a line of force.

2.3.1. The Potential Produced by a Continuous Charge Distribution.

So far we have limited our discussion of field intensities and potentials to the idealized case of point charges. However, real charges, that is, electrons and protons, have a small but finite extent, and we must see whether or not this fact modifies our results in any way. We shall see in Section 2.7.1 that the potential and the electric field intensity outside a spherically symmetrical charge distribution are the same as they would be if the charge were all concentrated in a point at the center of the sphere.

Before discussing the calculation of potential at a point inside a distributed charge, we should point out that there is often great advantage in treating discrete charges as though they were continuously distributed. Protons and electrons are so small compared to the dimensions of ordinary apparatus that we may consider a small volume $\Delta\tau$ and define an average charge density ρ, measured in coulombs/meter³, as

$$\Delta Q / \Delta\tau,$$

where ΔQ is the total charge within $\Delta\tau$. The volume $\Delta\tau$ may be assumed large enough such that the fluctuations in ΔQ with time, or those from one $\Delta\tau$ to a neighboring one, are negligible, yet small enough such that integral calculus remains valid even though the volume element is not allowed to become smaller than $\Delta\tau$. Thus, instead of summing the potentials of a large number of individual charges, we may integrate over the continuous distribution $\rho(x, y, z)$. An element of charge $\rho\, d\tau$ contributes an element of potential dV at a point P outside $d\tau$

$$dV = \frac{1}{4\pi\epsilon_0} \frac{\rho\, d\tau}{r}, \qquad (2\text{-}15)$$

where r is the distance from $d\tau$ to P and

$$V = \frac{1}{4\pi\epsilon_0} \int_\infty \frac{\rho\, d\tau}{r}. \qquad (2\text{-}16)$$

We must now ask whether or not the potential V is defined when P is inside the continuously distributed charge. At first sight it appears that the dV contributed by the charge element $\rho\, d\tau$ at P is infinite, since r is zero. However, consider the situation where the volume element $d\tau$ is a spherical shell of thickness dr and radius r centered on P. The charge in this shell contributes at P a dV of $(\rho/4\pi\epsilon_0)(4\pi r^2/r)\, dr$. If we consider another shell of smaller radius we see that it contributes a smaller dV because as r decreases, $d\tau$ in the numerator decreases more rapidly than does r in the denominator. The potential V therefore converges, and the integral is finite. A similar argument shows that the field intensity $\mathbf{E}$ also converges.

2.4. Gauss's Law

Gauss's law relates the flux of $\mathbf{E}$ over a closed surface to the total charge enclosed within the surface. Consider the case shown in Figure 2-3, in which a point charge Q is located inside a closed surface S at a point P. We can calculate the flux of the electric field intensity $\mathbf{E}$ through the closed surface as follows. The flux of $\mathbf{E}$ through the element of area $\mathbf{da}$ is

$$\mathbf{E} \cdot \mathbf{da} = \frac{Q}{4\pi\epsilon_0} \frac{\mathbf{r}_1 \cdot \mathbf{da}}{r^2} = \frac{Q}{4\pi\epsilon_0} \frac{da'}{r^2}, \qquad (2\text{-}17)$$

where da' is the projection of **da** on a plane normal to $\mathbf{r}_1$. Then

$$\mathbf{E} \cdot \mathbf{da} = \frac{Q}{4\pi\epsilon_0}\, d\Omega, \qquad\qquad (2\text{-}18)$$

where $d\Omega$ is the element of solid angle subtended by **da** at the point P.

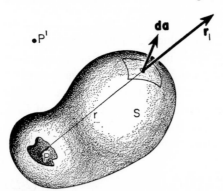

The element of solid angle $d\Omega$ subtended at a point P by an element of surface **da** is defined as follows. We first draw a straight line from every point on the periphery of **da** to the point P; we then draw a sphere of radius r having P as its center, such that r is less than the shortest distance from P to the periphery of **da**. The cone of lines from **da** to P intercepts an area da' on the surface of the sphere; the *solid angle* $d\Omega$ enclosed within the cone is defined as

Figure 2-3. *A point charge Q located at P inside a closed surface S. The total flux of the electric field intensity* **E** *through the surface S is Q/ε_0.*

$$d\Omega = \frac{da'}{r^2}.$$

The unit of solid angle is called the *steradian*. If **da** is part of a surface S which completely surrounds P, then the total solid angle subtended by the surface at P is 4π steradians.

To find the total flux of **E** in our problem, we integrate over the whole surface S:

$$\int_S \mathbf{E} \cdot \mathbf{da} = \frac{Q}{\epsilon_0}. \qquad\qquad (2\text{-}19)$$

If the point charge Q were outside the surface at some point P', the solid angle subtended by the surface S at P' would be zero. The situation remains unchanged if the surface is convoluted such that a line drawn outward from P cuts the surface at more than one point. The total solid angle subtended by the closed surface is still 4π at an inside point P and is still zero at an outside point P'.

If more than one point charge resides within S, the fluxes add algebraically, and the total flux of **E** leaving the volume is simply the total enclosed charge divided by ϵ_0. This is *Gauss's law*.

Gauss's law provides us with a powerful method for calculating the electric field intensity **E** due to simple charge distributions whose symmetry is such that the field is constant and normal over the entire surface S. This law has many applications, and we shall use it frequently.

If the charge enclosed by the surface S is distributed continuously, then the total enclosed charge Q is given by

$$Q = \int_\tau \rho \, d\tau, \qquad (2\text{-}20)$$

where ρ is the charge density and τ is the volume enclosed by the surface S. Then

$$\int_S \mathbf{E} \cdot \mathbf{da} = \frac{1}{\epsilon_0} \int_\tau \rho \, d\tau, \qquad (2\text{-}21)$$

or, using the divergence theorem,

$$\int_\tau \mathbf{\nabla} \cdot \mathbf{E} \, d\tau = \frac{1}{\epsilon_0} \int_\tau \rho \, d\tau. \qquad (2\text{-}22)$$

This equation is valid for any closed surface in the field, thus the integrands must be equal. Hence, at every point in the field,

$$\mathbf{\nabla} \cdot \mathbf{E} = \frac{\rho}{\epsilon_0}. \qquad (2\text{-}23)$$

This differential equation gives us information about the derivatives of $\mathbf{E}$ with respect to the coordinates, but it does not give us the field $\mathbf{E}$ itself.

2.4.1. The Average Potential Over a Spherical Surface in a Charge-free Region.

As an illustration of Gauss's law, we shall now show that, in a region of space where the charge density ρ is everywhere zero, the average potential over any spherical surface is equal to the value of the potential at the center of the sphere. To demonstrate this, let us consider a sphere of radius r, as in Figure 2-4, and compute the average potential $\overline{V}$ over the surface:

$$\overline{V} = \frac{1}{4\pi r^2} \int_S V \, da. \qquad (2\text{-}24)$$

We can introduce r under the integral sign because the integral is evaluated over a spherical surface for which r is a constant. Then

$$\overline{V} = \frac{1}{4\pi} \int_S \frac{V \, da}{r^2} = \frac{1}{4\pi} \int_S V \, d\Omega. \qquad (2\text{-}25)$$

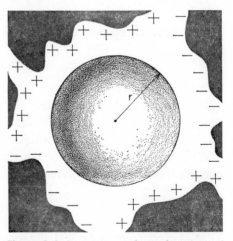

Figure 2-4. *Imaginary spherical surface of radius r in a charge-free region. It can be shown that the average potential over the surface is equal to the potential at the center.*

The solid angle $d\Omega$ is that subtended by da at the center of the sphere.

Since Eq. *2-25* is valid for all values of *r*, we can differentiate $\overline{V}$ with respect to *r*:

$$\frac{d\overline{V}}{dr} = \frac{1}{4\pi} \int_S \frac{dV}{dr}\, d\Omega. \qquad (2\text{-}26$$

We can differentiate with respect to *r* under the integral sign since the order of differentiation and integration is immaterial in this case. We next go back to da/r^2 instead of $d\Omega$ and remove r^2 from under the integral sign. Then

$$\frac{d\overline{V}}{dr} = -\frac{1}{4\pi r^2} \int_S E_r\, da. \qquad (2\text{-}27)$$

Now $E_r\, da$ is the flux of **E** through the spherical surface. The integral must be zero, since by hypothesis no charge is enclosed. Then $\overline{V}$ is independent of *r* for all values of *r*. If we let *r* approach zero, $\overline{V}$ approaches *V* at the origin. Thus, no matter how large *r* may be, the average potential over the surface of the sphere is always equal to the potential at the center of the sphere.

2.5. The Equations of Poisson and of Laplace

If we introduce into Eq. *2-23* the electrostatic potential *V*, as in Eq. *2-10*,

$$\nabla^2 V = -\frac{\rho}{\epsilon_0}. \qquad (2\text{-}28)$$

This is *Poisson's equation*. In a region of the field where the charge density ρ is zero,

$$\nabla^2 V = 0, \qquad (2\text{-}29)$$

which is *Laplace's equation*.

The general problem of finding the electrostatic potential function corresponding to a given charge distribution amounts to finding a solution of either Laplace's or Poisson's equation which will satisfy the given boundary conditions.

We can understand some of the significance of Laplace's equation if we examine it in Cartesian coordinates. In this coordinate system

$$\frac{\partial^2 V}{\partial x^2} + \frac{\partial^2 V}{\partial y^2} + \frac{\partial^2 V}{\partial z^2} = 0. \qquad (2\text{-}30)$$

Thus, at every point in the field, the second partial derivatives of the potential *V* in each of the three coordinate directions must add up to zero. This means that there can be no maximum or minimum of potential in a charge-free region; at a maximum or a minimum, the second partial derivatives are all different from zero and all necessarily have the same sign, hence their sum cannot add up to zero.

It is important to note that (a) the equations of Poisson and of Laplace,

(b) Gauss's law, and (c) the conservative character of the electrostatic field all follow directly from Coulomb's inverse square law.

2.6. Conductors

We have considered until now that our charges were situated in a vacuum, with no matter of any kind in the neighborhood. What happens if charges are situated on conductors, or if conductors are placed in an electrostatic field?

A conductor can be defined as a body within which charges can flow freely. Since we are dealing here with electrostatics, we assume a priori that the electric charges have reached their equilibrium positions and are fixed in space. We recognize, of course, that if a charge distribution on a conductor is suddenly disturbed it takes a finite time for the charges to redistribute themselves so as to reach their new positions. Then, under such static conditions, there must be zero electric field within a conductor, for otherwise charges would flow within the conductor, which is contrary to our hypothesis. We conclude, then, that the potential V must be the same throughout a conductor.

Thus, if a conductor is charged, the charges arrange themselves such that the net electric field due to all the charges can be zero inside the conductor. If a conductor is placed in an electric field, charge again flows temporarily within it so as to produce a second field which, added to the first, will give a net field equal to zero.

The significant fact concerning a conductor is that it is impossible to have net charge in one region of a conductor without having another set of charges, somewhere, to make the net electric field intensity within the conductor equal to zero. For example, it is impossible to have a charge density on one surface of an isolated plane conducting plate without having an identical charge density on the other side so as to produce within the plate two fields of equal intensity but of opposite direction. Or, if one plate of a parallel-plate capacitor is charged on the inside face, an equal and opposite charge must exist on the inside face of the opposite plate in order that **E** inside the plates can be zero.

Coulomb's law applies within conductors, even though the *net* field is zero. Then Gauss's law, as well as the property of the electrostatic field of being conservative, and the equations of Poisson and of Laplace, which all rest on Coulomb's law, still apply if conductors are present in the field.

Since the electric field intensity **E** must be zero everywhere within a conductor, we must have $\nabla \cdot \mathbf{E} = \rho/\epsilon_0 = 0$. Then the charge density ρ within a conductor must be everywhere zero. As a corollary, any net charge on a conductor must reside on its surface.

At the surface of a conductor, the electric field intensity **E** must be normal, for if there were a tangential component of **E**, charges would flow along the surface, which is contrary to our hypothesis. Then, according to Gauss's law, just outside the surface, $\mathbf{E} = \sigma/\epsilon_0$, where σ is the surface charge density.

It is remarkable that this electric field intensity σ/ϵ_0 can be found from Gauss's law by considering only the charges in the immediate neighborhood of the point considered, although the field is of course due to *all* the charges present, whether on the conductor being considered or elsewhere.

A hollow conductor has a charge on its inner surface equal in magnitude and opposite in sign to any charge which may be enclosed within the hollow. This is readily demonstrated by considering a Gaussian surface that lies within the conductor and which encloses the hollow. Since $\mathbf{E}$ is everywhere zero on this surface, the total enclosed charge must be zero.

2.7. Fields Produced by Some Simple Charge Distributions

A problem often encountered in electrostatics is that of finding the electric field intensity $\mathbf{E}$ produced by a given charge distribution. The vector $\mathbf{E}$ can be found in several different ways. First, we can use Eq. *2-3* for an element of charge and integrate over the whole charge distribution. We must of course keep in mind that the field intensity is a vector quantity. Another way consists in writing down the potential produced by an element of charge, integrating over the whole charge to get the potential, and then calculating its gradient, which gives the field intensity according to Eq. *2-10*. The potential calculation is generally simpler because the potential is a scalar quantity which can be integrated more easily than the vector $\mathbf{E}$. A third way is to use Gauss's law if the charge distribution possesses a symmetry which ensures constancy of the field intensity over certain imaginary surfaces in the field. These three types of calculations will be illustrated by various examples in the following sections.

Very often, the charge distribution possesses neither the symmetry required to permit using Gauss's law nor the simplicity required for the direct integration of either the field intensity or the potential. Then we must look to other methods described in Chapter 4 and in Appendix D.

It is important to note that only relatively simple charge distributions can be dealt with exactly by analytical means. Arbitrary charge distributions can be dealt with only by approximate or by numerical methods.

For this reason we shall restrict our discussion below to simple idealized charge distributions which permit straightforward calculation. This will illustrate the basic principles and will lead us to results of value in many practical problems.

2.7.1. Uniform Spherical Charge Distribution. Field at an External Point. We shall first consider the electric field intensity produced by a uniform spherical charge distribution of radius R and of uniform charge density ρ, as in Figure 2-5. Our problem is to find $\mathbf{E}$ as a function of the distance z from the center of the sphere to a point P outside the sphere.

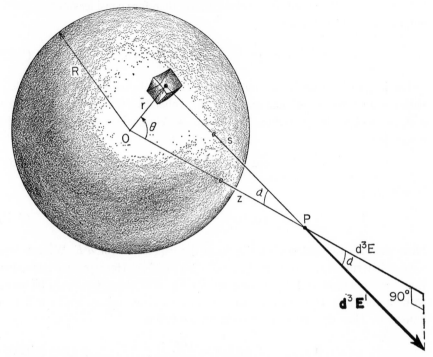

Figure 2-5. *An element of charge at the point (r, θ) inside a uniform, spherical charge distribution produces an element of electrostatic field intensity $\mathbf{d^3E'}$ at a point P outside the sphere. The projection of $\mathbf{d^3E'}$ on the axis joining P and the center of the sphere is d^3E.*

CALCULATION OF $\mathbf{E}$ FROM COULOMB'S LAW. Let us first calculate $\mathbf{E}$ directly from Eq. *2-3*. We can find the contribution to $\mathbf{E}$ due to the charge $\rho\, d\tau$ in the element of volume $d\tau$ and then integrate the resultant expression over the whole sphere. It is convenient to use spherical coordinates, since the charge has spherical symmetry. Then the volume element is $dr\, r\, d\theta\, r \sin \theta\, d\phi$. The charge in this volume produces a field at the point P which is directed away from the volume element if ρ is positive and toward the volume element if ρ is negative. Its magnitude is

$$d^3E' = \frac{1}{4\pi\epsilon_0}\frac{\rho r^2 \sin \theta\, dr\, d\theta\, d\phi}{s^2}, \qquad (2\text{-}31)$$

where s is the distance from the volume element to the point P. The axis along which $\theta = 0$ can be taken to be the line OP. The element of field intensity is written d^3E' since it is a third order differential.

It is obvious from the symmetry of the charge distribution that $\mathbf{E}$ must be radial. This is because the tangential field component produced by a given charge element will be canceled by an equal and opposite component produced by a symmetrically placed charge element. We therefore consider only the radial component of $\mathbf{E}$ and write

$$d^3 E = \frac{1}{4\pi\epsilon_0} \frac{\rho r^2 \sin\theta \, dr \, d\theta \, d\phi}{s^2} \cos\alpha. \tag{2-32}$$

The integration over the azimuth angle ϕ is straightforward, and the angle ϕ varies from 0 to 2π. We can carry out the other two integrations by using r and s as independent variables. To do this, we eliminate α with the aid of the cosine law:

$$\cos\alpha = \frac{s^2 + z^2 - r^2}{2sz}. \tag{2-33}$$

Similarly,

$$\cos\theta = \frac{r^2 + z^2 - s^2}{2rz}. \tag{2-34}$$

Now we wish to eliminate $\sin\theta \, d\theta$ from the expression for $d^3 E$. We can find $\sin\theta \, d\theta$ in terms of r, z, and s by differentiating Eq. 2-34. Here we must remember that z is a constant and that if we integrate Eq. 2-32 along θ, r would be taken to be a constant. Thus we must differentiate Eq. 2-34, taking both r and z as constants. Then the proper expression for $\sin\theta \, d\theta$ is

$$\sin\theta \, d\theta = \frac{s \, ds}{rz}. \tag{2-35}$$

Substituting Eqs. 2-33 and 2-35 in Eq. 2-32, we then obtain

$$E = \frac{\rho\pi}{4\pi\epsilon_0 z^2} \int_{r=0}^{r=R} \int_{s=z-r}^{s=z+r} r\left(1 + \frac{z^2 - r^2}{s^2}\right) ds \, dr, \tag{2-36}$$

$$\mathbf{E} = \frac{1}{4\pi\epsilon_0} \frac{(4/3)\pi R^3 \rho}{z^2} \mathbf{r}_1 = \frac{1}{4\pi\epsilon_0} \frac{Q}{z^2} \mathbf{r}_1, \tag{2-37}$$

where Q is the total charge $(4/3)\pi R^3 \rho$ and $\mathbf{r}_1$ is the radial unit vector directed outward. The vector $\mathbf{E}$ is directed outward along OP if Q is positive and inward along OP if Q is negative.

The above result is the same as would be obtained if the total charge Q were concentrated at the center of the sphere. This is due to the requirement that, by symmetry, all the lines of force must be radial. Then their density, and hence $\mathbf{E}$, at an outside point P, is the same whether the charges are concentrated at the point O or distributed with spherical symmetry around O. We say that there is spherical symmetry if the charge density is either constant or depends only on the distance r from the center of the sphere.

CALCULATION OF **E** FROM THE POTENTIAL. To compute the field intensity **E** from the potential V, we use the same element of charge as above. Then, from the definition of V,

$$d^3V = \frac{1}{4\pi\epsilon_0} \frac{\rho r^2 \sin\theta \, dr \, d\theta \, d\phi}{s}. \tag{2-38}$$

There is no $\cos\alpha$ term now, since V is a scalar. We carry out the integration as before by eliminating θ and integrating over ϕ, s, and r. The result is

$$V = \frac{1}{4\pi\epsilon_0} \frac{Q}{z}. \tag{2-39}$$

The electrostatic potential V, like **E**, is the same as if the total charge Q were concentrated at the center of sphere. To find **E**, we now calculate ∇V. By symmetry, **E** must be radial, hence

$$\mathbf{E} = -\nabla V = -\frac{\partial V}{\partial z}\mathbf{r_1}, \tag{2-40}$$

$$= \frac{1}{4\pi\epsilon_0} \frac{Q}{z^2}\mathbf{r_1}. \tag{2-41}$$

as previously.

CALCULATION OF **E** FROM GAUSS'S LAW. The simplest way to compute the field intensity in this case is to use Gauss's law. Consider an imaginary sphere of radius z concentric with the charged sphere. We know that **E** must be radial. Then, according to Gauss's law,

$$4\pi z^2 E = \frac{Q}{\epsilon_0} \tag{2-42}$$

and, again,

$$\mathbf{E} = \frac{1}{4\pi\epsilon_0} \frac{Q}{z^2}\mathbf{r_1}. \tag{2-43}$$

If the charge were not distributed with spherical symmetry, Gauss's law would still be true, of course, but then **E** would be a function of θ, and of ϕ, and would not be constant over the imaginary sphere. Gauss's law would then only give the average value of the normal component of **E** over the imaginary sphere.

2.7.2. Uniform Spherical Charge Distribution. Field at an Internal Point.

Let us now calculate the field intensity at a point P' within the charge distribution as in Figure 2-6. We can proceed as in the case of the external point P, first writing down the contribution from an element of charge either to **E** or to V and then integrating over the whole charge distribution. However, the integration is difficult to carry out, and we shall simplify the problem by dividing it into two distinct parts.

We draw an imaginary sphere of radius z through the point P', as in Figure 2-6, to divide the charge distribution into two parts. We then calculate the electric field intensity due to the charge contained within the sphere of radius z and that due to the charge contained within the hollow outer sphere of inner and outer radii z and R, respectively. Then, by the principle of superposition, the resultant field intensity for the two charge systems must be the vector sum of the two component field intensities.

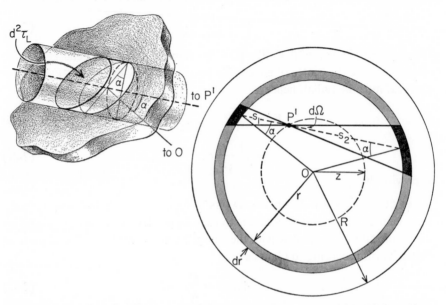

Figure 2-6. *To find the electrostatic field intensity* **E** *at a point* P' *inside a uniform spherical charge distribution, we divide the sphere into a shell and a core by means of an imaginary sphere of radius* z. *Then any pair of volume elements such as those shown in the shell produces equal and opposite fields at* P'. *The field at* P' *is thus due solely to the charges in the core. The exploded view shows one of the volume elements in detail.*

The separation of the charge into two systems is especially advantageous in this case because, as we shall see, the field produced by the hollow outer sphere at a point on its inner surface, or at any point within the hollow, is zero. This can be demonstrated as follows, without integrating.

We draw a small cone of solid angle $d\Omega$, having a vertex at the point P' and extending in both directions as in Figure 2-6, and consider the volume which these small cones intercept within a spherical shell of radius r and thickness dr concentric with the sphere. On the left, the volume element is

$$d^2\tau_L = \frac{s_1^2 \, d\Omega}{\cos \alpha} \, dr, \qquad (2\text{-}44)$$

whereas on the right it is

$$d^2\tau_R = \frac{s_2^2\, d\Omega}{\cos\alpha}\, dr. \tag{2-45}$$

The charge in the left-hand volume element contributes at P' a field of magnitude

$$d^2E = \frac{\rho}{4\pi\epsilon_0 s_1^2}\frac{s_1^2\, d\Omega}{\cos\alpha}\, dr, \tag{2-46}$$

which is directed toward the left if ρ is positive. Similarly, the charge on the left contributes an identical field, opposite in direction, with the result that the two fields cancel. This result is valid for any $d\Omega$ and any dr, thus the field due to the hollow sphere at a point on its inner surface, or at any point within the hollow, is zero.

A much simpler way of showing that the field due to the hollow sphere is zero anywhere inside the hollow is to use Gauss's law. Imagine a concentric spherical surface within the hollow. Then, according to Gauss's law, the average radial field intensity over this surface must be zero, since there is no enclosed charge. Now the symmetry of the problem requires that $\mathbf{E}$, if it exists, be radial. Hence $\mathbf{E}$ must be zero at every point on a spherical surface within the hollow.

CALCULATION OF $\mathbf{E}$ FROM COULOMB'S LAW. With the electric field intensity of the hollow sphere thus disposed of, we can calculate the contribution to $\mathbf{E}$ due to the inner sphere of radius z, just as we did in the case of the external point P, except that here $r = z$:

$$\mathbf{E} = \frac{1}{4\pi\epsilon_0}\frac{(4/3)\pi z^3\rho}{z^2}\,\mathbf{r}_1, \tag{2-47}$$

$$= \frac{\rho z}{3\epsilon_0}\,\mathbf{r}_1. \tag{2-48}$$

The electric field intensity thus increases linearly with z inside the spherical charge distribution.

CALCULATION OF $\mathbf{E}$ FROM THE POTENTIAL. We can arrive at the same result by first calculating the potential V as a function of z within the charge distribution. To do this, we could proceed by direct integration. However, it will be easier and more instructive to divide the charge distribution into two parts as above and to proceed as follows.

Let us first consider the hollow shell. We have seen that there is no electric field inside a hollow sphere of charge. Then all points within the hollow must be at the same potential. Thus, instead of calculating the potential at a point on the interior surface of the shell, we can calculate the potential at the center of the shell, where the integration is more easily performed. We choose our elementary volume to be a thin shell of radius r and of thickness dr. Thus the part of V which is due to the hollow sphere is

$$\frac{1}{4\pi\epsilon_0}\int_z^R \frac{\rho 4\pi r^2\, dr}{r} = \frac{\rho}{2\epsilon_0}(R^2 - z^2). \tag{2-49}$$

Next we compute the potential due to the interior sphere of radius z. The calculation is the same as for an external point, except that the integration is carried out only to $r = z$. This term is

$$\frac{1}{4\pi\epsilon_0}\frac{\rho(4/3)\pi z^3}{z} = \frac{\rho}{3\epsilon_0}z^2. \tag{2-50}$$

By adding these two contributions, we obtain the potential V at a point P' at a radius z inside the spherical charge distribution:

$$V = \frac{\rho}{\epsilon_0}\left(\frac{R^2}{2} - \frac{z^2}{6}\right). \tag{2-51}$$

The potential V can also be written as

$$V = \frac{Q}{4\pi\epsilon_0 R^3}\frac{(R^2 - z^2)}{2} + \frac{Q}{4\pi\epsilon_0 R}. \tag{2-52}$$

The second term is the potential at the surface of the sphere; the first term is the increase above the surface value for the interior points. The value of $\mathbf{E}$ is then

$$\mathbf{E} = -\boldsymbol{\nabla}V = -\frac{\partial V}{\partial z}\mathbf{r}_1 = \frac{\rho z}{3\epsilon_0}\mathbf{r}_1. \tag{2-53}$$

CALCULATION OF $\mathbf{E}$ FROM GAUSS'S LAW. To calculate the field intensity at the internal point from Gauss's law, we draw an imaginary surface of

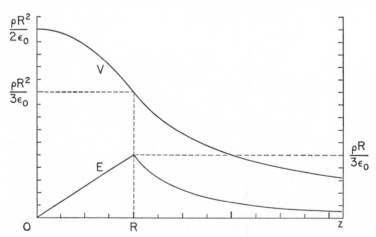

Figure 2-7. *In a uniform spherical charge distribution, the electric field intensity E rises linearly from the center to the surface of the sphere and falls off as the inverse square of the distance outside the sphere. On the other hand, the electric potential inside the sphere falls from a maximum at the center in parabolic fashion, and as the inverse first power of the distance outside the sphere.*

radius z through the point P'. Symmetry requires that the field intensity be radial, thus, according to Gauss's law,

$$4\pi z^2 E = \frac{\rho(4/3)\pi z^3}{\epsilon_0},\qquad(2\text{-}54)$$

or

$$\mathbf{E} = \frac{\rho z}{3\epsilon_0}\,\mathbf{r}_1,\qquad(2\text{-}55)$$

as in Eq. *2-48*.

Figure 2-7 shows $\mathbf{E}$ and V for our spherical charge distribution of radius R as a function of the radial position z of the point considered.

2.7.3. Infinite Sheet of Charge. Consider an infinite sheet of charge of uniform surface density σ as in Figure 2-8.

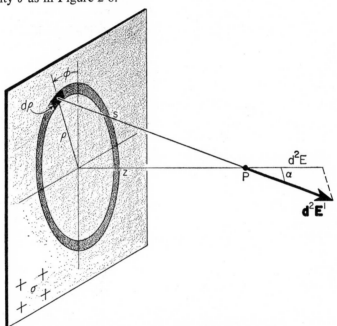

Figure 2-8. *An element of charge at the point (ρ, ϕ) on an infinite sheet of charge produces an electrostatic field intensity $\mathbf{d}^2\mathbf{E}'$ at a point P. The projection of $\mathbf{d}^2\mathbf{E}'$ on the normal to the sheet is d^2E.*

CALCULATION OF $\mathbf{E}$ FROM COULOMB'S LAW. We can compute the value of $\mathbf{E}$ at a point P located at a distance z from the sheet by direct application of Coulomb's law. It is convenient to use cylindrical coordinates, with the origin at O and with OP as axis. An element of charge $\sigma r\, d\phi\, dr$ produces at P a field which is directed away from the element, if σ is positive, and whose magnitude is

$$d^2 E' = \frac{1}{4\pi\epsilon_0} \frac{\sigma r \, d\phi \, dr}{s^2}. \tag{2-56}$$

By symmetry, the field $\mathbf{E}$ must be perpendicular to the sheet because the component of the above field which is perpendicular to OP is canceled by an equal and opposite component produced by a symmetrically placed charge element. We must therefore multiply by $\cos \alpha$ to obtain the normal component of field, $d^2 E$:

$$d^2 E = \frac{1}{4\pi\epsilon_0} \frac{\sigma r \, d\phi \, dr}{s^2} \cos \alpha. \tag{2-57}$$

If we eliminate s, integrate ϕ between the limits 0 and 2π, and integrate α between 0 and $\pi/2$, then

$$E = \frac{\sigma}{2\epsilon_0}. \tag{2-58}$$

The vector $\mathbf{E}$ is directed away from the sheet if σ is positive and toward the sheet if σ is negative.

POTENTIAL. In the previous section, we computed $\mathbf{E}$ from the gradient of V. If we try to find V in the present case by integrating over the sheet the contributions $d^2 V$ due to the charge elements according to Eq. 2-15, we find an infinite value for V. This is because Eq. 2-15 assumes that $V = 0$ at all points infinitely remote from the region considered. In the present case, V cannot be made equal to zero at infinity since the charged sheet itself extends to infinity. Equation 2-15 therefore does not apply, and we cannot use this second method for computing $\mathbf{E}$.

We can, however, find the electrostatic potential V from Eq. 2-58 since we must have, by symmetry,

$$E = -\frac{dV}{dz}. \tag{2-59}$$

Thus

$$V = -\frac{\sigma}{2\epsilon_0} z + V_0. \tag{2-60}$$

Here V_0 is a constant of integration which determines the plane over which the value of V is arbitrarily chosen to be zero.

CALCULATION OF $\mathbf{E}$ FROM GAUSS'S LAW. Here again, Gauss's law provides us with a simple method for calculating $\mathbf{E}$. We consider a cylinder with its axis perpendicular to the sheet and extending on either side as in Figure 2-9. By symmetry $\mathbf{E}$ must be directed along the normal to the sheet of charge. There is no flux through the sides of the cylinder, since $\mathbf{E}$ is everywhere parallel to the sides, hence the only flux is through the ends. If we let S be the cross-sectional area of the cylinder, then

$$2ES = \frac{\sigma S}{\epsilon_0}, \tag{2-61}$$

and

$$E = \frac{\sigma}{2\epsilon_0},$$
(2-62)

as in Eq. *2-58*.

Again Gauss's law gives the total field intensity **E** produced by *all* the charges of the system, despite the fact that we have included within the Gaussian surface only a small part of the charges.

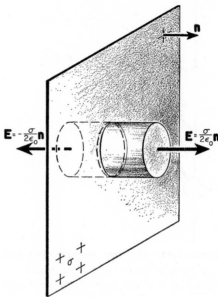

Figure 2-9

The electric field intensity produced by an infinite sheet of charge can be calculated from Gauss's law by using a cylindrical Gaussian surface with its axis perpendicular to the sheet. Then $E = \sigma/2\epsilon_0$ on either side.

2.7.4. Conducting Plate With a Surface Charge Density σ. We consider now a similar problem in which we have a conducting plate with a charge density σ on *each* of its surfaces, as in Figure 2-10. If we calculate the field intensity at a point P outside the conductor as above, we find that

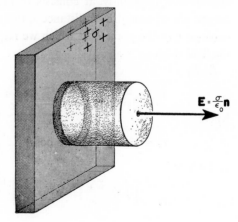

Figure 2-10

*The electric field intensity E outside a conducting surface is calculated from Gauss's law by using a Gaussian cylinder with one face in the conductor. Then $E = \sigma/\epsilon_0$. The vector **n** is a unit vector normal to the surface and pointing right.*

$$E = \frac{\sigma}{\epsilon_0}, \qquad (2\text{-}63)$$

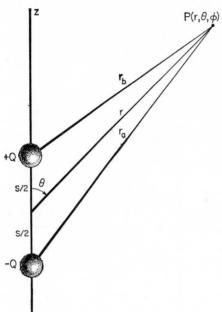

since *both* sheets of charge contribute to the field.

We can also obtain the same result through Gauss's law. We use a cylindrical Gaussian surface with one face inside the conducting plate and one face outside, as in Figure 2-10. Since the field intensity is zero within the conductor, and since there is no flux through the sides of the cylinder, the only flux through the Gaussian surface is that through the end which is outside the conductor. Then, according to Gauss's law, **E** is given by Eq. *2-63*.

Note that the electric field within the conductor is zero, since the electric field intensity contributed by the charges on the left-hand side of the plate is just equal and opposite to that contributed by the charges on the right-hand side.

Figure 2-11. *The two charges +Q and −Q form a dipole. The electrostatic potential at P is the sum of the potentials due to the individual charges.*

2.8. The Dipole

The dipole shown in Figure 2-11 is one type of charge distribution which is encountered frequently. It consists of positive and negative charges of equal magnitude separated by a distance s, this distance being small compared to the distance r to the point P at which we require the electrostatic potential V and the field intensity **E**.

At P,

$$V = \frac{Q}{4\pi\epsilon_0}\left(\frac{1}{r_b} - \frac{1}{r_a}\right), \qquad (2\text{-}64)$$

where

$$r_a^2 = r^2 + \left(\frac{s}{2}\right)^2 + rs\cos\theta \qquad (2\text{-}65)$$

and where

$$\frac{r}{r_a} = \left[1 + \left(\frac{s}{2r}\right)^2 + \frac{s}{r}\cos\theta\right]^{-1/2}, \qquad (2\text{-}66)$$

$$\frac{r}{r_a} = 1 - \frac{1}{2}\left(\frac{s^2}{4r^2} + \frac{s}{r}\cos\theta\right) + \frac{3}{8}\left(\frac{s^2}{4r^2} + \frac{s}{r}\cos\theta\right)^2 - \cdots, \qquad (2\text{-}67)$$

or, if we neglect terms of order higher than $\frac{s^2}{r^2}$,

$$\frac{r}{r_a} = 1 - \frac{s}{2r}\cos\theta + \frac{s^2}{4r^2}\frac{3\cos^2\theta - 1}{2}. \qquad (2\text{-}68)$$

Similarly,

$$\frac{r}{r_b} = 1 + \frac{s}{2r}\cos\theta + \frac{s^2}{4r^2}\frac{3\cos^2\theta - 1}{2}, \qquad (2\text{-}69)$$

hence

$$V = \frac{Qs}{4\pi\epsilon_0 r^2}\cos\theta \qquad (r^2 \gg s^2). \qquad (2\text{-}70)$$

It is interesting to note that the potential due to a dipole falls off as the *square* of the distance r, whereas the potential from a single point charge varies only as $1/r$. This comes from the fact that the charges in a dipole appear close together for an observer at some distance away, and that their fields cancel more and more as the distance r is increased.

We define the dipole moment $\mathbf{p} = Q\mathbf{s}$ as a vector quantity whose magnitude is Qs and which is directed from the negative to the positive charge. Then

$$V = \frac{\mathbf{p}\cdot\mathbf{r}_1}{4\pi\epsilon_0 r^2}, \qquad (2\text{-}71)$$

or

$$V = \frac{\mathbf{p}}{4\pi\epsilon_0}\cdot\nabla\left(\frac{1}{r}\right), \qquad (2\text{-}72)$$

where $\mathbf{r}_1$ is the unit radial vector (see Problem 1-21).

The components of $\mathbf{E}$ in spherical coordinates can be computed from the gradient of V:

$$E_r = -\frac{\partial V}{\partial r} = \frac{2p}{4\pi\epsilon_0 r^3}\cos\theta, \qquad (2\text{-}73)$$

$$E_\theta = -\frac{1}{r}\frac{\partial V}{\partial\theta} = \frac{p}{4\pi\epsilon_0 r^3}\sin\theta, \qquad (2\text{-}74)$$

$$E_\phi = -\frac{1}{r\sin\theta}\frac{\partial V}{\partial\phi} = 0. \qquad (2\text{-}75)$$

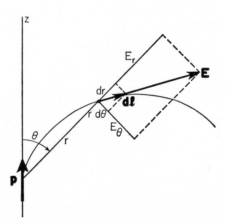

Figure 2-12. *A dipole* $\mathbf{p}$ *produces an electrostatic field intensity* $\mathbf{E}$ *with components* E_r *and* E_θ *at the point* (r, θ). *The element* $d\mathbf{l}$ *of the line of force is parallel to* $\mathbf{E}$ *at the point.*

The electric field intensity of a dipole thus falls off as the *cube* of the distance.

The equation for the lines of force of a dipole can be found by considering Figure 2-12, which shows an element $d\mathbf{l}$ of a line of force in grossly exaggerated form. The components of **E** and of **dl** are proportional, since the line element **dl** and the vector **E** are parallel, thus

$$\frac{r\,d\theta}{dr} = \frac{E_\theta}{E_r}. \qquad (2\text{-}76)$$

According to Eqs. *2-73* and *2-74*,

$$\frac{E_\theta}{E_r} = \frac{\sin\theta}{2\cos\theta}. \qquad (2\text{-}77)$$

Then

$$\frac{dr}{r} = \frac{2d(\sin\theta)}{\sin\theta}, \qquad (2\text{-}78)$$

thus

$$r = A\sin^2\theta. \qquad (2\text{-}79)$$

This equation determines the family of lines of force, the constant A being a parameter which varies from one line of force to another. The lines of force

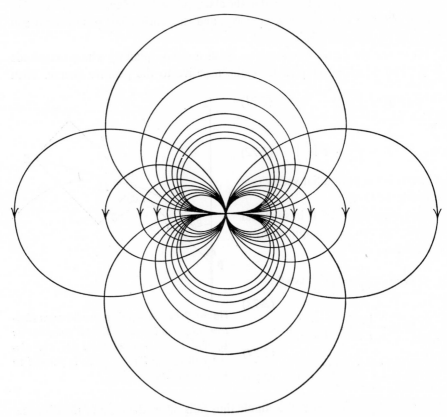

Figure 2-13. *The lines of force (arrows) and the equipotential lines for the dipole of Figure 2-11. In the central region the lines come too close together to be shown.*

and the equipotential lines, which are everywhere perpendicular to the lines of force, are shown in Figure 2-13. Rotating the equipotential lines about the *z*-axis generates the equipotential surfaces.

2.9. The Linear Quadrupole

The linear quadrupole is an arrangement of four charges, as in Figure 2-14. The separation *s* of the charges is assumed to be small compared to the distance *r* to the point *P*. At *P*,

$$V = \frac{1}{4\pi\epsilon_0}\left(\frac{Q}{r_a} - \frac{2Q}{r} + \frac{Q}{r_b}\right), \quad (2\text{-}80)$$

$$= \frac{Q}{4\pi\epsilon_0 r}\left(\frac{r}{r_a} + \frac{r}{r_b} - 2\right). \quad (2\text{-}81)$$

The ratios r/r_a and r/r_b can be expanded just as for the dipole, the only difference being that *s* must now be used instead of $s/2$. Thus, neglecting terms of order higher than s^2/r^2,

$$\frac{r}{r_a} = 1 - \frac{s}{r}\cos\theta + \frac{s^2}{r^2}\frac{(3\cos^2\theta - 1)}{2},$$
$$(2\text{-}82)$$

and

$$\frac{r}{r_b} = 1 + \frac{s}{r}\cos\theta + \frac{s^2}{r^2}\frac{(3\cos^2\theta - 1)}{2},$$
$$(2\text{-}83)$$

hence

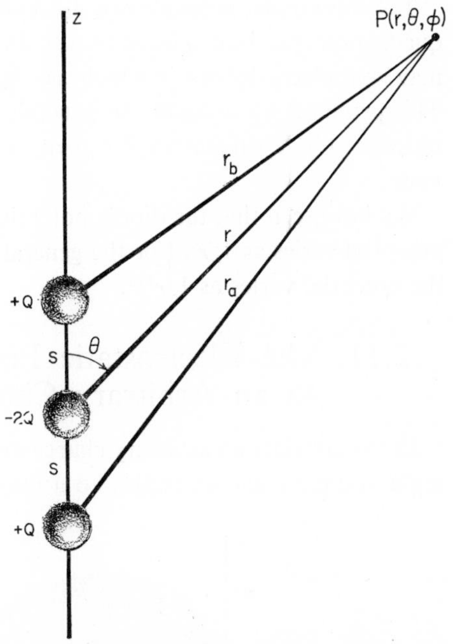

Figure 2-14. *Charges* $+Q$, $-2Q$, *and* $+Q$ *arranged along a line to form an axial quadrupole.*

$$V = \frac{2Qs^2}{4\pi\epsilon_0 r^3}\frac{(3\cos^2\theta - 1)}{2} \quad (r^2 \gg s^2). \quad (2\text{-}84)$$

The electrostatic potential *V* due to a linear quadrupole thus varies inversely as the *cube* of the distance, whereas the electrostatic field intensity **E**, calculated as in Eqs. *2-73*, *2-74*, and *2-75*, varies inversely as the *fourth* power of the distance. The fields of the three charges $+Q$, $-2Q$, and $+Q$ cancel almost completely for $r \gg s$.

2.10. Multipoles

It is possible to extend the dipole and quadrupole concepts to larger numbers of positive and negative charges located at small distances from each other.

Such charge arrangements are known as *multipoles* and are defined as follows. A single point charge is called a *monopole*. A *dipole* is produced by displacing a monopole through a small distance s_1 and replacing the original monopole by another of the same magnitude but of opposite sign. Likewise, a *quadrupole* is produced by displacing a dipole by a small distance s_2 and then replacing the original dipole by one of equal magnitude but of opposite sign. For the linear quadrupole, $s_2 = s_1 = s$.

The multipole concept can be continued indefinitely. For example, the quadrupole may be displaced by a small distance s_3, and the original quadrupole may be replaced by one in which the signs of all the charges have been changed. This produces an *octupole*. In general, we can produce 2^l *poles*, where l is the number of independent displacements s_1, s_2, $\cdots$ required to specify the arrangement.

We have seen that the dipole potential varies as $1/r^2$ and that the quadrupole potential varies as $1/r^3$. For the general multipole, characterized by the letter l, the potential varies as $1/r^{l+1}$.

2.11. The Electrostatic Potential V Due to an Arbitrary Charge Distribution

Let us consider an arbitrary charge distribution of density $\rho(x', y', z')$ occupying a volume τ and extending to a maximum distance $r_{\max}$ from the origin of

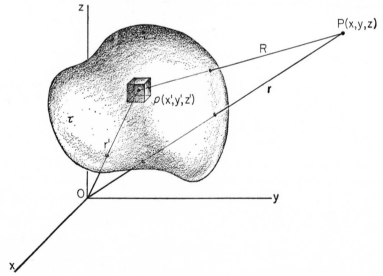

Figure 2-15. *An arbitrary charge distribution of density ρ within a volume τ produces an electrostatic potential V at a point $P(x, y, z)$ outside τ.*

coordinates O. We select O either within the volume or close to it. This distribution is illustrated in Figure 2-15.

We wish to find the electrostatic potential V at some point $P(x, y, z)$. This is given by

$$V = \int_\tau \frac{\rho \, d\tau}{4\pi\epsilon_0 R}, \tag{2-85}$$

where R is the distance between the point of observation P and the position $P'(x', y', z')$ of the element of charge $\rho \, d\tau$:

$$R = [(x - x')^2 + (y - y')^2 + (z - z')^2]^{1/2}. \tag{2-86}$$

In Eq. 2-85 the point of observation $P(x, y, z)$ is taken to be fixed, thus R is a function of the variables x', y', and z'.

Since R is a function of x', y', and z', let us expand $1/R$ as a Taylor series near the origin:

$$\frac{1}{R} = \frac{1}{r} + \left(x' \frac{\partial}{\partial x'} + y' \frac{\partial}{\partial y'} + z' \frac{\partial}{\partial z'}\right)_0 \left(\frac{1}{R}\right) \tag{2-87}$$
$$+ \frac{1}{2!} \left(x' \frac{\partial}{\partial x'} + y' \frac{\partial}{\partial y'} + z' \frac{\partial}{\partial z'}\right)_0^2 \left(\frac{1}{R}\right) + \cdots,$$

where the indices O are meant to indicate that the derivatives must be evaluated at the origin.

Now

$$\frac{\partial}{\partial x'} \left(\frac{1}{R}\right) = -\frac{1}{R^2} \frac{\partial R}{\partial x'}, \tag{2-88}$$

$$= \frac{x - x'}{R^3}, \tag{2-89}$$

and

$$\left[\frac{\partial}{\partial x'} \left(\frac{1}{R}\right)\right]_0 = \frac{x}{r^3}, \tag{2-90}$$

$$= \frac{l}{r^2}, \tag{2-91}$$

where

$$l = \frac{x}{r} \tag{2-92}$$

is the cosine of the angle formed between the vector r and the x-axis. The other first derivatives with respect to y' and z' are given by similar expressions.

The second derivatives required for evaluating the third term on the right-hand side of Eq. 2-87 are calculated similarly, the substitution $x' = 0$ and $R = r$ being made only at the end.

The result of the calculation is that the electrostatic potential V at the point P is given by

$$V = \int_\tau \frac{1}{r} \frac{\rho \, d\tau}{4\pi\epsilon_0} + \int_\tau \frac{1}{r^2} \, (lx' + my' + nz') \frac{\rho \, d\tau}{4\pi\epsilon_0} \qquad (2\text{-}93)$$

$$+ \int_\tau \frac{1}{r^3} \Big[3mny'z' + 3nlz'x' + 3lmx'y'$$

$$+ \frac{1}{2}(3l^2 - 1)x'^2 + \frac{1}{2}(3m^2 - 1)y'^2 + \frac{1}{2}(3n^2 - 1)z'^2 \Big] \frac{\rho \, d\tau}{4\pi\epsilon_0} + \cdots,$$

where l, m, and n are the direction cosines of the line joining the origin to the point of observation P. The series converges, since, by hypothesis, $r > r_{max}$, thus r is larger than either x', y', or z', whereas l, m, and n are no greater than unity.

Let us now examine the various terms successively. The first term is merely the potential which we would have at P if the whole charge were concentrated at the origin. It is called the *monopole term* and is zero only if the net charge is zero. If the charges are all of the same sign, then it is the most important term of the series since it involves only the first power of $1/r$.

The second term varies as $1/r^2$, as does the electrostatic potential of a dipole. Let us find the value of this term when the charge distribution is simply a dipole as in Figure 2-11. The integral must then be evaluated over the two charges Q and $-Q$ situated at $z' = s/2$ and $z' = -s/2$ respectively. The result is the value of V for the dipole, as in Eq. *2-70*. The second term T_2 of Eq. *2-93* can thus be taken to be a *dipole term*. In fact it can be written as

$$T_2 = \frac{\mathbf{p} \cdot \mathbf{r}_1}{4\pi\epsilon_0 r^2} \qquad (2\text{-}94)$$

if we set

$$\mathbf{p} = \int_\tau (x'\mathbf{i} + y'\mathbf{j} + z'\mathbf{k})\rho \, d\tau, \qquad (2\text{-}95)$$

$\mathbf{r}_1$ being the unit vector along $\mathbf{r}$ in the direction of P:

$$\mathbf{r}_1 = l\mathbf{i} + m\mathbf{j} + n\mathbf{k}. \qquad (2\text{-}96)$$

The quantity $\mathbf{p}$ is called the *dipole moment of the charge distribution* and can be written as

$$\mathbf{p} = \int_\tau \mathbf{r}'\rho \, d\tau. \qquad (2\text{-}97)$$

It is a vector whose components are

$$p_x = \int_\tau x'\rho \, d\tau,$$

$$p_y = \int_\tau y'\rho \, d\tau, \qquad (2\text{-}98)$$

$$p_z = \int_\tau z'\rho \, d\tau.$$

The dipole moment of an extended charge distribution can also be defined in terms of the vector distance $\bar{\mathbf{r}}'$ from the origin to the center of charge, which is defined in a manner analogous to the center of mass in mechanics:

$$\bar{\mathbf{r}}' = \frac{\int_\tau \mathbf{r}'\rho \, d\tau}{\int_\tau \rho \, d\tau}, \tag{2-99}$$

$$= \frac{\int_\tau \mathbf{r}'\rho \, d\tau}{Q}, \tag{2-100}$$

$$\mathbf{p} = Q\bar{\mathbf{r}}', \tag{2-101}$$

$$p_x = Q\bar{x}', \qquad p_y = Q\bar{y}', \qquad p_z = Q\bar{z}', \tag{2-102}$$

where Q is the net charge in the distribution.

If the net charge Q is zero, then $\bar{\mathbf{r}}' \longrightarrow \infty$ from Eq. *2-100* and $\mathbf{p}$ is indeterminate from Eq. *2-101*. Equation *2-97*, however, always determines $\mathbf{p}$ unambiguously. When $Q = 0$, the dipole moment is independent of the choice of origin (see Problem 2-30).

If the net charge is *not* zero, the dipole moment of the distribution can always be made zero by choosing the origin at the center of charge such that $\bar{\mathbf{r}}' = 0$.

Let us now consider the third term T_3 of Eq. *2-93*. It involves a $1/r^3$ factor as in the case of the linear quadrupole in Section 2.9. If we calculate T_3 for the linear quadrupole with charges Q, $-2Q$, and Q at $z = s$, $z = 0$, and $z = -s$ respectively, we find that it gives the electrostatic potential V of Eq. *2-84*. This third term can be rewritten as follows:

$$T_3 = \frac{1}{4\pi\epsilon_0 r^3}\left[3mn \int_\tau y'z'\rho \, d\tau + 3nl \int_\tau z'x'\rho \, d\tau \right. \tag{2-103}$$

$$+ 3lm \int_\tau x'y'\rho \, d\tau + \frac{1}{2}(3l^2 - 1)\int_\tau x'^2\rho \, d\tau$$

$$\left. + \frac{1}{2}(3m^2 - 1)\int_\tau y'^2\rho \, d\tau + \frac{1}{2}(3n^2 - 1)\int_\tau z'^2\rho \, d\tau \right],$$

where the integrals depend solely on the distribution of charge within the volume τ, and not on the position of the point of observation P.

These six integrals specify a quantity called the *quadrupole moment* for the charge distribution, and we write that

$$p_{xx} = \int_\tau x'^2\rho \, d\tau = Q\bar{x}'^2, \tag{2-104}$$

$$p_{yy} = \int_\tau y'^2\rho \, d\tau = Q\overline{y'^2}, \tag{2-105}$$

$$p_{zz} = \int_\tau z'^2\rho \, d\tau = Q\overline{z'^2}, \tag{2-106}$$

$$p_{yz} = p_{zy} = \int_\tau y'z'\rho \, d\tau = Q\overline{y'z'}, \tag{2-107}$$

$$p_{zx} = p_{xz} = \int_\tau z'x'\rho \, d\tau = Q\overline{z'x'}, \tag{2-108}$$

$$p_{xy} = p_{yx} = \int_\tau x'y'\rho \, d\tau = Q\overline{x'y'}, \tag{2-109}$$

where the bars indicate that the average value is to be taken. The quadrupole moment so defined is more complicated than a vector, since it requires six components to specify it. Such a quantity is called a *tensor*.

If the charge distribution is symmetrical about an axis, as in the atomic nucleus, for example, and if the axis of symmetry is chosen to be the z-axis, then the elements of charge at (x', y', z') and at $(-x', y', z')$ are equal, their contributions to the integral of Eq. *2-108* cancel, and

$$p_{zz} = 0. \tag{2-110}$$

Similarly,

$$p_{yz} = 0, \tag{2-111}$$

and

$$p_{xy} = 0. \tag{2-112}$$

Also, by symmetry

$$p_{xx} = p_{yy}. \tag{2-113}$$

In such cases it is convenient to define a single quantity q, often called the quadrupole moment of the distribution:

$$q = 2(p_{zz} - p_{xx}), \tag{2-114}$$

$$= \int_\tau \rho(3z^2 - r^2) \, d\tau, \tag{2-115}$$

$$= Q\overline{(3z^2 - r^2)}. \tag{2-116}$$

The quadrupole potential at a point whose coordinates are (r, θ) is then

$$V_3 = \frac{q}{4\pi\epsilon_0} \frac{(3\cos^2\theta - 1)}{r^3}. \tag{2-117}$$

We must note here that, in general, the various multipole terms depend on the choice of the origin, except for the first one, which is proportional to the net charge of the system. The second term, which is proportional to the dipole moment, is also independent of the choice of the origin for the special case in which the net charge is zero.

In summary, the potential produced by an arbitrary charge distribution is the same as that of: (a) a point charge equal to the net charge of the distribution, plus (b) a point dipole, with a dipole moment equal to the dipole moment of the distribution, plus (c) a point quadrupole with the quadrupole moment of the distribution, and so on, all located at the origin.

2.12. The Average Field Intensity Inside a Sphere Containing an Arbitrary Charge Distribution

In discussing dielectrics in the next chapter, we shall require the average electrostatic field intensity within a spherical surface enclosing an arbitrary charge distribution. Let us calculate the average field intensity at the interior point directly. To do this we shall first make the calculation for a single point charge.

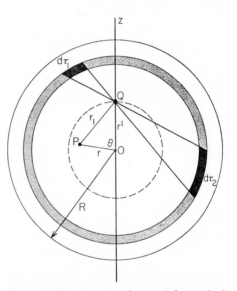

Figure 2-16 shows a point charge Q located at a distance r' from the center of a sphere of radius R. The z-axis is taken to be along the line joining the center of the sphere and the charge Q. By symmetry, the average field over the volume of the sphere must be along the z-axis.

We wish then to calculate

$$\bar{E}_z = \frac{\int_\tau E_z \, d\tau}{\int_\tau d\tau} = \frac{1}{\tau} \int_\tau E_z \, d\tau, \quad (2\text{-}118)$$

where τ is the volume of the sphere. This integral can be separated into two parts, one over the spherical shell between the radii r' and R, and one over the the sphere of radius r'.

Figure 2-16. *A point charge Q located at a distance r' from the center of a sphere of radius R. The average field intensity which Q produces within the sphere is proportional to the dipole moment of Q, is inversely proportional to the volume of the sphere, and is in the direction opposite to the dipole moment of Q. Figure 2-6 shows the elements of volume in detail.*

We can show that the integral over the outer volume is zero by using an argument somewhat analogous to that used in Section 2.7.2 to find the field inside a uniform spherical charge distribution. In Figure 2-16, the solid-angle element $d\Omega$ intercepts the volume elements $d\tau_1$ and $d\tau_2$ in the shell of thickness dr.

Since the value of E_z *decreases* as the square of the distance from Q whereas $d\tau$ *increases* as the square of the distance (see Eq. *2-44*), their product remains constant. However, at $d\tau_1$, E_z is positive, whereas at $d\tau_2$, E_z is negative, thus the two contributions to the integral cancel. The same is true for the whole outer shell, the contributions to the integral canceling in pairs.

To calculate $\int_\tau E_z \, d\tau$ over the inner volume, we consider point $P(x, y, z)$ in Figure 2-16. The potential at P is

$$V = \frac{1}{4\pi\epsilon_0} \frac{Q}{r_1}. \tag{2-119}$$

We can expand $1/r_1$ as in Eq. *2-67*, but now in terms of r/r' so as to obtain a converging series, since $r < r'$:

$$V = \frac{Q}{4\pi\epsilon_0} \frac{1}{r'} \left[1 + \frac{r}{r'} \cos\theta + \frac{1}{2} \frac{r^2}{r'^2} (3\cos^2\theta - 1) + \frac{1}{2} \frac{r^3}{r'^3} (5\cos^3\theta - 3\cos\theta) + \cdots \right] \tag{2-120}$$

This is the potential due to a series of multipoles. Recall that

$$r \cos\theta = z, \tag{2-121}$$

and that

$$\frac{\partial r}{\partial z} = \frac{\partial}{\partial z} (x^2 + y^2 + z^2)^{1/2} \tag{2-122}$$

$$= \frac{z}{r} = \cos\theta. \tag{2-123}$$

Then

$$E_z = -\frac{\partial V}{\partial z} = -\frac{Q}{4\pi\epsilon_0 r'^2} \left[1 + \frac{2z}{r'} + \frac{3}{2r'^2} (3z^2 - r^2) + \cdots \right]. \tag{2-124}$$

To compute $\frac{1}{\tau} \int_\tau E_z \, d\tau$ over the spherical volume of radius r', we return to polar coordinates and integrate each term of Eq. *2-124* in succession:

$$\bar{E}_{z1} = -\frac{Q}{4\pi\epsilon_0 r'^2 \tau} \int_0^\pi \int_0^{r'} 2\pi r^2 \sin\theta \, dr \, d\theta, \tag{2-125}$$

$$= -\frac{Qr'}{3\epsilon_0 \tau}; \tag{2-126}$$

$$\bar{E}_{z2} = -\frac{2Q}{4\pi\epsilon_0 r'^3 \tau} \int_0^\pi \int_0^{r'} 2\pi r^3 \cos\theta \sin\theta \, dr \, d\theta = 0; \tag{2-127}$$

$$\bar{E}_{z3} = -\frac{3Q}{8\pi\epsilon_0 r'^4 \tau} \left[\int_0^\pi \int_0^{r'} 6\pi r^4 \cos^2\theta \sin\theta \, dr \, d\theta - \int_0^\pi \int_0^{r'} 2\pi r^4 \sin\theta \, dr \, d\theta \right] = 0. \tag{2-128}$$

All the higher terms are also zero, and

$$\overline{E}_z = -\frac{Qr'}{3\epsilon_0} \cdot \frac{3}{4\pi R^3}, \qquad (2\text{-}129)$$

$$= -\frac{Qr'}{4\pi\epsilon_0 R^3}. \qquad (2\text{-}130)$$

According to Eq. *2-101*, Qr' is the dipole moment p of the charge Q, and

$$\overline{E} = -\frac{p}{4\pi\epsilon_0 R^3}. \qquad (2\text{-}131)$$

This average field intensity has been calculated for a single charge Q on the z-axis. For an arbitrary charge distribution the resultant field is the superposition of the fields due to the different charges, according to the theorem of superposition of Section 2.2. Then $\overline{E}$ is again given by Eq. *2-131* with p equal to the dipole moment of the arbitrary charge distribution within the sphere of radius R.

2.13. Capacitance

Because of the repulsion between similar charges, energy must be expended to charge a conductor. Accordingly, the potential of the conductor rises as charge is added, the magnitude of the potential being proportional to the amount of charge added and depending on the geometrical configuration of the conductor. The charge which must be added per unit increase in potential is defined as the *capacitance* of the conductor. Thus

$$C = \frac{Q}{V}. \qquad (2\text{-}132)$$

One might well ask why the capacitance C should be a constant for a given conductor. This can be shown as follows. We consider an isolated conductor carrying a charge Q, and its electrostatic potential $V(x, y, z)$. At the surface of the conductor the charge density is $\epsilon_0 E$, or $-\epsilon_0$ times the rate of change of V in the direction normal to the surface. Since the potential V satisfies Laplace's equation $\nabla^2 V = 0$ (Eq. *2-29*), and since this equation is linear, any multiple of V is also a solution. Let us therefore increase V by some constant factor α. Then the surface charge density will also increase by α, and the total charge Q on the conductor will likewise increase. The charge on an isolated conductor is therefore proportional to the potential on the conductor, and its capacitance C is a constant.

The unit of capacitance is the coulomb/volt or *farad*. Since the farad is a larger capacitance than can normally be achieved, the microfarad (10^{-6} farad) is the unit used in practice.

As a simple example, consider an isolated conducting sphere of radius R. When it carries a charge Q, its potential is given by

$$V = \frac{1}{4\pi\epsilon_0} \frac{Q}{R}, \tag{2-133}$$

thus its capacitance is

$$C = \frac{Q}{V} = 4\pi\epsilon_0 R. \tag{2-134}$$

For example, a sphere one meter in radius has a capacitance of about 100 micromicrofarads.

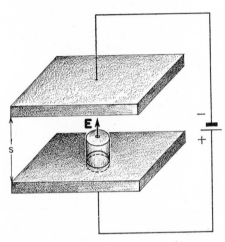

Figure 2-17. *The parallel-plate capacitor. The field intensity $\mathbf{E}$ is normal to the plates, and $E = \sigma/\epsilon_0$. End effects are neglected.*

For the case of two conductors the charge which must be transferred from one to the other per unit potential difference is defined as the capacitance between the two conductors. *Capacitors* consist of such pairs of conductors.

If two parallel conducting plates of area S separated by a distance s, as in Figure 2-17, are connected to the terminals of a battery, charge is transferred from one plate to the other, producing charge densities $+\sigma$ and $-\sigma$ on the inner surfaces. The field intensity $\mathbf{E}$ between the plates is readily found with the aid of a Gaussian surface having one end face within a plate and having sides perpendicular to the plates: it is σ/ϵ_0. The potential difference between the plates is

$$\Delta V = \frac{\sigma s}{\epsilon_0}, \tag{2-135}$$

and the capacitance is

$$C = \frac{Q}{\Delta V} = \frac{\sigma S}{\Delta V} = \epsilon_0 \frac{S}{s}. \tag{2-136}$$

It is useful to remember that the capacitance of a parallel-plate capacitor with a surface area of one square centimeter and a separation of one millimeter is about one micromicrofarad (10^{-12} farad).

In calculating the capacitance of the parallel-plate capacitor we have assumed that the field intensity $\mathbf{E}$ is everywhere perpendicular to the plates. This is not true in the fringing field at the edges of the plates, where the lines of force bow out into the space outside the plates. However, if the separation s is small compared to the linear extent of the plates, the above equation remains essentially correct.

Another example is that of a capacitor consisting of two concentric conducting spheres of radii R_1 and R_2, R_1 being the radius of the outer surface of the inner conductor and R_2 being that of the inner surface of the outer conductor, as shown in Figure 2-18. From Gauss's law, the field intensity between the conductors is given by

$$\mathbf{E} = \frac{Q}{4\pi\epsilon_0 r^2}\mathbf{r_1}, \qquad (2\text{-}137)$$

where Q is the positive charge which has been transferred from the outer to the inner conductor. The potential difference is

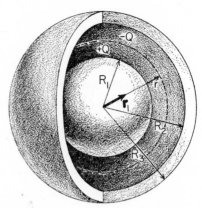

Figure 2-18. *Concentric spherical capacitor.*

$$\Delta V = \int_{R_2}^{R_1} \mathbf{E}\cdot\mathbf{dr}, \qquad (2\text{-}138)$$

$$= \frac{Q}{4\pi\epsilon_0 R_1} - \frac{Q}{4\pi\epsilon_0 R_2}. \qquad (2\text{-}139)$$

Thus the capacitance is

$$C = \frac{Q}{\Delta V} = 4\pi\epsilon_0\left(\frac{R_1 R_2}{R_2 - R_1}\right). \qquad (2\text{-}140)$$

If $R_2 \longrightarrow \infty$, $C \longrightarrow 4\pi\epsilon_0 R_1$, which is the capacitance calculated in Eq. *2-134* for the isolated sphere.

2.13.1. Coefficients of Capacitance and of Induction.

Consider two conductors, 1 and 2. Conductor 1 carries a charge Q_1 whereas conductor 2 is uncharged. Conductor 1 then has a potential $A_{11}Q_1$, and conductor 2 has a potential $A_{21}Q_1$, the coefficients A_{11} and A_{21} being constants which depend only on the geometry of the conductors. We then reverse the situation such that 1 is uncharged and 2 carries a charge Q_2. The potential becomes $A_{12}Q_2$ on conductor 1 and $A_{22}Q_2$ on 2. If the two fields are superposed,

$$V_1 = A_{11}Q_1 + A_{12}Q_2, \qquad (2\text{-}141)$$

$$V_2 = A_{21}Q_1 + A_{22}Q_2. \qquad (2\text{-}142)$$

For two different charges Q_1' and Q_2' we would have

$$V_1' = A_{11}Q_1' + A_{12}Q_2', \qquad (2\text{-}143)$$

$$V_2' = A_{21}Q_1' + A_{22}Q_2', \qquad (2\text{-}144)$$

with the same coefficients A_{11}, A_{12}, and so on.

We shall now show that $A_{12} = A_{21}$. This relation will be required below. It is a simple matter to show this equality for a pair of small conductors separated by a distance r, since both coefficients are equal to $1/4\pi\epsilon_0 r$.

For macroscopic conductors 1 and 2,

$$V_1 = \frac{1}{4\pi\epsilon_0}\left(\int_1 \frac{\sigma_1 \, da_1}{r} + \int_2 \frac{\sigma_2 \, da_2}{r}\right), \qquad (2\text{-}145)$$

where $\sigma_1 \, da_1$ and $\sigma_2 \, da_2$ are elements of charge on conductors 1 and 2, and r is the distance from these elements to the point on 1 where the potential V_1 is calculated.

Since it will be easier to pursue our reasoning in terms of summations, rather than integrals, we shall divide the two surfaces into infinitesimal elements of area which carry charges q_1, q_2, q_3, and so on. At position 1 the potential is

$$v_1 = \frac{1}{4\pi\epsilon_0}\left(\frac{q_2}{r_{12}} + \frac{q_3}{r_{13}} + \frac{q_4}{r_{14}} + \cdots\right),$$

where r_{12} is the distance between elements 1 and 2, and so forth. Since, by hypothesis, there are no point charges but rather a smooth distribution of charge over the surfaces, there is no $q_1/0$ term which would lead to an infinite value for v_1. We know that the potential has some finite value at each point.

We now consider a different charge distribution, such that q_1' replaces q_1, q_2' replaces q_2, and so on, and we form the summation

$$\begin{aligned}
\sum vq' = \frac{1}{4\pi\epsilon_0}&\left(0 + \frac{q_2}{r_{12}} + \frac{q_3}{r_{13}} + \frac{q_4}{r_{14}} + \cdots\right)q_1' \\
&+ \left(\frac{q_1}{r_{21}} + 0 + \frac{q_3}{r_{23}} + \frac{q_4}{r_{24}} + \cdots\right)q_2' \qquad (2\text{-}146) \\
&+ \left(\frac{q_1}{r_{31}} + \frac{q_2}{r_{32}} + 0 + \frac{q_4}{r_{34}} + \cdots\right)q_3' + \cdots.
\end{aligned}$$

It will be observed that r_{12} is the same as r_{21} and, similarly, that r_{31} equals r_{13}, $\cdots$. Thus

$$\sum vq' = \sum v'q. \qquad (2\text{-}147)$$

We then let the unprimed field correspond to $Q_1 = Q$, $Q_2 = 0$ and let the primed field correspond to $Q_1' = 0$, $Q_2' = Q$. The potentials on the conductors are V_1, V_2, V_1', V_2'. Then the summation $\sum vq'$ over conductor 1 gives $V_1 \sum q_1' = 0$ and $V_2 Q$ over conductor 2. Similarly, $\sum v'q$ gives $V_1 Q$ over conductor 1 and zero over conductor 2, such that

$$V_2 = V_1' \qquad (Q_1 = Q,\ Q_2 = 0,\ Q_1' = 0,\ Q_2' = Q). \qquad (2\text{-}148)$$

Substituting in Eqs. 2-142 and 2-143, we obtain the required result, namely, that $A_{12} = A_{21}$. More generally, when there are N conductors,

$$V_i = \sum_{j=1}^{N} A_{ij}Q_j, \qquad (2\text{-}149)$$

where

$$A_{ij} = A_{ji}. \tag{2-150}$$

Equation *2-149* can be rewritten more explicitly in the following form:

$$\begin{aligned}
V_1 &= A_{11}Q_1 + A_{12}Q_2 + A_{13}Q_3 + \cdots + A_{1N}Q_N, \\
V_2 &= A_{21}Q_1 + A_{22}Q_2 + A_{23}Q_3 + \cdots + A_{2N}Q_N, \\
V_3 &= A_{31}Q_1 + A_{32}Q_2 + A_{33}Q_3 + \cdots + A_{3N}Q_N, \\
&\quad\ldots\ldots\ldots\ldots\ldots\ldots\ldots\ldots\ldots\ldots\ldots\ldots, \\
V_N &= A_{N1}Q_1 + A_{N2}Q_2 + A_{N3}Q_3 + \cdots + A_{NN}Q_N.
\end{aligned} \tag{2-151}$$

It will be observed that the coefficient A_{13}, for example, is equal to the increase in potential produced in conductor 1 when the charge on conductor 3 is increased by one coulomb. From Eq. *2-150* this is exactly the same as the increase in potential produced in conductor 3 when the charge on conductor 1 is increased by one coulomb.

We have here a family of N simultaneous linear equations with N unknowns. All of the charges Q_i can therefore be determined if the potentials V_i and the coefficients A_{ij} are known. Thus

$$Q_i = \sum_{j=1}^{N} \frac{\Delta_{ij}}{\Delta} V_j, \tag{2-152}$$

where Δ is the determinant of all the A_{ij} coefficients. Δ_{ij} is the ijth minor determinant and is identical to Δ multiplied by $(-1)^{i+j}$, except that the ith row and the jth column are missing.

As an example, for two conductors the simultaneous equations are

$$V_1 = A_{11}Q_1 + A_{12}Q_2 \tag{2-153}$$

and

$$V_2 = A_{21}Q_1 + A_{22}Q_2. \tag{2-154}$$

According to Eq. *2-152* the solution for Q_1 is

$$Q_1 = V_1 \frac{\Delta_{11}}{\Delta} + V_2 \frac{\Delta_{12}}{\Delta}, \tag{2-155}$$

or

$$Q_1 = \frac{V_1 A_{22} - V_2 A_{12}}{A_{11}A_{22} - A_{21}A_{12}}, \tag{2-156}$$

which can be readily verified.

If we then write that

$$C_{ij} = \frac{\Delta_{ij}}{\Delta} \tag{2-157}$$

we obtain the relation

$$Q_i = \sum_{j=1}^{N} C_{ij}V_j, \tag{2-158}$$

where the coefficients C_{ij} depend solely on the geometry, since they involve only the coefficients A_{ij}. According to Eq. *2-150*, the determinant Δ is symmetrical about its diagonal, and

$$\Delta_{ij} = \Delta_{ji}, \tag{2-159}$$

thus

$$C_{ij} = C_{ji}. \tag{2-160}$$

Writing out Eq. *2-158* explicitly gives

$$
\begin{aligned}
Q_1 &= C_{11}V_1 + C_{12}V_2 + C_{13}V_3 + \cdots + C_{1N}V_N, \\
Q_2 &= C_{21}V_1 + C_{22}V_2 + C_{23}V_3 + \cdots + C_{2N}V_N, \\
Q_3 &= C_{31}V_1 + C_{32}V_2 + C_{33}V_3 + \cdots + C_{3N}V_N, \\
&\cdots\cdots\cdots\cdots\cdots\cdots\cdots\cdots\cdots\cdots\cdots\cdots, \\
Q_N &= C_{N1}V_1 + C_{N2}V_2 + C_{N3}V_3 + \cdots + C_{NN}V_N.
\end{aligned}
\tag{2-161}
$$

The coefficients C_{ij} are known as *coefficients of capacitance* when $i = j$ and as *coefficients of induction* when $i \neq j$. Their meaning can be understood as follows. If conductors $2, 3, 4, \cdots, N$ are connected together and to ground, such that $V_2 = V_3 = V_4 \cdots = V_N = 0$, then the charge Q_1 is simply $C_{11}V_1$, where C_{11} is the coefficient of capacitance between conductor 1 and all the other conductors connected together. Under such conditions V_1 and Q_1 have the same sign, and C_{11} is therefore a positive quantity. The presence of a charge Q_1 on conductor 1 induces a charge Q_2 of opposite sign on conductor 2, given by $C_{12}V_1$. Thus C_{12} is a negative quantity.

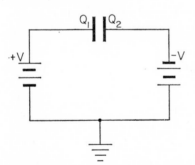

The same type of argument can be used for all the conductors: the coefficient C_{ii}, with equal indices, is a positive quantity and is called the coefficient of capacitance, or simply the *capacitance*, between the ith conductor and all other conductors connected together. On the other hand, the coefficient of induction C_{ij}, with different indices, is a negative quantity.

Figure 2-19. *A parallel-plate capacitor with its plates at potentials $+ V$ and $- V$. The charges on the two plates are Q_1 and Q_2.*

2.13.2. Examples. As an illustration of the above concepts, let us return to the parallel-plate capacitor and consider the case illustrated in Figure 2-19. The capacitor plates are not necessarily of the same size, but it is assumed that essentially all the lines of force emerging from one plate end on the other and that a negligible number go to other conductors, to ground, or extend to infinity. The net outward flux through a Gaussian surface enclosing both plates is then zero, and $Q_1 = - Q_2$.

From Eq. *2-158*,

$$Q_1 = C_{11}V + C_{12}(-V), \qquad (2\text{-}162)$$

$$Q_2 = C_{12}V + C_{22}(-V), \qquad (2\text{-}163)$$

and

$$C_{11} = C_{22}. \qquad (2\text{-}164)$$

The charge $C_{11}V$ is that which would appear on plate 1 if it were at potential V and if plate 2 were at ground. An extra charge $C_{12}(-V)$ is induced on plate 1 because plate 2 is at a potential $-V$. It will be recalled that C_{12} is a negative quantity, thus the charge $-C_{12}V$ is positive. By symmetry, $C_{11} = -C_{12}$ in this example.

In the general case of two conductors, we have defined the capacitance as the charge which must be transferred from one to the other to produce a unit potential difference between them. In the above example, the capacitance is $C_{11} = C_{22} = -C_{12}$.

Let us also define the coefficients of capacitance and of induction for the concentric spheres of Figure 2-18. We have, using Q_1 for the charge on the inner sphere and Q_2 for the charge on the outer,

$$Q_1 = C_{11}V_1 + C_{12}V_2, \qquad (2\text{-}165)$$

and

$$Q_2 = C_{21}V_1 + C_{22}V_2. \qquad (2\text{-}166)$$

The flux through a Gaussian surface enclosing only the inner sphere depends only on the charge Q_1 on that sphere, hence

$$V_1 - V_2 = \frac{Q_1}{4\pi\epsilon_0}\left(\frac{1}{R_1} - \frac{1}{R_2}\right), \qquad (2\text{-}167)$$

$$= \frac{Q_1}{4\pi\epsilon_0}\frac{(R_2 - R_1)}{R_1 R_2}. \qquad (2\text{-}168)$$

Note that $C_{11}V_1 = Q_1$ when $V_2 = 0$ and that sphere 1 is at potential V_1. Thus from the above equation,

$$C_{11} = 4\pi\epsilon_0 \frac{R_1 R_2}{R_2 - R_1}. \qquad (2\text{-}169)$$

Moreover, $C_{21}V_1$ is the charge on sphere 2 when it is grounded, and sphere 1 is at potential V_1. Since there is no field outside 2, Gauss's law shows that $Q_1 = -Q_2$, and therefore

$$C_{21} = -4\pi\epsilon_0 \left(\frac{R_1 R_2}{R_2 - R_1}\right). \qquad (2\text{-}170)$$

Since C_{12} is always equal to C_{21} we now require only C_{22}. When sphere 1 is grounded and sphere 2 is at potential V_2, part of the charge on sphere 2 is on its inner surface and part on its outer surface. The total charge on sphere 2 is $C_{22}V_2$. The induced charge on sphere 1 is then equal in magnitude and opposite in sign to the charge on the inner surface of the outer sphere, and, from Eq. *2-167*,

$$Q_{2i} = 4\pi\epsilon_0 \left(\frac{R_1 R_2}{R_2 - R_1} \right) V_2, \qquad (2\text{-}171)$$

where the subscript i indicates the inner surface of sphere 2. In addition, there is a charge Q_{20} on the outer surface of sphere 2, since it is now at a potential other than zero, such that

$$V_2 = \frac{Q_{20}}{4\pi\epsilon_0 R_3}, \qquad (2\text{-}172)$$

where R_3 is the radius of the outer surface of sphere 2. Thus

$$Q_{20} = 4\pi\epsilon_0 R_3 V_2, \qquad (2\text{-}173)$$

and

$$C_{22} = 4\pi\epsilon_0 \left(\frac{R_1 R_2}{R_2 - R_1} + R_3 \right). \qquad (2\text{-}174)$$

The capacitance of the outer sphere therefore depends on both the inner and the outer fields.

2.14. Potential Energy of a Charge Distribution

Let us consider a set of point charges distributed in space as in Figure 2-20. We shall assume that the charge configuration is of finite extent in order that

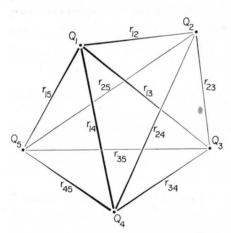

the potential at infinity can be taken to be zero, as usual. We shall also assume that no other charges are present. Each individual charge is situated in the electric field produced by the other charges, at a point where the potential V due only to the *other* charges has some definite value. Each charge thus has associated with it a definite potential energy, either positive or negative, and the system as a whole has stored in it a potential energy which we shall calculate. The charges are assumed to remain in equilibrium under the action of the electric forces and of other forces which we shall assume to be mechanical. Once we have calculated the potential energy, we shall be able to calculate the electrostatic forces and, therefore, the mechanical forces in equilibrium with them.

Figure 2-20. *Set of point charges Q_1, Q_2, . . . Q_5 separated by distances r_{12}, . . . r_{45}.*

Let $Q_1, Q_2, Q_3, \cdots, Q_N$ be the N charges; let r_{12} be the distance between Q_1 and Q_2, let r_{13} be the distance between Q_1 and Q_3, and so on, as in Figure 2-20. Now let Q_1 recede to infinity very slowly, such that the electrostatic and the mechanical forces are always in equilibrium. In this way there is no acceleration and, therefore, no kinetic energy involved. The change in the potential energy W_1 of the charge must be equal to the work which is done by, or against, the mechanical forces. This change W_1 is the product of the charge Q_1 and the potential V_1 produced by the *other* charges at the original position of Q_1. We shall assume that there is no charge at infinity and that the potential there is zero. Then

$$W_1 = \frac{Q_1}{4\pi\epsilon_0}\left(\frac{Q_2}{r_{12}} + \frac{Q_3}{r_{13}} + \cdots + \frac{Q_N}{r_{1N}}\right). \qquad (2\text{-}175)$$

We have chosen the sign of W_1 such that energy is withdrawn from the system if W_1 is positive. Note that all the charges except Q_1 are represented in the series of terms within the parentheses.

Now let Q_2 recede to a point infinitely distant from Q_1. The change W_2 in the potential energy of Q_2 is given by

$$W_2 = \frac{Q_2}{4\pi\epsilon_0}\left(\frac{Q_3}{r_{23}} + \frac{Q_4}{r_{24}} + \cdots + \frac{Q_N}{r_{2N}}\right). \qquad (2\text{-}176)$$

This series has only $N - 2$ terms within the brackets, the Q_1 and Q_2 terms being absent. We continue the process for all the remaining charges, there being progressively fewer terms in the series for the potential energy changes, until finally the Nth charge can be removed without any change in energy, since it is left in a zero field once all the other charges have been removed.

The total change W in potential energy is then

$$W = W_1 + W_2 + W_3 + \cdots + W_N \qquad (2\text{-}177)$$

$$= \frac{Q_1}{4\pi\epsilon_0}\left(0 + \frac{Q_2}{r_{12}} + \frac{Q_3}{r_{13}} + \frac{Q_4}{r_{14}} + \cdots + \frac{Q_N}{r_{1N}}\right)$$

$$+ \frac{Q_2}{4\pi\epsilon_0}\left(\quad\; 0 + \frac{Q_3}{r_{23}} + \frac{Q_4}{r_{24}} + \cdots + \frac{Q_N}{r_{2N}}\right)$$

$$+ \frac{Q_3}{4\pi\epsilon_0}\left(\qquad\qquad 0 + \frac{Q_4}{r_{34}} + \cdots + \frac{Q_N}{r_{3N}}\right) \qquad (2\text{-}178)$$

$$\cdots\cdots\cdots\cdots\cdots\cdots\cdots$$

$$+ \frac{Q_N}{4\pi\epsilon_0}\left(\qquad\qquad\qquad\qquad\quad 0\right).$$

Let us now rewrite the array of terms within the parentheses, adding in, below the diagonal line of zeros, the terms which are equal to their counterparts on the other side of the diagonal. Then every term of the series appears twice, and

$$2W = \frac{Q_1}{4\pi\epsilon_0}\left(0 \quad + \frac{Q_2}{r_{12}} + \frac{Q_3}{r_{13}} + \frac{Q_4}{r_{14}} + \cdots + \frac{Q_N}{r_{1N}}\right)$$

$$+ \frac{Q_2}{4\pi\epsilon_0}\left(\frac{Q_1}{r_{21}} + 0 \quad + \frac{Q_3}{r_{23}} + \frac{Q_4}{r_{24}} + \cdots + \frac{Q_N}{r_{2N}}\right)$$

$$+ \frac{Q_3}{4\pi\epsilon_0}\left(\frac{Q_1}{r_{31}} + \frac{Q_2}{r_{32}} + 0 \quad + \frac{Q_4}{r_{34}} + \cdots + \frac{Q_N}{r_{3N}}\right) \qquad (2\text{-}179)$$

$$\cdots\cdots\cdots\cdots\cdots\cdots\cdots\cdots\cdots\cdots\cdots$$

$$+ \frac{Q_N}{4\pi\epsilon_0}\left(\frac{Q_1}{r_{N1}} + \frac{Q_2}{r_{N2}} + \frac{Q_3}{r_{N3}} + \frac{Q_4}{r_{N4}} + \cdots + \quad 0\right).$$

Thus the first line is Q_1V_1, the second line is Q_2V_2, and so forth, such that

$$2W = Q_1V_1 + Q_2V_2 + Q_3V_3 + \cdots + Q_NV_N, \qquad (2\text{-}180)$$

and the total change in potential energy is

$$W = \frac{1}{2}\sum_{i=1}^{N} Q_iV_i, \qquad (2\text{-}181)$$

where V_i is the potential *in the undisturbed system* due to all the charges except Q_i at the point occupied by Q_i. We have *not* taken into account the self energy of the individual point charges, that is, the energy which would be liberated if each one were allowed to expand to an infinite volume.

For a continuous charge distribution of density $\rho(x, y, z)$ we can make a similar argument to calculate the energy of the system, but the argument must be made carefully. For example, in the absence of any other charges, we can bring a single charge Q to a given point without doing any work at all; but if we assemble the charge at the point by first bringing in a charge $Q/2$ and then a second charge $Q/2$ we must do work against the field of the first charge when we bring in the second.

We can calculate the potential energy for the continuous distribution correctly by removing the charge to infinity just as we have done for discrete charges. We must calculate the energy dW which we can recover from the system for each element of charge dQ which we remove. The simplest way to do this is to decrease the whole distribution uniformly from the initial density ρ to zero so that at any instant the density at every point is $\alpha\rho$ where α is a parameter lying in the range from 0 to 1. When the density at a point is $\alpha\rho$ the charge dQ' in a volume element $d\tau$ at that point is

$$dQ' = \alpha\rho \, d\tau, \qquad (2\text{-}182)$$

and the potential V' is

$$V' = \alpha V, \qquad (2\text{-}183)$$

where V is the initial potential at the point. If we decrease the charge density at every point in the distribution from $\alpha\rho$ to $(\alpha - d\alpha)\rho$ the charge in a volume element $d\tau$ decreases by

$$d^2Q = d\alpha\, \rho\, d\tau, \tag{2-184}$$

and the energy withdrawn from the system in removing d^2Q from this particular volume element is

$$d^2W = V'\, d^2Q, \tag{2-185}$$

$$= \alpha V\, d\alpha\, \rho\, d\tau. \tag{2-186}$$

If we repeat the operation for all the volume elements in the volume τ,

$$dW = \int_\tau \alpha V\, d\alpha\, \rho\, d\tau, \tag{2-187}$$

and, to decrease the charge density to zero everywhere,

$$W = \int_0^1 \alpha\, d\alpha \int_\tau \rho V\, d\tau, \tag{2-188}$$

or

$$W = \frac{1}{2} \int_\tau \rho V\, d\tau. \tag{2-189}$$

This equation is analogous to Eq. *2-181*, which was calculated for point charges, except that we have now taken the self energies into account. The integral in Eq. *2-189* may be evaluated over any arbitrary volume τ which contains all charges in the system, there being no contribution from the elements of volume in which $\rho = 0$. Then, if there are surface charge distributions σ,

$$W = \frac{1}{2} \int_S \sigma V\, da, \tag{2-190}$$

although this energy is implicitly included in Eq. *2-189*.

The factor $1/2$ appears in Eqs. *2-181* and *2-189* because the potential at the position of a given charge at the time it is removed to infinity is less, in general, than the potential at the same point in the original charge distribution. On the average, the potential at the time of removal is just one-half the potential in the original distribution.

2.14.1. Energy Density in an Electric Field. The potential energy W of the charge distribution can be related to the electric field intensity due to the charge distribution as follows. According to Poisson's equation,

$$\rho = -\epsilon_0 \nabla^2 V \tag{2-191}$$

at every point in the field. If we substitute Eq. *2-189* into Eq. *2-191*, then

$$W = -\frac{\epsilon_0}{2} \int_\tau V \nabla^2 V\, d\tau, \tag{2-192}$$

where τ is again any volume containing all the charges in the system

We may simplify this equation through the vector identity of Problem 1-14.

$$\nabla \cdot f\mathbf{A} = f(\nabla \cdot \mathbf{A}) + \mathbf{A} \cdot \nabla f, \tag{2-193}$$

where f and $\mathbf{A}$ are scalar and vector functions respectively. Let $f = V$, and $\mathbf{A} = \nabla V$. Then

$$V \nabla^2 V = \nabla \cdot (V \nabla V) - (\nabla V)^2, \tag{2-194}$$

and

$$W = -\frac{\epsilon_0}{2}\left[\int_\tau \nabla \cdot (V \nabla V)\, d\tau - \int_\tau (\nabla V)^2\, d\tau\right]. \tag{2-195}$$

Using the divergence theorem, we can transform the first term on the right side of this equation into a surface integral over the surface S bounding the volume τ such that

$$W = -\frac{\epsilon_0}{2}\left[\int_S (V \nabla V)\cdot \mathbf{da} - \int_\tau (\nabla V)^2\, d\tau\right]. \tag{2-196}$$

Now τ can be any volume which includes all the charge in the system. We are thus free to choose the bounding surface S at a large distance from the charge distribution. Then in the first integral V falls off at least as fast as $1/r$, since the monopole term falls off as $1/r$, whereas the dipole, quadrupole, and higher terms fall off as $1/r^2$, $1/r^3$, and so forth, as we saw in Section 2.10. Then ∇V falls off at least as fast as $1/r^2$. Since the surface area increases as r^2, the whole integral decreases at least as fast as $1/r$ and can be made arbitrarily small by choosing the surface S sufficiently far off. We are then left with

$$W = \frac{\epsilon_0}{2}\int_\tau E^2\, d\tau, \tag{2-197}$$

since $|\mathbf{E}| = -|\nabla V|$. The volume τ need not be infinite, but only large enough to include all points at which $\mathbf{E}$ differs from zero. This quantity takes into account the self energies and is always positive.

Equation 2-197 shows that the energy associated with a charge distribution, that is, the energy required to assemble all the charges, starting with a configuration in which they are all infinitely far apart, may be calculated by associating with each point of the field an energy density

$$\frac{dW}{d\tau} = \frac{\epsilon_0}{2} E^2, \tag{2-198}$$

measured in joules/meter^3. However, the assignment of such an energy density does not necessarily mean that the energy is localized in the field. There are two ways of computing the energy required to establish the field: one in terms of charge density and potential, as in Eq. 2-189, and one in terms of the field intensity, as in Eq. 2-197. In the first case the integrand is zero whenever the charge density ρ is zero. In the second case it is zero whenever the electric field intensity $\mathbf{E}$ is zero. Does the energy reside in the charges themselves, or does it reside in the field? These questions are meaningless. Our concept of energy density merely represents one way of computing the total energy in the system.

As an example of the validity of the energy density concept for calculating the energy stored in an electric field, let us consider an isolated spherical conductor of radius R and surface charge density σ. From Eq. *2-190*,

$$W = \frac{1}{2} \int_S \sigma V \, da, \qquad (2\text{-}199)$$

which leads at once to the familiar

$$W = \frac{1}{2} QV. \qquad (2\text{-}200)$$

In this case

$$V = \frac{Q}{4\pi\epsilon_0 R}, \qquad (2\text{-}201)$$

and

$$W = \frac{Q^2}{8\pi\epsilon_0 R}. \qquad (2\text{-}202)$$

In addition, from Eq. *2-197*, we have

$$W = \frac{\epsilon_0}{2} \int_\tau E^2 d\tau, \qquad (2\text{-}203)$$

where

$$E = \frac{Q}{4\pi\epsilon_0 r^2} \qquad (r > R). \qquad (2\text{-}204)$$

Then, integrating

$$W = \frac{\epsilon_0}{2} \int_R^\infty \left(\frac{Q}{4\pi\epsilon_0 r^2} \right)^2 4\pi r^2 \, dr, \qquad (2\text{-}205)$$

we obtain

$$W = \frac{Q^2}{8\pi\epsilon_0 R}, \qquad (2\text{-}206)$$

which is the result obtained above (Eq. *202*).

2.15. Forces on Conductors

An element of charge $\sigma \, da$ on the surface of a conductor experiences the electrostatic field of all the other charges in the system and is therefore subject to an electrostatic force. In a static field, this force must be perpendicular to the surface of the conductor, for otherwise the charges would move along the surface. Since the charge $\sigma \, da$ is bound to the conductor by internal forces, the force acting on $\sigma \, da$ is transmitted to the conductor itself.

To calculate the magnitude of this force, let us consider a conductor with a surface charge density σ and a field $\mathbf{E}$ at the surface. From Gauss's law, the electric field intensity just outside the conductor is

$$E = \frac{\sigma}{\epsilon_0} \qquad (2\text{-}207)$$

and is perpendicular to the conducting surface. Now the force on the element of charge $\sigma \, da$ is *not* $\mathbf{E}\sigma \, da$, since the field which acts on $\sigma \, da$ is the field due only to the *other* charges in the system.

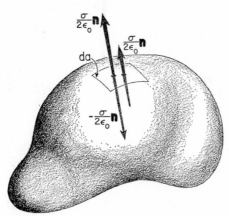

Figure 2-21. *The local charge density at the surface of a conductor gives rise to oppositely directed electric field intensities* $\sigma/2\epsilon_0$ *as shown by the two arrows on the left; the other charges on the conductor give rise to the field* $\sigma/2\epsilon_0$ *shown by the arrow on the right. The net result is* σ/ϵ_0 *outside, and zero inside. The vector* $\mathbf{n}$ *is a unit vector normal to the conductor surface, and it points outwards.*

Let us calculate first the electric field intensity (Figure 2-21) produced by $\sigma \, da$ itself. We can do this by direct integration from Coulomb's law, as in Section 2.7.3. Arbitrarily close to the surface, the part of the field arising from $\sigma \, da$ is $\sigma/2\epsilon_0$. The element of charge $\sigma \, da$ itself therefore produces exactly half the total field at a point lying in the surface. This is qualitatively reasonable since the nearby charge is much more effective than the more distant charge.

Now if $\sigma \, da$ produces half the field, then all the other charges must produce the other half, and the field intensity acting on $\sigma \, da$ must be $\sigma/2\epsilon_0$. These fields are illustrated in Figure 2-21. The local surface charge $\sigma \, da$ produces an electric field intensity $\sigma/2\epsilon_0$ outside the conductor and $\sigma/2\epsilon_0$ inside. Superposed over these fields there is a further field intensity $\sigma/2\epsilon_0$ directed outward, produced by all the other charges on the conductor. The net result is an outward field intensity of σ/ϵ_0 outside, and a zero field inside.

The force on the conductor surface is therefore

$$dF = \frac{\sigma}{2\epsilon_0} \, \sigma \, da, \qquad (2\text{-}208)$$

and the force per unit area is

$$\frac{dF}{da} = \frac{\sigma^2}{2\epsilon_0}, \qquad (2\text{-}209)$$

$$= \frac{\epsilon_0 E^2}{2}. \qquad (2\text{-}210)$$

The force per unit area is just equal to the energy density in the field.

We have arrived at Eq. *2-210* for an idealized case in which the surface charge lies in an infinitely thin plane sheet. This is of course never true in practice, since surfaces of conductors are rough on a microscopic scale, thus we really have a volume distribution of charge. Equation *2-210* nevertheless remains valid. The proof of this statement will be left as a problem at the end of the chapter.

We can also calculate the forces acting on conductors by considering how the energy of the system changes for a small virtual change in its geometry. It is generally easier to proceed in this way than it is to use surface charge densities and field intensities as above.

2.15.1. Forces on a Parallel-plate Capacitor. As a simple example, let us consider a parallel-plate capacitor of area S and plate separation s carrying a charge density $+\sigma$ on one plate and $-\sigma$ on the other, as in Figure 2-22. We shall assume that the separation of the plates is small compared to their linear extent, in order that the parallel-plate capacitor approximation will be valid. Then, from Eq. *2-197*, the energy associated with the electrostatic field between the plates is

$$W = \frac{\epsilon_0}{2} E^2 Ss. \qquad (2\text{-}211)$$

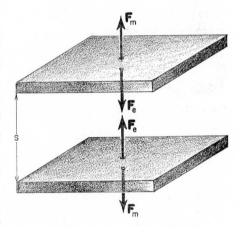

If the plates are now insulated, such that the charges remain constant, and if the plates are moved closer together by a small distance ds, the field intensity $\mathbf{E}$ remains the same according to Gauss's law. The volume between the plates decreases, however, hence the energy in the field also decreases. Since we must

Figure 2-22. *A charged parallel-plate capacitor with its plates insulated. The plates are held in equilibrium by a mechanical force F_m which acts on each plate in a direction tending to increase the separation s, and by an electric force F_e tending to decrease the separation.*

have conservation of energy, the energy lost by the field has gone into work against the mechanical forces $\mathbf{F}_m$ holding the plates apart. Then

$$\frac{\epsilon_0}{2} E^2 S \, ds = F_m \, ds, \qquad (2\text{-}212)$$

$$F_m = \frac{\epsilon_0}{2} E^2 S, \qquad (2\text{-}213)$$

and

$$\frac{F_m}{S} = \frac{\epsilon_0}{2} E^2, \tag{2-214}$$

$$= \frac{\sigma^2}{2\epsilon_0}. \tag{2-215}$$

Since the electrical force $\mathbf{F}_e$ is in equilibrium with the mechanical force, it must be of equal magnitude and oriented so as to pull the plates together. The forces are indicated in Figure 2-22.

It is instructive to examine this same problem for the case in which the potential difference between the plates is kept constant during the displacement ds. From Eq. *2-211*, the expression for electrostatic energy, we obtain the relation

$$W = \frac{\epsilon_0}{2} \frac{(\Delta V)^2}{s} S. \tag{2-216}$$

If the plates move closer together, such that s decreases, the electrostatic energy increases by an amount

$$dW = -\frac{\epsilon_0}{2} \frac{(\Delta V)^2}{s^2} ds, \tag{2-217}$$

ds being negative.

But now the charge on the plates increases in the process, since

$$Q = C(\Delta V), \tag{2-218}$$

or

$$Q = \frac{\epsilon_0 S}{s} \Delta V, \tag{2-219}$$

hence

$$dQ = -\frac{\epsilon_0 S(\Delta V)}{s^2} ds. \tag{2-220}$$

Thus dQ is positive when the plates move closer together. The battery must take positive charge from the negative plate, raise it through the potential difference ΔV, and put it on the positive plate. In this process the battery supplies an amount of energy

$$dW_B = dQ \, \Delta V, \tag{2-221}$$

or

$$dW_B = -\frac{\epsilon_0 S(\Delta V)^2}{s^2} ds. \tag{2-222}$$

The battery therefore does an amount of work equal to twice the increase in the electrostatic field energy. The other half goes into work against the mechanical forces. Thus

$$dW_m = \frac{dW_B}{2} = \frac{\epsilon_0}{2} E^2 S \, ds. \tag{2-223}$$

and

$$\frac{F_m}{S} = \frac{\epsilon_0}{2} E^2,$$ (2-224)

or

$$\frac{F_m}{S} = \frac{\sigma^2}{2\epsilon_0},$$ (2-225)

which are Eqs. *2-214* and *2-215*.

Had we equated mechanical work to change in field energy in this case we would have found the wrong sign for the force, since the field energy increases when the plates move together. It is therefore important to include all the energy changes when applying the principle of conservation of energy to a system.

2.16. Summary

It is found empirically that the force exerted by a point charge Q_a on a point charge Q_b in a vacuum is given by

$$\mathbf{F}_{ab} = \frac{1}{4\pi\epsilon_0} \frac{Q_a Q_b}{r^2} \mathbf{r}_1.$$ (2-2)

This is *Coulomb's law*. We consider the force $\mathbf{F}_{ab}$ as being the product of the *electrostatic field intensity* $\mathbf{E}_a$, where

$$\mathbf{E}_a = \frac{Q_a}{4\pi\epsilon_0 r^2} \mathbf{r}_1,$$ (2-3)

and of the charge Q_b. The *principle of superposition* for electrostatic fields then follows from the fact that $\mathbf{E}_a$ is proportional to the charge producing it.

The central nature of the Coulomb force makes $\mathbf{E}$ conservative and leads to the concept of *potential:*

$$\boldsymbol{\nabla} \times \mathbf{E} = 0,$$ (2-9)

hence

$$\mathbf{E} = -\boldsymbol{\nabla} V.$$ (2-10)

Gauss's law follows from the fact that $\mathbf{E}$ is central *and* falls off as $1/r^2$. It can be stated either in integral or in differential form:

$$\int_S \mathbf{E} \cdot \mathbf{da} = \frac{1}{\epsilon_0} \int_\tau \rho \, d\tau,$$ (2-21)

or

$$\boldsymbol{\nabla} \cdot \mathbf{E} = \frac{\rho}{\epsilon_0}.$$ (2-23)

Poisson's equation,

$$\nabla^2 V = -\frac{\rho}{\epsilon_0},$$ (2-28)

then follows from the differential statement of Gauss's law and from the definition of potential.

The electrostatic field produced by simple charge distributions can be calculated in three different ways: (a) by evaluating $\mathbf{E}$ for an element of charge and integrating over the complete charge distribution, (b) by calculating V in the same manner and then finding its gradient, or (c) by using Gauss's law. The fields due to more complex charge distributions can be calculated by other methods described in Chapter 4 and in Appendix D.

The *dipole*, the *quadrupole*, and, in the general case, the *multipole*, are of particular interest. The potential produced by an arbitrary charge distribution is the same as that produced by a point charge, a point dipole, a point quadrupole, and so forth, all situated at the origin and each having moments equal to those of the charge distribution.

We have discussed the concept of *capacitance* for some simple capacitors as well as for the general case. The relations between the charges Q_i on a set of conductors and their potentials V_i is

$$V_i = \sum_{j=1}^{N} A_{ij} Q_j, \qquad (2\text{-}149)$$

where $A_{ij} = A_{ji}$. Inversely,

$$Q_i = \sum_{j=1}^{N} C_{ij} V_j, \qquad (2\text{-}158)$$

where the C's are the coefficients of capacitance when $i = j$ or the coefficients of induction when $i \neq j$. The former is the capacitance between conductor i and all other conductors connected together. The coefficient of induction C_{ij} gives the charge induced on conductor i, when it is grounded, per unit potential of conductor j. We have found that $C_{ij} = C_{ji}$.

The *potential energy* associated with the charge distribution can be written either as

$$W = \frac{1}{2} \int_\tau \rho V \, d\tau \qquad (2\text{-}189)$$

or as

$$W = \frac{\epsilon_0}{2} \int_\tau E^2 \, d\tau. \qquad (2\text{-}197)$$

In Eq. *2-189* τ must be chosen to include all the charge distribution ρ; in Eq. *2-197* it must include all regions of space in which the field intensity $\mathbf{E}$ is nonvanishing. The assignment of *energy density* $\epsilon_0 E^2/2$ to every point in space therefore leads to the correct potential energy for the whole charge distribution.

Finally, *electrostatic forces* exerted on charges or on conductors can be calculated either (a) directly from Coulomb's law or (b) from the principle of energy conservation by considering an infinitesimal virtual displacement and equating the work done *by* the forces to the increase in potential energy of the system. The force per unit area on a conductor is $\sigma^2/2\epsilon_0$ and is perpendicular to the surface.

Problems

2-1. Show that ϵ_0 is expressed in farads/meter, that E is expressed in volts/meter, and that the volt is a joule/coulomb.

2-2. Show that the permittivity of free space ϵ_0 can be defined as follows. If a potential difference of one volt is established across a capacitor formed of two parallel plates spaced one meter apart in a vacuum, then, neglecting edge effects, the absolute value of the charge density in coulombs/meter² on either plate is numerically equal to ϵ_0.

2-3. Calculate the electric field intensity E which would be just sufficient to balance the gravitational force on an electron.

If this electric field were produced by a second electron located below the first one, what would be the distance between the two electrons? (The charge on an electron is $e = -1.6 \times 10^{-19}$ coulomb and its mass is $m = 9.1 \times 10^{-31}$ kilogram.)

2-4. In 1906, in the course of a historic experiment which demonstrated the small size of the atomic nucleus, Rutherford observed that an alpha particle ($Q = 2 \times 1.6 \times 10^{-19}$ coulomb) with a kinetic energy of 7.68×10^6 electron-volts ($= 7.68 \times 10^6 \times 1.6 \times 10^{-19}$ joule) making a head-on collision with a gold nucleus ($Q = 79 \times 1.6 \times 10^{-19}$ coulomb) is repelled.

What is the distance of closest approach at which the electrostatic potential energy is equal to the initial kinetic energy?

What is the maximum force of repulsion?

What is the maximum acceleration in g's?

2-5. At an earlier stage in the development of atomic theory, J. J. Thompson had proposed an atom consisting of a positive charge Ze, where Z is an integer and e is the fundamental unit of charge (1.6×10^{-19} coulomb), uniformly distributed throughout a sphere of radius a. The electrons, of charge $-e$, were considered to be point charges embedded in the positive charge.

Find the force acting on an electron as a function of its distance r from the center of the sphere.

What type of motion does the electron execute?

What is the frequency?

How does the frequency compare to that of visible light radiated by atoms?

2-6. A hollow conducting sphere of radius R carries a charge Q uniformly distributed over its surface. Find the electric field intensity $\mathbf{E}$ outside at a distance z from the center by using Coulomb's law and integrating over the surface of the sphere.

2-7. A hemispherical surface is uniformly charged with a surface density σ.

Find the electric field intensity at the center O of the sphere by direct integration from Coulomb's law.

Find the field intensity at O by first calculating the potential V at a point P on the axis of symmetry and then differentiating with respect to the distance z along this axis.

2-8. A thin infinite conducting plate carries a surface charge density σ. Show that one-half of the electric field intensity $\mathbf{E}$ at a point situated z meters from the surface of the plate is due to the charge located on the plate within a circle of radius $\sqrt{3}z$.

2-9. An electric field exists everywhere in the z direction. What can you conclude about the values of the partial derivatives of E_z with respect to x, to y, and to z (a) if the charge density ρ is zero (b) if the charge density ρ is not zero?

2-10. A two-dimensional electrostatic field varies with the coordinates x and y but is independent of z. Show that the average value of the potential V on any circle parallel to the xy-plane equals the potential at the center of the circle, provided the charge density in the region is zero.

2-11. Making use of the property demonstrated in Problem 2-10, find the potential distribution within a square two of whose adjacent edges are maintained at 100 volts and whose other two edges are at 0 and 50 volts. To find an approximate solution construct a square grid of 36 points. Of these, 20 will be on the edges of the square and 16 in the interior. Guess at the potentials for the interior points of the grid. Next correct the guesses by starting at an interior point nearest one corner of the square and making the potential at that point the average of the potentials at the four nearest points. Remember that the potentials on the edges of the square are fixed. Correct all the interior potentials successively, then repeat the correction for all the points. Sketch in some equipotentials.

2-12. Two infinite parallel plates separated by a distance s are at potentials 0 and V_0. Use Poisson's equation to find the potential V in the region between the plates where the space charge density is $\rho = \rho_0(x/s)$. The distance x is measured from the plate at zero potential.

What are the surface densities on the plates?

2-13. Using Gauss's law, show that there can be no discontinuity in the electrostatic field intensity $\mathbf{E}$ at the surface of a charge distribution of uniform density ρ.

2-14. Find the potential V and the electric field intensity $\mathbf{E}$ both inside and outside a uniform spherical charge distribution of density ρ and of radius R, using only the equations of Poisson and of Laplace and appropriate boundary conditions. Hint: Use the result obtained in the preceding problem.

2-15. Calculate the electrostatic field intensity in volts/meter at the surface of an iodine nucleus (53 protons and 74 neutrons). Find the electrostatic potential at the center of the nucleus. Assume that the charge density is uniform and that the radius of the nucleus is given by $R = 1.25 \times 10^{-15} A^{1/3}$ meters, where A is the total number of particles in the nucleus.

2-16. A spherical charge distribution is given by

$$\rho = \rho_0 \left(1 - \frac{r^2}{a^2} \right); \qquad (r \leq a)$$

$$\rho = 0 \qquad\qquad (r > a).$$

Calculate the total charge Q.

Find the electric field intensity $\mathbf{E}$ and the potential V outside the charge distribution.

Find **E** and V inside.

Show that the maximum value of E is at $(r/a) = 0.745$.

The above charge distribution applies very roughly to light nuclei. Draw graphs showing ρ, E, and V as functions of r/a for calcium (atomic number 20) assuming $\rho_0 = 5.0 \times 10^{25}$ coulombs/meter^3 and $a = 4.5$ fermis (1 fermi $= 10^{-15}$ meter).

2-17. Use Gauss's law to find the electrostatic field intensity inside an infinitely long cylindrical charge distribution of radius a and uniform charge density ρ.

2-18. A 1.00-microampere beam of protons is accelerated through a difference of potential of 10,000 volts. Calculate the charge density once the protons have been accelerated, assuming that the current density is uniform within a diameter of 2.00 millimeters and is zero outside this diameter.

Calculate the radial electric field strength both inside and outside the beam.

Draw a graph of the radial electric field strength for values of r ranging from zero to 1.00 centimeters.

Now let the beam be situated along the axis of a grounded cylindrical conducting tube with an inside radius of 1.00 centimeters. Draw a graph of V inside the tube.

2-19. The axial electric field intensity E_z on the axis of the accelerating tube in a particular type of ion accelerator is given approximately by

$$E_z = E_{z0} + kz^2,$$

where z is measured from the center of the tube along its axis. The azimuthal component E_ϕ equals zero. Show that the radial electric field intensity in the neighborhood of the axis is $E_r = -kzr$, assuming that the charge density is zero.

Draw a rough sketch of the lines of force in a radial plane.

What is the maximum charge density in coulombs/meter^3 which can be tolerated if the value calculated above for the radial field is to be accurate within 5% at the ends of the tube? The accelerating tube is 1.00 meter long, E_{z0} is 7.5×10^5 volts/meter and k is 1.00×10^6 volts/meter^3.

2-20. Find the potential due to an infinite line charge of density λ coulombs/meter (a) by direct integration, (b) by using Gauss's law.

Why does the first method give an infinite answer?

Show that $V = -(\lambda/2\pi\epsilon_0) \ln (r/a)$. What is the physical interpretation of "a"?

2-21. Using the result from Problem 2-20, show that the potential due to two parallel line charges of opposite polarity is given by $(\lambda/2\pi\epsilon_0) \ln (r_1/r_2)$, where r_1 is the distance from the point considered to the negative line, and r_2 is the corresponding distance to the positive line. What is "a" in this case?

2-22. A potential difference V is applied between two coaxial cylinders of radii r_1 and r_2 respectively. Show that the electric field intensity E at the surface of the inner cylinder has a minimum value of V/r_1 when $r_1 = r_2/e$, where e is the base of natural logarithms.

2-23. A potential difference V is applied between two concentric spheres of radii r_1 and r_2. Show that the electric field intensity E at the surface of the inner sphere has a minimum value of $2V/r_1$ for $r_1 = r_2/2$.

2-24. The high voltage electrode of an ion accelerator is hemispherical and is concentric with the hemispherical end of a tank within which it is enclosed. The radius of the tank is 48.3 centimeters. The high voltage electrode is maintained at a potential of 5.0×10^5 volts, and the tank is grounded. Assuming a true spherical geometry, draw a curve of the electric field intensity E at the surface of the electrode for electrode radii ranging from 10 to 35 cm.

What range of radii can be tolerated if the electric field intensity can deviate by 10% from the minimum value?

2-25. A hollow conductor of arbitrary shape carries a charge Q, the surface charge density in a given region being σ. Then, according to Gauss's law, the electric field intensity just outside the shell is σ/ϵ_0. If now a small section of the shell is removed, small enough such that the charge distribution at all other points remains essentially unchanged, show that the electric field intensity in the hole is $\sigma/2\epsilon_0$.

2-26. The electric field intensity at the surface of a real conductor falls from its external value E_0 to zero in a finite distance δ. The surface charge density σ is distributed throughout this layer. Show that $\sigma = \displaystyle\int_0^\delta \rho(x)\,dx = \epsilon_0 E_0$.

Use $\nabla \cdot \mathbf{E} = \rho/\epsilon_0$ to show that the force per unit area on the surface is $dF/da = \sigma^2/2\epsilon_0$.

2-27. Find the equation for the equipotential surfaces of a dipole.

2-28. Calculate the potential for a dipole exactly and identify the quadrupole and octupole terms.

2-29. Consider an imaginary sphere of radius a centered on a dipole of moment $\mathbf{p}$. Show that the electrostatic energy associated with the region of space outside the sphere is $W = (p^2/3\epsilon_0 a^3)$ by integrating the energy density from $r = a$ to $r = \infty$.

2-30. Show that the dipole moment of an arbitrary charge distribution is independent of the choice of origin, provided the net charge in the distribution is zero.

2-31. Compute the dipole moment of a spherical shell with a surface charge density $\sigma = \sigma_0 \cos\theta$, where θ is the polar angle.

2-32. Find the capacitance per unit length of a capacitor consisting of a pair of infinite coaxial cylinders having inner and outer radii a and b respectively.

2-33. Find the time required for the plates (mass m_0 per unit area) of a parallel-plate capacitor to come together when released from a separation x_0 (a) when the plates are charged with a charge density σ and then insulated, and (b) when the plates are maintained at a constant potential difference V.

2-34. Two capacitors of capacitance C_1 and C_2 have charges Q_1 and Q_2 respectively. Calculate the amount of energy dissipated when they are connected in parallel.

How is this energy dissipated?

2-35. A capacitor consisting of two concentric spheres is arranged such that the outer sphere can be separated and the inner removed without disturbing the charges on either. The radius of the inner sphere is a, that of the outer sphere is b, and the charges are Q and $-Q$ respectively. If the inner sphere is removed and the outer restored to its original form, find the increase in energy when the two spheres are separated by a large distance. Where does the energy come from?

2-36. According to the Special Theory of Relativity, a particle at rest has an energy $W = mc^2$ where m is the particle's mass and c is the velocity of light. Imagine that this energy is the electrostatic energy of the charge distribution on an electron. Find the radius of the electron (a) if the charge e is uniformly distributed throughout its spherical volume, and (b) if the charge e is uniformly distributed over its spherical surface.

2-37. A variable capacitor consists of two thin coaxial cylinders of radii a and b, $(b - a \ll a)$ free to move with respect to each other in the axial direction. Using energy methods compute the magnitude and direction of the force on the inner cylinder when it is displaced with respect to the outer one. Explain how this force arises.

CHAPTER 3

Dielectrics

So far we have limited our discussion to electrostatic fields in free space; in this chapter we shall examine the phenomena which result from the introduction of a dielectric material into an electrostatic field. It will be shown that these phenomena modify a previously established field not only at points within the dielectric itself, but also at points outside.

Dielectrics differ from conductors in that they have no free charges which can move through the material under the influence of an electric field. Conductors possess electrons which can move freely, making it impossible to establish a static electric field within them, since these electrons continue to move until they are distributed so as to neutralize all external fields. In dielectrics, on the other hand, all the electrons are bound to their parent molecules, and the only motion possible in the presence of an electric field is a displacement of the positive and negative charges of the molecules in opposite directions. The displacement is usually small compared to atomic dimensions.

A dielectric in which this charge separation has taken place is said to be *polarized*, and its molecules possess induced dipole moments (Section 2.8). These dipoles as a group produce their own field, which adds to that produced by the external charges. The dipole field and the external field can be comparable in magnitude.

In addition to the charge separation, an external field can also polarize a dielectric by orienting molecules which possess permanent dipole moments. A water molecule, for example, possesses just such a permanent dipole moment and is thus called a *polar* molecule. Such a molecule experiences a torque which tends to align it with the field, but collisions arising from the thermal motion of the molecules tend to destroy the alignment. An equilibrium polarization is established in which there is, on the average, a net alignment. We shall at first limit our discussion to the induced type of polarization, although all the general conclusions we shall draw are equally applicable to polar dielectrics, which will be discussed in Section 3.9.

82

3.1 The Electric Polarization **P**

The displacement of charges within the atoms and molecules of a dielectric makes each atom or molecule a dipole with a particular moment **p**. We shall treat these dipoles both from a *molecular* and from a *macroscopic* point of view. On the molecular scale we shall consider the fields of individual dipoles, whereas on the macroscopic scale we shall consider only the average fields produced by large numbers of dipoles. In the end, we shall deal with dielectrics entirely from the macroscopic point of view. We must, however, justify this procedure by first examining carefully the molecular aspect. If one is interested in individual atomic interactions, then the fields must necessarily be treated on a molecular scale.

The *electric polarization* **P** is the dipole moment per unit volume at a given point and is a macroscopic quantity. If **p** is the *average electric dipole moment per molecule* in a small volume τ and N is the number of molecules per unit volume, then

$$\mathbf{P} = N\mathbf{p}. \tag{3-1}$$

It will be recalled from Problem 2-30 that the dipole moment of a charge distribution is independent of the origin of coordinates provided the net charge in the distribution is zero, as it is in molecules.

The volume τ over which we define **P** must be large enough such that there is no significant fluctuation in **P** from one instant to the next or from one τ to a nieghboring one. We expect relative statistical fluctuations of the order of $1/(N\tau)^{1/2}$, which sets a lower limit on the magnitude of τ. For example, if $N = 10^{25}$ molecules/meter^3 and $\tau = 10^{-18}$ meter^3, the expected statistical fluctuation in **P** is about 0.03%.

On the other hand, if τ is too large, significant errors might be made in replacing sums by integrals. For example, consider a small cube of side l and volume $\tau = l^3$, as in Figure 3-1. If the cube contains a point charge Q at its center, then at a point P at a distance $r \gg l$ the potential is

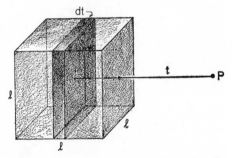

Figure 3-1. *A charge Q is assumed to be spread with uniform density $\rho = Q/l^3$ throughout the volume of the cube. The charge in the thin layer of thickness dt and surface area l^2 is $(Q/l^3)l^2\,dt$.*

$$V = \frac{1}{4\pi\epsilon_0}\frac{Q}{r}. \tag{3-2}$$

However, if the charge is distributed uniformly throughout the cube with a density $\rho = Q/l^3$,

$$V = \frac{1}{4\pi\epsilon_0}\int_\tau \frac{\rho\,d\tau}{t} \approx \frac{1}{4\pi\epsilon_0}\int_{r-\frac{l}{2}}^{r+\frac{l}{2}} \frac{Q}{l^3}\frac{l^2\,dt}{t}, \qquad (3\text{-}3)$$

where t is the distance from the point P to an arbitrary point within the cube, as in Figure 3-1.

Integrating and expanding the resultant logarithmic factor in powers of l/r, we obtain

$$V \approx \frac{Q}{4\pi\epsilon_0 l}\left[\frac{l}{r}+\frac{l^3}{12r^3}\right]. \qquad (3\text{-}4)$$

Comparing this approximate potential with the exact potential in Eq. 3-2, we find the relative error to be

$$\frac{\Delta V}{V} \approx \frac{l^2}{12r^2}. \qquad (3\text{-}5)$$

With $\tau = 10^{-18}$ meter^3 and $l = 10^{-6}$ meter the error is small even when r is a small fraction of a millimeter. Fortunately, molecules are so small that this type of approximation can be made with high accuracy.

3.2. Field at an Exterior Point

Figure 3-2 shows a block of dielectric material with a dipole moment **P** per unit volume, **P** being a function of position within the dielectric. Let us calculate the electrostatic potential V which the dipoles produce at a point O outside. This potential can then be added to that produced by all the other charges in the system to give the total potential. The negative gradient of this total potential at the point O is the resultant field intensity.

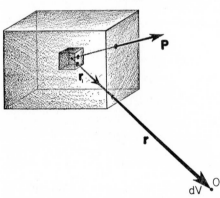

*Figure 3-2. Block of dielectric with dipole moment **P** per unit volume. The dipoles within the element of volume shown give rise to an electrostatic potential dV at the point O.*

At the point O the potential dV due to the dipole moment **P** $d\tau$ is

$$dV = \frac{1}{4\pi\epsilon_0}\frac{\mathbf{P}\cdot\mathbf{r}_1}{r^2}\,d\tau, \qquad (3\text{-}6)$$

$$= \frac{1}{4\pi\epsilon_0}\left[\mathbf{P}\cdot\nabla\left(\frac{1}{r}\right)\right]d\tau. \qquad (3\text{-}7)$$

where ∇ is evaluated at $d\tau$ (see Problem 1-21). Integrating over the block of dielectric gives V:

$$V = \frac{1}{4\pi\epsilon_0} \int_\tau \left[\mathbf{P} \cdot \mathbf{\nabla} \left(\frac{1}{r} \right) \right] d\tau. \tag{3-8}$$

This integration can be carried out analytically only for simple geometries and only if $\mathbf{P}$ is a simple function of position within the dielectric. Furthermore, $\mathbf{P}$ is never known a priori, although we can often deduce it from measurable quantities. We shall nevertheless assume, for the time being, that $\mathbf{P}$ is known.

Equation *3-8* can be put into a form which facilitates physical interpretation by transforming it through the vector identity of Problem 1-14:

$$\mathbf{\nabla} \cdot f\mathbf{A} = f\mathbf{\nabla} \cdot \mathbf{A} + \mathbf{A} \cdot \mathbf{\nabla} f, \tag{3-9}$$

where f and $\mathbf{A}$ are scalar and vector functions respectively. Let $1/r$ be the scalar and $\mathbf{P}$ the vector function. Then

$$V = \frac{1}{4\pi\epsilon_0} \int_\tau \left(\mathbf{\nabla} \cdot \frac{\mathbf{P}}{r} \right) d\tau - \frac{1}{4\pi\epsilon_0} \int_\tau \frac{\mathbf{\nabla} \cdot \mathbf{P}}{r} d\tau. \tag{3-10}$$

We can use the divergence theorem to express the first term as a surface integral,

$$V = \frac{1}{4\pi\epsilon_0} \int_S \frac{\mathbf{P} \cdot \mathbf{da}}{r} - \frac{1}{4\pi\epsilon_0} \int_\tau \frac{\mathbf{\nabla} \cdot \mathbf{P}}{r} d\tau, \tag{3-11}$$

where S is the surface which bounds the volume τ of the dielectric.

3.2.1. The Bound Charge Densities ρ' and σ'. Both terms of Eq. *3-11* have a $1/r$ dependence, the first involving a surface integral and the second a volume integral. These are exactly the expressions for the potential produced by surface and volume charge distributions having densities

$$\sigma' = \mathbf{P} \cdot \mathbf{n} \tag{3-12}$$

and

$$\rho' = -\mathbf{\nabla} \cdot \mathbf{P} \tag{3-13}$$

respectively, where $\mathbf{n}$ is the unit *outward* normal vector at the surface of the dielectric. The dielectric may therefore be replaced by the charge distributions σ' and ρ', and the problem may be treated as a free space potential problem, at least for points outside the dielectric. We shall see later that we can also use the same procedure to find a macroscopic potential at points within the dielectric.

We can demonstrate with the aid of Figure 3-3 that the densities σ' and ρ' represent actual accumulations of charge. Let us first consider the surface density σ'. We imagine a small element of surface $\mathbf{da}$ within the dielectric. Under the action of the field, an average charge separation $\mathbf{s}$ is produced in the molecules. Positive charge crosses the surface by moving in the direction of the field; negative charge crosses it by moving in the opposite direction. For the purpose of our calculation, we may consider all the positive charge to be in the form of

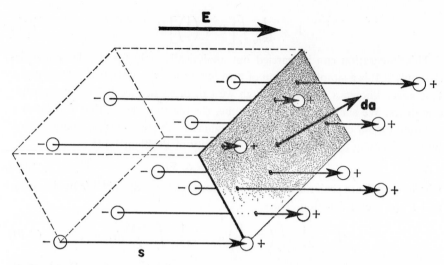

Figure 3-3. *Under the action of an electrostatic field* **E,** *which is the resultant of an external field and of the field of dipoles within the dielectric, positive and negative charges in the molecules are separated by an average distance* **s.** *In the process a net charge* $dQ' = NQ\mathbf{s} \cdot \mathbf{da}$ *crosses the surface* **da,** *N being the number of molecules/meter³, and Q the sum of the positive charges in a molecule. The circles indicate the centers of charge for the positive and for the negative charges in one molecule.*

point charges Q and all the negative charge to be in the form of point charges $-Q$. Furthermore, we may consider the negative charges to be fixed and the positive charges to move a distance **s**. The amount of charge dQ' which crosses **da** is then just the total amount of positive charge within the imaginary parallelepiped shown in Figure 3-3. The volume of this parallelepiped is

$$d\tau = \mathbf{s} \cdot \mathbf{da}, \qquad (3\text{-}14)$$

thus

$$dQ' = NQ\mathbf{s} \cdot \mathbf{da}, \qquad (3\text{-}15)$$

where N is the number of molecules per unit volume and $Q\mathbf{s}$ is the dipole moment **p** of a molecule. Then

$$dQ' = \mathbf{P} \cdot \mathbf{da}. \qquad (3\text{-}16)$$

If **da** is on the surface of the dielectric material, dQ' accumulates there in a layer of thickness $\mathbf{s} \cdot \mathbf{n}$. Since the thickness of the layer is of the order of the dimensions of a molecule, we may treat the charge as a surface distribution with a density

$$\sigma' = \frac{dQ'}{da} = \mathbf{P} \cdot \mathbf{n}. \qquad (3\text{-}17)$$

The surface charge density σ' is thus equal to the normal component of the polarization vector at the surface, as in Eq. *3-12.*

We can show similarly that $-\nabla \cdot \mathbf{P}$ represents a volume density of charge. The net charge which flows out of a volume τ across an element **da** of its surface is $\mathbf{P} \cdot \mathbf{da}$, as we found above. The net charge which flows out across the entire surface bounding τ is thus

$$Q' = \int_S \mathbf{P} \cdot \mathbf{da}, \qquad (3\text{-}18)$$

and the net charge which remains within the volume τ must be $-Q'$. If ρ' is the volume density of the charge remaining within this volume, then

$$\int_\tau \rho' \, d\tau = -Q' = -\int_S \mathbf{P} \cdot \mathbf{da}, \qquad (3\text{-}19)$$

$$= -\int_\tau (\nabla \cdot \mathbf{P}) \, d\tau. \qquad (3\text{-}20)$$

Since this equation must be true for all τ, the integrands must be equal at every point, and the net induced charge density is

$$\rho' = -\nabla \cdot \mathbf{P}, \qquad (3\text{-}21)$$

as in Eq. *3-13*.

We refer to σ' and ρ' as either *bound, polarization,* or *induced* charge densities, as distinguished from *free* or *conductible* charges. Bound charges are those which accumulate through the displacements which occur on a molecular scale in the polarization process. *Free* charges are those which can move over macroscopic distances, as do the conduction electrons in a conductor. Coulomb's law applies to any net accumulation of charge, regardless of other matter which may be present.

3.3. Field at an Interior Point

It is often necessary to know the electrostatic potential and the field intensity at points within a dielectric. We may wish to know, for example, the potential difference or the capacitance between two conductors separated by a dielectric.

Let us first define ϵ as the electric field intensity at a particular instant of time at a particular point within the dielectric. This is a rapidly fluctuating quantity, both with regard to position and to time. It reaches enormous magnitudes at the surfaces of nuclei, as shown in Problem 2-15. There are also large variations in its direction: on one side of a nucleus, ϵ is in one direction, and on the other it is in the opposite direction. Thermal agitation of the molecules also produces large time fluctuations at any given point.

We shall call $\bar{\epsilon}$ the *time* average of the electric field intensity at a particular point.

The *macroscopic electric field intensity* **E,** which is what we really wish to know in the dielectric, is the *space and time* average of the field ϵ, and we shall call it $\bar{\epsilon}$. Thus

$$\mathbf{E} \equiv \bar{\epsilon} = \frac{1}{\tau} \int_\tau \bar{\epsilon} \, d\tau. \tag{3-22}$$

We shall choose the volume τ large enough such that statistical fluctuations are negligible, but small enough such that, for example, the polarization vector $\mathbf{P}$ does not change significantly from one side to the other.

The macroscopic field intensity $\mathbf{E}$ is a slowly varying function of the coordinates and is independent of the time in the static case. It is this field intensity which we shall integrate in order to calculate potential differences. We shall show that this macroscopic field intensity and the corresponding potential within the dielectric can be calculated from the bound charge distributions σ' and ρ' discussed above, exactly as in Eq. *3-11*. This is not intuitively obvious, however, hence the calculation must be done carefully.

There are two reasons why the type of calculation used for the exterior point might not be valid at an interior point. In the first place, near the point considered there may be large numbers of molecules for which our expressions for the dipole field are not valid, since Eq. *2-70* requires that the distance between the dipole and the point considered be much larger than the dimensions of the dipole. In the second place, near this point there are large numbers of molecules for which the approximations involved in replacing sums by integrals might not be valid.

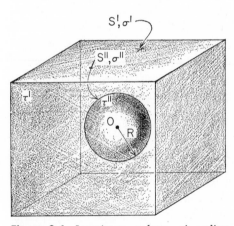

To calculate the macroscopic field $\mathbf{E}$ inside a dielectric, let us consider Figure 3-4, which shows a small imaginary sphere of radius R with a point O as its center. The surface S'' of this sphere divides the dielectric into two volumes, τ' outside and τ'' inside. The radius R is chosen such that the potential at O may be calculated for all the polarized material outside S'' by treating O as an exterior point as in Section 3.2. The molecules within S'' are too close to O to be treated in this fashion and must be handled differently. The volume τ'' is macroscopically small, and the macroscopic quantities $\mathbf{E}$, $\mathbf{P}$, and $\rho' = -\boldsymbol{\nabla} \cdot \mathbf{P}$ do not vary significantly from one side to the other.

Figure 3-4. *Imaginary sphere of radius R, volume τ'' and surface S'' inside a block of dielectric. The remaining volume is τ', and its outside surface is S'. The surface charge densities are σ' and σ''.*

Let us now calculate the total electric field intensity $\bar{\epsilon}$ which the dipoles of the dielectric produce at the point O. It is somewhat simpler in this case to calculate the field intensity directly than it is to first calculate the potential. We can state that

$$\bar{\epsilon} = \bar{\epsilon}' + \bar{\epsilon}'', \qquad (3\text{-}23)$$

where $\bar{\epsilon}'$ is the time-averaged field contributed at the point O by the polarized dielectric in the volume τ' and $\bar{\epsilon}''$ is that contributed by the dielectric in τ''. The macroscopic field intensity $\mathbf{E}$ is then given by the space average of $\bar{\epsilon}$:

$$\mathbf{E} = \bar{\bar{\epsilon}}' + \bar{\bar{\epsilon}}'', \qquad (3\text{-}24)$$

$$= \frac{1}{\tau} \int_\tau (\bar{\epsilon}' + \bar{\epsilon}'')\, d\tau, \qquad (3\text{-}25)$$

where τ is a suitably chosen small volume which can be τ''.

3.3.1. Field Produced by the Distant Dipoles. Point O is external to the volume τ', thus we can calculate $\bar{\epsilon}'$ from (a) the bound volume charge ρ' in the

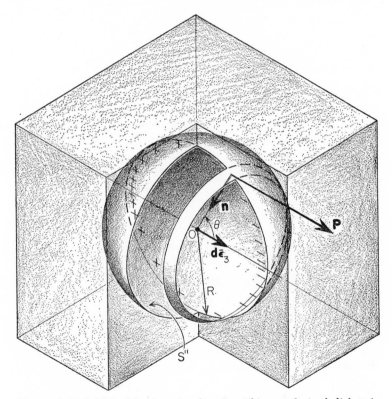

Figure 3-5. *Spherical cavity of radius R within a polarized dielectric, the charges shown being due to the polarization $\mathbf{P}$. The charges on the annular element give rise to the electric field intensity $d\bar{\epsilon}_3$.*

volume τ', (b) the bound surface charge σ' on the outer surface S', and (c) the bound surface charge σ'' on the inner surface S''. This latter surface is not real, but the discussion in Section 3.2 applies even when only a portion of the dielectric is under consideration, as it is here.

Each element of polarization charge $\rho'\, d\tau$ in τ' contributes an element of field

$$d\bar{\varepsilon}' = \frac{1}{4\pi\epsilon_0} \frac{\rho'\, d\tau}{r^2}\, \mathbf{r}_1, \tag{3-26}$$

where $\mathbf{r}_1$ is the unit vector in the direction from $d\tau$ to the point O and r is the distance from $d\tau$ to O. With similar consideration of the surface charges σ' and σ'',

$$\bar{\varepsilon}' = \frac{1}{4\pi\epsilon_0}\left(\int_{\tau'} \frac{\rho'\, d\tau}{r^2}\, \mathbf{r}_1 + \int_{S'} \frac{\sigma'\, da'}{r^2}\, \mathbf{r}_1 + \int_{S''} \frac{\sigma''\, da''}{r^2}\, \mathbf{r}_1 \right). \tag{3-27}$$

Let us calculate the third term, which we shall call $\bar{\varepsilon}'_3$. Figure 3-5 shows the spherical surface S'' with an axis drawn parallel to the polarization vector $\mathbf{P}$. The polarization charge density on the surface S'' is

$$\sigma'' = \mathbf{P}\cdot\mathbf{n} = -P\cos\theta, \tag{3-28}$$

and the charge on the annulus of width $R\, d\theta$ contributes an element of field intensity at O given by

$$d\bar{\varepsilon}'_3 = \frac{1}{4\pi\epsilon_0} \frac{P\cos\theta}{R^2}\, 2\pi R^2 \sin\theta\, d\theta \cos\theta. \tag{3-29}$$

The first $\cos\theta$ factor comes from σ''; the second comes from taking the component of the field intensity in the axial direction, since symmetry requires the resultant field to be in that direction. On performing the integration over the whole surface S'', we find that

$$\bar{\varepsilon}'_3 = \frac{\mathbf{P}}{3\epsilon_0}. \tag{3-30}$$

3.3.2. Field Produced by the Near Dipoles. Now we must inquire into the space average of the field intensity $\bar{\varepsilon}''$ due to the polarized material within the surface S''. The method of calculating this space average is indicated in Figure 3-6. In principle, we first find the field intensity at the point O due to the dipoles within the spherical surface S'' centered on O. Then we repeat the calculation for another point O' displaced from O. The spherical surface of radius R must be displaced also, in order to keep it centered on O'. We repeat the calculation for many other points O', all lying within some suitably small volume—which may be τ''. We then average the field intensities for all the O' points.

Now all the spherical surfaces surrounding the O' points have the same number of dipoles in them, and $\mathbf{P}$, the dipole moment per unit volume, is the same throughout every sphere, since we have chosen a small radius for the spheres.

All that varies from one O' to another is the fact that sometimes the point lies in a high-field region, within a molecule, for example, and other times it lies in a low-field region. Since **P** does not change significantly over the distances of interest, we may compute the aver- age in question simply by taking one sphere S'' and finding the average field intensity within its volume. We need consider only the dipoles within it. This is merely the average which we calculated in Eq. *2-131* stated in terms of the total dipole moment within the sphere. Thus

$$\bar{\mathbf{\varepsilon}}'' = -\frac{N(4/3)\pi R^3 \mathbf{p}}{4\pi\epsilon_0 R^3}, \quad (3\text{-}31)$$

$$= -\frac{\mathbf{P}}{3\epsilon_0}. \quad (3\text{-}32)$$

where N is the number of molecules per unit volume and **p** is the average dipole moment per molecule.

Thus the average field which the nearby molecules contribute is equal in magnitude and opposite in direc- tion to that part of the field contrib-

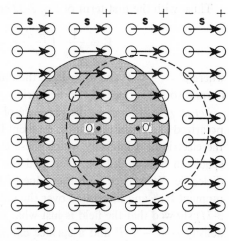

Figure 3-6. *To find the space-averaged field intensity produced by the dipoles, we calculate the field intensity at O due to the dipoles within the spherical surface S'' and then repeat this calculation for many other points O' at the center of other neighboring spherical surfaces.*

uted by all the other molecules through the bound charge on the inner surface S''. Equation *3-25* then leads to

$$\mathbf{E} = \frac{1}{4\pi\epsilon_0} \int_{\tau'} \frac{\rho' \, d\tau}{r^2} \mathbf{r}_1 + \frac{1}{4\pi\epsilon_0} \int_{S'} \frac{\sigma' \, da}{r^2} \mathbf{r}_1. \quad (3\text{-}33)$$

The first integral is calculated only over that portion of the dielectric which is outside the spherical surface S''. It would of course be simpler to calculate if it were extended to the complete volume τ of the dielectric, but then the error would be

$$\frac{1}{4\pi\epsilon_0} \int_{\tau''} \frac{\rho' \, d\tau}{r^2} \mathbf{r}_1.$$

Since the bound charge density ρ' does not vary significantly over the small sphere τ'', this integral is merely the field intensity at the center of a uniform spherical charge distribution. For every element of charge giving an element of electric field intensity in one direction, there is a symmetrical element of charge giving a field in the opposite direction, thus the integral is zero. The first integral of Eq. *3-33* can therefore be extended to the complete volume τ of the dielectric without changing its magnitude. It represents only the contribution of the non-local dipoles to the field at O, even when it is evaluated over the whole dielectric volume.

Thus, with the first term of Eq. *3-33* so modified we can write

$$\mathbf{E} = \frac{1}{4\pi\epsilon_0} \int_\tau \frac{\rho' \, d\tau}{r^2} \, \mathbf{r}_1 + \frac{1}{4\pi\epsilon_0} \int_S \frac{\sigma' \, da}{r^2} \, \mathbf{r}_1, \qquad (3\text{-}34)$$

where $\rho' = -\boldsymbol{\nabla}\cdot\mathbf{P}$ and $\sigma' = \mathbf{P}\cdot\mathbf{n}$, the unit vector $\mathbf{n}$ pointing outward along the normal to the surface of the dielectric.

Let us recapitulate. In the presence of an electric field, a dielectric becomes polarized and acquires a dipole moment $\mathbf{P}$ per unit volume. We wish to calculate the electric field intensity which these elementary dipoles produce throughout space. In Section 3.2 we calculated the field for a point situated outside the dielectric. We started with the value of the electric potential V for a dipole of moment $\mathbf{P} \, d\tau$ and integrated over the volume τ of the dielectric. The result (Eq. *3-11*) showed that the field is just what we would expect from a volume charge density $\rho' = -\boldsymbol{\nabla}\cdot\mathbf{P}$ and a surface charge density $\sigma' = \mathbf{P}\cdot\mathbf{n}$. We then showed that these two quantities do indeed represent real accumulations of charge.

We then calculated the electric field intensity at a point inside the dielectric. This calculation required the definition of $\boldsymbol{\epsilon}$, the instantaneous electric field intensity at a particular point in the dielectric; the definition of its time average $\bar{\boldsymbol{\epsilon}}$; and the definition of its time and space average $\bar{\bar{\boldsymbol{\epsilon}}}$. This last quantity is just the macroscopic electric field intensity $\mathbf{E}$. In this calculation we obtained $\mathbf{E}$ directly, and not the potential V. We divided the dielectric into two regions, a small sphere of volume τ'' centered on the point O considered, and the remaining volume τ'. The field intensity at O due to the dipoles in τ', comprises three terms arising from (a) the volume charge density in τ', (b) the surface charge density on the outside surface of the dielectric, and (c) the surface charge density on the sphere τ''. It turns out that this last term is just canceled by the field at O due to the dipoles within the sphere τ''. We also found that the first term can be extended without error to the complete volume τ of the dielectric.

The macroscopic field intensity $\mathbf{E}$ at a point inside a dielectric can therefore be found by replacing the dielectric with the bound charge densities ρ' and σ' in exactly the same manner as for an external point. That is, we have found that the charge densities ρ' and σ' represent actual accumulations of charge, even though bound, and that they produce electrostatic field intensities according to Coulomb's law. This is true inside as well as outside the dielectric.

In calculating the macroscopic field $\mathbf{E}$ we have said nothing about the field of the external charge distribution which is responsible for the polarization in the first place. It simply adds at every point to the field produced by the polarized dielectric, to produce the total macroscopic field.

3.4. The Local Field

Although the above discussion clarifies our understanding of polarization effects in dielectrics, it cannot be used for calculating the macroscopic field **E**, since we do not know as yet how to determine the polarization vector **P**. We must eventually be able to calculate the electrostatic potential and field intensity at any point, either inside or outside a dielectric without knowing **P**. We must be able to calculate the potential and the field intensity knowing only the potentials of, or the charges on, the conductors, plus the geometry and characteristics of the conductors and dielectrics in the system.

In order to achieve this, let us calculate the average field intensity acting on some particular molecule in the dielectric. We shall call this the *local field* and shall designate it $\bar{\varepsilon}_{loc}$. We define $\bar{\varepsilon}_{loc}$ in the following way. Imagine that we stop the thermal motion of all the molecules in the dielectric at some particular instant. We remove the molecule in question, keeping all the other molecules frozen in position, and calculate the space-averaged electrostatic field intensity in the cavity previously occupied by the molecule. We replace the molecule, return the system to normal temperature, and repeat the process many times. The resultant time average of the space-averaged field intensity in the cavity is $\bar{\varepsilon}_{loc}$.

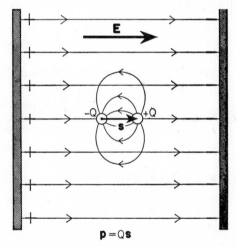

We expect the local field to be *larger* than the macroscopic field **E**, since the local field includes only the field of the *other* molecules in the system, whereas the macroscopic field includes the field of all the molecules, including the one in question. In Section 2.12 we found that the average field intensity within a sphere containing an arbitrary charge distribution is in the direction opposite to the dipole moment of the distribution. Thus the molecule in question contributes an average field in the

Figure 3-7. *The field of an individual dipole.*

direction opposite that of the macroscopic field intensity **E**, as indicated in Figure 3-7.

We have that

$$\bar{\varepsilon}_{loc} = \frac{1}{\tau_m} \int_{\tau_m} (\bar{\varepsilon} - \bar{\varepsilon}_m) \, d\tau, \qquad (3\text{-}35)$$

where $\bar{\epsilon}$ is the time-averaged electrostatic field intensity at a point within the volume occupied by the molecule, $\bar{\epsilon}_m$ is the time-averaged field at the same point produced by the molecule's own charge distribution, and τ_m is the molecular volume.

The above integral can be put in a tractable although somewhat inaccurate form by replacing the average over the molecular volume in the first term by the average over a macroscopically small volume τ of the dielectric, such that

$$\bar{\epsilon}_{\text{loc}} \approx \frac{1}{\tau} \int_\tau \bar{\epsilon} \, d\tau - \frac{1}{\tau_m} \int_{\tau_m} \bar{\epsilon}_m \, d\tau. \tag{3-36}$$

The first term is just the macroscopic field $\mathbf{E}$, hence

$$\bar{\epsilon}_{\text{loc}} \approx \mathbf{E} - \frac{1}{\tau_m} \int_{\tau_m} \bar{\epsilon}_m \, d\tau. \tag{3-37}$$

Numerical evaluation of the second term in this equation would require detailed information about the shape and charge distribution of the molecule, information which is available only from a quantum-mechanical description of the system. However, we can make the calculation in general terms, assuming only the shape of the molecule. If we select the simplest shape—the sphere—then the second term of Eq. *3-37* can be readily evaluated from Eq. *2-131*. We have

$$\frac{1}{\tau_m} \int_{\tau_m} \bar{\epsilon}_m \, d\tau = -\frac{\mathbf{p}}{4\pi\epsilon_0 R^3}, \tag{3-38}$$

where $\mathbf{p}$ is the dipole moment of the molecule and R is its radius, or

$$\frac{1}{\tau_m} \int_{\tau_m} \bar{\epsilon}_m \, d\tau = -\frac{\mathbf{P}}{4\pi\epsilon_0 N R^3}, \tag{3-39}$$

$$= -\frac{\mathbf{P}}{3\epsilon_0 N \tau_m}. \tag{3-40}$$

If we further assume that

$$\tau_m = \frac{1}{N}, \tag{3-41}$$

then

$$\bar{\epsilon}_{\text{loc}} \approx \mathbf{E} + \frac{\mathbf{P}}{3\epsilon_0}. \tag{3-42}$$

This expression for the local field is at best approximate, owing to the approximations which have gone into it. First we averaged the field intensity in Eq. *3-35* over a volume containing a large number of molecules, instead of over the volume of only one molecule, thereby including space between molecules, where $\bar{\epsilon}$ may be different from what it is within a molecule. We also assumed a spherical shape for the molecule. Usually, this is a good assumption, but we then assumed that $\tau_m = \frac{1}{N}$, that is, we assumed that all of space is filled with molecular volumes, which contradicts the assumption of spherical shape. Nonetheless, dielectric behavior predicted from Eq. *3-42* agrees surprisingly well with experimental data for many substances.

Fortunately, our dielectric theory does not require that Eq. *3-42* be quantitatively accurate; our conclusions will all be valid if only

$$\bar{\epsilon}_{loc} = \mathbf{E} + b\,\frac{\mathbf{P}}{\epsilon_0}, \qquad (3\text{-}43)$$

where b is a constant which depends on the nature of the dielectric.

3.4.1. The Lorentz Calculation for the Local Field.*

Before carrying the theory further, let us examine Lorentz's classical calculation,† which is the usual method of finding the local field. In the Lorentz calculation we do not average the field intensity over a molecular volume; we define the local field at a single point at the center of the molecule in question.

The calculation is similar to that of Section 3.3 for the macroscopic electrostatic field intensity $\mathbf{E}$. We divide the dielectric into two regions by a small imaginary sphere of radius R, as in Figure 3-4; the center of the sphere is fixed at the position of the molecule, where we wish to calculate the local field. As in Section 3.3,

$$\bar{\epsilon}_{loc} = \bar{\epsilon}' + \bar{\epsilon}\,', \qquad (3\text{-}44)$$

where $\bar{\epsilon}'$ is the time-averaged field produced by the polarized dielectric in the volume τ' and $\bar{\epsilon}''$ is that produced by the polarized dielectric in the small volume τ''. We write $\bar{\epsilon}_{loc}$ with one bar to indicate only time-averaging, since we are calculating the local field at a single point.

The radius R is chosen large enough such that we can calculate $\bar{\epsilon}'$ macroscopically from the bound charge densities ρ', σ', and σ'', as in Eq. *3-27*. We saw in Eq. *3-33* that the terms involving ρ' and σ' give the macroscopic field $\mathbf{E}$ due to the polarization of the dielectric. From Eq. *3-30* the term involving σ'' is $\mathbf{P}/3\epsilon_0$. Altogether,

$$\bar{\epsilon}_{loc} = \frac{1}{4\pi\epsilon_0}\int_{\tau'}\frac{\rho'\,d\tau}{r^2}\,\mathbf{r}_1 + \frac{1}{4\pi\epsilon_0}\int_{S'}\frac{\sigma'\,da}{r^2}\,\mathbf{r}_1 + \frac{\mathbf{P}}{3\epsilon_0} + \bar{\epsilon}'', \qquad (3\text{-}45)$$

$$= \mathbf{E} + \frac{\mathbf{P}}{3\epsilon_0} + \bar{\epsilon}''. \qquad (3\text{-}46)$$

From here on the line of reasoning departs from that of Section 3.3, since we do not wish to average $\bar{\epsilon}_{loc}$ over a volume. We need only calculate $\bar{\epsilon}''$, that is, the field contributed at the one point by the molecules within the small volume τ''.

---

*This section may be omitted without losing continuity.
† H. A. Lorentz, *Theory of Electrons* (Dover, New York, 1952).

In some special cases, $\bar{\varepsilon}''$ is zero. For example, if the dielectric material is a liquid or a gas, the thermal agitation of the molecules insures that the field from the nearby molecules averages to zero. If the dielectric is crystalline, with the atoms arrayed in a cubic lattice, it is found upon summing contributions of the individual polarized atoms within the small sphere that $\bar{\varepsilon}'' = 0$.

For cases in which $\bar{\varepsilon}'' = 0$ we have

$$\bar{\varepsilon}_{loc} = \mathbf{E} + \frac{\mathbf{P}}{3\epsilon_0}, \tag{3-47}$$

which is known as the *Lorentz form of the local field*.

In general $\bar{\varepsilon}''$ will not be zero. It will, however, be proportional to $\mathbf{P}$, since the field produced by an individual dipole is proportional to its dipole moment, which is in turn proportional to $\mathbf{P}$ by definition. In general, then,

$$\bar{\varepsilon}_{loc} = \mathbf{E} + b\frac{\mathbf{P}}{\epsilon_0}, \tag{3-48}$$

where b is a constant whose magnitude depends on the characteristics of the dielectric material.

So far we have discussed dielectrics consisting of only one type of molecule. In the more general case,

$$\mathbf{P} = N_1\mathbf{p}_1 + N_2\mathbf{p}_2 + \cdots, \tag{3-49}$$

where N_1 is the number of molecules of the first type per unit volume, with the average dipole moment $\mathbf{p}_1$, N_2 is the number of the second type per unit volume, and so on. The theory is not otherwise modified.

3.5. The Displacement Vector $\mathbf{D}$

We found in Sections 3.2 and 3.3 that the field produced by the atomic and molecular dipoles of a polarized dielectric can be calculated from the bound charge densities and from Coulomb's law, just as for any other charge distribution. Let us investigate the implications of this fact for Gauss's law, which is a direct consequence of Coulomb's law and of the concept of electrostatic field intensity.

Gauss's law relates the flux of the electric field intensity vector $\mathbf{E}$ through a closed surface to the net charge Q enclosed within that surface as follows:

$$\int_S \mathbf{E} \cdot \mathbf{da} = \int_\tau \mathbf{\nabla} \cdot \mathbf{E} \, d\tau, \tag{3-50}$$

$$= \frac{Q}{\epsilon_0}. \tag{3-51}$$

For dielectrics, Q must include bound as well as free charges:

$$Q = \int_\tau (\rho + \rho') \, d\tau, \tag{3-52}$$

where the integration is intended to cover both the surface and the volume densities of bound charges. If we substitute Eqs. *3-50* and *3-51* into Eq. *3-52* and equate the integrands of the volume integrals, then

$$\mathbf{\nabla} \cdot \mathbf{E} = \frac{\rho + \rho'}{\epsilon_0} \tag{3-53}$$

at every point. This is the differential form of Gauss's law for dielectrics. If there are surface charge distributions σ' present they extend over a finite thickness and can also be described by a volume density ρ'.

Now, from Eq. *3-21*,

$$\rho' = -\mathbf{\nabla} \cdot \mathbf{P}. \tag{3-54}$$

Then for any dielectric

$$\mathbf{\nabla} \cdot \mathbf{E} = \frac{1}{\epsilon_0}(\rho - \mathbf{\nabla} \cdot \mathbf{P}), \tag{3-55}$$

or

$$\mathbf{\nabla} \cdot (\epsilon_0 \mathbf{E} + \mathbf{P}) = \rho. \tag{3-56}$$

Equation *3-56* is especially significant. It states that the vector $\epsilon_0 \mathbf{E} + \mathbf{P}$ is such that its divergence depends only on the *free* charge density ρ. This vector is called the *electric displacement* and is designated by **D**:

$$\mathbf{D} = \epsilon_0 \mathbf{E} + \mathbf{P}. \tag{3-57}$$

Thus

$$\boxed{\mathbf{\nabla} \cdot \mathbf{D} = \rho.} \tag{3-58}$$

This equation states *Gauss's law in its general form*. It is applicable to any dielectric medium as well as to a vacuum. *It is also the first of Maxwell's four fundamental equations of electromagnetism.* In deriving this equation we have based our arguments on (a) Coulomb's law, (b) the concept of electric field intensity, and (c) the demonstration that the field of the dipoles in a polarized medium can be calculated everywhere from the bound charge densities.

In integral form Gauss's law for **D** becomes

$$\int_S \mathbf{D} \cdot \mathbf{da} = \int_\tau \rho \, d\tau. \tag{3-59}$$

Thus the flux of the displacement vector **D** through a closed surface is equal to the *free* charge enclosed by the surface. This latter form is often more useful for determining **D** and **E**.

From the definition of the displacement vector,

$$\mathbf{E} = \frac{\mathbf{D}}{\epsilon_0} - \frac{\mathbf{P}}{\epsilon_0}. \tag{3-60}$$

The electrostatic field intensity **E** is therefore the difference between two different fields. The first term $\mathbf{D}/\epsilon_0$ represents a field whose sources are the free charges, since

$$\nabla \cdot \left(\frac{\mathbf{D}}{\epsilon_0}\right) = +\frac{\rho}{\epsilon_0}. \tag{3-61}$$

Likewise, $-\mathbf{P}/\epsilon_0$ represents a field whose sources are the bound charges, since

$$\nabla \cdot \left(\frac{\mathbf{P}}{\epsilon_0}\right) = -\frac{\rho'}{\epsilon_0}. \tag{3-62}$$

The "lines of force" of $\mathbf{D}$ begin or end only on free charges, whereas the lines of $\mathbf{E}$ begin or end on either free or polarization charges. This does not mean, however, that the magnitude and direction of $\mathbf{D}$ at a particular point depend only on the free charges. The only quantity which depends on the free

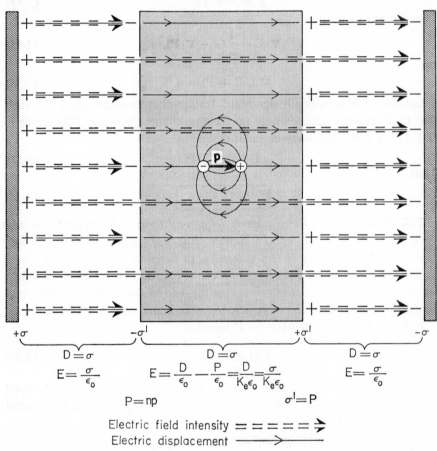

Electric field intensity $= = = = = \Rightarrow$
Electric displacement $\longrightarrow$

Figure 3-8. *A block of dielectric of coefficient K_e located between the plates of a parallel-plate capacitor. Molecules of the dielectric are polarized with a dipole moment $\mathbf{p}$, leading to a polarization $\mathbf{P}$. The displacement vector $\mathbf{D}$ depends only on the free charges $\pm\sigma$ and is the same inside and outside the dielectric. The electric field intensity $\mathbf{E}$, on the other hand, is reduced inside the dielectric because the polarization charges $\pm\sigma'$ produce a field in the opposite direction.*

charges alone is $\nabla \cdot \mathbf{D}$. To find $\mathbf{D}$, we must integrate Eq. *3-58*, subject to whatever boundary conditions obtain in the particular field. Figure 3-8 shows the vectors $\mathbf{P}$, $\mathbf{E}$, and $\mathbf{D}$ and the bound charge density σ' for a dielectric between the plates of a parallel-plate capacitor.

3.6. The Electric Susceptibility χ_e

In order to relate $\mathbf{D}$ and $\mathbf{E}$ in more practical terms, let us now examine the relationship between the polarization vector $\mathbf{P}$ and the macroscopic field intensity $\mathbf{E}$. To do this, let us consider the dipole moment $\mathbf{p}$ induced in a single molecule. The magnitude of $\mathbf{p}$ depends on the local field $\bar{\mathbf{\epsilon}}_{\text{loc}}$: the positive and negative charges are separated under the action of the local field until the restoring force, which is an internal electrostatic force arising from their separation, just balances the local field force.

In most dielectrics, the molecular charge separation is directly proportional to, and is in the same direction as, the local field. Thus

$$\mathbf{p} = \alpha \bar{\mathbf{\epsilon}}_{\text{loc}}, \tag{3-63}$$

$$= \alpha \left(\mathbf{E} + b \frac{\mathbf{P}}{\epsilon_0} \right), \tag{3-64}$$

where the constant α is known as the *molecular polarizability*. Dielect ics which show this simple dependence of polarization on local field are said to be *linear* and isotropic. Many commercially important dielectrics are *homogeneous* as well as linear and isotropic. We shall designate such materials as *Class A dielectrics* and shall confine our attention to them for the time being.

The dipole moment per unit volume is then

$$\mathbf{P} = N\mathbf{p}, \tag{3-65}$$

$$= N\alpha \left(\mathbf{E} + b \frac{\mathbf{P}}{\epsilon_0} \right), \tag{3-66}$$

where N is again the number of molecules per unit volume. Solving this equation for $\mathbf{P}$, we obtain

$$\mathbf{P} = \frac{N\alpha}{1 - (N\alpha b/\epsilon_0)} \mathbf{E}, \tag{3-67}$$

$$= \epsilon_0 \chi_e \mathbf{E}, \tag{3-68}$$

where χ_e is a dimensionless constant known as the *electric susceptibility* of the dielectric. The constant ϵ_0 is included explicitly in Eq. *3-68* simply to make χ_e dimensionless. For a Class A dielectric, the polarization vector $\mathbf{P}$ is thus proportional to the macroscopic field $\mathbf{E}$ as well as to the local field $\bar{\mathbf{\epsilon}}_{\text{loc}}$.

3.6.1. The Dielectric Coefficient K_e. For a Class A dielectric we have, from Eqs. *3-57* and *3-68*,

$$\mathbf{D} = \epsilon_0(1 + \chi_e)\mathbf{E}, \tag{3-69}$$

$$= K_e\epsilon_0\mathbf{E}, \tag{3-70}$$

where

$$K_e = 1 + \chi_e \tag{3-71}$$

is a dimensionless constant known either as the *dielectric coefficient*, the *dielectric constant*, or the *relative permittivity* of the dielectric material. In a vacuum, $\chi_e = 0$, and $K_e = 1$.

A number of typical dielectric coefficients are given in Table 3-1.

TABLE 3-1. Dielectric Coefficients of Various Materials

Material	Dielectric Coefficient
O_2 gas at 1 atm and 25°C	1.00052
Petroleum oil	2.2
Silicone oil	2.2–2.8
Polyethylene	2.3
Polystyrene	2.6
Lucite	3.2
Mylar	3.2
Quartz	3.8
Mica	5.4
Pyrex glass	4.8
Porcelain	5.5–9.0
Ethyl alcohol	26
Water	81
TiO_2	100
$BaTiO_3$	up to 10,000

The dielectric coefficient depends on the frequency of the electric field; the values shown in Table 3-1 apply only to the electrostatic case we have been discussing. The materials with very large dielectric coefficients are not Class A dielectrics, and the dipole moments responsible for their dielectric coefficients may not be of the simple induced type we have been discussing. There may also be marked temperature effects in the dielectric behavior.

With $\mathbf{D}$ proportional to $\mathbf{E}$, as in Eq. *3-70*, we have

$$\nabla \cdot \mathbf{E} = \frac{\rho}{K_e\epsilon_0}, \tag{3-72}$$

and

$$\nabla^2 V = -\frac{\rho}{K_e\epsilon_0}. \tag{3-73}$$

This is *Poisson's equation for Class A dielectrics*. If the dielectric is not Class A, we must write

$$\nabla^2 V = -\frac{(\rho + \rho')}{\epsilon_0}. \tag{3-74}$$

The bound charge density ρ' is related to the free charge density ρ in a Class A dielectric as follows:

$$\mathbf{P} = \mathbf{D} - \epsilon_0 \mathbf{E}, \tag{3-75}$$

$$= \frac{K_e - 1}{K_e} \mathbf{D}, \tag{3-76}$$

thus, if the dielectric is homogenous,

$$\nabla \cdot \mathbf{P} = \left(\frac{K_e - 1}{K_e}\right) \nabla \cdot \mathbf{D}, \tag{3-77}$$

and

$$-\rho' = \left(\frac{K_e - 1}{K_e}\right) \rho. \tag{3-78}$$

Thus, at any point in a homogeneous, isotropic, linear dielectric, ρ' must be zero if ρ is zero. Usually, $\rho = 0$, and the polarization charges are located only on the surfaces of the dielectric, thus $\nabla \cdot \mathbf{P} = 0$.

3.7. Calculation of Electrostatic Fields Involving Dielectrics

We are now in a position to calculate electrostatic fields involving Class A dielectrics.

If the symmetry of the field is simple and if the charge density ρ is zero, as it often is, we can usually integrate the Maxwell equation

$$\nabla \cdot \mathbf{D} = \rho \tag{3-79}$$

to find the displacement vector $\mathbf{D}$. The constant of integration can be determined from the boundary conditions which can be, for example, the charge densities on the conductors. The integral form of the Maxwell equation, that is,

$$\int_S \mathbf{D} \cdot d\mathbf{a} = \int_\tau \rho \, d\tau, \tag{3-80}$$

is often more useful than Eq. *3-79* for determining $\mathbf{D}$.

Once $\mathbf{D}$ is determined, $\mathbf{E}$ can be found at once from Eq. *3-70*,

$$\mathbf{E} = \frac{\mathbf{D}}{K_e \epsilon_0}, \tag{3-81}$$

provided that the dielectric coefficient K_e is known. It is then a simple step from $\mathbf{E}$ to potential difference, capacitance, or other physical quantities depending on $\mathbf{E}$.

3.7.1. The Parallel-Plate Capacitor.

As a simple example, we shall consider a parallel plate capacitor with a dielectric of coefficient K_e completely filling the space between the plates, as in Figure 3-9. We assume that the separation of the plates is small compared to the linear extent of the plates, in order that we may neglect fringing effects at the edges.

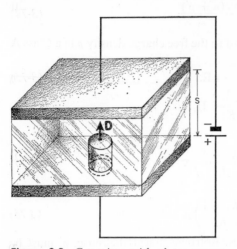

Figure 3-9. *Capacitor with plates separated by a dielectric.*

The surface charge densities $+\sigma$ on the lower plate and $-\sigma$ on the upper plate produce a uniform electrostatic field intensity directed upward. The polarization in the dielectric produces a bound surface charge density $-\sigma'$ on the lower surface of the dielectric and $+\sigma'$ on the upper surface. These bound charges produce a uniform electrostatic field intensity directed downward, with the result that the net field between the plates is *less* than it would be without the dielectric and with the same charges on the plates. Thus the potential difference between the plates is decreased, and the capacitance is increased by the presence of the dielectric.

To calculate the capacitance quantitatively, we can apply Gauss's law for the displacement vector **D** to a cylinder with its base within the conducting material of one plate, its sides perpendicular to the plates, and its upper surface in the dielectric, as in Figure 3-9. Since **D** and **E** must be perpendicular to the plates, the only flux of **D** through the Gaussian surface is through the top. Thus

$$D = \sigma \qquad (3\text{-}82)$$

and is perpendicular to the plates. We also have, from Eq. *3-81*,

$$E = \frac{\sigma}{K_e \epsilon_0}. \qquad (3\text{-}83)$$

The potential difference between the plates is

$$\Delta V = Es, \qquad (3\text{-}84)$$

$$= \frac{\sigma s}{K_e \epsilon_0}, \qquad (3\text{-}85)$$

and the capacitance is

$$C = \frac{Q}{\Delta V} = \frac{\sigma S}{\Delta V}, \qquad (3\text{-}86)$$

$$\frac{K_e \epsilon_0 S}{s}, \qquad (3\text{-}87)$$

where S is the area of one plate. The capacitance is therefore increased by a factor K_e through the presence of the dielectric.

The measurement of the capacitance of a suitable capacitor with and without dielectric provides a convenient method for determining the dielectric coefficient.

3.7.2. The Free Charge σ, the Bound Charge σ', and the Displacement D at a Dielectric-Conductor Boundary.

It is instructive to examine the relationship between the bound surface charge density σ' and the free surface charge density σ at the interface between a dielectric and a conductor. At the lower plate of the capacitor considered above,

$$\sigma' = \mathbf{P} \cdot \mathbf{n} = -P, \tag{3-88}$$

since $\mathbf{n}$ is the outward normal to the dielectric surface and is in the direction opposite to $\mathbf{P}$. Thus

$$-\sigma' = P = D - \epsilon_0 E, \tag{3-89}$$

$$= \frac{K_e - 1}{K_e} D, \tag{3-90}$$

$$= \frac{K_e - 1}{K_e} \sigma. \tag{3-91}$$

Thus the bound charge density σ' is of opposite sign and is smaller in magnitude by the factor $(K_e - 1)/K_e$ than the free charge density σ. This relationship is always true whenever a Class A dielectric is in contact with a conductor.

The free charge density σ on a conductor in contact with *any* dielectric is always equal to the displacement vector $\mathbf{D}$ just inside the surface of the dielectric, as we can show from Gauss's law by the same argument used in the case of the parallel-plate capacitor. Furthermore, if a conducting surface is introduced into a dielectric so as to be coincident with an equipotential surface, then the free surface charge density σ on the conductor at a particular point is equal in magnitude to the displacement vector $\mathbf{D}$ in the dielectric at that point.

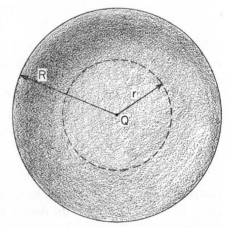

Figure 3-10. *Dielectric sphere with a point charge Q at the center.*

3.7.3. Dielectric Sphere with a Point Charge at Its Center.

As a further example of electrostatic fields in dielectrics, let us consider a Class A dielectric sphere of radius R and dielectric coefficient K_e with a point charge Q embedded at the center as in Figure 3-10.

Again, we can find the displacement vector $\mathbf{D}$ from Gauss's law. We draw an imaginary sphere of radius $r < R$ and use it as a Gaussian surface. Then

$$\mathbf{D} = \frac{Q}{4\pi r^2}\,\mathbf{r}_1, \tag{3-92}$$

and

$$\mathbf{E} = \frac{Q}{4\pi\epsilon_0 K_e r^2}\,\mathbf{r}_1. \tag{3-93}$$

In addition,

$$\mathbf{P} = \frac{K_e - 1}{K_e}\,\mathbf{D}, \tag{3-94}$$

$$= \left(\frac{K_e - 1}{K_e}\right)\frac{Q}{4\pi r^2}\,\mathbf{r}_1. \tag{3-95}$$

At the outer surface of the sphere,

$$\sigma_0' = \mathbf{P}\cdot\mathbf{n} = P, \tag{3-96}$$

$$= \left(\frac{K_e - 1}{K_e}\right)\frac{Q}{4\pi R^2}. \tag{3-97}$$

The total amount of bound charge on the outer surface is thus

$$Q' = \frac{K_e - 1}{K_e}\,Q. \tag{3-98}$$

Since there is no volume density of free charge, there should be no volume density of bound charge, as we saw in the last section. This is correct, as we can calculate directly:

$$\rho' = -\boldsymbol{\nabla}\cdot\mathbf{P}, \tag{3-99}$$

$$= -\frac{1}{r^2}\frac{\partial}{\partial r}(r^2 P), \tag{3-100}$$

$$= 0. \tag{3-101}$$

There is also bound charge on the surface of the cavity containing the free charge Q at the center. This can be calculated as follows. Let the radius of the cavity be δ. Then if $-\sigma_c'$ is the density of bound charge on the cavity surface, the total bound charge on the cavity is

$$Q'' = -\sigma_c' 4\pi\delta^2, \tag{3-102}$$

$$= -\left(\frac{K_e - 1}{K_e}\right)\frac{Q}{4\pi\delta^2}\,4\pi\delta^2, \tag{3-103}$$

$$= -\left(\frac{K_e - 1}{K_e}\right)Q. \tag{3-104}$$

The dielectric as a whole therefore remains neutral, as must be expected.

The net charge at the center is then

$$Q_{net} = Q - \left(\frac{K_e - 1}{K_e}\right)Q, \tag{3-105}$$

or

$$Q_{net} = \frac{Q}{K_e}, \tag{3-106}$$

and is smaller than the free charge by the factor K_e. This accounts for the reduction of the field intensity within the dielectric by the factor K_e, as in Eq. *3-93*.

It is instructive to compare the field intensity outside the sphere to that inside. Outside, from Gauss's law,

$$\mathbf{D} = \frac{Q}{4\pi r^2}\mathbf{r_1}, \tag{3-107}$$

and

$$\mathbf{E} = \frac{Q}{4\pi \epsilon_0 r^2}\mathbf{r_1}, \tag{3-108}$$

which is to be compared to Eq. *3-93* for the field inside the sphere. At the surface of the sphere the electrostatic field intensity is discontinuous, the magnitude just outside the surface being K_e times as large as the magnitude just inside the surface. The difference is due to the bound charges which produce an opposing field within the dielectric.

If we compute the potential as a function of distance from the center of the sphere, we find that it undergoes a discontinuity in slope at the dielectric surface. However, the potential itself is continuous.

3.8 The Clausius-Mossotti Equation

Let us return now to the basic polarization mechanism in a nonpolar dielectric and compute the dielectric coefficient K_e in terms of the molecular properties. We shall assume the Lorentz form of Eq. *3-47* for the local field:

$$\bar{\epsilon}_{loc} = \mathbf{E} + \frac{\mathbf{P}}{3\epsilon_0}. \tag{3-109}$$

As we saw, this equation is not necessarily correct, in that the factor multiplying $\mathbf{P}/\epsilon_0$ may differ from $\frac{1}{3}$, but $\frac{1}{3}$ is of the right order of magnitude.

If we set $b = \frac{1}{3}$, then from Eq. *3-66*,

$$\mathbf{P} = N\alpha\left(\mathbf{E} + \frac{\mathbf{P}}{3\epsilon_0}\right), \tag{3-110}$$

or

$$\epsilon_0(K_e - 1)\mathbf{E} = N\alpha\left(\mathbf{E} + \frac{K_e - 1}{3}\mathbf{E}\right), \tag{3-111}$$

and

$$\frac{K_e - 1}{K_e + 2} = \frac{N\alpha}{3\epsilon_0}, \tag{3-112}$$

where N is the number of molecules per unit volume and α is the molecular polarizability.

If the dielectric is a compound consisting of a number of different types of molecules or atoms, Eq. *3-112* becomes

$$\frac{K_e - 1}{K_e + 2} = \frac{1}{3\epsilon_0} \sum_i N_i \alpha_i, \qquad (3\text{-}113)$$

where N_i and α_i are the appropriate quantities for the ith type of molecule or atom.

Equation *3-112*, or *3-113*, is known as the *Clausius-Mossotti equation.* It relates the dielectric coefficient K_e to the mass density of a material, since

$$N = \frac{\rho}{M} N_A, \qquad (3\text{-}114)$$

where ρ is the mass density, N_A is Avogadro's number, and M is the molecular weight. In m.k.s. units, ρ is expressed in kilograms/meter³, N_A is the number of molecules in one kilogram molecular weight, or 6.02×10^{26}, and M is the kilogram molecular weight (for example, the kilogram molecular weight of oxygen is 32 kilograms). Then

$$\frac{M}{\rho} \frac{K_e - 1}{K_e + 2} = \frac{N_A}{3\epsilon_0} \alpha = \alpha_M. \qquad (3\text{-}115)$$

The quantity α_M is called the *molar polarization.*

Equation *3-115* shows that the quantity $(K_e - 1)/\rho(K_e + 2)$ is independent of density if our model for the polarization is valid. This prediction of the Clausius-Mossotti equation is borne out in a wide variety of gases and is approximated in nonpolar liquids. Table 3-2, taken from a paper by Michels, Sanders and Schipper,[*] shows, for hydrogen, remarkable agreement between theory and experiment.

TABLE 3-2.   Test of the Clausius-Mossotti Equation in Hydrogen at 24.9°C

Pressure (atmospheres)	Density × 10³ (grams/centimeter³)	K_e	$\left(\dfrac{K_e - 1}{K_e + 2}\right)\dfrac{1}{\rho}$
7.96	0.324	1.00192	1.973
30.03	1.206	1.00730	2.013
88.13	3.421	1.02083	2.015
255.04	8.984	1.05540	2.019
478.78	14.955	1.09310	2.013
814.62	21.755	1.13766	2.016
1425.36	30.357	1.19500	2.011

[*] A. Michels, P. Sanders, and A. Schipper, *Physica* **2,** 753 (1935).

Examination of Eq. *3-112* shows that K_e must increase rapidly and tend to infinity as the number of molecules per unit volume approaches the critical value N_c, where

$$\frac{N_c\alpha}{3\epsilon_0} = 1. \qquad (3\text{-}116)$$

Physically, the expression $K_e \longrightarrow \infty$ corresponds to the dielectric volume being filled with infinitely polarizable, that is, conducting, molecules. In gases and in liquids, the polarizabilities are relatively small, with the result that this condition is never approached, and the Clausius-Mossotti equation is valid.

In crystalline solids, however, the interactions of the dipoles with each other produce polarizations which are more complicated than those of our simple model, and the Clausius-Mossotti equation is not valid.

3.9. Polar Molecules

Let us now investigate the behavior of dielectrics in which the molecules possess permanent dipole moments. Molecules consisting of two or more dissimilar atoms exhibit such permanent moments. For example, if two atoms are held together by ionic bonds, in which one atom carries a positive and the other a negative charge, it is clear from the separation of the ionic charges that the molecules are polar. Other mechanisms exist by which other molecular types can also have permanent moments. Diatomic molecules consisting of two similar atoms never have permanent moments because there is no asymmetrical way for them to arrange themselves.

In addition to their permanent dipole moments, polar molecules also exhibit induced moments of the type we have been discussing, but for the time being we shall neglect these induced moments and focus our attention on the permanent moments.

If a permanent dipole is oriented in a uniform local electrostatic field intensity ϵ (*from now on, for simplicity, we shall drop the subscript* "loc"), such that the dipole moment $\mathbf{p}$

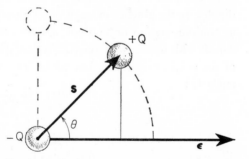

Figure 3-11. *Dipole with a permanent dipole moment* $\mathbf{p} = Q\mathbf{s}$ *oriented at an angle* θ *with respect to the local electrostatic field intensity* ϵ. *The potential energy is shown to be* $-\mathbf{p}\cdot\epsilon$

makes an angle with ϵ, as in Figure 3-11, a torque $\mathbf{p} \times \epsilon$ will act on the dipole and will tend to align it with the field. An unaligned dipole therefore has greater energy than an aligned one.

We can calculate the potential energy which the dipole possesses when it has an orientation θ relative to the field ϵ by finding how much work we must do to introduce a dipole with such an orientation into the field. Let us bring the dipole from infinity, where the field intensity is zero, to the final position indicated in Figure 3-11. The potential V is assumed to be zero at $z = 0$. The energy required to bring the charge $-Q$ from $z = 0$ to z in the field ϵ, *which is assumed to be fixed*, is

$$W_- = (-Q)(-\epsilon z). \tag{3-117}$$

Similarly, for the charge $+Q$,

$$W_+ = Q[-\epsilon(z + s \cos \theta)]. \tag{3-118}$$

The net potential energy of the dipole is then

$$W = -Q\epsilon s \cos \theta, \tag{3-119}$$

$$= -\mathbf{p} \cdot \boldsymbol{\epsilon}. \tag{3-120}$$

It is minimum when $\mathbf{p}$ is parallel to $\boldsymbol{\epsilon}$.

3.9.1. The Langevin Equation.

We shall now limit our discussion to gaseous and liquid polar dielectrics. In these dielectrics, thermal agitation brings about collisions between molecules which tend to destroy any alignment with a field ϵ. Between collisions, the field ϵ exerts a restoring torque with the result that, on the average, there is a net alignment, and consequently a net dipole moment $\mathbf{P}$ per unit volume.

To compute this net polarization, we consider a unit volume containing N dipoles. In the absence of an external electrostatic field, the dipoles are oriented at random, and, at any instant, dN are oriented at angles lying between θ and $\theta + d\theta$ with respect to a given direction. The fraction dN/N is merely the ratio of the solid angle corresponding to the angular interval $d\theta$ to the total solid angle 4π:

$$\frac{dN}{N} = \frac{2\pi \sin \theta \, d\theta}{4\pi}, \tag{3-121}$$

$$= \frac{\sin \theta \, d\theta}{2}. \tag{3-122}$$

If the dipoles are subject to a local electrostatic field ϵ, the solid-angle elements are no longer equally probable, since a dipole has a potential energy W which depends on its orientation relative to the field. It is shown in statistical mechanics* that if a large number of molecules with a distribution of energies are in statistical equilibrium, the number possessing a particular energy W is proportional to $e^{-W/kT}$, where k is the Boltzmann constant 1.380×10^{-23} joule/degree and T is the absolute temperature in degrees Kelvin.

---

* See, for example, Richtmyer, Kennard, and Lauritsen, *Introduction to Modern Physics* (McGraw-Hill, New York, 1955), p. 168.

In the present case, the dipoles whose axes lie in the range between θ and $\theta + d\theta$, measured from the direction of ϵ, all possess an energy $W = -\mathbf{p} \cdot \epsilon$. Then the number of dipoles lying in the interval θ to $\theta + d\theta$ is

$$dN = Ce^{\mathbf{p} \cdot \epsilon/kT} \sin \theta \, d\theta, \qquad (3\text{-}123)$$

where the constant C must be chosen such that the total number of molecules in a unit volume is N:

$$N = C \int_0^{\pi} e^{\mathbf{p} \cdot \epsilon/kT} \sin \theta \, d\theta. \qquad (3\text{-}124)$$

Now the molecules whose moments lie in the angular interval θ to $\theta + d\theta$ possess a total dipole moment $d\mathbf{P}'$ given by

$$d\mathbf{P}' = \mathbf{p} \, dN, \qquad (3\text{-}125)$$

and the resultant moment, which must be in the direction of the field intensity ϵ by symmetry, is

$$d\mathbf{P} = p \, dN \cos \theta \, \mathbf{k}, \qquad (3\text{-}126)$$

where $\mathbf{k}$ is a unit vector in the direction of the field ϵ. Then

$$P = Np \frac{\displaystyle\int_0^{\pi} e^{u \cos \theta} \sin \theta \cos \theta \, d\theta}{\displaystyle\int_0^{\pi} e^{u \cos \theta} \sin \theta \, d\theta}, \qquad (3\text{-}127)$$

where we have set

$$u = \frac{p\epsilon}{kT}. \qquad (3\text{-}128)$$

Writing now

$$t = \frac{\mathbf{p} \cdot \epsilon}{kT} = u \cos \theta, \qquad (3\text{-}129)$$

we obtain

$$P = \frac{\dfrac{Np}{u} \displaystyle\int_{-u}^{+u} e^t t \, dt}{\displaystyle\int_{-u}^{+u} e^t \, dt}, \qquad (3\text{-}130)$$

$$= \frac{Np}{u} \frac{[te^t - e^t]_{-u}^{+u}}{[e^t]_{-u}^{+u}}, \qquad (3\text{-}131)$$

$$= Np \left(\coth u - \frac{1}{u} \right), \qquad (3\text{-}132)$$

$$= Np \left(\coth \frac{p\epsilon}{kT} - \frac{kT}{p\epsilon} \right). \qquad (3\text{-}133)$$

Equation *3-133* is known as the *Langevin equation* because it was first derived by Langevin in 1905 for magnetic dipoles.

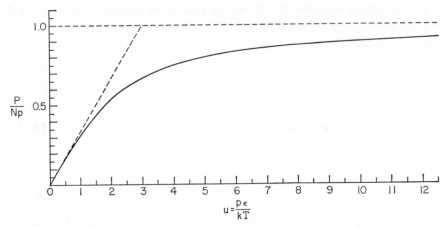

Figure 3-12. *The Langevin function.*

Figure 3-12 shows P/Np as a function of u. For large values of $u = p\epsilon/kT$, that is, for large fields and low temperatures, there is a saturation effect, and P tends toward

$$P_0 = Np \qquad (3\text{-}134)$$

as an asymptotic value. This corresponds to the case in which all the dipoles are aligned with the field and the polarization is maximum.

The region of practical interest is the region where $p\epsilon/kT$ is small compared to unity. At room temperature $kT \sim 4 \times 10^{-21}$ joule, whereas a typical dipole moment is of the order of 10^{-30} coulomb-meter. Thus, even with a field intensity of 10^7 volts/meter, $p\epsilon/kT$ is only of the order of 2×10^{-3}. We can therefore expand the exponentials in Eq. *3-133* and retain only the terms up to u^3. Then

$$P = Np \left[\frac{2 + u^2}{2u[1 + (u^2/6)]} - \frac{1}{u} \right], \qquad (3\text{-}135)$$

$$= Np \left[\frac{1}{2u} (2 + u^2)\left(1 - \frac{u^2}{6}\right) - \frac{1}{u} \right], \qquad (3\text{-}136)$$

$$= \frac{Npu}{3}, \qquad (3\text{-}137)$$

$$= \frac{Np^2}{3kT} \epsilon. \qquad (3\text{-}138)$$

Thus when $p\epsilon \ll kT$, the polarization is proportional to the field which produces it, the susceptibility is inversely proportional to the absolute temperature, and the dielectric is linear.

From a practical point of view, the only feature which distinguishes a polar from a nonpolar dielectric is the temperature dependence of the susceptibility and, therefore, of the dielectric coefficient.

3.9.2. The Debye Equation. Let us now consider the case in which there are both induced and permanent dipoles, as in any real polar dielectric. Combining Eqs. *3-63*, *3-65*, and *3-138*, we obtain

$$\mathbf{P} = N\left(\alpha + \frac{p^2}{3\,kT}\right)\epsilon, \qquad (3\text{-}139)$$

where ϵ again indicates the local electric field intensity. Using now Eq. *3-47* for the Lorentz local field,

$$\epsilon = \mathbf{E} + \frac{\mathbf{P}}{3\epsilon_0}, \qquad (3\text{-}140)$$

or, for a linear dielectric (Eqs. *3-68* and *3-71*),

$$\epsilon = \left(\frac{K_e + 2}{3}\right)\mathbf{E}. \qquad (3\text{-}141)$$

Then

$$\epsilon_0(K_e - 1)\mathbf{E} = N\left(\alpha + \frac{p^2}{3kT}\right)\left(\frac{K_e + 2}{3}\right)\mathbf{E} \qquad (3\text{-}142)$$

or

$$\frac{K_e - 1}{K_e + 2} = \frac{N}{3\epsilon_0}\left(\alpha + \frac{p^2}{3kT}\right). \qquad (3\text{-}143)$$

Multiplying by the molecular weight M and dividing by the mass density ρ, as we did in discussing the Clausius-Mosotti equation, we find a new expression for the molar polarization which is valid for polar dielectrics:

$$\alpha_M = \frac{M}{\rho}\left(\frac{K_e - 1}{K_e + 2}\right) = \frac{N_A}{3\epsilon_0}\left(\alpha + \frac{p^2}{3kT}\right). \qquad (3\text{-}144)$$

This is known as the *Debye equation*, after Debye, who first derived it in 1912. This expression is similar to Eq. *3-115*, except for the term $p^2/3kT$, which comes from the alignment of the polar molecules.

In principle, the Debye equation can be used to determine both the polarizability α and the permanent dipole moment p of a molecule. Plotting $(M/\rho)(K_e - 1)/(K_e + 2)$ versus $1/T$ gives a straight line, as in Figure 3-13, whose intercept on the vertical axis is $N_A\alpha/3\epsilon_0$ and whose slope is $N_A p^2/9\epsilon_0 k$, where N_A is Avogadro's number and k is the Boltzmann constant. In practice, this equation provides a reliable way of measuring α and p only for gases, where the dielectric coefficient differs only slightly from unity, and for dilute solutions of polar molecules in a nonpolar solvent.

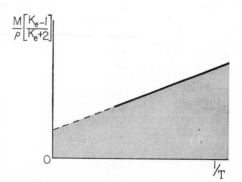

Figure 3-13. *The polarizability α and the dipole moment per molecule p can be determined from the intercept on the vertical axis and from the slope of this curve.*

We have made one important assumption in deriving the Debye equation. We have assumed that it is the Lorentz local field $\bar{\epsilon}_{loc} = \mathbf{E} + (\mathbf{P}/3\epsilon_0)$ which is responsible both for the induced and the oriented polarization. We saw that the factor $\frac{1}{3}$ is only approximate. Furthermore, as regards the orientation forces, there is another more subtle effect which further invalidates Eq. *3-144*. As a permanent dipole turns, part of the local field turns with it and is always aligned with the dipole, hence it can play no part in orienting the dipole. This comes about because the field of the dipole polarizes the surrounding molecules, and these in turn produce a field at the dipole which is in the same direction as its moment. Furthermore, molecular associations in liquids and in solids complicate the problem. The result is that dielectric behavior in liquids and especially in crystalline solids is more complicated than the simple picture we have developed here. The molar polarization of water, for example, shows little temperature dependence, even though water has a large permanent dipole moment of 6.2×10^{-30} coulomb-meter. The basic features of the polarization process are as we have discussed them, but a precise determination of molecular polarizability and of permanent dipole moment must rest on a more sophisticated treatment.*

Table 3-3 lists the magnitude of the permanent dipole moments for a number of polar molecules.

TABLE 3-3.   Polar Molecules and Their Dipole Moments

Molecule	Permanent Dipole Moment (10^{-30} coulomb-meters)
CO	0.3
HI	1.3
HCl	3.3
Ethyl iodide	6.0
H_2O	6.2
Acetone	10.
Nitrobenzene	14.
NaI	16.
KCl	21.
CsCl	33.

3.10. Frequency Dependence of the Dielectric Coefficient

We have discussed so far two basic polarization processes. We first discussed *induced* polarization, in which the center of negative charge in an atom or mole-

* See for example C. J. F. Böttcher, *Theory of Electric Polarization* (Elsevier, Amsterdam, 1952).

cule is displaced relative to the center of positive charge when an external field is applied. This type of polarization is also called *electronic*. We then considered *orientational* polarization in which molecules with a permanent dipole moment tend to be aligned by an external field, the magnitude of the susceptibility being inversely proportional to the temperature. There is also a third basic polarization process which we may call *ionic*. This process occurs in ionic crystals, in which ions of one sign may move with respect to ions of the other sign when an external field is applied.

The dependence of the dielectric coefficient on the frequency of the external field can be understood qualitatively from these different polarization processes. Water, for example, has a dielectric coefficient of 81 in an electrostatic field, and a dielectric coefficient of about 1.8 at optical frequencies. The large static value is attributable to the orientation of the permanent dipole moments, but the rotational inertia of the molecules is much too large for any significant response at optical frequencies. The electronic motion at optical frequencies may be either greater or lesser than the motion at zero frequency, depending on the magnitude of the frequency as compared to frequencies which are characteristic of the atomic system. Similarly, the dielectric coefficient K_e of sodium chloride is 5.6 in an electrostatic field and 2.3 at optical frequencies. The larger static value is attributed to ionic motion, which again is impossible at high frequencies.

3.11. Solid Dielectrics

Most of our discussion of dielectrics so far has been in terms of gases or liquids, because the polarization process is simplest for these substances. However, from a practical viewpoint, solids are of great importance, and our theory would not be complete without some mention of them. Induced, orientational, and ionic polarizations also occur in solids. In crystalline solids, however, they depend on the molecular structure and on the type of lattice. In many substances the dielectric coefficient decreases by a large factor as the temperature is lowered through the freezing point. In nitrobenzene, for example, the dielectric coefficient K_e falls from about 35 to about 3 in passing through the freezing point at 279°K. In the solid state, the permanent dipole moments of the nitrobenzene molecules are fixed rigidly in the crystal lattice and cannot rotate under the influence of an external field.

3.12. Nonlinear, Anisotropic, and   Nonhomogeneous Dielectrics

All dielectric materials are linear at sufficiently small field intensities. They are almost always linear at the field intensities which are of practical interest.

Anisotropy is the most common departure from the ideal Class A dielectric behavior. Crystalline solids commonly have different dielectric properties in different crystal directions because the charges which constitute the atoms of the crystal are able to move more easily in some directions than in others. The result is that the susceptibility depends on direction, thus the polarization vector **P** is, in general, not in the same direction as the resultant field intensity **E**. Then

$$P_x = \epsilon_0(\chi_{exx}E_x + \chi_{exy}E_y + \chi_{exz}E_z) \qquad (3\text{-}145)$$

or, more generally,

$$P_i = \epsilon_0 \sum_j \chi_{eij}E_j, \qquad (3\text{-}146)$$

where the subscripts i and j represent the three coordinate directions x, y, and z. All three components of **P** depend on all three components of **E**, with different susceptibilities for each. The susceptibility χ_e thus has nine components and is a tensor. Actually, there are only six independent components, and, if the coordinate axes are properly chosen, these six components reduce to three. The relationship between **P** and **E** is still linear but is more complicated than for isotropic dielectrics.

For anisotropic dielectrics, Eq. 3-56 still applies:

$$\nabla \cdot (\epsilon_0 \mathbf{E} + \mathbf{P}) = \rho,$$

where ρ is the free charge density. It is again useful to define the displacement vector as in Eq. 3-57

$$\mathbf{D} = \epsilon_0 \mathbf{E} + \mathbf{P},$$

except that now **D**, **E** and **P** are in general not all in the same direction.

The relation between the displacement vector **D** and the electric field intensity vector **E** must now be written as

$$D_i = \epsilon_0 \sum_j K_{eij}E_j, \qquad (3\text{-}147)$$

where K_{ij} is a tensor which, again, has six independent components. The relationship between **D** and **E** is still linear, and the general features of the discussion of Class A dielectrics are valid.

Nonhomogeneity is of little practical importance, but there is one fact which we should point out. If the dielectric coefficient is a function of position in the dielectric, then a volume density of bound charge may exist when there is no corresponding volume density of free charge (see Eq. 3-78). Demonstration of this fact will be left as an exercise.

3.13. Potential Energy of a Charge Distribution in the Presence of Dielectrics

If dielectrics are present in the vicinity of a charge distribution, we may still calculate the energy of the system in the manner of Section 2.14. We allow each free charge to recede to infinity as before, except that now the potential at a given point in the field depends on the geometry and on the characteristics of the dielectric. The calculation leads us again to Eq. *2-189*:

$$W = \frac{1}{2} \int_\tau \rho V \, d\tau, \tag{3-148}$$

where the volume τ is any volume which includes all the free charges in the system.

So as restrict the calculation to free charges, we write

$$\rho = \nabla \cdot \mathbf{D}. \tag{3-149}$$

We then use the vector identity of Problem 1-14 to obtain

$$W = \frac{1}{2} \int_\tau V(\nabla \cdot \mathbf{D}) \, d\tau, \tag{3-150}$$

$$= \frac{1}{2} \int_\tau (\nabla \cdot V\mathbf{D}) \, d\tau - \frac{1}{2} \int_\tau (\mathbf{D} \cdot \nabla V) \, d\tau. \tag{3-151}$$

Then, transforming the first term to a surface integral gives

$$W = \frac{1}{2} \int_S V\mathbf{D} \cdot d\mathbf{a} + \frac{1}{2} \int_\tau (\mathbf{D} \cdot \mathbf{E}) \, d\tau. \tag{3-152}$$

As in Section 2.14, V falls off at least as fast as $1/r$, D falls off at least as fast as $1/r^2$, and da increases as r^2. The first integral falls off at least as fast as $1/r$ and goes to zero as the surface S recedes to infinity. Thus

$$W = \frac{1}{2} \int_\tau (\mathbf{D} \cdot \mathbf{E}) \, d\tau, \tag{3-153}$$

where τ is any volume which includes all the points where $\mathbf{D}$ and $\mathbf{E}$ differ from zero. This expression is independent of the type of dielectric present in the system and is completely general.

As for free space, we may define an energy density

$$\frac{dW}{d\tau} = \frac{1}{2} \mathbf{D} \cdot \mathbf{E}, \tag{3-154}$$

which is useful in calculating the work required to assemble a charge distribution.

In the special case of a Class A dielectric in which

$$\mathbf{D} = K_e \epsilon_0 \mathbf{E}, \tag{3-155}$$

we have

$$W = \frac{1}{2} \int_\tau K_e \epsilon_0 E^2 \, d\tau. \tag{3-156}$$

3.14. Forces on Dielectrics

A dielectric material placed in an electric field is subject to forces which arise from the interaction of the electric field with the dipoles in the dielectric.

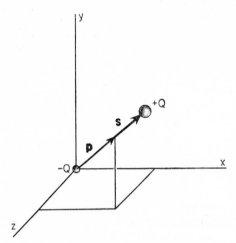

Figure 3-14. *Dipole of moment* **p** *located in an electrostatic field of intensity* **E** *whose components are functions of the coordinates.*

Although these forces are ordinarily small, they are readily measurable, and they give rise to the phenomenon of electrostriction.

A dipole in a uniform electrostatic field experiences a torque

$$\mathbf{T} = \mathbf{p} \times \mathbf{E} \qquad (3\text{-}157)$$

which tends to align it with the field, but the net force is zero. There can be a net force only if the field is nonuniform, such that one end of the dipole is subject to a greater force than the other.

Let us calculate the force which a dipole experiences in a nonuniform electrostatic field. We select axes as in Figure 3-14 and set the field intensity at the origin to be

$$\mathbf{E} = E_x\mathbf{i} + E_y\mathbf{j} + E_z\mathbf{k}. \qquad (3\text{-}158)$$

Then the x-component of the force on the dipole is

$$F_x = Q\left(E_x + \frac{\partial E_x}{\partial x}\mathbf{s}\cdot\mathbf{i} + \frac{\partial E_x}{\partial y}\mathbf{s}\cdot\mathbf{j} + \frac{\partial E_x}{\partial z}\mathbf{s}\cdot\mathbf{k}\right) - QE_x, \qquad (3\text{-}159)$$

$$= \frac{\partial E_x}{\partial x}p_x + \frac{\partial E_x}{\partial y}p_y + \frac{\partial E_x}{\partial z}p_z, \qquad (3\text{-}160)$$

and, similarly,

$$F_y = \frac{\partial E_y}{\partial x}p_x + \frac{\partial E_y}{\partial y}p_y + \frac{\partial E_y}{\partial z}p_z, \qquad (3\text{-}161)$$

$$F_z = \frac{\partial E_z}{\partial x}p_x + \frac{\partial E_z}{\partial y}p_y + \frac{\partial E_z}{\partial z}p_z. \qquad (3\text{-}162)$$

Then

$$\mathbf{F} = \left(p_x\frac{\partial}{\partial x} + p_y\frac{\partial}{\partial y} + p_z\frac{\partial}{\partial z}\right)(E_x\mathbf{i} + E_y\mathbf{j} + E_z\mathbf{k}), \qquad (3\text{-}163)$$

$$= (p\cdot\nabla)\mathbf{E}. \qquad (3\text{-}164)$$

3.14.1. Pressure Rise Due to a Gradient in Electric Field Intensity.

To gain a qualitative understanding of the nature of this force, let us consider a parallel-plate capacitor immersed in a liquid dielectric, as in Figure 3-15. A vertical dipole situated on the median plane of the capacitor in the fringe-field is acted on by two forces, as illustrated in Figure 3-16. Since the forces acting on the charges at the ends of the dipole are not quite perpendicular to the median plane, there is a net force directed toward the high field region between the capacitor plates. As a result, the dipoles in the fringe field press inward, producing an increase in pressure between the plates.

We can calculate the increase in pressure from the electrostatic force on a small volume of the liquid.

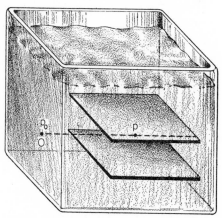

Figure 3-15. *A parallel-plate capacitor is immersed in a liquid dielectric. When the capacitor is charged, the fluid pressure is higher between the plates than it is outside at O.*

The resulting differential equation can then be integrated to find the pressure difference between a point within the capacitor and one outside the field.

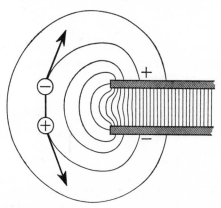

Figure 3-16. *Dipole in the fringe-field of a capacitor. The dipole lines up with the field and is subject to a net force directed toward the high-field region.*

Let us calculate this pressure difference $p - p_0$ approximately by considering an element of volume at the point O of Figure 3-15. Such a volume is shown in Figure 3-17. We assume the liquid to be incompressible. We choose the z-axis perpendicular to the capacitor plates and the x- and y-axes parallel to the plates, as indicated in Figure 3-17. At the point O in Figure 3-15, the field intensity **E** is in the z direction, hence the dipole moment **P** $d\tau$ of the volume element is also in the z direction. Thus, at the point O, both the electric field intensity **E** and the dipole moment **P** $d\tau$ are oriented along the z-axis. Thus the terms involving p_x and p_y in Eq. 3-164 are zero.

Since $E_y = 0$, $\partial E_y/\partial z = 0$. Also, since E_z is a maximum on the median plane,

$\partial E_z/\partial z = 0$. We are then left with a net force $d\mathbf{F}$ acting on the element of volume $d\tau$, which is given by

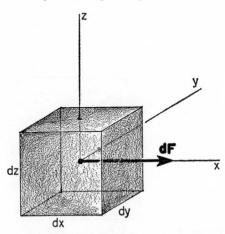

$$dF = P \, d\tau \frac{\partial E_z}{\partial z} \mathbf{i}. \quad (3\text{-}165)$$

Now, since $\nabla \times \mathbf{E} = 0$,

$$\frac{\partial E_x}{\partial z} = \frac{\partial E_z}{\partial x}, \quad (3\text{-}166)$$

and

$$dF = P \, d\tau \frac{\partial E_z}{\partial x} \mathbf{i}, \quad (3\text{-}167)$$

$$= P \, d\tau \frac{\partial E}{\partial x} \mathbf{i}, \quad (3\text{-}168)$$

Figure 3-17. *An element of volume of liquid dielectric at the point O of Figure 3-15 experiences a force* **dF** *toward the high-field region of the capacitor.*

since E_z is the only component of $\mathbf{E}$ at a point on the median plane of the capacitor. The quantity $\mathbf{P}$, however, is proportional to $\mathbf{E}$,

$$\mathbf{P} = \epsilon_0(K_e - 1)\mathbf{E}, \quad (3\text{-}169)$$

thus

$$d\mathbf{F} = \epsilon_0(K_e - 1)E \frac{dE}{dx} \, d\tau \, \mathbf{i}, \quad (3\text{-}170)$$

$$= \frac{\epsilon_0(K_e - 1)}{2} \frac{d(E^2)}{dx} \, d\tau \, \mathbf{i}. \quad (3\text{-}171)$$

Since the volume element is in equilibrium, this electrostatic force must be balanced by a difference in pressure on the left and right faces. If the pressure is p on the left face and $p + (dp/dx) \, dx$ on the right face, then

$$\frac{dp}{dx} = \frac{\epsilon_0(K_e - 1)}{2} \frac{d}{dx} (E^2), \quad (3\text{-}172)$$

and

$$p = \frac{\epsilon_0(K_e - 1)}{2} E^2 + p_0, \quad (3\text{-}173)$$

where p_0 is the hydrostatic pressure at a point on the median plane but outside the electric field, and p is the pressure at a point where the electric field intensity is E. The pressure within the capacitor thus exceeds the pressure in the external region by the amount

$$\epsilon_0(K_e - 1)E^2/2.$$

In deriving this equation we have made a simplifying assumption which invalidates it to some extent. We have considered the dielectric constant K_e to be strictly constant, whereas K_e may depend on the density of the fluid and hence on the pressure, since the fluid is compressible. Had we taken the dependence of K_e on density into account,* we would have found that

$$\nabla p = \frac{\epsilon_0}{2} \nabla \left(E^2 \frac{dK_e}{d\rho} \rho \right), \qquad (3\text{-}174)$$

where ρ is the mass density of the dielectric liquid. Integrating this equation leads to

$$p = \frac{1}{2} \epsilon_0 E^2 \frac{dK_e}{d\rho} \rho + p_0. \qquad (3\text{-}175)$$

We may use the Clausius-Mossotti equation (Eq. *3-115*) relating the dielectric coefficient K_e and the mass density ρ to obtain the pressure p in terms of K_e and ρ. Differentiating Eq. *3-115* leads to

$$\rho \frac{dK_e}{d\rho} = \frac{(K_e + 2)(K_e - 1)}{3}, \qquad (3\text{-}176)$$

thus

$$p = \frac{\epsilon_0 E^2}{2} \frac{(K_e + 2)(K_e - 1)}{3} + p_0. \qquad (3\text{-}177)$$

This is the correct relation between pressure and electric field intensity. For example, an electrostatic field intensity of 5×10^7 volts/meter is required in order to produce a pressure difference of one atmosphere when the dielectric coefficient $K_e = 5$. This dependence of pressure on elec-

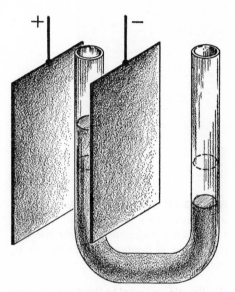

Figure 3-18. *The liquid dielectric rises as shown into the high-field region when the electric field is applied.*

tric field intensity can be observed in a U-tube as in Figure 3-18. When the electric field is applied, the liquid between the plates rises by an amount which depends both on the dielectric coefficient and on the electric field intensity in the liquid. This electric field intensity depends in turn on the geometry of the tube cross section and is calculated from Laplace's equation.

3.14.2. Pressure Rise in the Surface Layer. At the surface of the dielectric there is a rise in pressure which can be understood with the aid of Figure 3-19. The electric field intensity is assumed to be normal to the surface. The bound charge σ' resides in a thin layer of thickness t inside which the electric field

---

* This calculation is most readily made by using energy methods. See W. K. H. Panofsky and M. Phillips, *Classical Electricity and Magnetism* (Addison-Wesley, 1955), p. 92.

intensity rises from a value E in the interior of the dielectric to E_0 outside. The dipoles whose positive charges constitute the surface charge layer experience the field E on their negative ends and a field which is greater than E on their positive ends. The resultant force per unit area is directed to the right, and

$$\frac{dF}{da} = \sigma' \frac{(E_0 + E)}{2} - \sigma'E = \frac{\sigma'}{2}(E_0 - E). \qquad (3\text{-}178)$$

It can be shown that this result is independent of the manner in which E varies

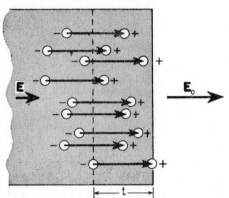

Figure 3-19. *The bound surface density σ' extends over a finite layer of thickness t in which the electrostatic field intensity rises from $\mathbf{E}$ inside the dielectric to $\mathbf{E}_o$ outside.*

inside the dielectric. Since the lines of force are normal to the surface, the field E_0 outside the dielectric is larger than the field E inside the dielectric by a factor equal to the dielectric coefficient:

$$E_0 = K_e E, \qquad (3\text{-}179)$$

such that

$$\frac{dF}{da} = \frac{\sigma'}{2} E(K_e - 1). \qquad (3\text{-}180)$$

The bound surface charge density σ' depends on the field intensity in the dielectric, since

$$\sigma' = \mathbf{P} \cdot \mathbf{n} = \epsilon_0(K_e - 1)E_n, \qquad (3\text{-}181)$$

where E_n is the component of the field intensity inside the dielectric in the direction normal to the dielectric surface. In our case this is the total intensity. Then

$$\frac{dF}{da} = \frac{\epsilon_0(K_e - 1)^2 E^2}{2}. \qquad (3\text{-}182)$$

Since this is, again, an electrical force which must be balanced by a difference in pressure, pressure must rise in passing through the surface layer into the dielectric.

In this derivation we have again made a simplifying assumption which invalidates the result to some extent. In this case K_e varies in going from the body of the dielectric to the surface through the surface layer. When this variation is taken into account, it is found that, for those substances to which the Clausius-Mossotti equation can be applied,

$$\frac{dF}{da} = \frac{\epsilon_0(K_e - 1)^2 E^2}{3} \qquad (3\text{-}183)$$

if $\mathbf{E}$ is perpendicular to the dielectric surface.

3.14.3. Net Reduction of the Force Pulling the Capacitor Plates Together. We can now calculate the total force per unit area with which the liquid dielectric of Figure 3-15 pushes against the capacitor plates. There is one rise in pressure in passing through the fringe field into the region between the plates, and another rise in pressure in passing out of the dielectric through the surface layer. From our approximate equations for these pressures, the total pressure at the surface of the capacitor plate is

$$p_{tot} = \frac{\epsilon_0(K_e - 1)^2 E^2}{2} + \frac{\epsilon_0(K_e - 1)E^2}{2} + p_0. \qquad (3\text{-}184)$$

Since the hydrostatic pressure on the outside surface of the capacitor plate is p_0, $p_{tot} - p_0$ is the excess pressure tending to push the capacitor plates apart, and

$$p_{tot} - p_0 = \frac{\epsilon_0}{2} E^2 K_e(K_e - 1). \qquad (3\text{-}185)$$

The capacitor plates are charged conductors, however, thus the electric field intensity acting on the charges on the plates produces a force which tends to pull the plates together. The magnitude of this force per unit area is

$$\frac{dF}{da} = \frac{\sigma^2}{2\epsilon_0}, \qquad (3\text{-}186)$$

as on any conductor charged with a surface charge density σ. This pressure exceeds that pushing the plates apart. Since the field intensity within the dielectric is given by

$$E = \frac{\sigma}{K_e\epsilon_0}, \qquad (3\text{-}187)$$

we can write the pressure on the conductor in terms of the charge density on the capacitor plate:

$$p_{tot} - p_0 = \frac{\epsilon_0}{2} \frac{\sigma^2}{K_e^2 \epsilon_0^2} K_e(K_e - 1) = \frac{\sigma^2}{2\epsilon_0} \frac{(K_e - 1)}{K_e}. \qquad (3\text{-}188)$$

Then the net force per unit area with which the capacitor plates are pulled together is

$$\left(\frac{dF}{da}\right)_{net} = \frac{\sigma^2}{2\epsilon_0} - \frac{\sigma^2}{2\epsilon_0} \frac{(K_e - 1)}{K_e} = \frac{\sigma^2}{2K_e\epsilon_0}. \qquad (3\text{-}189)$$

Thus the attractive force on the capacitor plates is reduced by the factor K_e over what it would be if the plates carried the same charge density in free space. Had we used the correct equations for the pressure rises in the liquid, the force between the capacitor plates would have been reduced by the same factor.

Calculations of the forces between charged conductors immersed in a liquid dielectric always show that the force is reduced by the factor K_e. There is a tendency to think of this as representing a reduction in the electrical forces between the charges on the conductors, as though Coulomb's law for the interaction of two charges should have the dielectric coefficient included in its denominator. This is incorrect, however. The strictly electric forces between charges on the conductors are not influenced by the presence of the dielectric medium. The medium is polarized, however, and the interaction of the electric field with the polarized medium results in an increased fluid pressure on the conductors which reduces the net forces acting on them.

3.15. Summary

When a dielectric material is placed in an electric field the positive charges in the molecules are displaced with respect to the negative charges, and the molecules become *polarized*, giving an induced dipole moment per unit volume **P** which we call the *polarization* vector. We examined the potential which the dipoles in the polarized material produce at an external point and found it to be the same as the potential produced by surface and volume distributions of charge σ' and ρ':

$$\sigma' = \mathbf{P} \cdot \mathbf{n}, \tag{3-12}$$

$$\rho' = -\nabla \cdot \mathbf{P}. \tag{3-13}$$

We saw that σ' and ρ' represent real accumulations of charge, which we referred to as *bound* charge distributions.

To calculate the electrostatic field intensity at an internal point in the dielectric we distinguished between the electric field intensity on the *molecular* scale ϵ and the *macroscopic* electric field intensity **E**, which is the space and time average $\bar{\epsilon}$ of ϵ. By dividing the dielectric into "near" and "far" regions we showed that the macroscopic field can be calculated from the same bound charge distributions σ' and ρ':

$$\mathbf{E} = \frac{1}{4\pi\epsilon_0} \int_\tau \frac{\rho' \, d\tau}{r^2} \, \mathbf{r}_1 + \frac{1}{4\pi\epsilon_0} \int_S \frac{\sigma' \, da}{r^2} \, \mathbf{r}_1. \tag{3-34}$$

The electric field intensity produced by charges external to the dielectric must be included to find the total macroscopic field.

In order to put the calculation of the macroscopic electric field intensity and potential on a practical basis, we defined the *local electric field* intensity $\bar{\epsilon}_{loc}$, which is the space and time average of the electric field intensity acting on a particular molecule. The local field intensity is larger than the macroscopic intensity **E**, since $\bar{\epsilon}_{loc}$ excludes the molecule's own field, which is in the direction opposite to **E**. We made two different calculations of $\bar{\epsilon}_{loc}$, one involving a simple averaging of the molecule's own field intensity over its volume, and another involving the field intensities of the "near" and "far" dipoles, according to Lorentz's original method. Both methods lead to

$$\bar{\epsilon}_{loc} \approx \mathbf{E} + \frac{\mathbf{P}}{3\epsilon_0}. \tag{3-42}$$

This is only an approximate result, but our subsequent results are valid as long as

$$\bar{\bar{\epsilon}}_{loc} = \mathbf{E} + b\frac{\mathbf{P}}{\epsilon_0}, \tag{3-43}$$

which is well justified in practice.

By applying Gauss's law to a volume within a dielectric, and including bound charge ρ' as well as free charge ρ, we found that we could define the *displacement vector* $\mathbf{D}$ as

$$\mathbf{D} = \epsilon_0\mathbf{E} + \mathbf{P}, \tag{3-57}$$

which has special significance in that its divergence depends only on the free charge density ρ:

$$\boxed{\nabla \cdot \mathbf{D} = \rho.} \tag{3-58}$$

This is the first of Maxwell's four equations.

To examine further the relationship between the vectors $\mathbf{D}$, $\mathbf{E}$, and $\mathbf{P}$ we assumed that the dipole moment of an individual molecule depends linearly on the local field:

$$\mathbf{p} = \alpha\bar{\bar{\epsilon}}_{loc}, \tag{3-63}$$

where α is the *molecular polarizability*. This led us to the dependence of the polarization vector $\mathbf{P}$ on the macroscopic field intensity $\mathbf{E}$:

$$\mathbf{P} = \epsilon_0\chi_e\mathbf{E}, \tag{3-68}$$

where χ_e is a dimensionless constant called the *electric susceptibility*. This led at once to the relationship between the displacement vector $\mathbf{D}$ and the field intensity $\mathbf{E}$:

$$\mathbf{D} = \epsilon_0(1 + \chi_e)\mathbf{E}, \tag{3-69}$$

$$= K_e\epsilon_0\mathbf{E}, \tag{3-70}$$

where K_e is called the *dielectric coefficient*.

In a linear, homogeneous, isotropic dielectric, which we refer to as *Class A*, we showed that the bound charge density ρ' is always related to the free charge density ρ by

$$-\rho' = \left(\frac{K_e - 1}{K_e}\right)\rho. \tag{3-78}$$

We calculated the electrostatic field intensity in some simple cases involving Class A dielectrics. These calculations amount to integrations of the Maxwell equation

$$\nabla \cdot \mathbf{D} = \rho \tag{3-58}$$

making use of the boundary conditions that obtain in the particular problem. In problems with simple symmetries Gauss's law for the displacement vector $\mathbf{D}$,

$$\int_S \mathbf{D} \cdot \mathbf{da} = \int_\tau \rho \, d\tau, \tag{3-80}$$

is the simplest method of solution. Once $\mathbf{D}$ is known, $\mathbf{E}$ is immediately available from Eq. *3-70* provided the dielectric coefficient K_e is known.

We showed that the dielectric coefficient is related to the mass density and to the molecular polarization of a dielectric through the *Clausius-Mossotti equation*,

$$\alpha_M = \frac{M}{\rho}\frac{K_e - 1}{K_e + 2} = \frac{N_A}{3\epsilon_0}\alpha, \qquad (3\text{-}115)$$

where α_M is the *molar polarization*, M is the molecular weight, N_A is Avogadro's number, α is the molecular polarization, and ρ is the mass density.

We discussed *polar molecules* which have a permanent dipole moment. These moleculds, when placed in an electric field are subject to a torque which tends to align them with the field, while thermal agitation tends to destroy the alignment. We calculated the net alignment, and consequently the net dipole moment per unit volume, using the Boltzmann distribution. The result is the *Langevin equation:*

$$P = Np\left(\coth\frac{p\epsilon}{kT} - \frac{kT}{p\epsilon}\right), \qquad (3\text{-}133)$$

where N is the number of dipoles per unit volume, p is the permanent dipole moment per molecule, ϵ is the local electric field intensity, k is the Boltzmann constant, and T is the absolute temperature. We showed that this result corresponds to a linear dielectric for field intensities and absolute temperatures of practical interest.

Combining the results for induced dipoles with those for fixed dipoles we arrived at the molar polarization for polar dielectrics:

$$\alpha_M = \frac{M}{\rho}\left(\frac{K_e - 1}{K_e + 2}\right) = \frac{N_A}{3\epsilon_0}\left(\alpha + \frac{p^2}{3kT}\right), \qquad (3\text{-}144)$$

where p is the permanent dipole moment of the molecules in question. This equation is known as the *Debye equation*. It affords a method of determining α, the molecular polarization, and p, the permanent dipole moment per molecule, through the temperature dependence of the electric susceptibility.

We discussed nonisotropic dielectrics and showed that the same basic approach as for Class A dielectrics is valid, except that the vectors $\mathbf{D}$, $\mathbf{E}$, and $\mathbf{P}$ are no longer necessarily in the same direction, with the result that the electric susceptibility and the dielectric coefficient have different magnitudes in different directions at a given point in the material.

We calculated the potential energy of a charge distribution in the presence of dielectrics and found that, as for free space,

$$W = \frac{1}{2}\int_\tau \rho V \, d\tau. \qquad (3\text{-}148)$$

On relating the charge density ρ to the displacement vector $\mathbf{D}$ through the Maxwell equation we found that

$$W = \frac{1}{2} \int_\tau (\mathbf{D} \cdot \mathbf{E}) \, d\tau. \qquad (3\text{-}153)$$

As in the free space case, we defined an energy density

$$\frac{dW}{d\tau} = \frac{1}{2} (\mathbf{D} \cdot \mathbf{E}), \qquad (3\text{-}154)$$

which is useful in calculating the work required to assemble a charge distribution.

Finally, we calculated the forces acting on dielectrics in electric fields. The field produces a torque on a dipole tending to align it with the field; if there is a gradient of the field intensity there is a net force acting on the dipole,

$$\mathbf{F} = (\mathbf{p} \cdot \nabla)\mathbf{E}. \qquad (3\text{-}164)$$

We considered the simple case of a parallel-plate capacitor submerged in a liquid dielectric. Dipoles in the fringe field of the capacitor are subject to a force tending to pull them into the high-field region, leading to an increased fluid pressure in the high-field region. Using approximate methods we calculated this pressure to be

$$p = \frac{\epsilon_0(K_e - 1)}{2} E^2 + p_0, \qquad (3\text{-}173)$$

where p is the pressure at a point where the electric field intensity is E and where p_0 is the hydrostatic pressure in the field-free region.

We showed that there is a further pressure rise in passing through the surface layer of the dielectric, since the ends of the dipoles lying in the surface layer are subject to a greater force than are the ends lying in the interior of the dielectric. The force acting on the surface layer is

$$\frac{dF}{da} = \frac{\epsilon_0(K_e - 1)^2 E^2}{2}, \qquad (3\text{-}182)$$

and this must be balanced by a higher pressure at the outer boundary than at the inner boundary of the surface layer.

The net result of the two pressure rises—one in passing through the fringe field, and one in passing through the surface layer—is a reduction of the force pulling the capacitor plates together. The net force acting on the plates per unit area is

$$\left(\frac{dF}{da}\right)_{net} = \frac{\sigma^2}{2K_e \epsilon_0}, \qquad (3\text{-}189)$$

which is K_e (the dielectric coefficient), times smaller than in free space. The reduction in net force arises from the interaction of the electric field with the dipoles of the dielectric, which results in a rise in the fluid pressure at the surface of the plates.

Problems

3-1. A sample of diamond has a density of 3.5 grams/centimeter^3 and a polarization of 10^{-7} coulomb/meter^2. The number of atoms per unit volume is given by $N\rho/A$, where N is Avogadro's number, ρ is the mass density, and A is the atomic weight of carbon. Compute the average dipole moment per atom.

Find the average separation between centers of positive and negative charge. Carbon has a nucleus with charge $+6e$, surrounded by 6 electrons.

3-2. A sphere of linear, isotropic, homogeneous dielectric material has a radius R and a uniform electrical polarization $\mathbf{P}$ parallel to the polar axis of spherical coordinates.

Show that the electric field at points outside the sphere is simply that of an electric dipole at the center of the sphere.

Find the moment of this dipole.

3-3. Consider a large block of dielectric material polarized uniformly with a dipole moment per unit volume $\mathbf{P}$. A small spherical cavity is made in the dielectric. Assuming that the polarization elsewhere is undisturbed, what is the electrostatic field intensity at the center of the cavity? What is its direction? Neglect external fields.

3-4. A long cylindrical cavity is cut in a uniformly polarized dielectric parallel to the polarization vector. Find the electrostatic field intensity which the polarized dielectric produces on the axis of the cavity, assuming that the polarization outside the cavity is undisturbed.

3-5. Show that in a long needle-like cavity oriented parallel to the polarization vector in a dielectric, an electric charge Q will experience a force $\mathbf{F} = Q\mathbf{E}$, where $\mathbf{E}$ is the electrostatic field intensity in the undisturbed dielectric.

Show that in a thin disk-like cavity with its flat faces perpendicular to the polarization vector, a charge Q experiences a force $\mathbf{F} = Q\mathbf{D}/\epsilon_0$, where $\mathbf{D}$ is the displacement vector in the undisturbed dielectric.

3-6. Consider a thin disk of dielectric, of radius R and thickness t, permanently polarized with a dipole moment per unit volume $\mathbf{P}$ parallel to the axis of the disk. Find the electrostatic field intensity at a point on the axis at a distance z from the disk.

Calculate $\mathbf{E}$ and $\mathbf{D}$ inside the disk.

3-7. Consider a spherical distribution of dipoles arranged in a cubic lattice, all of the same moment $\mathbf{p}$ and all aligned in the same direction. Show that the electric field intensity contributed by the dipoles at a lattice point at the center of the sphere is zero. Hint: Express the dipole field intensity components of Eqs. 2-73, 2-74, and 2-75 in rectangular coordinates before summing the contributions of the individual dipoles.

3-8. Show that the electric susceptibility and the dielectric coefficient, as defined in the text, are dimensionless constants.

3-9. The dielectric constant of the material between the plates of a parallel-plate capacitor varies linearly from one plate to the other. If K_1 and K_2 are the values at the two plates, and if the plate separation is s, find the capacitance per unit area.

3-10. A dielectric sphere of radius R contains a uniform density of free charge ρ.

Find the potential at the center (a) by line integration of E (use Gauss's law) and (b) by integration of Coulomb's law over the sphere.

3-11. A dielectric sphere of dielectric coefficient K_e and radius a is polarized such that $P = (K/r)\mathbf{r}_1$, $\mathbf{r}_1$ being the unit radial vector. Calculate the volume and the surface density of induced charge. What distribution of free charge is involved in this polarization? Calculate the potential inside and outside the sphere. Sketch a curve of potential versus distance from $r = 0$ to $r = \infty$.

3-12. Calculate the capacitance of a parallel-plate capacitor with plate separation s and surface area S when the space between the plates is partially filled with a dielectric slab of area S but of thickness $t < s$. Neglect edge effects.

3-13. A capacitor is formed of two concentric spherical conducting shells of radii r_1 and r_2. The space between the spheres is filled with a dielectric of coefficient K_1 from $r = r_1$ to $r = r_3$, where $r_1 < r_3 < r_2$, and with a dielectric of coefficient K_2 from r_3 to r_2. Calculate the capacitance.

3-14. Calculate the capacitance per unit length of two long coaxial cylindrical conductors in free space.

If the space between the cylinders were filled with a dielectric, how would the dielectric constant have to depend on the distance r from the axis in order that the electric field intensity be independent of r?

What would be the volume density of bound charge?

3-15. A conducting wire carrying a charge Q per unit length is embedded along the axis of a circular cylinder of dielectric. The radius of the wire is a; the radius of the cylinder is b. Show that the bound charge on the outer surface of the dielectric is equal to the bound charge on the inner surface, except for sign.

Show that the net charge along the axis is Q/K_e per unit length, K_e being the dielectric coefficient.

Show that the volume density of bound charge is zero.

3-16. The dipole moment of the H_2O molecule is 6.2×10^{-30} coulomb-meter. Find the maximum polarization of water vapor at a temperature of $100°C$ and a pressure of 760 millimeters of mercury.

3-17. Show that a nonhomogeneous dielectric can have a volume density ρ' of bound charge in the absence of a free charge density ρ.

Calculate ρ' in this case.

3-18. A dipole of moment $\mathbf{p}$ is lined up with the y-axis at the origin of coordinates. A second dipole of moment $\mathbf{p}$ is centered at the point (a, a) and is pointed toward the origin. Calculate the force on the second dipole.

3-19. A plane parallel capacitor is composed of two electrodes of area A separated by a *solid* dielectric of thickness t and dielectric coefficient K_e, the electrodes being pressed on the dielectric but not bound to it. The capacitor is connected to a source of voltage V. Both the thickness of the dielectric t and the voltage V are constant. Calculate the force of attraction between the plates.

If $A = 68$ square inches, $t = 0.030$ inch, $K_e = 3.0$, and $V = 60$ kilovolts, calculate the force of attraction in tons.

3-20. The solid dielectric of the capacitor in the preceding problem is removed, and the plates are submerged in a liquid of the same dielectric coefficient, such that the space between the plates is always filled with dielectric. Calculate the force of attraction in tons.

3-21. A dielectric slab which just fits between the plates of a parallel-plate capacitor is withdrawn such that only part of the slab remains within the capacitor. The plates are maintained at a fixed potential difference by a battery. Show by a qualitative argument that a force acts on the dielectric slab, and give the direction of this force.

Calculate the magnitude of the force from the energy associated with the system.

Does the expression for the force have the right limiting value when the slab is completely within the space between the plates? Discuss.

3-22. The capacitor in the above problem is charged, and the battery is then disconnected. Calculate the force of attraction on the dielectric slab, and compare with the above result. Explain.

3-23. A concentric spherical capacitor of radii r_1 and r_2 contains a fluid of dielectric coefficient K_e between its electrodes. If the potential difference between the electrodes is V, calculate the fluid pressure due to the electric field as a function of the radius.

Find the pressure acting on the inner sphere.

CHAPTER 4

Electrostatic
Fields II

Up to this point, our discussion of electrostatic fields has been limited to simple charge distributions where the electric field intensity and potential at arbitrary points in the field could be found either by direct integration from Coulomb's law or by application of Gauss's law.

We shall now consider in this chapter more complex cases of the following two general types.

(1) The charges or the potentials are specified for each of several conductors, and we are required to find the electric field intensity and potential in the space around the conductors.

(2) Conductors or dielectrics are introduced into previously known fields, and we are required to find the modified field and the charge densities or polarizations.

In every case we must find a solution either of Poisson's equation,

$$\nabla^2 V = -\rho/\epsilon_0, \qquad (4\text{-}1)$$

or of Laplace's equation,

$$\nabla^2 V = 0, \qquad (4\text{-}2)$$

if the charge density ρ is equal to zero. We shall usually be concerned with charge-free regions and Laplace's equation. There are, however, important cases involving space charge where $\rho \neq 0$, as in thermionic vacuum tubes, which we shall also study. Appendix D describes a widely used method for calculating two-dimensional electrostatic fields when ρ is equal to zero.

Once the electrostatic field is known it is possible to deduce many other quantities, such as charge densities and total charges on conductors, differences

129

in potential between conductors, capacitances, focusing properties of electro-static lenses, vacuum tube characteristics, and so forth.

4.1. Boundary Conditions

The solution of either Poisson's or Laplace's equation must always be con-sistent with certain conditions at the boundaries between different media in the field.

4.1.1. Potential. The electrostatic potential V must satisfy the following con-ditions.

(1) It must go to zero at infinity if the charge distributions are of finite extent.

(2) It must be constant throughout any conductor, since, by assumption, all charges are at rest.

(3) It must be continuous across any boundary, because a discontinuous potential would imply an infinitely large field intensity, which is physically impossible.

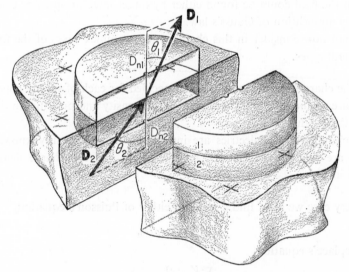

Figure 4-1. *Gaussian cylinder on the interface between two different media 1 and 2. The difference* $D_{1n} - D_{2n}$ *between the* normal *components of* **D** *is equal to the surface charge density* σ.

4.1.2. Normal Component of the Displacement Vector. Consider a short Gaussian cylinder drawn about a boundary surface as in Figure 4-1. The end faces of the cylinder are parallel to the boundary, and the height of the cylinder approaches zero such that the end faces are arbitrarily close to the boundary. From Gauss's law,

$$\int_S \mathbf{D} \cdot \mathbf{da} = \int_S \sigma \, da, \tag{4-3}$$

where σ is the free charge density on the boundary surface. The only flux of $\mathbf{D}$ is through the end faces, since the area of the other surface is arbitrarily small. If the end area S is small enough such that $\mathbf{D}$ and σ do not vary significantly over it, then

$$D_{1n} - D_{2n} = \sigma. \tag{4-4}$$

There are two different boundary cases which we can distinguish as follows.

(1) The boundary is between two dielectric media. The surface charge density σ is generally zero in this case, and so D_n is continuous across the boundary.

(2) The boundary is between a conductor and a dielectric. Since the displacement $\mathbf{D}$ is necessarily zero in the conductor, $D_n = \sigma$ in the dielectric material, σ being the free charge density on the surface of the conductor.

4.1.3. Tangential Component of the Electric Field Intensity. This boundary

condition follows from the fact that the electrostatic field is conservative, that is, the line integral of $\mathbf{E} \cdot \mathbf{dl}$ around a closed path is zero. Consider the path shown in Figure 4-2, with two sides parallel to the boundary and arbitrarily close to it. The other two sides are perpendicular to the boundary. In calculating this line integral, only the first two sides of the path are important, since the lengths of the other two approach zero. If the path is small enough such that E_t does not vary significantly over it,

$$E_{t1}L - E_{t2}L = 0, \tag{4-5}$$

or

$$E_{t1} = E_{t2}. \tag{4-6}$$

The tangential component of $\mathbf{E}$ is therefore continuous across the boundary.

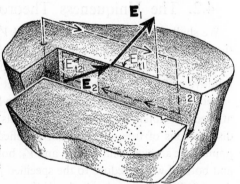

Figure 4-2. *Closed path of integration crossing the interface between two different media 1 and 2. Whatever be the surface charge density σ, the tangential components of $\mathbf{E}$ on either side of the interface are equal: $E_{t1} = E_{t2}$.*

If the boundary lies between a dielectric and a conductor, then $\mathbf{E} = 0$ in the conductor, and $E_t = 0$ in both media. The electrostatic field intensity $\mathbf{E}$ is therefore always normal to the surface of a conductor.

4.1.4. Bending of Lines of Force.

It follows from the boundary conditions that the **D** and **E** vectors change direction at the boundary between two dielectrics. In Figure 4-3,

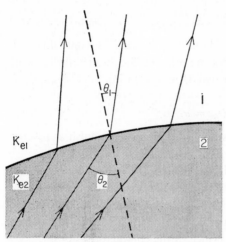

$$D_1 \cos \theta_1 = D_2 \cos \theta_2 \qquad (4\text{-}7)$$

or

$$K_{e1}\epsilon_0 E_1 \cos \theta_1 = K_{e2}\epsilon_0 E_2 \cos \theta_2, \qquad (4\text{-}8)$$

and

$$E_1 \sin \theta_1 = E_2 \sin \theta_2. \qquad (4\text{-}9)$$

Then, dividing the second equation by the third, we obtain

$$K_{e1} \cot \theta_1 = K_{e2} \cot \theta_2 \qquad (4\text{-}10)$$

or

$$\frac{K_{e1}}{K_{e2}} = \frac{\tan \theta_1}{\tan \theta_2}. \qquad (4\text{-}11)$$

Figure 4-3. *Lines of* **D** *or of* **E** *crossing the interface between two different media 1 and 2. The lines change direction in such a way that* $K_{e1} \tan \theta_2 = K_{e2} \tan \theta_1$.

The larger angle from the normal is in the medium with the larger dielectric constant.

4.2. The Uniqueness Theorem

We shall demonstrate that a potential V which satisfies both Poisson's equation and the boundary conditions pertinent to a particular field is the only possible potential. Therefore, any such potential we can devise, whether by intuitive or formal methods, is the correct one.

Let us consider a finite region of space which may contain charged conductors at specified potentials, dielectric materials of specified properties, and volume distributions of free charges with specified densities. We assume that at each point there are two solutions, V_1 and V_2, both of which satisfy Poisson's equation and both of which reduce to the specified potentials on the surfaces of the conductors. This does *not* imply that a given point can be at two different potentials at the same time. Our assumption is that either one or the other of two different fields can exist in the region for which boundary conditions are specified.

Corresponding to V_1 and V_2, there are the electrostatic field intensities $\mathbf{E}_1$ and $\mathbf{E}_2$, thus

$$\mathbf{E}_1 = -\nabla V_1, \qquad \mathbf{E}_2 = -\nabla V_2 \qquad (4\text{-}12)$$

at every point in the field.

We have assumed that Poisson's equation is satisfied by both V_1 and V_2 everywhere. Then

$$\nabla \cdot \mathbf{D}_1 = \rho, \qquad \nabla \cdot \mathbf{D}_2 = \rho. \qquad (4\text{-}13)$$

We now focus our attention on the difference between the two solutions and call it V_3:

$$V_3 = V_2 - V_1. \qquad (4\text{-}14)$$

Then the corresponding displacement vectors $\mathbf{D}_1$, $\mathbf{D}_2$, and $\mathbf{D}_3$ are such that

$$\mathbf{D}_3 = \mathbf{D}_2 - \mathbf{D}_1, \qquad (4\text{-}15)$$

and so

$$\nabla \cdot \mathbf{D}_3 = \nabla \cdot \mathbf{D}_2 - \nabla \cdot \mathbf{D}_1 = 0 \qquad (4\text{-}16)$$

at every point. On the surfaces of the conductors and at infinity, $V_3 = 0$, since both V_1 and V_2 reduce to the specified boundary values.

We now use the vector identity

$$\nabla \cdot f\mathbf{A} = f(\nabla \cdot \mathbf{A}) + \mathbf{A} \cdot \nabla f, \qquad (4\text{-}17)$$

where f is any scalar function and $\mathbf{A}$ is any vector function. Integrating over a volume τ and using the divergence theorem, we find that

$$\int_S f\mathbf{A} \cdot d\mathbf{a} = \int_\tau f(\nabla \cdot \mathbf{A})\, d\tau + \int_\tau (\mathbf{A} \cdot \nabla f)\, d\tau. \qquad (4\text{-}18)$$

Then if we set $f = V_3$ and $\mathbf{A} = \mathbf{D}_3$,

$$\int_S V_3 \mathbf{D}_3 \cdot d\mathbf{a} = \int_\tau V_3(\nabla \cdot \mathbf{D}_3)\, d\tau + \int_\tau (\mathbf{D}_3 \cdot \nabla V_3)\, d\tau, \qquad (4\text{-}19)$$

where the surface integral on the left side is to be evaluated for all the surfaces which bound the volume over which the integrals on the right are to be evaluated. Let us take this volume to be the volume external to the conductors, extending to infinity in all directions.

The surface integral is then to be evaluated over all the conductor surfaces and over an imaginary surface of infinite radius. Since the quantity V_3 is zero on all the conductor surfaces, this portion of the integral is zero. To evaluate the integral over the surface of infinite radius, we consider the integral over a finite sphere and let its surface recede to infinity. Both V_2 and V_1 must fall off as $1/r$ at sufficiently large distances, since all the charge in the system will appear as a point charge from a distance large in comparison to the dimensions of the charge system. Then V_3, the difference between V_2 and V_1, must also fall as $1/r$. Now $\mathbf{D}_3$ must fall off as ∇V_3, or as $1/r^2$. Since the area S over which the integration is performed increases as r^2, the whole integral falls off as $1/r$ and approaches zero at infinity. The left side of the equation is thus zero.

The first term on the right is zero, since $\nabla \cdot \mathbf{D}_3 = 0$ at every point. We are thus left with the second term on the right, which must be identically equal to zero. Thus

$$\int_\tau (\mathbf{D}_3 \cdot \mathbf{E}_3)\, d\tau = 0. \qquad (4\text{-}20$$

In homogeneous, isotropic, linear dielectrics the quantity $\mathbf{D} \cdot \mathbf{E} = K_e \epsilon_0 E^2$ is intrinsically positive, and the only way in which the integral can be zero is to have $\mathbf{D}_3$ and $\mathbf{E}_3$ equal to zero at every point.

It then follows that

$$\nabla V_2 = \nabla V_1 \qquad \qquad (4\text{-}21)$$

or that V_2 can differ from V_1 at most by a constant. Since V_1 and V_2 must be the same both on the surfaces of the conductors and at infinity, they must be the same everywhere. Therefore $V_2 = V_1$, and there is only one possible potential V.

This proof of the uniqueness of the solution to Poisson's equation is valid as long as $\mathbf{D} \cdot \mathbf{E}$ is an intrinsically positive quantity in all the dielectric material in the system.

4.3. Images

The method of images involves the conversion of an electrostatic field into another equivalent field which is simpler to calculate. It is particularly useful for point charges near conductors. We shall find that it is possible in certain cases to replace the conductors by one or more point charges in such a way that the conductor surfaces are replaced by equipotential surfaces at the same potentials. Since the boundary conditions are then conserved, the electric field thus found must be the correct one for the entire region outside the conductors.

4.3.1. Point Charge Near an Infinite Grounded Conducting Plane. As a first example, consider a point charge $+Q$ at a distance D to the left of an infinite conducting plane connected to ground as in Figure 4-4a. This plane may

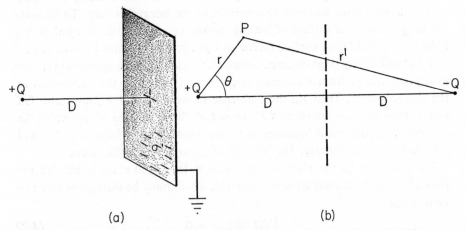

Figure 4-4. (a) *Point charge Q near a grounded conducting plane.* (b) *The conducting plane has been replaced by the image charge $-Q$ to calculate the field at P.*

be taken to be at a fixed potential of zero, whatever be the charges induced on it. This is because the earth has a large capacitance of $4\pi\epsilon_0$ (radius) ≈ 600 micro-farads, thus the addition or subtraction of even large amounts of charge has a negligible effect on its potential. It is clear that if we remove the grounded conductor and replace it by a charge $-Q$ at a distance D behind the plane, then every point of the plane will be equidistant from $+Q$ and from $-Q$ and will thus be at zero potential. In the region to the left of the plane the two point charges must therefore give the proper solution for the point and the plane. The charge $-Q$ is said to be the *image* of the charge $+Q$ in the plane.

The potential V at a point P, whose coordinates are r and θ as shown in Figure 4-4b, is given by

$$4\pi\epsilon_0 V = \frac{Q}{r} - \frac{Q}{r'}, \tag{4-22}$$

where

$$r' = \sqrt{r^2 + 4D^2 - 4rD\cos\theta} \tag{4-23}$$

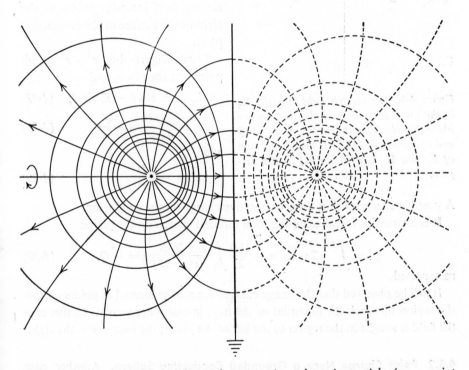

Figure 4-5. *Lines of force (shown by arrows) and equipotentials for a point charge near a grounded conducting plane. The equipotentials near the charge can-not be shown because they are too close together. The equipotential surfaces are generated by rotating the figure about the axis designated by the curved arrow. The image field to the right of the conducting plane is indicated by broken lines.*

and where the components of the electric field intensity at P are the components of ∇V,

$$4\pi\epsilon_0 E_r = -4\pi\epsilon_0 \frac{\partial V}{\partial r} = \frac{Q}{r^2} - \frac{Q(r - 2D\cos\theta)}{r'^3} \qquad (4\text{-}24)$$

and

$$4\pi\epsilon_0 E_\theta = -4\pi\epsilon_0 \frac{1}{r}\frac{\partial V}{\partial\theta} = -\frac{2QD\sin\theta}{r'^3}. \qquad (4\text{-}25)$$

The lines of force and the equipotentials are shown in Figure 4-5.

The induced charge density σ' on the surface of the conducting plane is readily found from the normal component of the electric field intensity at the conductor, since

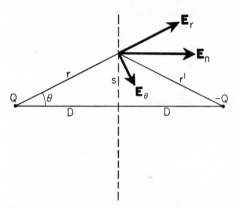

$$E_n = \sigma'/\epsilon_0. \qquad (4\text{-}26)$$

In this particular case the surface charge density is negative, and the electric field intensity points to the right at the surface of the conducting plate.

From Figure 4-6, $r = r'$ at all points on the plane, and

Figure 4-6. *The electric field intensity $\mathbf{E}_n$ at the surface of the grounded conducting plane is calculated from the fields of Q and of its image $-Q$. It is the vector sum of $\mathbf{E}_r$ and $\mathbf{E}_\theta$, and is normal to the surface.*

$$E_n = E_r \cos\theta - E_\theta \sin\theta, \qquad (4\text{-}27)$$

$$= \frac{2QD}{4\pi\epsilon_0 r^3} = -\frac{\sigma'}{\epsilon_0}, \qquad (4\text{-}28)$$

and

$$\sigma' = -\frac{QD}{2\pi r^3}. \qquad (4\text{-}29)$$

A positive charge Q thus induces negative charge on the conductor.

It is instructive to calculate the total induced charge on the plane:

$$Q' = \int_0^\infty \sigma' 2\pi s\, ds = -\frac{QD}{2}\int_0^\infty \frac{2s\, ds}{(s^2 + D^2)^{3/2}} = -Q, \qquad (4\text{-}30)$$

as expected.

It will be observed that the image charges are always located at points *outside* the region in which the potential or the field intensity are sought. In this case the field is sought in the region to the left of the plane; the image is to the right.

4.3.2. Point Charge Near a Grounded Conducting Sphere.

Another case which can be dealt with readily by the image method is that of a point charge near a grounded conducting sphere, as in Figure 4-7a. We remove the conductor and try to find the position and magnitude of an "image" charge $-Q'$, as in Figure 4-7b, which will make the potential zero on the spherical surface.

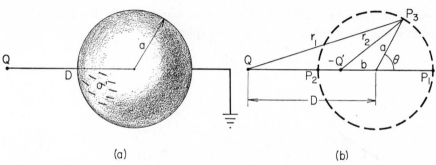

Figure 4-7. (*a*) *Point charge Q at a distance D from the center of a grounded conducting sphere of radius a. When Q is positive, the induced surface charge density σ′ is negative.* (*b*) *The boundary condition V = 0 on the spherical surface is satisfied by the original charge Q and its image −Q′.*

It is clear from the symmetry of the problem that if such a charge exists it must lie on the line connecting Q and the center of the sphere. We begin by making the potential zero at the points P_1 and P_2. Then

$$\frac{Q}{(D+a)} - \frac{Q'}{(a+b)} = 0, \tag{4-31}$$

and

$$\frac{Q}{(D-a)} - \frac{Q'}{(a-b)} = 0. \tag{4-32}$$

Solving these two equations gives

$$Q' = \frac{a}{D}\,Q, \tag{4-33}$$

and

$$b = \frac{a^2}{D}. \tag{4-34}$$

We still have to find whether this charge arrangement will make the potential zero at a general point P_3 on the surface of the sphere. At P_3

$$4\pi\epsilon_0 V = \frac{Q}{r_1} - \frac{Q'}{r_2}, \tag{4-35}$$

where

$$r_1 = \sqrt{(D^2 + a^2 + 2Da\cos\theta)} \tag{4-36}$$

and

$$r_2 = \sqrt{(b^2 + a^2 + 2ba\cos\theta)}. \tag{4-37}$$

Taking Q' and b as in Eqs. *4-33* and *4-34* does in fact make $V = 0$ at P_3, as required.

Since the original point charge and the image charge $-Q'$ satisfy the boundary condition, they must give the correct potential and field intensity at every point in the space outside the conducting sphere.

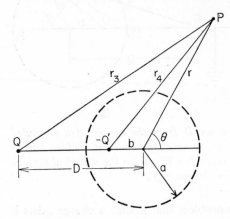

Figure 4-8

The electrostatic potential V at the point $P(r, \theta)$ is calculated from Q and its image $-Q'$.

We can now write down the potential at an arbitrary point $P(r, \theta)$ as in Figure 4-8:

$$4\pi\epsilon_0 V = \frac{Q}{r_3} - \frac{(a/D)Q}{r_4}, \tag{4-38}$$

where

$$r_3 = \sqrt{D^2 + r^2 + 2Dr\cos\theta} \tag{4-39}$$

and

$$r_4 = \sqrt{\left(\frac{a^2}{D}\right)^2 + r^2 + 2\frac{a^2}{D}r\cos\theta}. \tag{4-40}$$

Then, to find the electrostatic field intensity at P, we merely have to calculate ∇V.

As in the case of the point charge and the plane, we calculate the induced charge density σ' from the value of the field intensity on the surface of the sphere. We calculate E_r and evaluate it at $r = a$:

$$4\pi\epsilon_0 E_r = \frac{Q(r + D\cos\theta)}{r_3^3} - \frac{aQ\left(r + \frac{a^2}{D}\cos\theta\right)}{Dr_4^3}, \tag{4-41}$$

and, at $r = a$,

$$\sigma' = \epsilon_0 E_r = -\frac{Q(D^2 - a^2)}{4\pi a(D^2 + a^2 + 2Da\cos\theta)^{3/2}}. \tag{4-42}$$

It is again instructive to integrate this density over the whole surface of the sphere to get the total induced charge:

$$Q' = \int_0^\pi \sigma' 2\pi a^2 \sin\theta \, d\theta = -\frac{a}{D}Q. \tag{4-43}$$

The total induced charge on the real conducting sphere is thus the same as the image charge which replaced the sphere. This must be true from Gauss's law. If we draw a Gaussian surface just outside the sphere, then the flux of **E** through this surface must be the same, no matter whether the conducting sphere is present or whether it is replaced by the image charge, since the fields outside the sphere are identical in either case. Thus the charge enclosed by the Gaussian surface must also be the same in both cases.

Figure 4-9 shows the field and potential distributions for a point charge in the vicinity of a grounded conducting sphere.

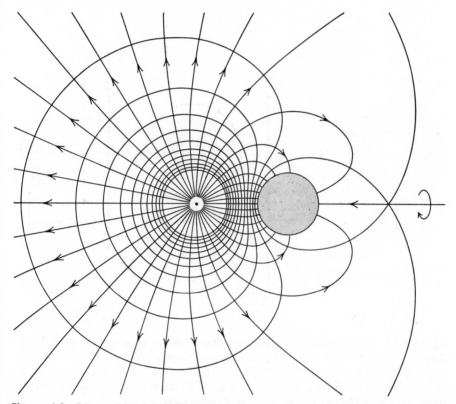

Figure 4-9. *Lines of force (indicated by arrows) and equipotentials for a point charge near a conducting sphere. The equipotential surfaces are generated by rotating the figure about the axis identified by the curved arrow. The equipotentials in the vicinity of the point charge are again not shown because they are too close together.*

4.3.3. Point Charge Near a Charged Conducting Sphere. If the sphere is at a potential other than zero, we may still determine the field by the method of images. We first replace the conducting sphere with an image charge Q', as in

the case of the grounded sphere. This makes the surface occupied by the sphere an equipotential. We next add a second image charge at the center to raise the spherical surface to the required potential.

If we are given a sphere of radius a with a charge Q_s on it, and if its center is at a distance $D > a$ from a point charge Q, we replace the sphere by an image charge $Q' = (a/D)Q$ at a distance $b = a^2/D$ from the center, plus a charge $(Q_s - Q')$ at the center. The surface density of charge is then $\sigma' + \sigma''$, where σ' is the nonuniform distribution calculated from Q and Q' and where σ'' is the uniform distribution calculated from $(Q_s - Q')$.

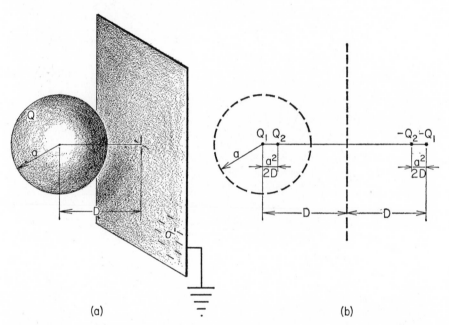

(a)   (b)

Figure 4-10. (a) *Conducting sphere carrying a charge Q near a grounded conducting plane. When Q is positive, the induced surface charge density σ' is negative. The plane is assumed to be infinite. (b) The field outside the sphere and to the left of the conducting plane is calculated by successive approximations by using the image charges $Q_1, Q_2, \ldots$ and $-Q_1, -Q_2, \ldots$*

4.3.4. Images by Successive Approximations. Charged Sphere Near a Grounded Conducting Plane.

Some fields may be determined by the method of images through successive approximations. As an illustration we shall consider the case of a charged sphere near a grounded plane. Assume that we wish to calculate the capacitance of this system; we wish to replace both the sphere and the plane by a set of point charges which will maintain these surfaces as equipotentials.

First, we put a charge Q_1 at the center of the sphere, as in Figure 4-10b. This makes the sphere, but not the plane, an equipotential. Next we put the image $-Q_1$ of Q_1 to the right of the plane. This makes the plane an equipotential but destroys the spherical equipotential, so we put the image Q_2 of $-Q_1$ inside the sphere. This makes the sphere again an equipotential but upsets the plane. We continue the process, which converges rapidly, until we have the required precision. The charges and their locations are shown in Table 4-1.

TABLE 4-1. Images for the Case of a Charged Sphere Near a Grounded Conducting Plane

Right of Plane		Left of Plane	
Charge	Distance from Center of Sphere	Charge	Distance from Center of Sphere
		Q_1	0
$-Q_1$	$2D$	$Q_2 = (a/2D)Q_1$	$a^2/2D$
$-Q_2$	$2D - (a^2/2D)$	$Q_3 = \dfrac{a}{\left(2D - \dfrac{a^2}{2D}\right)} \dfrac{a}{2D} Q_1$	$\dfrac{a^2}{2D - (a^2/2D)}$
		$\quad = \dfrac{(a/2D)^2}{1 - (a/2D)^2} Q_1$	$\quad = \dfrac{a^2/2D}{1 - (a/2D)^2}$

If we set $(a/2D) = r$, then

$$Q_1 = Q_1, \tag{4-44}$$

$$Q_2 = rQ_1, \tag{4-45}$$

$$Q_3 = \frac{r^2}{1 - r^2} Q_1, \tag{4-46}$$

$$Q_4 = \frac{r^3}{(1 - r^2)\left(1 - \dfrac{r^2}{1 - r^2}\right)} Q_1, \tag{4-47}$$

$$Q_5 = \frac{r^4}{(1 - r^2)\left(1 - \dfrac{r^2}{1 - r^2}\right)\left[1 - \dfrac{r^2}{1 - [r^2/(1 - r^2)]}\right]} Q_1, \tag{4-48}$$

and so on. It is now easy to calculate V and $\mathbf{E}$. The equipotentials and the lines of force are shown in Figure 4-11.

The total charge is

$$Q = Q_1\left(1 + r + \frac{r^2}{1 - r^2} + \cdots\right). \tag{4-49}$$

Now only Q_1 contributes to the potential of the sphere. The charges $-Q_1$ and

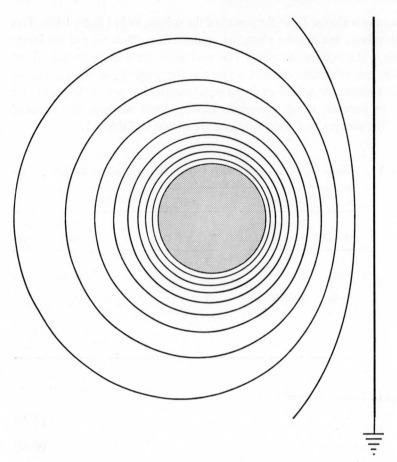

Figure 4-11. *Equipotentials for a charged sphere near a grounded conducting plane.*

Q_2 make the potential of the sphere zero; since the same is true of all the following pairs of charges, the potential of the sphere is

$$V = \frac{Q_1}{4\pi\epsilon_0 a}. \tag{4-50}$$

The capacitance between the sphere and the plane is then

$$C = \frac{Q}{V} = \frac{Q_1(1 + r + \cdots)}{Q_1/4\pi\epsilon_0 a} = 4\pi\epsilon_0 a(1 + r + \cdots). \tag{4-51}$$

The presence of the plane therefore increases the capacitance of the sphere.

4.3.5. Image Forces. The force which acts between a point charge and a conductor can be calculated in several ways. Consider the case in which the conductor is an infinite plane. An annulus of charge of width ds at distance s from the foot of the perpendicular, as in Figure 4-12, exerts a force **dF** on Q in the direction perpendicular to the plane as follows:

$$dF = \frac{Q\sigma' 2\pi s\, ds}{4\pi\epsilon_0 r^2} \cos\theta. \qquad (4\text{-}52)$$

This will be an attractive force if we use the absolute value of the induced charge density calculated in Eq. *4-29*. Thus

$$dF = \frac{Q^2 D}{2\pi r^3}\frac{2\pi s\, ds}{4\pi\epsilon_0 r^2} \cos\theta \qquad (4\text{-}53)$$

or, expressing s and r in terms of the angle θ,

$$F = \frac{Q^2}{4\pi\epsilon_0 D^2} \int_0^{\pi/2} \cos^3\theta \sin\theta\, d\theta, \qquad (4\text{-}54)$$

$$= \frac{Q^2}{4\pi\epsilon_0 (2D)^2}. \qquad (4\text{-}55)$$

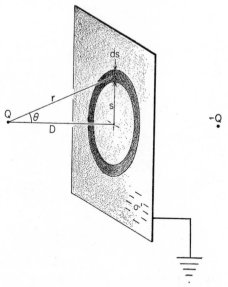

Figure 4-12. *The force of attraction between a point charge Q and an infinite grounded conducting plane can be calculated directly from Coulomb's law by using the induced charge density σ'. This, in turn, is calculated from Q and the image charge $-Q$. The ring element shown is used for the integration. The force is equal to that between Q and its image $-Q$.*

From Newton's third law, this is also the magnitude of the net force acting on the plane.

We can see that the force acting on Q must be given by Eq. *4-55* in a simple way. Since the field in the region to the right of the plane is correctly given by Q and its image $-Q$, Coulomb's law leads to Eq. *4-55* directly. This is always true. *The force between a point charge and a conductor is always given correctly by the Coulomb force between the point charge and the image charges.*

4.4. Images in Dielectrics. Charge Near a Semi-infinite Dielectric

The method of images can also be used to determine fields in the presence of dielectrics. As an example, consider the case of a point charge Q at a distance D in front of a semi-infinite block of Class A dielectric material, as in Figure 4-13. The field of the charge Q polarizes the dielectric, and a negative induced surface charge density σ' is produced on the surface. The resultant field at any point can then be computed by replacing the dielectric with this surface charge and treating the problem as if these charges, together with Q, were in free space.

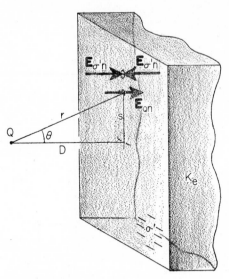

The value of σ' must of course be known as a function of the coordinates on the surface before the electrostatic potential or field intensity can be calculated.

To find σ' we can proceed in the following manner. Consider a point just inside the dielectric at a distance s from the foot of the perpendicular, as in Figure 4-13. At this point there is a resultant electrostatic field intensity $\mathbf{E}_i$ with a normal component E_{ni}. The normal component of the polarization produced by this resultant field is given by

$$P_n = \epsilon_0(K_e - 1)E_{ni} \quad (4\text{-}56)$$

and

$$\sigma' = P_n. \quad (4\text{-}57)$$

Figure 4-13. *Point charge Q near the plane surface of a large block of dielectric. The quantity $E_{\sigma'n}$ is the normal component of $\mathbf{E}$ due to the induced surface charge density σ'; E_{Qn} is the normal component of $\mathbf{E}$ due to the charge Q.*

Now E_{ni} is the superposition of two parts: one arising from the point charge Q, and another arising from σ'. Applying Gauss's law to a suitable closed surface with faces on either side of the boundary, we find that the normal component of the field arising from σ' is

$$E_{\sigma'n} = \frac{\sigma'}{2\epsilon_0}. \quad (4\text{-}58)$$

It is oriented in the direction pointing toward the boundary, the surface charges being negative if Q is positive, and it has the same magnitude on either side of the boundary. The part of the field arising from Q is readily calculated from Coulomb's law:

$$E_{Qn} = \frac{Q}{4\pi\epsilon_0} \frac{D}{(s^2 + D^2)^{3/2}}, \quad (4\text{-}59)$$

which is the same, both in magnitude and direction, on either side of the boundary. Altogether then, the normal component of the polarization just inside the dielectric is given by

$$P_n = \sigma' = \epsilon_0(K_e - 1)\left[\frac{QD}{4\pi\epsilon_0(s^2 + D^2)^{3/2}} - \frac{\sigma'}{2\epsilon_0}\right], \quad (4\text{-}60)$$

$$= \frac{(K_e - 1)QD}{2\pi(K_e + 1)(s^2 + D^2)^{3/2}}. \quad (4\text{-}61)$$

At this stage we could calculate the potential and the field intensity at any point, either within the dielectric or in free space, by using Coulomb's law, integrating over the σ' distribution, and adding the contribution from the point charge Q. But this is not the simplest way to deal with this field. We shall find instead a set of image charges which will satisfy the boundary conditions.

To find these charges, we confine our attention to the boundary and write down the normal components of the resultant field for a point just inside the dielectric, E_{ni}, and just outside, E_{no}. For the inside point the normal component of the field arising from the surface charge σ' subtracts from that arising from Q. For the outside point they add. Altogether,

$$E_{ni} = \left[1 - \left(\frac{K_e - 1}{K_e + 1}\right)\right] \frac{QD}{4\pi\epsilon_0(s^2 + D^2)^{3/2}} \tag{4-62}$$

$$= \left(\frac{2}{K_e + 1}\right) \frac{QD}{4\pi\epsilon_0(s^2 + D^2)^{3/2}} \tag{4-63}$$

and

$$E_{no} = \left[1 + \left(\frac{K_e - 1}{K_e + 1}\right)\right] \frac{QD}{4\pi\epsilon_0(s^2 + D^2)^{3/2}} \tag{4-64}$$

$$= \left(\frac{2K_e}{K_e + 1}\right) \frac{QD}{4\pi\epsilon_0(s^2 + D^2)^{3/2}}. \tag{4-65}$$

It will be observed that the normal component of **D** is continuous across the boundary. We assured this condition when we used Gauss's law to compute σ'.

Can we now find a set of image charges which will give the normal field components of Eqs. *4-58* and *4-59* and also make the tangential component of **E** continuous across the boundary? We can save some time if we recall that an image charge is always *outside* the region in which the field is to be determined. We consider first a point outside the dielectric surface. We see from Eq. *4-64* that E_{no} will be properly given by the charge $+Q$ together with an image charge

$$Q' = -\frac{(K_e - 1)}{(K_e + 1)} Q \tag{4-66}$$

located at a distance D behind the boundary, as in Figure 4-14a.

For a point inside the dielectric there are, at first glance, two sets of point charges which will give the proper normal component of **E**: (a) the point charge Q together with an image charge

$$Q' = +\frac{(K_e - 1)}{(K_e + 1)} Q \tag{4-67}$$

at the image position behind the boundary and (b) a single image charge

$$Q'' = +\frac{2}{K_e + 1} Q, \tag{4-68}$$

which replaces Q. The first of these can be ruled out because we always want the image charge to be outside the region in which the field is required. The

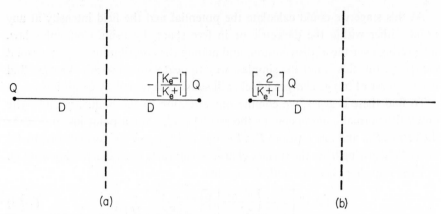

Figure 4-14. (a) When the dielectric is replaced by the image charge $-[(K_e - 1)/(K_e + 1)]Q$, the field is unaffected outside the dielectric. (b) When the dielectric is removed and $[2/(K_e + 1)]Q$ is substituted for Q, the field is unaffected in the region previously occupied by the dielectric.

image charge must therefore be located outside of the dielectric, as in Figure 4-14b.

What we have done, then, is the following. In order to find the field outside the dielectric we replaced the dielectric by an image charge $Q' = -\dfrac{K_e - 1}{K_e + 1} Q$ located at a distance D behind the boundary, as in Figure 4-14a. Then, in order to find the field inside the dielectric, we replaced both Q and the dielectric with a

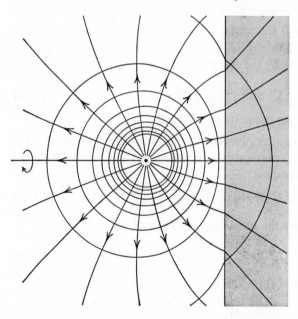

Figure 4-15

Lines of force (identified by arrows) and equipotentials for a point charge near a dielectric. As usual, the equipotential surfaces are generated by rotating the figure about the axis indicated by the curved arrow. The equipotentials near the point charge are not shown.

single charge $Q'' = +\dfrac{2}{K_e + 1} Q$ at the position of Q, as in Figure 4-14b. Since these combinations of charges produce fields which satisfy the boundary conditions, we know from the uniqueness theorem that they provide the correct solution. The shape of the field is shown in Figure 4-15.

In general, for two media having dielectric constants K_{e1} and K_{e2}, with the point charge Q in the first medium, the point charges which give the correct field are the following:

$$Q' = -\frac{K_{e2} - K_{e1}}{K_{e2} + K_{e1}} Q \tag{4-69}$$

at the image position together with Q gives the field in the first medium, and

$$Q'' = +\frac{2K_{e2}}{K_{e2} + K_{e1}} Q \tag{4-70}$$

at the position of Q gives the field in the second medium.

4.5. General Solution of Laplace's Equation*

The methods which we have considered until now for the calculation of electrostatic fields are useful only in special cases. We shall discuss here a more general method which will involve solving Poisson's equation,

$$\nabla^2 V = -\frac{\rho}{\epsilon_0}. \tag{4-71}$$

To begin with, we shall confine our attention to problems in which the charge density ρ is equal to zero, thus we shall have to deal with Laplace's equation,

$$\nabla^2 V = 0. \tag{4-72}$$

Solutions of Laplace's equation are known as *harmonic functions*, and there are an infinite number of them. These functions have a number of general properties, of which we shall use the following one. If the functions V_1, V_2, V_3, $\cdots$ are solutions, then any linear combination $A_1V_1 + A_2V_2 + A_3V_3 + \cdots$ of these functions, where the A's are arbitrary constants, is also a solution. This can be demonstrated readily by substitution into the original equation.

4.5.1. Solutions in Rectangular Coordinates. It is usually possible to find solutions of Laplace's equation which will satisfy required boundary conditions by the process of *variable separation*. In Cartesian coordinates, for example, we can usually find a solution of the form

$$V = X(x) Y(y) Z(z), \tag{4-73}$$

where $X(x)$, $Y(y)$, and $Z(z)$ are functions only of the variables x, y, and z,

* Sections 4.5 to 4.6.3 may be omitted without losing continuity.

respectively. We can then fit boundary conditions by adding a series of such solutions multiplied by suitable coefficients. The uniqueness theorem assures us that the solution thus found is the proper solution.

We can find the form of the functions $X(x)$, $Y(y)$, and $Z(z)$ by substituting V of Eq. *4-73* into Laplace's equation. Then

$$YZ\frac{d^2X}{dx^2} + ZX\frac{d^2Y}{dy^2} + XY\frac{d^2Z}{dz^2} = 0, \qquad (4\text{-}74)$$

where we have written total instead of partial derivatives, since the X, Y, and Z

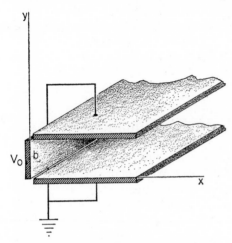

functions are each a function of a single variable. On dividing through by XYZ, we find that

$$\frac{1}{X}\frac{d^2X}{dx^2} + \frac{1}{Y}\frac{d^2Y}{dy^2} + \frac{1}{Z}\frac{d^2Z}{dz^2} = 0. \qquad (4\text{-}75)$$

Now since the second and third terms are independent of x, and since the three terms must add to zero at all points, the first term must also be independent of x. It is therefore constant in value, and

$$\frac{1}{X}\frac{d^2X}{dx^2} = C_1. \qquad (4\text{-}76)$$

Similarly,

$$\frac{1}{Y}\frac{d^2Y}{dy^2} = C_2, \qquad (4\text{-}77)$$

$$\frac{1}{Z}\frac{d^2Z}{dz^2} = C_3. \qquad (4\text{-}78)$$

Figure 4-16. *Grounded, plane-parallel electrodes terminated by a plane electrode at potential V_0. The electrodes are assumed to be infinite in the direction perpendicular to the paper and are assumed to extend infinitely on the right.*

Then

$$C_1 + C_2 + C_3 = 0. \qquad (4\text{-}79)$$

The problem now becomes one of solving the three *ordinary* differential equations, subject to the condition of Eq. *4-79* and to the boundary conditions.

4.5.2. Field Between Two Grounded Semi-infinite Parallel Electrodes Terminated by a Plane Electrode at Potential V_0.

As an example, consider Figure 4-16, which shows two grounded, semi-infinite, parallel electrodes separated by a distance b. The plane at $x = 0$ is occupied by a conducting electrode maintained at a potential V_0. The problem is to find the potential V at any point between the plates.

Since the plates have infinite extent in the positive and negative z directions, the potential must be independent of z, thus the last term of Eq. *4-75*, together with the constant C_3, is zero. We must therefore solve the two ordinary differential equations

$$\frac{d^2 X}{dx^2} - k^2 X = 0 \qquad (4\text{-}80)$$

and

$$\frac{d^2 Y}{dy^2} + k^2 Y = 0, \qquad (4\text{-}81)$$

where we have substituted k^2 for C_1 and $-k^2$ for C_2 to eliminate square roots in the solution. The choice between C_1 and C_2 as the negative constant is immaterial; the boundary conditions will force us to the same final solution in either case.

Equation *4-81* is solved by setting

$$Y = A \sin ky + B \cos ky, \qquad (4\text{-}82)$$

where A and B are arbitrary constants. This can be easily verified by substitution.

Our value of Y must satisfy the boundary conditions

$$V = 0 \qquad (y = 0, y = b), \qquad (4\text{-}83)$$
$$V = V_0 \qquad (x = 0), \qquad (4\text{-}84)$$
$$V \longrightarrow 0 \qquad (x \longrightarrow \infty). \qquad (4\text{-}85)$$

In order to have $V = 0$ at $y = 0$ we must have $B = 0$; and in order to have $V = 0$ at $y = b$ we must have

$$kb = n\pi \qquad (n = 1, 2, \cdots), \qquad (4\text{-}86)$$

thus

$$Y = A \sin \frac{n\pi y}{b} \qquad (n = 1, 2, \cdots). \qquad (4\text{-}87)$$

The value $n = 0$ must be omitted, for it corresponds to a sine term which is zero, and therefore to zero field.

Turning now to the X equation, we have

$$\frac{d^2 X}{dx^2} - \left(\frac{n\pi}{b}\right)^2 X = 0, \qquad (4\text{-}88)$$

thus

$$X = G e^{n\pi x/b} + H e^{-n\pi x/b}, \qquad (4\text{-}89)$$

where G and H are arbitrary constants. We can again verify this solution by substitution. The condition that $V \longrightarrow 0$ as $x \longrightarrow \infty$ requires that $G = 0$.

Altogether then, we have

$$V'(x, y) = C \sin \frac{n\pi y}{b} e^{-n\pi x/b}, \qquad (4\text{-}90)$$

where C is another arbitrary constant.

The solution as it is will obviously satisfy the boundary conditions stated in

Eqs. *4-83* and *4-85*. It will not, however, satisfy Eq. *4-84*. We therefore take an infinite sum of such solutions and set

$$V(x, y) = \sum_{n=1}^{\infty} C_n \sin \frac{n\pi y}{b} e^{-n\pi x/b}. \qquad (4\text{-}91)$$

To evaluate the coefficients C_n, we use the boundary condition at $x = 0$, namely,

$$V(0, y) = V_0 = \sum_{n=1}^{\infty} C_n \sin \frac{n\pi y}{b}. \qquad (4\text{-}92)$$

The expression on the right is called a *Fourier series*. It can be shown that the functions in Eq. *4-92*, provided an infinite series of cosine terms is also included, constitute a *complete* set of functions. This means that *an arbitrary boundary condition can be satisfied with such an infinite series.*

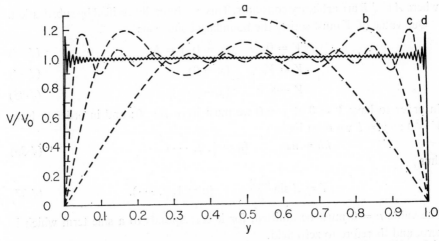

Figure 4-17. *The condition $V = V_0$ as satisfied by a Fourier series taking (a) only the first term, (b) the first 3 terms, (c) the first 10 terms, and (d) the first 100 terms. The Fourier series provides an increasingly better approximation as the number of terms is increased.*

Using a technique devised by Fourier, we multiply both sides of Eq. *4-92* by $\sin [(p\pi y)/b]$, where p is an integer, and integrate from $y = 0$ to $y = b$:

$$\int_0^b V_0 \sin \frac{p\pi y}{b} dy = \int_0^b \sum_{n=1}^{\infty} C_n \sin \frac{n\pi y}{b} \sin \frac{p\pi y}{b} dy. \qquad (4\text{-}93)$$

On the left-hand side,

$$\int_0^b V_0 \sin \frac{p\pi y}{b} dy = \begin{cases} \dfrac{2bV_0}{p\pi} & \text{if } p \text{ is odd,} \\ 0 & \text{if } p \text{ is even,} \end{cases} \qquad (4\text{-}94)$$

whereas on the right-hand side,

$$\int_0^b C_n \sin\frac{n\pi y}{b} \sin\frac{p\pi y}{b} \, dy = \begin{cases} 0 & \text{if } p \neq n, \\ C_n \dfrac{b}{2} & \text{if } p = n. \end{cases} \tag{4-95}$$

Thus, for a given p, the only term of the infinite series on the right-hand side of Eq. *4-93* which differs from zero is the one for which $n = p$. Functions with such properties are said to be *orthogonal*.

Combining Eqs. *4-94* and *4-95*, we find that

$$C_n = \begin{cases} \dfrac{4V_0}{n\pi} & \text{if } n \text{ is odd,} \\ 0 & \text{if } n \text{ is even.} \end{cases} \tag{4-96}$$

We can now write down the potential V at any point (x, y):

$$V(x, y) = \frac{4V_0}{\pi} \sum_{n=1,3,5,\ldots}^{\infty} \frac{1}{n} \sin\frac{n\pi y}{b} e^{-n\pi x/b}. \tag{4-97}$$

The successive terms in the series become progressively less important because of the $(1/n)$ factor in the coefficients and because of the negative exponential factor involving n. The degree of approximation which one achieves at $x = 0$

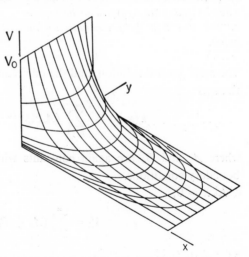

Figure 4-18

Three-dimensional plot of the potential V for the configuration of Figure 4-16. The ∪-shaped curves are equipotentials; the others show the intersections of the potential surface with planes parallel to the xV-plane.

with one, three, ten, and one hundred terms of the series is indicated in Figure 4-17. At $x = b$ the first term alone gives a good approximation. The equipotentials are shown in Figure 4-18.

4.5.3. Field Between Two Grounded Parallel Electrodes Terminated on Two Opposite Sides by Plates at Potentials V_1 and V_2. As a more complicated example, consider Figure 4-19, where two grounded plane parallel electrodes of

width a are separated by a distance b and extend to infinity in the other direction. The plane at $x = 0$ is occupied by a conducting surface maintained at a potential V_1, and the plane at $x = a$ is occupied by a conductor maintained at a potential V_2. The problem is again to find the electrostatic potential V at any point between the plates.

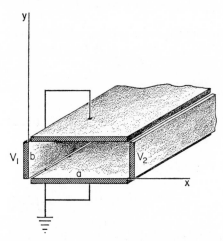

Since the plates have infinite extent in the positive and negative z directions, there is no z dependence of the potential, hence the last term of Eq. *4-75*, together with the constant C_3 in Eq. *4-79*, is again zero. Since the Y part of the solution is identical with that of the previous example, Eq. *4-87* is again valid, as are Eqs. *4-88* and *4-89*.

From this point on, the solution differs from that of the previous example, since the boundary conditions are different. Here we have

$$V = V_1 \text{ at } x = 0 \qquad (4\text{-}98)$$

and

$$V = V_2 \text{ at } x = a. \qquad (4\text{-}99)$$

Figure 4-19. *Grounded plane-parallel electrodes terminated on two sides with plane electrodes at potentials V_1 and V_2. The electrodes are assumed to be infinite in the direction perpendicular to the paper.*

The most general solution, and the one required to satisfy the boundary conditions, is

$$V(x, y) = \sum_{n=1}^{\infty} (A_n e^{-n\pi x/b} + B_n e^{n\pi x/b}) \sin \frac{n\pi y}{b}, \qquad (4\text{-}100)$$

where A_n and B_n are again constants which must be determined from the boundary conditions.

At $x = 0$,

$$V_1 = \sum_{n=1}^{\infty} (A_n + B_n) \sin \frac{n\pi y}{b}. \qquad (4\text{-}101)$$

The coefficients are evaluated by the same Fourier method used in the previous example. On multiplying by $\sin \frac{p\pi y}{b}$ and integrating from $y = 0$ to $y = b$, we have again, out of the whole infinite series, only one term corresponding to $p = n$:

$$V_1 \int_0^b \sin \frac{n\pi y}{b} \, dy = (A_n + B_n) \frac{b}{2}, \qquad (4\text{-}102)$$

thus

$$A_n + B_n = \begin{cases} \dfrac{4V_1}{n\pi} & \text{if } n \text{ is odd,} \\ 0 & \text{if } n \text{ is even.} \end{cases} \qquad (4\text{-}103)$$

We can find another relationship between A_n and B_n by using the boundary condition at $x = a$: from Eq. *4-100*,

$$V_2 = \sum_{n=1}^{\infty} (A_n e^{-n\pi a/b} + B_n e^{n\pi a/b}) \sin \frac{n\pi y}{b}. \qquad (4\text{-}104)$$

Multiplying by $\sin \dfrac{p\pi y}{b}$ and integrating from $y = 0$ to $y = a$, as before, we find that

$$A_n e^{-n\pi a/b} + B_n e^{n\pi a/b} = \begin{cases} \dfrac{4V_2}{n\pi} & \text{if } n \text{ is odd,} \\ 0 & \text{if } n \text{ is even,} \end{cases} \qquad (4\text{-}105)$$

and from Eqs. *4-103* and *4-105*,

$$A_n = \frac{4}{n\pi} \left(\frac{V_1 - V_2 e^{-n\pi a/b}}{1 - e^{-2n\pi a/b}} \right) \qquad (4\text{-}106)$$

and

$$B_n = \frac{4e^{-n\pi a/b}}{n\pi} \left(\frac{V_2 - V_1 e^{-n\pi a/b}}{1 - e^{-2n\pi a/b}} \right), \qquad (4\text{-}107)$$

where $n = 1, 3, 5, \cdots$. The potential V at any point (x, y) is given by Eq. *4-100* with A_n and B_n as above.

The degree of approximation achieved with a few terms of the final solution using these coefficients in Eq. *4-100* will be left as a problem at the end of the chapter. Figure 4-20 shows the equipotentials for the case where $V_1 = V_2 = V_0$.

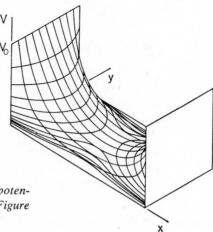

Figure 4-20

A three-dimensional plot of the potential V for the configuration of Figure 4-19 with $V_1 = V_2 = V_0$.

4.6. Solutions of Laplace's Equation in Spherical Coordinates. Legendre's Equation. Legendre Polynomials

Although electrostatic fields can usually be calculated in Cartesian coordinates, certain cases of symmetry are best treated in spherical polar coordinates. Laplace's equation then takes the form

$$\nabla^2 V = \frac{1}{r^2} \frac{\partial}{\partial r} \left(r^2 \frac{\partial V}{\partial r} \right) + \frac{1}{r^2 \sin \theta} \frac{\partial}{\partial \theta} \left(\sin \theta \frac{\partial V}{\partial \theta} \right)$$

$$+ \frac{1}{r^2 \sin^2 \theta} \frac{\partial^2 V}{\partial \phi^2} = 0. \qquad (4\text{-}108)$$

The solutions of this equation are known as *spherical harmonic functions*.

We shall restrict ourselves here to problems with axial symmetry, that is, to problems in which V is independent of the angle ϕ. Equation *4-108* then reduces to

$$\frac{\partial}{\partial r} \left(r^2 \frac{\partial V}{\partial r} \right) + \frac{1}{\sin \theta} \frac{\partial}{\partial \theta} \left(\sin \theta \frac{\partial V}{\partial \theta} \right) = 0. \qquad (4\text{-}109)$$

As in Cartesian coordinates, we seek solutions in which the variables are separated and set

$$V(r, \theta) = R(r) \, \Theta(\theta), \qquad (4\text{-}110)$$

where R is a function only of r and Θ is a function only of θ. Substituting $V = R\Theta$ into Eq. *4-109*, we obtain

$$\Theta \frac{\partial}{\partial r} \left(r^2 \frac{\partial R}{\partial r} \right) + \frac{R}{\sin \theta} \frac{\partial}{\partial \theta} \left(\sin \theta \frac{\partial \Theta}{\partial \theta} \right) = 0, \qquad (4\text{-}111)$$

and dividing through by $R\Theta$ gives

$$\frac{1}{R} \frac{d}{dr} \left(r^2 \frac{dR}{dr} \right) + \frac{1}{\Theta \sin \theta} \frac{d}{d\theta} \left(\sin \theta \frac{d\Theta}{d\theta} \right) = 0. \qquad (4\text{-}112)$$

We have written total instead of partial derivatives, since the functions to be differentiated in each case are functions of a single variable.

Since the second term of Eq. *4-112* is independent of r, the first term must also be independent of r. The first term must therefore be constant, and we may write

$$\frac{1}{R} \frac{d}{dr} \left(r^2 \frac{dR}{dr} \right) = k \qquad (4\text{-}113)$$

and

$$\frac{1}{\Theta \sin \theta} \frac{d}{d\theta} \left(\sin \theta \frac{d\Theta}{d\theta} \right) = -k, \qquad (4\text{-}114)$$

since the sum of the two constants must equal zero.

Let us examine the R equation first. Multiplying both sides by R and differentiating the bracketed factors, we obtain the relation

$$r^2 \frac{d^2R}{dr^2} + 2r \frac{dR}{dr} - kR = 0. \qquad (4\text{-}115)$$

A function of the type

$$R = Ar^n + \frac{B}{r^{n+1}} \qquad (4\text{-}116)$$

is a solution of Eq. *4-115*. On substituting we find that n is related to k:

$$n(n+1) = k. \qquad (4\text{-}117)$$

Let us now examine Eq. *4-114* for Θ. We have

$$\frac{d}{d\theta}\left(\sin\theta \frac{d\Theta}{d\theta}\right) + n(n+1)\sin\theta\,\Theta = 0. \qquad (4\text{-}118)$$

It is convenient to change variables in this equation and to let

$$\mu = \cos\theta. \qquad (4\text{-}119)$$

Recall that for any function $f(\mu)$

$$\frac{df}{d\theta} = \frac{df}{d\mu}\frac{d\mu}{d\theta} = -\sin\theta\frac{df}{d\mu} = -\sqrt{1-\mu^2}\frac{df}{d\mu}. \qquad (4\text{-}120)$$

Thus Eq. *4-118* becomes

$$\frac{d}{d\mu}\left[(1-\mu^2)\frac{d\Theta}{d\mu}\right] + n(n+1)\Theta = 0. \qquad (4\text{-}121)$$

This is known as *Legendre's equation*. Its solutions are polynomials in $\cos\theta$ and are known as *Legendre polynomials*. They are designated by $P_n(\mu)$ or $P_n(\cos\theta)$:

$$\Theta = P_n(\mu) = P_n(\cos\theta), \qquad (4\text{-}122)$$

where n is called the *degree* of the polynomial. A different polynomial exists for each value of n. We shall limit our discussion to integral values of n.

Before proceeding to find solutions of Eq. *4-121*, we may point out an interesting property of Legendre's equation. The index n must satisfy Eq. *4-117*. But

$$n' = -(n+1) \qquad (4\text{-}123)$$

will equally satisfy this equation because

$$n'(n'+1) = n(n+1) = k. \qquad (4\text{-}124)$$

That is, Eq. *4-121* remains unchanged when the index n' is substituted for n. Hence the solutions must be the same, and

$$P_{-(n+1)}(\cos\theta) = P_n(\cos\theta). \qquad (4\text{-}125)$$

Therefore, for every solution of Laplace's equation of the form

$$V = Ar^n P_n(\cos\theta) \qquad (4\text{-}126)$$

there is another solution of the form

$$V = \frac{B}{r^{n+1}} P_n(\cos \theta). \tag{4-127}$$

This also follows directly from the R function of Eq. *4-116*.

Let us now proceed to find the Legendre polynomials $P_n(\cos \theta)$ which are solutions of Legendre's equation. We know from our experience with point charges that

$$V_1 = \frac{C}{r}, \tag{4-128}$$

is a solution of Laplace's equation, C being a constant. This is readily verified by substitution in Eq. *4-108*. Since we are looking for solutions of the form indicated in Eqs. *4-126* or *4-127*, it follows from the latter equation that

$$P_0'(\cos \theta) = 1. \tag{4-129}$$

We use a prime on the symbol P because the polynomials which we shall derive here differ from the Legendre polynomials by constant factors, as we shall see below. They are nevertheless solutions of Eq. *4-121*. Substituting $\Theta = P_0'(\cos \theta) = 1$ and $n = 0$ into Eq. *4-121* does in fact solve it.

Having found the solution $P_0'(\cos \theta)$, how can we find $P_1'(\cos \theta)$ and all the other polynomials corresponding to all the possible integral values of the index n in Eq. *4-118*? We shall do this starting with Eq. *4-128*, but first we must know that any partial derivative of a solution of Laplace's equation with respect to any of the Cartesian coordinate variables is also a solution. This is easily demonstrated by substituting dV/dx in Laplace's equation and remembering that the order of differentiation in partial derivatives is immaterial.

Let us therefore find the negative partial derivative of Eq. *4-128* with respect to z:

$$-\frac{\partial}{\partial z}\left(\frac{C}{r}\right) = +\frac{C}{r^2}\frac{\partial r}{\partial z} \tag{4-130}$$

and

$$\frac{\partial r}{\partial z} = \frac{\partial}{\partial z}(x^2 + y^2 + z^2)^{1/2} = \frac{z}{r} = \cos \theta. \tag{4-131}$$

Equation *4-130* thus gives us a new solution of Laplace's equation:

$$V_2 = C\frac{\cos \theta}{r^2}. \tag{4-132}$$

Comparing once again with Eq. *4-127* we see that

$$P_1'(\cos \theta) = \cos \theta. \tag{4-133}$$

Substitution of $P_1'(\cos \theta) = \cos \theta$ for Θ into Eq. *4-121* shows that it is really a solution when $n = 1$.

Equation *4-126* shows another possible solution for a given $P_n(\cos \theta)$. In this case we have, in addition to V_2, another solution:

$$V_2' = DrP_1'(\cos \theta) = Dr \cos \theta. \tag{4-134}$$

To find $P_2'(\cos \theta)$, we differentiate V_2 with respect to z:

$$V_3 = -\frac{\partial}{\partial z}\left(C \frac{\cos \theta}{r^2}\right) = -\frac{\partial}{\partial z}\left(C \frac{z}{r^3}\right) = C \frac{(3 \cos^2 \theta - 1)}{r^3}. \tag{4-135}$$

Comparing this with Eq. *4-127*,

$$P_2'(\cos \theta) = (3 \cos^2 \theta - 1). \tag{4-136}$$

Again there is another solution:

$$V_3' = Fr^2(3 \cos^2 \theta - 1), \tag{4-137}$$

which corresponds to Eq. *4-126*. We shall stop here, but we could continue to find further polynomials in this way by repeated partial differentiations with respect to z.

It is convenient to multiply the above polynomials by normalizing factors to make them equal to unity at $\cos \theta = 1$. Thus Eq. *4-136* must be multiplied by the factor $\frac{1}{2}$ to make $P_2(\cos \theta) = 1$ when $\cos \theta = 1$. The *general form of the normalized Legendre polynomial* is

$$P_n(\cos \theta) = \frac{1}{2^n n!} \frac{\partial^n}{\partial(\cos \theta)^n} (\cos^2 \theta - 1)^n. \tag{4-138}$$

The first five are shown in Table 4-2; those for $n = 1, 2,$ and 3 are plotted as functions of θ in Figure 4-21.

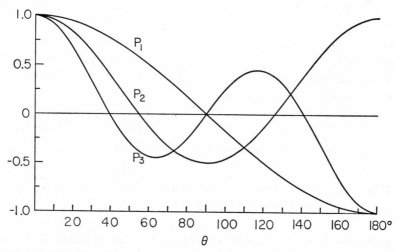

Figure 4-21. *The first three Legendre polynomials.*

TABLE 4-2.   Legendre Polynomials

n	$P_n(\cos \theta)$
0	1
1	$\cos \theta$
2	$\frac{3}{2} \cos^2 \theta - \frac{1}{2}$
3	$\frac{5}{2} \cos^3 \theta - \frac{3}{2} \cos \theta$
4	$\frac{35}{8} \cos^4 \theta - \frac{15}{4} \cos^2 \theta + \frac{3}{8}$

A general solution of Laplace's equation in spherical polar coordinates, assuming axial symmetry, is therefore the following:

$$V = \sum_{n=0}^{\infty} A_n r^n P_n(\cos \theta) + \sum_{n=0}^{\infty} B_n r^{-(n+1)} P_n(\cos \theta). \qquad (4\text{-}139)$$

The various terms are shown in Table 4-3.

TABLE 4-3.   Solutions of Laplace's Equation in Spherical Polar Coordinates in the Case of Axial Symmetry

n	$r^n P'_n (\cos \theta)$	$r^{-(n+1)} P'_n \cos \theta$
0	1	r^{-1}
1	$r \cos \theta$	$r^{-2} \cos \theta$
2	$\frac{1}{2} r^2 (3 \cos^2 \theta - 1)$	$\frac{1}{2} r^{-3} (3 \cos^2 \theta - 1)$
3	$\frac{1}{2} r^3 (5 \cos^3 \theta - 3 \cos \theta)$	$\frac{1}{2} r^{-4} (5 \cos^3 \theta - 3 \cos \theta)$
4	$\frac{1}{8} r^4 (35 \cos^4 \theta - 30 \cos^2 \theta + 3)$	$\frac{1}{8} r^{-5} (35 \cos^4 \theta - 30 \cos^2 \theta + 3)$

It can be shown that the functions in Eq. *4-139* are a *complete set of functions*, thus an arbitrary boundary condition with axial symmetry can be satisfied with such an infinite series. Moreover, any function of the polar angle θ can be represented as a series of Legendre polynomials, provided the function is continuous within the range of θ considered and provided the function has a finite number of maxima and minima.

It can be shown that

$$\int_{-1}^{+1} P_m(\cos \theta) P_n(\cos \theta) \, d(\cos \theta) = \begin{cases} 0 & \text{if } m \neq n, \\ \dfrac{2}{2n+1} & \text{if } m = n. \end{cases} \qquad (4\text{-}140)$$

This property of *orthogonality* of the Legendre polynomials is important in evaluating the coefficients of Eq. *4-139*.

4.6.1. Conducting Sphere in a Uniform Electrostatic Field. To illustrate the use of Eq. *4-139* in calculating electrostatic fields, we consider the case of an

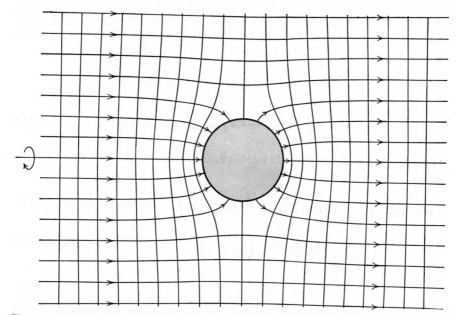

Figure 4-22. *Lines of force (indicated by arrows) and equipotentials for a conducting sphere in a uniform electrostatic field. The lines of force are normal at the surface of the sphere, and there is zero electric intensity inside. Observe that the field is hardly disturbed at distances larger than one radius from the surface of the sphere.*

insulated conducting sphere situated in a uniform electrostatic field E_0, as in Figure 4-22.

At any point, either inside or outside the sphere, the electric field intensity is that due to the induced charges plus E_0. We assume that the charges which produce E_0 are so far away that they are unaffected by the presence of the sphere. The induced charges arrange themselves on the conducting sphere such that the total field is zero *inside*. Outside the sphere, the total field is of course not zero; we shall calculate it by solving Laplace's equation.

The field is best described in terms of spherical polar coordinates with the origin at the center of the sphere and the polar axis along E_0. Our boundary conditions are then

$$V = 0 \qquad\qquad (r = a), \qquad (4\text{-}141)$$

$$V = -E_0 z = -E_0 r \cos\theta \qquad (r = \infty). \qquad (4\text{-}142)$$

At $r = a$, from Eqs. *4-139* and *4-141*,

$$0 = \sum_{n=0}^{\infty} A_n a^n P_n(\cos\theta) + \sum_{n=0}^{\infty} B_n a^{-(n+1)} P_n(\cos\theta). \qquad (4\text{-}143)$$

The method of evaluating the coefficients A_n and B_n is similar to that which we used for evaluating the C_n's of Eq. 4-92. We multiply both sides of the equation by $P_m(\cos\theta)$ and integrate from $\cos\theta = -1$ to $+1$:

$$0 = \sum_{n=0}^{\infty} \int_{-1}^{+1} A_n a^n P_n(\cos\theta) P_m(\cos\theta)\, d(\cos\theta)$$

$$+ \sum_{n=0}^{\infty} \int_{-1}^{+1} B_n a^{-(n+1)} P_n(\cos\theta) P_m(\cos\theta)\, d(\cos\theta). \qquad (4\text{-}144)$$

According to Eq. 4-140, the only nonvanishing terms are those for which $n = m$, thus

$$0 = A_n a^n \int_{-1}^{+1} P_n^2(\cos\theta)\, d(\cos\theta) + B_n a^{-(n+1)} \int_{-1}^{+1} P_n^2(\cos\theta)\, d(\cos\theta), \quad (4\text{-}145)$$

$$= A_n a^n \left(\frac{2}{2n+1}\right) + B_n a^{-(n+1)}\left(\frac{2}{2n+1}\right). \qquad (4\text{-}146)$$

Thus

$$B_n = -A_n a^{2n+1}. \qquad (4\text{-}147)$$

As $r \longrightarrow \infty$ the potential V is given by Eq. 4-142, all the terms involving inverse powers of r go to zero, and

$$-E_0 r P_1(\cos\theta) = \sum_{n=0}^{\infty} A_n r^n P_n(\cos\theta). \qquad (4\text{-}148)$$

Inspection of Eq. 4-148 shows that the only term which is not zero on the right hand side is that for which $n = 1$. We can show this in a formal manner by multiplying both sides by $P_m(\cos\theta)$ and integrating from $\cos\theta = -1$ to $+1$. By either method we find that

$$A_1 = -E_0 \qquad (4\text{-}149)$$

and all the other A_n's are zero. Then all the B's are zero except B_1:

$$B_1 = -A_1 a^3 = E_0 a^3. \qquad (4\text{-}150)$$

Finally, the potential at any point (r, θ) is

$$V(r, \theta) = -E_0 r \cos\theta + E_0 \frac{a^3 \cos\theta}{r^2}, \qquad (4\text{-}151)$$

$$= -E_0\left(1 - \frac{a^3}{r^3}\right) r \cos\theta. \qquad (4\text{-}152)$$

The field intensity, illustrated in Figure 4-22, is then readily found from V:

$$E_r = -\frac{\partial V}{\partial r} = E_0\left(1 + \frac{2a^3}{r^3}\right)\cos\theta, \qquad (4\text{-}153)$$

$$E_\theta = -\frac{1}{r}\frac{\partial V}{\partial \theta} = -E_0\left(1 - \frac{a^3}{r^3}\right)\sin\theta. \qquad (4\text{-}154)$$

The surface density of induced charge on the sphere is found easily, since we know that at the surface of the conductor,

$$(E_r)_{r=a} = \frac{\sigma}{\epsilon_0}. \tag{4-155}$$

Then

$$\sigma = 3\epsilon_0 E_0 \cos\theta. \tag{4-156}$$

Returning now to Eq. *4-151*, we observe that the first term is the potential corresponding to the uniform field intensity $\mathbf{E}_0$. The second term has the form of the potential due to a dipole (Section 2.8). In fact, if we replace the sphere by a dipole of moment

$$p = 4\pi\epsilon_0 E_0 a^3 \tag{4-157}$$

located at the center, the field outside the surface previously occupied by the sphere will remain unchanged. We shall examine the image aspect of this field in the problems at the end of this chapter.

We could also have determined the field quickly from Eq. *4-139* by a less formal method. We must have the term $-E_0 r \cos\theta$ to fit the condition at infinity. No other function with positive powers of r can be included. This one term, however, is inadequate to fit the condition at $r = a$, where V must be independent of θ. We must therefore add another function which also includes the $\cos\theta$ factor in order that the coefficient of $\cos\theta$ can be zero at $r = a$. Then

$$V = -E_0 r \cos\theta + \frac{B\cos\theta}{r^2}. \tag{4-158}$$

We finally choose a value for B which will make $V = 0$ at $r = a$. Our solution satisfies both Laplace's equation and the boundary conditions; it must therefore be the correct solution, according to the uniqueness theorem.

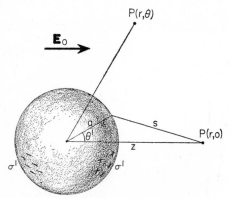

Figure 4-23. *The electrostatic potential V at $P(r, \theta)$ can be calculated from the applied electric field intensity $\mathbf{E}_o$ and the induced surface charge density σ'. We first calculate V on the axis of symmetry at $P(r, \theta)$ by a simple integration. This value is then used as a boundary condition to determine the coefficients of the Legendre polynomials in the series for V at any point $P(r, \theta)$.*

There is still another method of calculating this same field which will add to our understanding of the physical phenomenon and which will illustrate further the use of Legendre polynomials. Consider Figure 4-23. As indicated previously, the potential at any point (r, θ) arises from two charge distributions: (1) that which produces the electric field intensity $\mathbf{E}_0$ and which resides on electrodes situated far away, and (2) that which is induced on the surface of the sphere. This latter distribution is unknown, and we denote it by $\sigma(\theta')$. We use a prime on θ to distinguish it from the polar angle for a point (r, θ) outside the sphere. At the general point (r, θ) the total potential from these two sources must be of the form shown in Eq. *4-139*.

Now it is possible to compute from Coulomb's law the potential at a point P on the axis $\theta = 0$ at a distance $r = z$ from the center of the sphere:

$$V = -E_0 z + \frac{1}{4\pi\epsilon_0} \int_0^\pi \frac{\sigma(\theta') 2\pi a^2 \sin\theta' \, d\theta'}{s}, \tag{4-159}$$

where a is the radius of the sphere and s is the distance from a point on the sphere to P as in Figure 4-23.

$$s = \sqrt{z^2 + a^2 - 2az \cos\theta'} \tag{4-160}$$

$$= z \sqrt{1 + \frac{a^2}{z^2} - \frac{2a}{z} \cos\theta'}. \tag{4-161}$$

Expanding $1/s$ and grouping terms involving the same power of (a/z), we obtain

$$\frac{1}{s} = \frac{1}{z}\left[1 + \frac{a}{z} \cos\theta' + \left(\frac{3}{2}\cos^2\theta' - \frac{1}{2}\right)\frac{a^2}{z^2} \right.$$
$$\left. + \left(\frac{5}{2}\cos^3\theta' - \frac{3}{2}\cos\theta'\right)\frac{a^3}{z^3} + \cdots \right], \tag{4-162}$$

$$= \frac{1}{z} + \frac{a}{z^2} P_1(\cos\theta') + \frac{a^2}{z^3} P_2(\cos\theta') + \cdots. \tag{4-163}$$

We have already seen that any function of the polar angle θ can be expanded as a series of Legendre polynomials. Thus

$$\sigma(\theta') = b_0 + b_1 P_1(\cos\theta') + b_2 P_2(\cos\theta') + \cdots, \tag{4-164}$$

where $b_0, b_1, \cdots$ are constants. Equation *4-159* then becomes

$$V = -E_0 z + \frac{a^2}{2\epsilon_0} \int_{-1}^{+1} [b_0 + b_1 P_1(\cos\theta') + b_2 P_2(\cos\theta') + \cdots]$$
$$\times \left[\frac{1}{z} + \frac{a}{z^2} P_1(\cos\theta') + \frac{a^2}{z^3} P_2(\cos\theta') + \cdots \right] d(\cos\theta'). \tag{4-165}$$

The orthogonality property of the Legendre polynomials makes this an easy integral to evaluate, thus

$$V = -E_0 z + \frac{a^2}{2\epsilon_0}\left(\frac{2b_0}{z} + \frac{2b_1}{3}\frac{a}{z^2} + \frac{2b_2}{5}\frac{a^2}{z^3} + \cdots \right). \tag{4-166}$$

Thus, when $\theta = 0$ and $r = z$, the general solution for V shown in Eq. *4-139* must reduce to the above form, and we can match coefficients term by term to find V at *any* point (r, θ) outside the sphere. On doing this we find that all the A_n's are zero, except for

$$A_1 = -E_0, \qquad (4\text{-}167)$$

and that

$$B_n = \frac{b_n}{2n+1} \frac{a^{n+2}}{\epsilon_0}. \qquad (4\text{-}168)$$

To evaluate the b_n's, we use the fact that the potential is zero at $r = a$. Substituting the above coefficients into Eq. *4-139* and setting $r = a$, we have

$$0 = -E_0 a P_1(\cos\theta) + \frac{b_0 a}{\epsilon_0} + \frac{b_1 a}{3\epsilon_0} P_1(\cos\theta) + \frac{b_2 a}{5\epsilon_0} P_2(\cos\theta) + \cdots, \quad (4\text{-}169)$$

which must be true for all θ. Thus both the term $b_0 a/\epsilon_0$, which is independent of θ, and the coefficients of all the P_n's must be equal to zero. Thus

$$b_0 = 0, \qquad (4\text{-}170)$$

and

$$-E_0 a + \frac{b_1 a}{3\epsilon_0} = 0, \qquad (4\text{-}171)$$

or

$$b_1 = 3\epsilon_0 E_0. \qquad (4\text{-}172)$$

All other b_n's are zero.

The potential V at any point (r, θ) is thus given by substituting into Eq. *4-139* $A_1 = -E_0$ as in Eq. *4-167*, and

$$B_1 = E_0 a^3, \qquad (4\text{-}173)$$

as in Eqs. *4-168* and *4-172*. The field is the same as that found in Eq. *4-151*.

The surface charge density $\sigma(\theta')$ on the conducting sphere can be obtained from Eq. *4-164* now that the b_n's are known: we find the value previously found in Eq. *4-156*.

4.6.2. Dielectric Sphere in a Uniform Electrostatic Field.

We can calculate this field by either of the formal methods discussed above if we write a general solution as in Eq. *4-139* for points outside the sphere and write another solution with different coefficients for points inside the sphere. The coefficients must be chosen such that the boundary conditions are satisfied:

$$V \longrightarrow -E_0 r \cos\theta \qquad (r \longrightarrow \infty);$$

V is continuous across the boundary $(r = a)$;

the normal component of **D** is continuous $(r = a)$.

Instead of following such a formal procedure, however, we shall write down a combination of spherical harmonics which will satisfy all the boundary conditions.

Outside the sphere, we must have $-E_0 r \cos\theta$ as one of the terms in the solution to satisfy the condition at $r \longrightarrow \infty$. Furthermore, this is the only harmonic with a positive power of r which we can permit, for otherwise the condition at $r \longrightarrow \infty$ would be violated. As regards this condition, all the terms with inverse powers of r are acceptable.

Consider now the solution for points inside the dielectric sphere. No inverse powers at all are permissible here, since such terms would make the potential infinite at the center. This is clearly impossible, since the only charges in the system are those which produce the field E_0 and those induced on the surface of the sphere, if we assume a Class A dielectric, with the result that no volume distribution of induced charge exists.

Writing V_0 for the potential outside the sphere and V_i for that inside, we have

$$V_0 = -E_0 r \cos \theta + \sum_{n=0}^{\infty} B_n r^{-(n+1)} P_n(\cos \theta), \qquad (4\text{-}174)$$

$$V_i = \sum_{n=0}^{\infty} C_n r^n P_n(\cos \theta). \qquad (4\text{-}175)$$

We also require that

$$V_0(a, \theta) = V_i(a, \theta) \qquad (4\text{-}176)$$

and that

$$-\left(\frac{\partial V_0(r, \theta)}{\partial r}\right)_{r=a} = -\left(K_e \frac{\partial V_i(r, \theta)}{\partial r}\right)_{r=a}, \qquad (4\text{-}177)$$

where K_e is the dielectric coefficient of the sphere. These are the second and third boundary conditions discussed above. Therefore

$$-E_0 a P_1(\cos \theta) + \frac{B_0}{a} + \frac{B_1 P_1(\cos \theta)}{a^2} + \frac{B_2 P_2(\cos \theta)}{a^3} + \cdots$$
$$= C_0 + C_1 a P_1(\cos \theta) + C_2 a^2 P_2(\cos \theta) + \cdots, \qquad (4\text{-}178)$$

and

$$E_0 P_1(\cos \theta) + \frac{B_0}{a^2} + \frac{2B_1 P_1(\cos \theta)}{a^3} + \frac{3B_2 P_2(\cos \theta)}{a^4} + \cdots$$
$$= -K_e C_1 P_1(\cos \theta) - 2K_e C_2 a P_2(\cos \theta) + \cdots. \qquad (4\text{-}179)$$

In order that Eqs. *4-178* and *4-179* be true for all values of θ, the coefficient of each Legendre polynomial on the left side must be equal to the coefficient of the same Legendre polynomial on the right side. Thus, from Eq. *4-178*,

$$\frac{B_0}{a} = C_0, \qquad (4\text{-}180)$$

$$-E_0 a + \frac{B_1}{a^2} = C_1 a, \qquad (4\text{-}181)$$

$$\frac{B_2}{a^3} = C_2 a^2, \cdots, \qquad (4\text{-}182)$$

and, from Eq. *4-179*,

$$\frac{B_0}{a^2} = 0, \qquad (4\text{-}183)$$

$$E_0 + \frac{2B_1}{a^3} = -K_e C_1, \tag{4-184}$$

$$\frac{3B_2}{a^4} = -2K_e C_2 a. \tag{4-185}$$

These sets of equations lead to the following values for the coefficients:

$$B_0 = C_0 = 0, \tag{4-186}$$

$$B_1 = \left(\frac{K_e - 1}{K_e + 2}\right) E_0 a^3, \tag{4-187}$$

$$C_1 = -\frac{3E_0}{K_e + 2}, \tag{4-188}$$

$$B_n = C_n = 0 \qquad (n > 1). \tag{4-189}$$

Thus

$$V_0(r, \theta) = -\left[1 - \left(\frac{K_e - 1}{K_e + 2}\right)\frac{a^3}{r^3}\right] E_0 r \cos \theta, \tag{4-190}$$

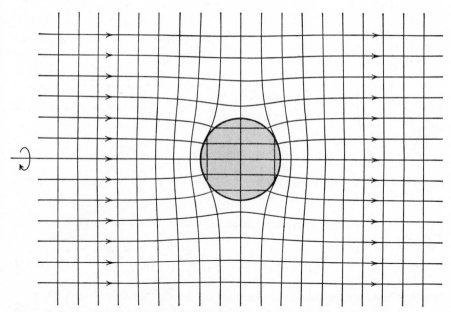

Figure 4-24.   *The field near a dielectric sphere in a uniform electrostatic field. The lines of electric displacement (indicated by arrows) crowd into the sphere as shown, with the result that D is larger inside than outside. Since there is no free charge at the surface of the sphere, the lines of D neither originate nor terminate there, and they are continuous across the boundary. The equipotentials spread out inside, corresponding to a lower electric field intensity E. The electric field intensity E is discontinuous at the surface, and the density of lines of force is lower inside than outside. As in the conducting sphere, the field is hardly disturbed at distances larger than one radius from the surface. The field inside is uniform.*

and

$$V_i(r, \theta) = -\left(\frac{3}{K_e + 2}\right) E_0 r \cos \theta = -\left(\frac{3}{K_e + 2}\right) E_0 z. \qquad (4\text{-}191)$$

We may calculate the field intensity inside and outside the sphere by calculating $-\nabla V$ from Eqs. *4-190* and *4-191*. It will be observed that the field inside the sphere is uniform, is along z, and is given by

$$E_i = \left(\frac{3}{K_e + 2}\right) E_0. \qquad (4\text{-}192)$$

The lines of force and equipotentials are shown in Figure 4-24.

4.6.3. Uniformly Charged Ring.

As a final example of a field involving spherical harmonics, let us consider a thin ring of radius a, carrying a charge Q as in

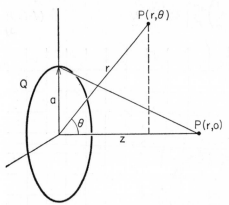

Figure 4-25. We wish to find the electrostatic potential V at a point $P(r, \theta)$ such that $r \geqq a$. The uniform charge on the ring assures azimuthal symmetry for the potential. Equation *4-139* again applies, but we can rule out all terms with positive powers of r since we require that $V \longrightarrow 0$ as $r \longrightarrow \infty$. The potential at P must therefore be of the form

$$V(r, \theta) = \sum_{n=0}^{\infty} B_n r^{-(n+1)} P_n(\cos \theta).$$

Figure 4-25. *A ring of radius a carrying a total charge Q.*

$$(4\text{-}193)$$

We shall proceed as we did in the latter part of Section 4.6.1. On the axis, where $\theta = 0$ and $r = z$, we have $P_n(\cos \theta) = 1$ and

$$V(z, 0) = \frac{B_0}{z} + \frac{B_1}{z^2} + \frac{B_2}{z^3} + \cdots. \qquad (4\text{-}194)$$

We can, however, calculate the potential on the axis directly from Coulomb's law, and if we expand the resultant expression in inverse powers of z we may match coefficients term by term with Eq. *4-194* to determine the B_n's. The axis thus provides us with the equivalent of a boundary condition.

Following this procedure, we have

$$V(z, 0) = \frac{Q}{4\pi\epsilon_0 (a^2 + z^2)^{1/2}} = \frac{Q}{4\pi\epsilon_0 z}\left(1 + \frac{a^2}{z^2}\right)^{-1/2}, \qquad (4\text{-}195)$$

$$= \frac{Q}{4\pi\epsilon_0 z}\left(1 - \frac{1}{2}\frac{a^2}{z^2} + \frac{3}{8}\frac{a^4}{z^4} - \frac{5}{16}\frac{a^6}{z^6} + \cdots\right). \qquad (4\text{-}196)$$

On matching coefficients with Eq. *4-194*, we find that

$$B_0 = \frac{Q}{4\pi\epsilon_0},$$ (4-197)

$$B_1 = 0,$$ (4-198)

$$B_2 = -\frac{Q}{4\pi\epsilon_0}\frac{a^2}{2},$$ (4-199)

$$B_3 = 0, \cdots,$$ (4-200)

and, from Eq. *4-193*,

$$V(r, \theta) = \frac{Q}{4\pi\epsilon_0}\left[\frac{1}{r} - \frac{1}{2}\frac{a^2}{r^3}\left(\frac{3}{2}\cos^2\theta - \frac{1}{2}\right) + \cdots\right].$$ (4-201)

Figure 4-26 shows the equipotential lines in this case. The components of the field intensity may be found, as usual, by calculating $-\nabla V$.

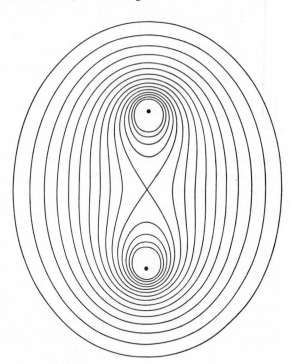

Figure 4-26

Equipotentials for a charged ring. None are shown in the vicinity of the ring, where they are too close together to be depicted graphically. At about two diameters from the ring the equipotentials are approximately circular, and the field is quite similar to that of a point charge.

4.7. Solutions of Poisson's Equation

We have as yet dealt only with solutions to Laplace's equation, since we have concerned ourselves only with cases in which the charge density ρ is zero. As we pointed out earlier, however, there are important fields in which a *space charge* exists and in which ρ is not zero. For these, we must find a solution of

Poisson's equation, and again the solution must be consistent with the boundary conditions which obtain in the particular problem. We have already shown in Section 4.2 that the solution is unique.

4.7.1. The Vacuum Diode. As an example of such a field let us find the potential distribution between the plates of a vacuum diode whose cathode and anode are plane parallel surfaces separated by a distance which is small compared to their linear extent. The anode is maintained at a positive potential V_0 relative to the cathode whose potential we shall take to be zero. The cathode is heated in order that electrons will be emitted thermionically and will be accelerated toward the anode under the action of the electric field. We shall assume that the electrons are emitted with zero velocity and that the current is not limited by the cathode temperature but can be increased at will by increasing V_0.

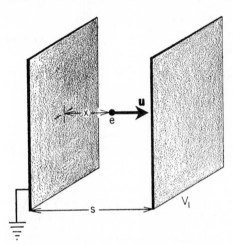

Since the electrons move in the space between the plates with finite velocity, they constitute a space charge whose density ρ is given by

$$\rho = \frac{J}{u}, \qquad (4\text{-}202)$$

Figure 4-27. *A plane-parallel vacuum diode. The cathode is grounded, and the anode is at a potential V_1. An electron of charge e moves toward the plate with a velocity **u**.*

where J is the current density in amperes/meter^2 at a point where the electron velocity is u meters/second. The space charge density ρ is then measured in coulombs/meter^3; since the electron carries a negative charge, ρ is negative. The current density J is also negative, since we take the velocity u as positive for motion from cathode to anode, as in Figure 4-27.

Since the potential can depend only on the coordinate x in the direction perpendicular to the plates, Poisson's equation reduces to

$$\frac{d^2V}{dx^2} = -\frac{\rho}{\epsilon_0}. \qquad (4\text{-}203)$$

Thus the second derivative of V with respect to x is everywhere positive, since ρ is a negative quantity, and, for a given potential difference between the plates, V is everywhere lower than the corresponding free space value.

Expressing ρ in terms of the current density J and of the velocity u, we have

$$\frac{d^2V}{dx^2} = \frac{J}{\epsilon_0 u}, \qquad (4\text{-}204)$$

where we now take J to be the magnitude of the current density, as read on a meter, without regard to sign.

From the conservation of energy, the velocity u is given by

$$\frac{1}{2} mu^2 = eV, \qquad (4\text{-}205)$$

where m is the mass of the electron. Substituting this value of u into Eq. *4-204* gives

$$\frac{d^2V}{dx^2} = \frac{J}{\epsilon_0}\left(\frac{m}{2eV}\right)^{1/2}. \qquad (4\text{-}206)$$

This equation can be integrated easily by first multiplying the left side by $2(dV/dx)\,dx$ and the right side by $2\,dV$, which are equivalent factors. Thus

$$\left(\frac{dV}{dx}\right)^2 = 4\frac{J}{\epsilon_0}\left(\frac{m}{2e}\right)^{1/2} V^{1/2} + A, \qquad (4\text{-}207)$$

where A is a constant of integration which can be evaluated from the magnitude of dV/dx at the cathode, where V is zero.

In the present case, $dV/dx = 0$ at the cathode, as can be seen from the following. If we establish the potential difference V_0 between the plates when the cathode is cold, that is, with no electrons available, the electric field intensity E_c at the surface of the cathode is positive and equal to V_0/s. But if we heat the cathode, electrons are emitted, the space charge is established, and E_c diminishes. If an unlimited supply of electrons is available, the space charge increases, and E_c falls until equilibrium is reached. As long as E_c is positive, the electrons emitted are accelerated toward the anode and cannot return to the cathode. The current is then limited by the cathode emission and not by V_0, as we assumed at the beginning. On the other hand, if E_c were negative the electrons could never leave the cathode and we would have no space charge. Thus E_c cannot be either positive or negative. At equilibrium, $E_c = 0$, thus the constant of integration A in Eq. *4-207* must be zero. Then

$$\frac{dV}{dx} = 2\left(\frac{J}{\epsilon_0}\right)^{1/2}\left(\frac{m}{2e}\right)^{1/4} V^{1/4}, \qquad (4\text{-}208)$$

and

$$V^{3/4} = \frac{3}{2}\left(\frac{J}{\epsilon_0}\right)^{1/2}\left(\frac{m}{2e}\right)^{1/4} x + B. \qquad (4\text{-}209)$$

The constant of integration B is zero since $V = 0$ at $x = 0$, and so

$$V = \left(\frac{9}{4}\frac{J}{\epsilon_0}\right)^{2/3}\left(\frac{m}{2e}\right)^{1/3} s^{4/3} \left(\frac{x}{s}\right)^{4/3}. \qquad (4\text{-}210)$$

When $x = s$, $V = V_0$, and so Eq. *4-210* can be written as

$$V = V_0 \left(\frac{x}{s}\right)^{4/3}. \qquad (4\text{-}211)$$

Expressing the field intensity E, the current density J, and the charge density ρ in similar fashion, we find that

$$E = \frac{4}{3}\frac{V_0}{s}\left(\frac{x}{s}\right)^{1/3},$$ (4-212)

$$J = \frac{4\epsilon_0}{9}\left(\frac{2e}{m}\right)^{1/2}\left(\frac{V_0^{3/2}}{s^2}\right),$$ (4-213)

$$= 2.335 \times 10^{-6}\frac{V^{3/2}}{s^2}$$ (amperes/meter^2).   (4-214)

Thus

$$\rho = \frac{4\epsilon_0}{9s^2}V_0\left(\frac{x}{s}\right)^{-2/3}.$$ (4-215)

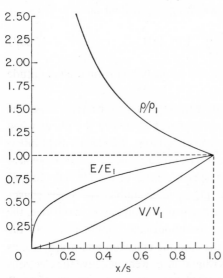

Figure 4-28. *The space charges density ρ, the electric field intensity E, and the electrostatic potential V as functions of the distance from the cathode in a plane-parallel infinite diode. The index 1 refers to the value at the anode. The distance between cathode and anode is s.*

Equation *4-214*, which is known as the *Child-Langmuir law*, is valid only for the plane parallel diode and for electrons emitted with zero velocity. Figure 4-28 shows the distribution of potential V, electric field intensity E, and charge density ρ in the plane parallel diode. One can show,[*] however, that, in general, no matter what the geometry of the diode may be, the current is related to the potential difference between cathode and anode by the relation

$$J = KV^{3/2},$$ (4-216)

where K is a constant.

In an actual diode, electrons are emitted with finite velocities, and the equilibrium field intensity E_c at the cathode is negative. In this case, a potential minimum is established at a small distance in front of the cathode and only electrons with velocities greater than a critical value can get past the potential minimum, which is a potential energy maximum for electrons.

4.8. Summary

In this chapter we have dealt with electrostatic problems which cannot easily be solved by direct integration from Coulomb's law or by application of Gauss's law. We have sought solutions of Poisson's equation

[*] K. R. Spangenberg, *Fundamentals of Electron Devices* (McGraw-Hill, 1957), p. 169.

$$\nabla^2 V = -\rho/\epsilon_0 \qquad (4\text{-}1)$$

or, more often, of Laplace's equation

$$\nabla^2 V = 0. \qquad (4\text{-}2)$$

The solutions of these equations must always be consistent with certain *boundary conditions* which necessarily prevail between different media.

(1) For charge distributions of finite extent the potential V must go to zero at infinity; it must be constant throughout a conductor; and it must be continuous across any physical boundary.

(2) The normal component of the displacement vector $\mathbf{D}$ differs on the two sides of a boundary by the free charge density σ residing on the boundary.

(3) The tangential component of the field intensity $\mathbf{E}$ is continuous across a boundary.

We showed that a potential V which satisfies both Poisson's equation and the pertinent boundary conditions is the only possible potential. Thus, any potential we can devise, whether by intuitive or formal methods, is the correct one. This is the *uniqueness theorem*.

We discussed the method of *images*, in which an electrostatic problem is converted into an equivalent problem which is simpler to solve. This method is particularly appropriate for point charges near conductors; we used it for the case of a point charge and a conducting plane, for the case of a point charge and a conducting sphere, and for the case of a sphere near a conducting plane. We showed that the electrostatic forces calculated for the image problem are the same as for the equivalent arrangement of charges and conductors which the images replace. We also showed how to find the field intensities by image methods in the case of a point charge near a dielectric slab.

We next found general solutions of Laplace's equation, such solutions being known as harmonic functions. We looked for solutions by the process of variable separation, first in rectangular coordinates. In this process we seek solutions of the form

$$V = X(x)Y(y)Z(z), \qquad (4\text{-}73)$$

where $X(x)$, $Y(y)$, and $Z(z)$ are functions only of x, y, and z, respectively. We showed that such solutions exist and that by taking linear combinations of them we can satisfy arbitrary boundary conditions. We showed how to find the solutions for two grounded, semi-infinite, parallel electrodes terminated by a plane electrode at a potential V_0, as well as for a pair of parallel plates extending to infinity in one direction and terminated by electrodes at arbitrary potentials on the other two sides. The series of sine and cosine terms which we use in rectangular coordinates to fit arbitrary boundary conditions are known as

Fourier series. The coefficients of the various terms in the series can be evaluated through the orthogonality of the sine and cosine functions. For example,

$$\int_0^b C_n \sin \frac{n\pi y}{b} \sin \frac{p\pi y}{b} \, dy = \begin{cases} 0 & \text{if } p \neq n, \\ C_n \dfrac{b}{2} & \text{if } p = n. \end{cases} \tag{4-95}$$

In spherical coordinates Laplace's equation was solved by the method of variable separation. We restricted ourselves to problems of axial symmetry, in which the potential is independent of the azimuth angle ϕ. In seeking solutions of the form

$$V(r, \theta) = R(r) \, \Theta(\theta), \tag{4-110}$$

we were led to two ordinary differential equations:

$$r^2 \frac{d^2 R}{dr^2} + 2r \frac{dR}{dr} - n(n+1)r = 0, \tag{4-115}$$

and Legendre's equation,

$$\frac{d}{d\mu} \left[(1 - \mu^2) \frac{d\Theta}{d\theta} \right] + n(n+1)\Theta = 0, \tag{4-121}$$

where $\mu = \cos \theta$.

The first equation is readily solved by functions of the type

$$R(r) = Ar^n + \frac{B}{r^{n+1}}. \tag{4-116}$$

The solutions of Legendre's equation are called *Legendre polynomials*, which we denote by $P_n(\cos \theta)$, there being a different polynomial for each value of the index n. We built up a set of these polynomials by making use of a property of harmonic functions, namely, that the derivative of such a function with respect to a rectangular coordinate is also a solution. The general form of the solutions we found by this method is

$$P_n(\cos \theta) = \frac{1}{2^n n!} \frac{\partial^n}{\partial(\cos \theta)^n} (\cos^2 \theta - 1)^n. \tag{4-138}$$

The general solution of Laplace's equation in spherical coordinates, if we assume axial symmetry, is then

$$V = \sum_{n=0}^{\infty} A_n r^n P_n(\cos \theta) + \sum_{n=0}^{\infty} B_n r^{-(n+1)} P_n(\cos \theta). \tag{4-139}$$

The individual terms of this equation constitute a complete set of functions; any arbitrary boundary value of the potential having axial symmetry can be satisfied with such a series. The coefficients in the series can be determined by using the specified potentials on the boundaries and by using the orthogonality property of the Legendre functions:

$$\int_{-1}^{+1} P_m(\cos\theta) P_n(\cos\theta)\, d(\cos\theta) = \begin{cases} 0 & \text{if } m \neq n \\ \dfrac{2}{2n+1} & \text{if } m = n. \end{cases} \qquad (4\text{-}140)$$

We used the general equation *4-139* to solve several typical problems: a conducting sphere in a uniform electrostatic field, which we examined from several points of view, a dielectric sphere in a uniform electrostatic field, and a uniformly charged ring.

We finally discussed the solution of Poisson's equation for the parallel-plate vacuum diode. This leads to the *Child-Langmuir law* relating the current density J to the potential difference V_0 between the plates:

$$J = \frac{4\epsilon_0}{9}\left(\frac{2e}{m}\right)^{1/2}\left(\frac{V_0^{3/2}}{s^2}\right). \qquad (4\text{-}213)$$

Problems

4-1. Two infinite conducting planes intersect at right angles, the line of intersection being the x-axis and the planes being the xz- and xy-planes. A charge Q is placed in the yz-plane at a distance a from the y-axis and b from the z-axis. Use the method of images to find the field intensity $\mathbf{E}$ at the surface of each conductor.

Compute the surface charge density σ.

Find the force $\mathbf{F}$ on the charge Q.

4-2. A conducting sphere of radius R bearing a charge Q is at a distance $d = 3R$ from an infinite, grounded, conducting plane. Determine the potential of the sphere within one percent.

4-3. The centers of two conducting spheres are separated by 25 centimeters. The radius of the first is 5 centimeters, and that of the second is 10 centimeters. The potential of the first is 10 volts; the second is grounded. What is the charge on each sphere, within one percent?

4-4. A grounded metal sphere of radius R is under the influence of an external point charge Q at point P. What fraction of the induced charge on the sphere can be seen from P?

4-5. A thin conducting spherical shell of radius a contains within it a point charge Q at a distance r from the center. Find, by the method of images, the charge density induced on the outside surface of the sphere.

Find also the force $\mathbf{F}$ on the charge Q.

Is the equilibrium point at the center stable, unstable, or neutral?

4-6. A charge Q is situated between two horizontal parallel conducting plates separated by a distance s. The charge Q is at a distance x above the lower plate. Calculate, the force due to the image charges, in the form of an infinite series.

Find an approximate value for the force when Q is situated (a) near one of the plates and (b) near the position $x = s/2$.

In the Millikan oil-drop experiment a small oil droplet carrying a few excess electrons is situated in the electric field between two charged parallel plates separated by a distance s. The force on the droplet is calculated from the electric field V/s, where V is the difference in potential between the plates. The above image force is neglected. Is this serious?

4-7. Find the force of attraction (or repulsion) between a point charge q and a conducting sphere of radius R carrying a charge Q if the distance from q to the center of the sphere is d.

Under what circumstances can this force be attractive even though q and Q are of the same sign?

How can you explain such an attractive force?

4-8. The energy of a point dipole $\mathbf{p}$ in a field $\mathbf{E}$ is $W = -\mathbf{p} \cdot \mathbf{E}$. Use the method of images to find the energy of a dipole $\mathbf{p}$ at a distance d from an infinite, grounded, conducting plane when the angle between $\mathbf{p}$ and the normal to the plane is θ.

Find the force and torque on the dipole due to the induced charges on the plane.

4-9. In Section 4.4 we calculated the surface charge density σ' induced on the plane surface of a block of dielectric by a point charge Q at a distance D in front of it. Show that this surface charge density and Q give the correct electrostatic potential V (a) at the foot of the perpendicular drawn from Q to the dielectric surface and (b) at a distance D behind the boundary.

4-10. A point charge Q is embedded in a semi-infinite, Class A dielectric block of dielectric coefficient K_e at a distance d below the surface. An induced charge density σ' is produced on the surface of the dielectric at the foot of the perpendicular drawn from Q to the surface. What is the sign of the induced charge?

In terms of σ', what is the electric field intensity (a) just inside the surface and (b) just outside the surface?

Calculate the magnitude of σ'. Do not attempt to use the method of images; start with more fundamental principles.

Show that your resulting field intensity, when σ' is substituted into the above results, satisfies the proper boundary conditions at the surface of the dielectric.

4-11. A point charge Q is situated midway between the plane and parallel faces of two large blocks of dielectric separated by a distance $2s$. Show that an infinite number of image charges are required to describe the field in the region between the dielectric blocks.

Draw a table showing the sign, magnitude, and position of the first six.

4-12. According to the uniqueness theorem, the Poisson equation $\nabla^2 V = -\rho/\epsilon_0$ can have only one solution if the potential V is determined at the boundaries of the field. Show that two solutions can differ at most by a constant if the normal component of ∇V is determined everywhere at the boundaries.

4-13. Are there solutions to Laplace's equation of the form $V(x, y, z) = X(x) + Y(y) + Z(z)$? Would such solutions be useful? Discuss.

4-14. Show that a harmonic function F is uniquely determined at all points within a given region by its value at the boundary.

Show also that F is identically equal to zero throughout the region if it vanishes at all points of its boundary.

4-15. Use the fact that $1/r$ is a solution of Laplace's equation to show that
$f = a \dfrac{\partial}{\partial x}\left(\dfrac{1}{r}\right)$, $g = b \dfrac{\partial^2}{\partial x^2}\left(\dfrac{1}{r}\right)$, and $h = c \dfrac{\partial^2}{\partial x\, \partial z}\left(\dfrac{1}{r}\right)$ are also solutions when a, b, and c are constants.

What arrangements of charges would produce the potentials f, g, and h?

4-16. Show that a sum of terms of the form $r^n \sin n\theta$ and $r^n \cos n\theta$, where n is any positive or negative integer, is a solution of Laplace's equation in two dimensions.

4-17. A linear distribution of charge, λ coulombs/meter, extends along the z-axis from $z = -a$ to $z = +a$. Show that the electrostatic potential V at any point for which $r > a$ is given by

$$4\pi\epsilon_0 V = \frac{2\lambda a}{r} P_0(\cos\theta) + \frac{2\lambda a^3}{3r^3} P_2(\cos\theta) + \frac{2\lambda a^5}{5r^5} P_4(\cos\theta) + \cdots .$$

4-18. With the electrode arrangement of Section 4.5.2 calculate the potential at $x = 0$, using the first five terms of the series. Perform the calculation for $y = 0.1b$, $0.2b$, and so on. Repeat the calculation at $x = b$, using only the first term of the series.

4-19. With the electrode arrangement of Section 4.5.3 calculate the potential at $x = 0$, using the first five terms of the series. Calculate V for $y = 0.1b, 0.2b$, and so on. Set $V_1 = V_2$.

4-20. Show that $V = -E_0[1 - (a^2/r^2)]r \cos\theta$ is the potential in the vicinity of a grounded, infinite, circular cylindrical conductor introduced into a previously uniform electrostatic field of intensity E_0, provided the axis of the cylinder is perpendicular to E_0.

4-21. A small hemispherical bump is raised on the inner surface of one plate of a parallel-plate capacitor. Find the resulting potential between the plates.

4-22. A grounded conducting sphere of radius a has point charges $+Q$ and $-Q$ situated on an extended diameter at distances $D > a$ to the right and left, respectively. Find the magnitude and position of the image charges within the sphere.

Now let D and Q approach infinity in such a way that Q/D^2 remains constant. Find the potential and field outside the sphere due to the image charges. Find the field in the vicinity of the sphere due to the charges $\pm Q$. Superposition of the two fields gives the field due to all the charges.

Find the surface charge density induced on the outside of the sphere. This is another way of calculating the field around an uncharged, conducting sphere introduced into a previously uniform field.

4-23. A charge Q is uniformly distributed throughout the volume of an ellipsoid of revolution whose semi-major axis is a and whose semi-minor axes are b. Find the electrostatic potential at any point in space outside the ellipsoid.

4-24. A hollow dielectric sphere with inner and outer radii a and $2a$, respectively, and dielectric coefficient $K_e = 3$ is placed in a previously uniform field E_0. Show that $E = (27/34)E_0$ in the hollow.

CHAPTER 5

Magnetic Fields of Steady Currents

Our discussion of electromagnetic field theory has been limited so far to the effects of charges at rest. We shall now discuss in this chapter the fields produced by charges in uniform motion, that is, by steady currents. In general, our results will also be applicable to time-dependent currents, provided that the rates of change are not too great. We shall point out the limits of applicability of our results where necessary.

5.1. Magnetic Forces

It is common laboratory experience that circuits carrying electric currents exert forces on each other. For example, the force between two parallel wires carrying currents I_a and I_b is proportional to $I_a I_b / \rho$, where ρ is the distance between the wires (Section 5.2.2). The force is attractive if the currents flow in the same direction and is repulsive if they flow in opposite directions. There is good evidence that all magnetic effects have their origin in charges moving in some way, the motion being either a translation, as in an electric current, or a rotation about an axis, as in a spinning electron.

In the general case of a pair of currents, as in Figure 5-1, the force which one current exerts on the other when both are in free space is given by a more complex expression, but it is again proportional to the product $I_a I_b$. It has been found experimentally to be

$$\mathbf{F}_{ab} = \frac{\mu_0}{4\pi} I_a I_b \oint_a \oint_b \frac{\mathbf{dl}_a \times (\mathbf{dl}_b \times \mathbf{r}_1)}{r^2}, \tag{5-1}$$

where $\mathbf{F}_{ab}$ is the force exerted *on* current I_a *by* current I_b, and where the line integrals are evaluated over the two wires. This is the *magnetic force law*. The vectors $\mathbf{dl}_a$ and $\mathbf{dl}_b$ point in the directions of positive current flow; $\mathbf{r}_1$ is a unit vector pointing from $\mathbf{dl}_b$ to $\mathbf{dl}_a$; and r is the distance between the two elements $\mathbf{dl}_a$ and $\mathbf{dl}_b$. The force is measured in newtons, the current in amperes, and the lengths in meters.

The meaning of the above double integral is as follows. We choose a fixed element $\mathbf{dl}_a$ on circuit a and add the vectors $\mathbf{dl}_a \times (\mathbf{dl}_b \times \mathbf{r}_1)/r^2$ corresponding to each element $\mathbf{dl}_b$ of circuit b. We then repeat the operation for all the other elements $\mathbf{dl}_a$ of circuit a and, finally, calculate the overall sum (In general, this integration cannot be performed analytically. We then divide the circuits into small finite elements and evaluate the sum numerically).

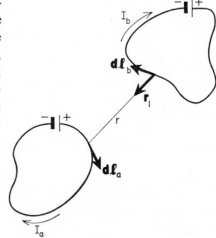

The constant μ_0 is called the *permeability of free space* and is *arbitrarily* taken to be *exactly*

$$4\pi \times 10^{-7} \text{ newton/ampere}^2$$

in rationalized m.k.s. units.

Since the constant of proportionality is fixed with absolute accuracy, Eq. *5-1* is

Figure 5-1. *Two currents I_a and I_b.*

used to define the magnitude of the ampere, as we shall see later on. It is also used to define the coulomb, since the ampere is a current of one coulomb/second.

Coulomb's law, Eq. *2-1*, gave us the force of interaction between stationary charges. The magnetic force law now states the force between charges moving with uniform velocities. In both laws there are constants of proportionality, ϵ_0 and μ_0, and it is the latter which is defined arbitrarily. The coulomb is thus defined not from Coulomb's law but from the magnetic force law. Thus it turns out experimentally that the value of ϵ_0 in Coulomb's law must be 8.85×10^{-12} farads/meter, as stated previously.

The force $\mathbf{F}_{ab}$ is expressed above in such a fashion that $\mathbf{dl}_a$ and $\mathbf{dl}_b$ do not play symmetrical roles. This is quite disturbing, since, from Newton's third law, we expect $\mathbf{F}_{ab}$ to equal $\mathbf{F}_{ba}$. The force $\mathbf{F}_{ab}$ can be expressed in a symmetrical and somewhat simpler form by expanding the triple vector product under the integral:

$$\frac{\mathbf{dl}_a \times (\mathbf{dl}_b \times \mathbf{r}_1)}{r^2} = \frac{\mathbf{dl}_b(\mathbf{dl}_a \cdot \mathbf{r}_1)}{r^2} - \frac{\mathbf{r}_1(\mathbf{dl}_a \cdot \mathbf{dl}_b)}{r^2}. \tag{5-2}$$

We can now show that the double integral of the first term on the right is zero:

$$\oint_a \oint_b \mathbf{dl}_b \frac{\mathbf{r}_1 \cdot \mathbf{dl}_a}{r^2} = \oint_b \mathbf{dl}_b \oint_a \frac{\mathbf{r}_1}{r^2} \cdot \mathbf{dl}_a, \tag{5-3}$$

or, from Problem 1-21,

$$\oint_a \oint_b d\mathbf{l}_b \frac{\mathbf{r}_1 \cdot d\mathbf{l}_a}{r^2} = -\oint_b d\mathbf{l}_b \oint_a \boldsymbol{\nabla} \left(\frac{1}{r}\right) \cdot d\mathbf{l}_a, \qquad (5\text{-}4)$$

where the gradient involves derivatives with respect to the coordinates of a point on circuit a. Then, from Stokes's theorem,

$$\oint_a \oint_b d\mathbf{l}_b \frac{\mathbf{r}_1 \cdot d\mathbf{l}_a}{r^2} = -\oint_b d\mathbf{l}_b \int_{S_a} \boldsymbol{\nabla} \times \boldsymbol{\nabla} \left(\frac{1}{r}\right) \cdot d\mathbf{a}_a = 0, \qquad (5\text{-}5)$$

where S_a is any surface bounded by circuit a. The last integral is zero, since the curl of a gradient is identically equal to zero.

We are thus left with the double integral of only the second term for the triple vector product $d\mathbf{l}_a \times (d\mathbf{l}_b \times \mathbf{r}_1)$, and

$$\mathbf{F}_{ab} = -\frac{\mu_0}{4\pi} I_a I_b \oint_a \oint_b \frac{\mathbf{r}_1 (d\mathbf{l}_a \cdot d\mathbf{l}_b)}{r^2}. \qquad (5\text{-}6)$$

We now have $\mathbf{F}_{ab} = -\mathbf{F}_{ba}$, since the unit vector $\mathbf{r}_1$ is directed toward the circuit on which the force is to be calculated, with the result that it is oriented in one direction for $\mathbf{F}_{ab}$ and in the opposite direction for $\mathbf{F}_{ba}$. Newton's third law therefore applies.

5.2. The Magnetic Induction B.
The Biot-Savart Law

Despite the fact that the above integral for $\mathbf{F}_{ab}$ is simpler and more symmetrical than that of Eq. *5-1*, it is not as interesting. The reason is that, with the above integral, the force cannot be expressed as the interaction of current a with the field of current b. We can perform such an operation on Eq. *5-1*, however, since

$$\mathbf{F}_{ab} = I_a \oint_a d\mathbf{l}_a \times \left(\frac{\mu_0}{4\pi} I_b \oint \frac{d\mathbf{l}_b \times \mathbf{r}_1}{r^2}\right), \qquad (5\text{-}7)$$

$$= I_a \oint_a d\mathbf{l}_a \times \mathbf{B}_b, \qquad (5\text{-}8)$$

where

$$\mathbf{B}_b = \frac{\mu_0}{4\pi} I_b \oint_b \frac{d\mathbf{l}_b \times \mathbf{r}_1}{r^2} \qquad (5\text{-}9)$$

can be taken to be the field of circuit b at the position of the element $d\mathbf{l}_a$ of circuit a.

The vector $\mathbf{B}$ is called the *magnetic induction*. It is expressed in webers/meter², the weber being a volt-second:

$$1 \text{ weber/meter}^2 = 10^4 \text{ gauss}.$$

The gauss is not an m.k.s. unit, but it is frequently used because of its convenient order of magnitude.

The above equation for **B** is called the *Biot-Savart law*. The integration can be performed analytically only for the simplest geometrical forms. It shows that the element of force **dF** on an element of wire of length **dl** carrying a current I in a region where the magnetic induction is **B** is given by

$$d\mathbf{F} = I\,d\mathbf{l} \times \mathbf{B}. \tag{5-10}$$

If the current I is distributed in space with a current density **J** amperes/meter², then I becomes $J\,da$ and must be put under the integral sign. Then $J\,da\,d\mathbf{l}$ can be written as $\mathbf{J}\,d\tau$, where $d\tau$ is an element of volume. Thus, in the general case, the magnetic induction **B** at a point in space is given by

$$\mathbf{B} = \frac{\mu_0}{4\pi} \int_\tau \frac{\mathbf{J} \times \mathbf{r}_1}{r^2}\,d\tau, \tag{5-11}$$

where the integration is carried out over any volume τ which includes all the currents.

It may well be asked here whether the above integral can be used to calculate **B** at a point inside a current-carrying conductor. Since r is the distance between the point of observation where **B** is measured and the point where the current density is **J**, it appears, at first sight, that the contribution of the local current density will be infinite because of the $1/r^2$ factor. The integral does not, in fact, diverge; it *does* apply within current carrying conductors. This can be seen by analogy with electrostatics, where the same problem arises in calculating the electric field intensity **E** inside a charge distribution. The components of **B** and of **E** both vary as $1/r^2$. Since those of **E** do remain finite within a charge distribution, those of **B** must also remain finite within a current distribution. It is assumed that both the charge density and the current density are finite.

Just as in electrostatics, where we considered lines of force to describe an electric field, we can draw *lines of magnetic induction* which are everywhere tangent to the direction of **B**.

Similarly, it is convenient to use the concept of *flux*, the flux of the magnetic induction **B** through a surface S being defined as the normal component of **B** integrated over S:

$$\Phi = \int_S \mathbf{B}\cdot d\mathbf{a}. \tag{5-12}$$

5.2.1. The Magnetic Induction Due to a Current Flowing in a Long Straight Wire. In a long straight wire carrying a current I, as in Figure 5-2, an element $I\,dl$ of the current will produce a magnetic induction dB as shown in the figure:

$$dB = \frac{\mu_0 I}{4\pi} \frac{dl \sin \phi}{r^2}. \tag{5-13}$$

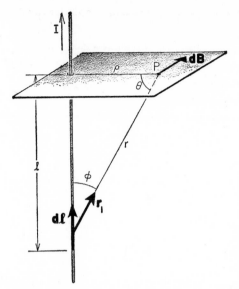

Figure 5-2

The magnetic induction **dB** *produced by an element* I **dl** *of an infinitely long straight current. The vector* **dB** *lies in a plane that is perpendicular to the wire and which passes through P.*

Expressing dl, $\sin\phi$, and r^2 in terms of the angle θ, we find that

$$B = \frac{\mu_0 I}{4\pi\rho} \int_{-\frac{\pi}{2}}^{+\frac{\pi}{2}} \cos\theta \, d\theta = \frac{\mu_0 I}{2\pi\rho}. \tag{5-14}$$

The magnitude of **B** thus falls off inversely as the *first* power of the distance from an infinitely long wire and is in the direction perpendicular to a plane containing the wire. The lines of **B** are circles lying in a plane perpendicular to the wire and are centered on it.

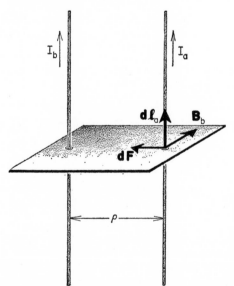

Figure 5-3

Two long parallel wires carrying currents in the same direction. The element of force **dF** *acting on the element* **dl**$_a$ *is in the direction shown.*

5.2.2. Force Between Two Long Parallel Wires. Definition of the Ampere.
Let us now examine the force between two infinitely long parallel wires carrying
currents I_a and I_b, separated by a distance ρ, as in Figure 5-3. The current I_b
produces a magnetic induction B_b as in the above equation at the position of
the current I_a. The force **dF** acting on an element dl_a of this current is then

$$\mathbf{dF} = I_a(\mathbf{dl}_a \times \mathbf{B}_b), \qquad (5\text{-}15)$$

$$dF = \frac{I_a \, dl_a \, \mu_0 \, I_b}{2\pi\rho}, \qquad (5\text{-}16)$$

and the force per unit length is

$$\frac{dF}{dl_a} = \frac{\mu_0 I_a I_b}{2\pi\rho}. \qquad (5\text{-}17)$$

The force is attractive if the currents are in the same direction and is repulsive
if they are in opposite directions.

   This equation provides us with a *definition of the ampere:* two long parallel
wires separated by a distance of one
meter exert on each other a force of
2×10^{-7} newton per meter of length
when the current in each is one ampere. This assumes that the diameters
of the wires are negligible compared
to their separation.

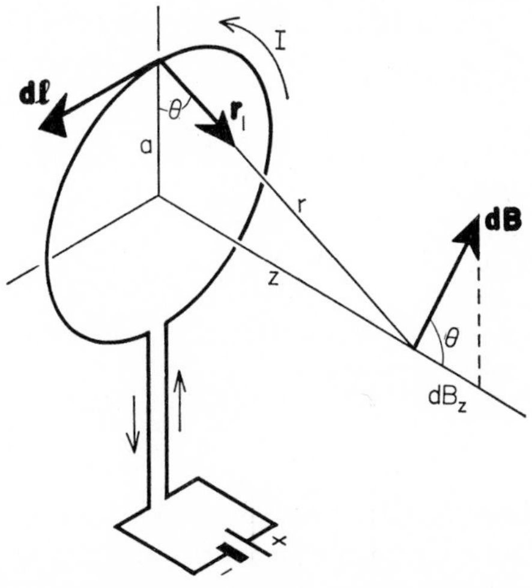

5.2.3. The Circular Loop. As a second example of the calculation of the
magnetic induction vector, we shall
determine the magnitude and direction of **B** on the axis of a circular
loop of radius a carrying a current
I, as in Figure 5-4. Points off the
axis will be considered in Section
5.12.3.

   An element I **dl** of current produces
a magnetic induction **dB** as indicated

Figure 5-4. *The magnetic induction* **dB**
produced by an element I **dl** *at a point on
the axis of circular current loop of radius
a. The projection of* **dB** *on the axis is* **dB**$_z$.

in the figure. By symmetry, the total magnetic induction will be along the axis,
and we need to calculate only dB_z:

$$dB_z = \frac{\mu_0 I}{4\pi} \frac{dl}{r^2} \cos\theta, \qquad (5\text{-}18)$$

hence

$$B_z = \frac{\mu_0 I}{4\pi} \frac{2\pi a}{r^2} \cos\theta, \qquad (5\text{-}19)$$

$$B_z = \frac{\mu_0 I a^2}{2(a^2 + z^2)^{3/2}}. \qquad (5\text{-}20)$$

The magnetic induction is maximum in the plane of the ring and drops off as z^3 for $z^2 \gg a^2$.

5.3. The Lorentz Force on a Point Charge Moving in a Magnetic Field

Let us now return to Eq. 5-8. The force on a current element $I\,\mathbf{dl}$ is

$$\mathbf{dF} = I\,\mathbf{dl} \times \mathbf{B} \qquad (5\text{-}21)$$

when the magnetic induction is $\mathbf{B}$.

Now, in terms of the current density $\mathbf{J}$ and of the cross-sectional area da of the conductor,

$$I\,\mathbf{dl} = \mathbf{J}\,da\,dl, \qquad (5\text{-}22)$$

$$= \mathbf{J}\,d\tau, \qquad (5\text{-}23)$$

where $d\tau$ is an element of volume with cross-sectional area da and length dl. Then

$$\mathbf{dF} = \mathbf{J} \times \mathbf{B}\,d\tau, \qquad (5\text{-}24)$$

or

$$\frac{\mathbf{dF}}{d\tau} = \mathbf{J} \times \mathbf{B}. \qquad (5\text{-}25)$$

If we set

$$\mathbf{J} = nQ\mathbf{u}, \qquad (5\text{-}26)$$

where n is the number of charge carriers per unit volume, Q is the charge on each one, and $\mathbf{u}$ is the average velocity of each carrier, then

$$\frac{1}{n}\frac{\mathbf{dF}}{d\tau} = Q(\mathbf{u} \times \mathbf{B}). \qquad (5\text{-}27)$$

Since $n\,d\tau$ is the number of charge carriers in the volume element $d\tau$, $\mathbf{dF}/(n\,d\tau)$ is the force per charge carrier, which we shall call $\mathbf{f}$.

The magnetic force on an individual charge is therefore

$$\mathbf{f} = Q(\mathbf{u} \times \mathbf{B}). \qquad (5\text{-}28)$$

This is known as the *Lorentz force*. It is perpendicular both to the velocity $\mathbf{u}$ and to the magnetic induction $\mathbf{B}$.

If we add to this the force which may arise from the presence of an electric field $\mathbf{E}$, the total force on a charge Q moving with a velocity $\mathbf{u}$ in both an electric and a magnetic field is

$$\mathbf{f} = Q[\mathbf{E} + (\mathbf{u} \times \mathbf{B})]. \qquad (5\text{-}29)$$

5.3.1. The Parallel-plate Magnetron. As an example of the motion of a charged particle under the action of both electric and magnetic fields, let us consider the parallel-plate magnetron shown in Figure 5-5. A uniform electric field $E = V/s$ is established between the plates of a parallel-plate capacitor, together with a uniform magnetic field B perpendicular to E. Electrons of charge $-Q$ are released with negligible velocity from the lower plate and are accelerated toward the upper plate by the electric field. Since the magnetic force is always at right angles to the velocity $\mathbf{u}$, the electrons describe a curved path.

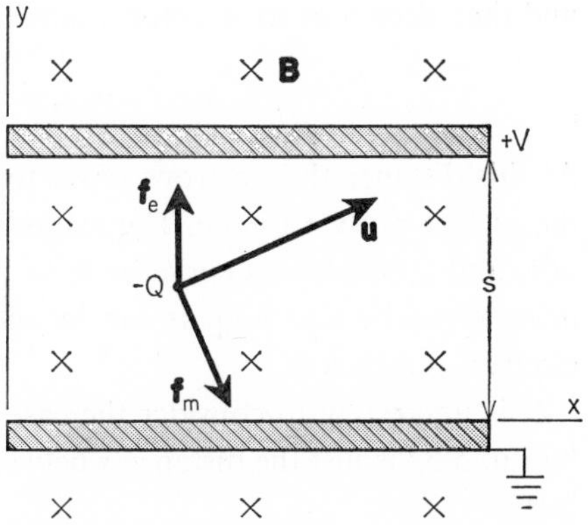

Let us find the velocity u of an electron as a function of the coordinates, of the potential V of the anode, and of the magnetic induction B. We consider an electron moving with a velocity $\mathbf{u}$ as indicated in the figure. The electric force $\mathbf{f}_e$ and the magnetic force $\mathbf{f}_m$ are as indicated, thus

$$f_x = QBu_y, \qquad (5\text{-}30)$$

or

$$m\frac{du_x}{dt} = QBu_y. \qquad (5\text{-}31)$$

Integrating this, we obtain

$$\int_0^t \frac{du_x}{dt}\,dt = \frac{Q}{m} B \int_0^t u_y\,dt, \qquad (5\text{-}32)$$

$$u_x = \frac{Q}{m} By. \qquad (5\text{-}33)$$

Figure 5-5. *Parallel-plate magnetron. The lower plate is grounded, and the upper plate is maintained at a potential V. An electron of charge −Q moves with a velocity u. The electric field exerts a force $\mathbf{f}_e$ on the electron; and the magnetic field, a force $\mathbf{f}_m$.*

The x-component of the velocity is thus proportional to y. It is zero at the cathode, and it increases with y.

We can now find the y-component of the velocity $\mathbf{u}$ from the conservation of energy. Since the magnetic force is always perpendicular to the velocity, it does no work and does not contribute to the kinetic energy of the electron. Then

$$\frac{1}{2} mu^2 = Q\frac{V}{s} y, \qquad (5\text{-}34)$$

where m is the electron's mass, which we assume to be the rest mass. Thus

$$\frac{1}{2} m(u_x^2 + u_y^2) = Q\frac{V}{s} y, \qquad (5\text{-}35)$$

$$u_y^2 = \frac{Q}{m}\left(2\frac{V}{s}y - \frac{QB^2}{m}y^2\right). \tag{5-36}$$

The y-component of the velocity is zero at the cathode. It increases at first, and then decreases to zero for a maximum y given by

$$y_{\max} = 2\,\frac{V}{s}\,\frac{m}{QB^2}. \tag{5-37}$$

At this distance the electrons move toward the right in a direction parallel to the surface of the cathode. The magnetic force is then directed toward the cathode, and the electrons curve back to it, the y-component of their velocity still being given by Eq. *5-36*. It can be shown that the trajectory described by an electron is a cycloid.

It is interesting to consider the case in which the maximum value of y given by Eq. *5-37* is just the distance s between the plates. The potential of the anode is then

$$V_{\mathrm{crit}} = \frac{1}{2}\frac{Q}{m}B^2 s^2. \tag{5-38}$$

If V is larger than this critical value, all of the electrons emitted by the cathode are collected by the anode. However, if V is smaller than V_{crit}, the electrons never reach the anode but return to the cathode.

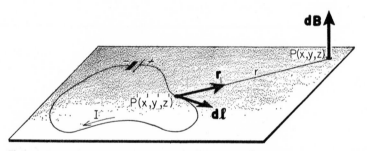

Figure 5-6. *A current element I* **dl** *at a source point P′ produces an element of magnetic induction* **dB** *at a field point P.*

5.4. The Divergence of the Magnetic Induction B.

We shall show that the divergence of the magnetic induction **B** is always zero. According to the Biot-Savart law, Eq. *5-9*,

$$\mathbf{B} = \frac{\mu_0 I}{4\pi}\oint\frac{\mathbf{dl}\times\mathbf{r}_1}{r^2}, \tag{5-39}$$

and

$$\mathbf{\nabla}\cdot\mathbf{B} = \frac{\mu_0 I}{4\pi}\mathbf{\nabla}\cdot\oint\frac{\mathbf{dl}\times\mathbf{r}_1}{r^2}, \tag{5-40}$$

where **B** is the magnetic induction at a field point $P(x, y, z)$ and the element of conductor **dl** carrying the current I is at a source point $P'(x', y', z')$, as in Figure 5-6.

Now it makes no difference whether we form the vector sum

$$(\mathbf{dl} \times \mathbf{r_1})/r^2$$

at the point P where we compute **B** and then take the divergence of the resultant vector or whether we compute first the divergence of the elementary vector $(\mathbf{dl} \times \mathbf{r_1})/r^2$ and then sum the resultant scalar quantity over all the circuit elements **dl**. That is, the differentiation and integration operations are interchangeable, thus

$$\nabla \cdot \mathbf{B} = \frac{\mu_0 I}{4\pi} \oint \nabla \cdot \left(\frac{\mathbf{dl} \times \mathbf{r_1}}{r^2} \right). \tag{5-41}$$

From Problem 1-23, we have

$$\nabla \cdot \left(\mathbf{dl} \times \frac{\mathbf{r_1}}{r^2} \right) = \frac{\mathbf{r_1}}{r^2} \cdot (\nabla \times \mathbf{dl}) - \mathbf{dl} \cdot \left(\nabla \times \frac{\mathbf{r_1}}{r^2} \right). \tag{5-42}$$

The first term on the right is zero, since **dl** is not a function of the coordinates x, y, and z of the field point P where we wish to calculate $\nabla \cdot \mathbf{B}$. Also, from Problem 1-21,

$$\nabla \times \frac{\mathbf{r_1}}{r^2} = -\nabla \times \nabla \left(\frac{1}{r} \right), \tag{5-43}$$

$$= 0, \tag{5-44}$$

since the curl of the gradient is always zero. Thus both terms on the right-hand side of Eq. *5-42* are zero, and, from Eq. *5-40*,

$$\boxed{\nabla \cdot \mathbf{B} = 0} \tag{5-45}$$

always.

This is the second of the four Maxwell equations. The first one we found was Eq. *3-58*. The present one follows directly from the Biot-Savart law for the magnetic force between currents.

The net flux of magnetic induction through any closed surface is always equal to zero, since

$$\int_S \mathbf{B} \cdot \mathbf{da} = \int_\tau (\nabla \cdot \mathbf{B}) \, d\tau. \tag{5-46}$$

$$= 0. \tag{5-47}$$

This result follows from the definition of the magnetic induction **B**, which itself is deduced from the empirical law describing the forces between current elements. There are no sources of magnetic induction at which the divergence of **B** would be different from zero, and, from Gauss's law (Section 2.4), there are no free magnetic charges corresponding to the free electrical charges in an electrostatic field.

5.5. The Vector Potential A

We have seen in Chapter 2 that the electrostatic field intensity $\mathbf{E}$ can be derived from the potential V through the relation $\mathbf{E} = -\nabla V$. We shall now show that the magnetic induction $\mathbf{B}$ is related to a certain quantity $\mathbf{A}$ through the equation $\mathbf{B} = \nabla \times \mathbf{A}$, where the vector $\mathbf{A}$ is called, by analogy, the *vector potential*. This is an important quantity; we shall have occasion to use it repeatedly both in this chapter and in Chapter 6. Later on, in Chapter 13 we shall find that V and $\mathbf{A}$ play fundamental roles in electromagnetic theory.

According to the Biot-Savart law, stated in Eq. *5-9*, the magnetic induction $\mathbf{B}$ at the point P of Figure 5-6 is given by

$$\mathbf{B} = \frac{\mu_0 I}{4\pi} \oint \frac{d\mathbf{l} \times \mathbf{r}_1}{r^2}. \tag{5-48}$$

Now, from Problem 1-21,

$$\frac{\mathbf{r}_1}{r^2} = -\nabla\left(\frac{1}{r}\right), \tag{5-49}$$

where the gradient operator implies differentiations with respect to the coordinates x, y, and z of the field point P. Then

$$\mathbf{B} = \frac{\mu_0 I}{4\pi} \oint \nabla\left(\frac{1}{r}\right) \times d\mathbf{l}. \tag{5-50}$$

We have removed the minus sign by inverting the order of the vectors in the vector product.

We may transform this equation through the vector identity of Problem 1-22:

$$\nabla \times (f\mathbf{C}) = f(\nabla \times \mathbf{C}) - (\mathbf{C} \times \nabla f). \tag{5-51}$$

Taking the scalar function to be $1/r$ and the vector function to be $d\mathbf{l}$, we obtain

$$\mathbf{B} = \frac{\mu_0 I}{4\pi}\left[\oint\left(\nabla \times \frac{d\mathbf{l}}{r}\right) - \oint\frac{1}{r}(\nabla \times d\mathbf{l})\right], \tag{5-52}$$

where the $\nabla \times$ operators again involve derivatives with respect to the coordinates x, y, and z of the field point P. Since $d\mathbf{l}$ is not a function of these coordinates, $\nabla \times d\mathbf{l}$ is zero, and

$$\mathbf{B} = \frac{\mu_0 I}{4\pi} \oint\left(\nabla \times \frac{d\mathbf{l}}{r}\right). \tag{5-53}$$

To obtain $\mathbf{B}$, we therefore compute $\nabla \times \dfrac{d\mathbf{l}}{r}$ at the point P for every element of the circuit and then add all the resulting vector elements together. Again, it makes no difference if we interchange the order of differentiation and integration, thus

$$\mathbf{B} = \frac{\mu_0 I}{4\pi} \nabla \times \left(\oint \frac{d\mathbf{l}}{r} \right), \tag{5-54}$$

$$= \nabla \times \left(\frac{\mu_0 I}{4\pi} \oint \frac{d\mathbf{l}}{r} \right), \tag{5-55}$$

$$= \nabla \times \mathbf{A}, \tag{5-56}$$

where

$$\mathbf{A} = \frac{\mu_0 I}{4\pi} \oint \frac{d\mathbf{l}}{r} \tag{5-57}$$

is the *vector potential* measured in webers/meter. If the current is distributed with a current density $\mathbf{J}$, then

$$\mathbf{A} = \frac{\mu_0}{4\pi} \int_\tau \frac{\mathbf{J}\, d\tau}{r}. \tag{5-58}$$

This integral, like that for $\mathbf{B}$, appears to diverge inside a current-carrying conductor because of the $1/r$ factor, but it actually does not. This can be seen from the fact that its components vary as $1/r$, like the electrostatic potential V, which does not diverge within a charge distribution.

Equation 5-56 relating $\mathbf{B}$ and $\mathbf{A}$ is a completely general result and is true under all circumstances, even for time-dependent currents and for points inside a conductor, where the current density is finite.

The result expressed as Eq. 5-45, namely, that

$$\nabla \cdot \mathbf{B} = 0$$

under all circumstances, follows immediately from the fact that $\mathbf{B}$ can be expressed as the curl of the vector potential $\mathbf{A}$, since the divergence of the curl of a vector is always zero, as we saw in Section 1.6.

The vector potential $\mathbf{A}$ is not uniquely defined by Eq. 5-57 or 5-58 in that we can add to it any term whose curl is zero without changing the value of $\mathbf{B}$ in any way. We have no reason at the moment to add such a term, however, and we shall use Eqs. 5-57 and 5-58 for defining the vector potential. This point will be discussed further in Chapter 13.

It must also be noted that $\mathbf{B}$ involves only the space derivatives of $\mathbf{A}$, and not the value of $\mathbf{A}$ itself. The value of $\mathbf{B}$ at a given point can thus be calculated only if $\mathbf{A}$ is known in the *region* around the point considered.

5.5.1. The Long Straight Wire.

We have already found the magnetic induction $\mathbf{B}$ for this case in Section 5.2.1, starting from the Biot-Savart law; we shall now calculate it from the vector potential $\mathbf{A}$.

Each element $I\,\mathbf{dl}$ of the current contributes to the vector potential an element

$$\mathbf{dA} = \frac{\mu_0 I}{4\pi}\frac{\mathbf{dl}}{r}, \qquad (5\text{-}59)$$

where $\mathbf{dA}$ is in the same direction as $\mathbf{dl}$. The elements $I\,\mathbf{dl}$ thus all contribute

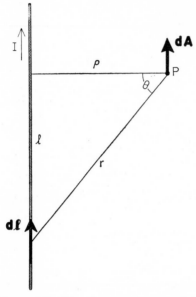

elements $\mathbf{dA}$ in the same direction. From the fundamental definition of the curl in terms of line integrals (Eq. *1-69*), and from the azimuthal symmetry of the field, $\nabla \times \mathbf{A} = \mathbf{B}$ is in the azimuthal direction around the conductor.

For an infinitely long conductor, $\mathbf{dA}$ is proportional to dl/l for values of l where $r \gg \rho$. Thus $A \longrightarrow \infty$ logarithmically. At first sight this is disturbing, but the fact that a function is infinite does not necessarily mean that its derivatives are also infinite; that is, $\mathbf{B}$ can be finite even though $\mathbf{A}$ is infinite.

Let us calculate $\mathbf{A}$ and $\mathbf{B}$ for a current of finite length, and then we can let the length go to infinity. Referring to Figure 5-7, we have

Figure 5-7. *The element of current $I\,\mathbf{dl}$ of a long straight current produces an element of vector potential $\mathbf{dA}$ at the point P.*

$$A_z = \frac{\mu_0 I}{4\pi}\int_{-L}^{L}\frac{dl}{(\rho^2 + l^2)^{1/2}}, \qquad (5\text{-}60)$$

$$A_z = \frac{\mu_0 I}{4\pi}\ln\left[l + (\rho^2 + l^2)^{1/2}\right]_{-L}^{+L}. \qquad (5\text{-}61)$$

For $L^2 \gg \rho^2$, we can expand the square root in terms of ρ^2/L^2 and keep only the lowest order term. Then

$$A_z = \frac{\mu_0 I}{4\pi}\ln\left[1 + \frac{4L^2}{\rho^2}\right]. \qquad (5\text{-}62)$$

To compute $\mathbf{B} = \nabla \times \mathbf{A}$, we use cylindrical coordinates, keeping in mind that $\mathbf{A}$ is parallel to the z-axis and is independent of ϕ:

$$\mathbf{B} = \frac{1}{\rho}\begin{vmatrix} \mathbf{i} & \mathbf{j}\rho & \mathbf{k} \\ \dfrac{\partial}{\partial\rho} & 0 & \dfrac{\partial}{\partial z} \\ 0 & 0 & A_z \end{vmatrix}, \qquad (5\text{-}63)$$

$$B_\rho = 0, \qquad (5\text{-}64)$$

$$B_z = 0, \qquad (5\text{-}65)$$

$$B_\phi = -\frac{\partial A_z}{\partial \rho}, \tag{5-66}$$

$$= \frac{\mu_0 I}{4\pi} \frac{\frac{8L^2}{\rho^3}}{1 + \frac{4L^2}{\rho^2}}, \tag{5-67}$$

$$\longrightarrow \frac{\mu_0 I}{2\pi \rho} \qquad (L \gg \rho). \tag{5-68}$$

This result is identical to Eq. *5-14*, which we deduced from the Biot-Savart law.

5.5.2. Pair of Long Parallel Wires. As a somewhat more complicated example, we now consider the case of two long parallel wires separated by a distance R and carrying currents I of equal magnitude but in opposite directions, as in Figure 5-8. We begin with wires of finite length L, use Eq. *5-62* for a single wire, and add the two vector potentials together. Then

$$A_z = \frac{\mu_0 I}{4\pi} \ln \left(\frac{\rho_a^2 + 4L^2}{\rho_a^2} \cdot \frac{\rho_b^2}{\rho_b^2 + 4L^2} \right). \tag{5-69}$$

In this case we may let $L \longrightarrow \infty$ before computing the curl, and

$$A_z = \frac{\mu_0 I}{4\pi} \ln \frac{\rho_b^2}{\rho_a^2}. \tag{5-70}$$

With the rectangular coordinates shown in Figure 5-8,

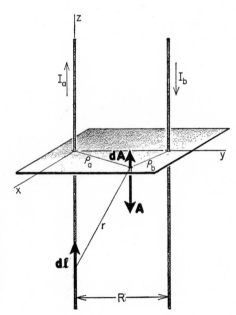

Figure 5-8

Pair of long parallel wires carrying currents of equal magnitude in opposite directions. The element of current I **dl** *produces the element of vector potential* **dA** *shown. The vector potential* **A** *is directed in the opposite direction, since the point considered is closer to* I_b *than to* I_a.

$$A_x = 0, \tag{5-71}$$

$$A_y = 0, \tag{5-72}$$

$$A_z = \frac{\mu_0 I}{4\pi} \ln\left[\frac{x^2 + (R-y)^2}{x^2 + y^2}\right], \tag{5-73}$$

$$B_x = \frac{\partial A_z}{\partial y}, \tag{5-74}$$

$$= \frac{\mu_0 I}{2\pi}\left[-\frac{(R-y)}{\rho_b^2} - \frac{y}{\rho_a^2}\right], \tag{5-75}$$

$$B_y = -\frac{\partial A_z}{\partial x}, \tag{5-76}$$

$$= -\frac{\mu_0 I}{2\pi}\left(\frac{x}{\rho_b^2} + \frac{x}{\rho_a^2}\right), \tag{5-77}$$

$$B_z = 0. \tag{5-78}$$

At the midpoint between the two conductors, where the magnitude of **B** must be double that for a single current, $x = 0$, $y = R/2$, hence

$$B_y = 0 \tag{5-79}$$

and

$$B_x = 2\frac{\mu_0 I}{2\pi\left(\dfrac{R}{2}\right)} \tag{5-80}$$

as expected.

5.6. The Line Integral of the Vector Potential A Over a Closed Curve

One interesting property of the vector potential **A** is the following. The magnetic flux Φ through a surface S is

$$\Phi = \int_S \mathbf{B} \cdot \mathbf{da}, \tag{5-81}$$

$$= \int_S \boldsymbol{\nabla} \times \mathbf{A} \cdot \mathbf{da}, \tag{5-82}$$

$$= \oint \mathbf{A} \cdot \mathbf{dl}. \tag{5-83}$$

The flux through S is thus given by the line integral of $\mathbf{A} \cdot \mathbf{dl}$ around the boundary of S. We shall use this result in Section 5.11.1, and also in the next chapter.

5.7. The Conservation of Charge
and the Equation of Continuity

Let us consider a surface S bounding a volume τ within a conductor carrying a current of density $\mathbf{J}$. According to all experiments to date, charge is always conserved, and the outward flux of $\mathbf{J}$ must therefore be equal to the rate of loss of charge within the volume:

$$\int_S \mathbf{J} \cdot \mathbf{da} = -\int_\tau \frac{\partial \rho}{\partial t}\, d\tau, \qquad (5\text{-}84)$$

where ρ is the net charge density. This is the *equation of continuity*.

Then, from the divergence theorem, we can replace the surface integral by a volume integral, and

$$\int_\tau \boldsymbol{\nabla} \cdot \mathbf{J}\, d\tau = -\int_\tau \frac{\partial \rho}{\partial t}\, d\tau. \qquad (5\text{-}85)$$

This equation being valid for all τ, we can equate the integrands, and, at every point, we then have

$$\boldsymbol{\nabla} \cdot \mathbf{J} = -\frac{\partial \rho}{\partial t}. \qquad (5\text{-}86)$$

This is the *law of conservation of charge* stated in differential form.

5.8 The Charge Density ρ in a Conductor

The above result permits us to find the charge density ρ in a conductor. The current density $\mathbf{J}$ in a conductor is given by

$$\mathbf{J} = \sigma \mathbf{E}, \qquad (5\text{-}87)$$

where σ is the conductivity. This is *Ohm's law* in its general form. As a rule, σ is a constant. Now, from Eq. 3-58,

$$\boldsymbol{\nabla} \cdot \mathbf{D} = \rho, \qquad (5\text{-}88)$$

so that

$$\boldsymbol{\nabla} \cdot \mathbf{J} = \sigma \boldsymbol{\nabla} \cdot \mathbf{E}, \qquad (5\text{-}89)$$

$$= \frac{\sigma \rho}{K_e \epsilon_0}, \qquad (5\text{-}90)$$

and, from the law of conservation of charge,

$$\frac{\partial \rho}{\partial t} = -\boldsymbol{\nabla} \cdot \mathbf{J} = -\frac{\sigma \rho}{K_e \epsilon_0}, \qquad (5\text{-}91)$$

$$\rho = \rho_0 \exp[-\sigma t / K_e \epsilon_0]. \qquad (5\text{-}92)$$

The free charge density ρ therefore decreases exponentially with time at a rate such that after a time $K_e \epsilon_0 / \sigma$, called the *relaxation time*, it is reduced to $1/e$ or

36.8% of its original value. For copper, $\sigma = 5.8 \times 10^7$ mhos/meter, and the dielectric coefficient K_e can be taken to be of the order of unity. The relaxation time is therefore of the order of 10^{-19} second. This is an extremely short time, even for optical frequencies, which are of the order of 10^{15} per second. Thus, in good conductors, the free volume charge density ρ can be set equal to zero, and any net charge density must be situated at the surface.

The time derivative of the charge density ρ is then

$$\frac{\partial \rho}{\partial t} = -\frac{\sigma}{K_e \epsilon_0} \rho_0 \exp[-\sigma t / K_e \epsilon_0], \qquad (5\text{-}93)$$

where the coefficient $\sigma / K_e \epsilon_0$ is enormous, being of the order of 10^{19} in a good conductor. This coefficient is of course most effective in the exponent, and, in a good conductor like copper, the quantity $-\nabla \cdot \mathbf{J}$ is extremely small, except over periods of time of the order of 10^{-18} second after charge has been introduced.

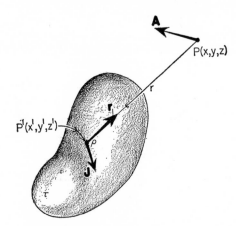

Figure 5-9

The currents within the volume τ produce a vector potential $\mathbf{A}$ at the field point $P(x, y, z)$. The current density at the source point $P'(x', y', z')$ is $\mathbf{J}$, and the charge density is ρ.

5.9. The Divergence of the Vector Potential A. The Lorentz Condition

Let us now calculate $\nabla \cdot \mathbf{A}$. From Eq. 5-58,

$$\nabla \cdot \mathbf{A} = \frac{\mu_0}{4\pi} \nabla \cdot \int_\tau \frac{\mathbf{J} \, d\tau}{r}, \qquad (5\text{-}94)$$

where $\mathbf{A}$ is evaluated at the field point $P(x, y, z)$, but where the volume element $d\tau$ is situated at the source point $P'(x', y', z')$ as in Figure 5-9. The volume τ is any volume enclosing all the currents. Since the derivatives in the divergence operator are calculated at the field point, the order of differentiation and integration is immaterial, and so

$$\nabla \cdot \mathbf{A} = \frac{\mu_0}{4\pi} \int_\tau \nabla \cdot \frac{\mathbf{J}}{r} \, d\tau. \qquad (5\text{-}95)$$

Using the vector identity of Problem 1-14, we find that

$$\mathbf{\nabla} \cdot \mathbf{A} = \frac{\mu_0}{4\pi} \left[\int_\tau \frac{\mathbf{\nabla} \cdot \mathbf{J}}{r} \, d\tau + \int_\tau \mathbf{J} \cdot \mathbf{\nabla} \left(\frac{1}{r} \right) d\tau \right]. \tag{5-96}$$

Note that **J** is not a function of the coordinates x, y, z of the field point which are involved in the operator $\mathbf{\nabla}$, but only of the coordinates x', y', and z' of the source point. Then $\mathbf{\nabla} \cdot \mathbf{J} \equiv 0$, and

$$\mathbf{\nabla} \cdot \mathbf{A} = \frac{\mu_0}{4\pi} \int_\tau \mathbf{J} \cdot \mathbf{\nabla} \left(\frac{1}{r} \right) d\tau. \tag{5-97}$$

Setting the gradient at the source point to be $\mathbf{\nabla}'(1/r)$, we have, from Problem 1-21,

$$\mathbf{\nabla} \left(\frac{1}{r} \right) = -\mathbf{\nabla}' \left(\frac{1}{r} \right), \tag{5-98}$$

thus

$$\mathbf{\nabla} \cdot \mathbf{A} = -\frac{\mu_0}{4\pi} \int_\tau \mathbf{J} \cdot \mathbf{\nabla}' \left(\frac{1}{r} \right) d\tau. \tag{5-99}$$

We return again to the vector identity of Problem 1-14, which gives

$$\mathbf{J} \cdot \mathbf{\nabla}' \left(\frac{1}{r} \right) = \mathbf{\nabla}' \cdot \left(\frac{\mathbf{J}}{r} \right) - \frac{1}{r} \mathbf{\nabla}' \cdot \mathbf{J}. \tag{5-100}$$

Then

$$\mathbf{\nabla} \cdot \mathbf{A} = -\frac{\mu_0}{4\pi} \left(\int_\tau \mathbf{\nabla}' \cdot \frac{\mathbf{J}}{r} \, d\tau - \int_\tau \frac{1}{r} \mathbf{\nabla}' \cdot \mathbf{J} \, d\tau \right). \tag{5-101}$$

The first integral on the right is similar to that of Eq. *5-95*, except that now the divergence of $\mathbf{J}/r$ is computed at P' rather than at P. Transforming this integral with the divergence theorem, we obtain

$$\mathbf{\nabla} \cdot \mathbf{A} = -\frac{\mu_0}{4\pi} \left(\int_S \frac{\mathbf{J}}{r} \cdot d\mathbf{a} - \int_\tau \frac{1}{r} \mathbf{\nabla}' \cdot \mathbf{J} \, d\tau \right), \tag{5-102}$$

where S is the surface enclosing the volume τ, within which the current **J** is confined. Everywhere on the surface, **J** is either zero or tangential, and thus

$$\mathbf{\nabla} \cdot \mathbf{A} = \frac{\mu_0}{4\pi} \int_\tau \frac{1}{r} \mathbf{\nabla}' \cdot \mathbf{J} \, d\tau. \tag{5-103}$$

Now, from Eq. *5-86* for the conservation of charge,

$$\mathbf{\nabla}' \cdot \mathbf{J} = -\frac{\partial \rho}{\partial t}, \tag{5-104}$$

and

$$\mathbf{\nabla} \cdot \mathbf{A} = -\frac{\mu_0}{4\pi} \int_\tau \frac{1}{r} \frac{\partial \rho}{\partial t} \, d\tau, \tag{5-105}$$

$$= -\mu_0 \frac{\partial}{\partial t} \int_\tau \frac{\rho}{4\pi r} \, d\tau, \tag{5-106}$$

where τ is again any volume within which the current $\mathbf{J}$ is confined. It can be infinite if required, for only the regions in which $\partial\rho/\partial t \neq 0$ will contribute to the right-hand side. Since the integral is simply $K_e\epsilon_0 V$ (Eq. *2-16*),

$$\boldsymbol{\nabla}\cdot\mathbf{A} = -K_e\epsilon_0\mu_0 \frac{\partial V}{\partial t}. \tag{5-107}$$

This is the *Lorentz condition* relating V and $\mathbf{A}$ for nonmagnetic materials; we shall return to it in Section 13.1.1. If V is constant,

$$\boldsymbol{\nabla}\cdot\mathbf{A} = 0. \tag{5-108}$$

5.10. The Curl of the Magnetic Induction B. Poisson's Equation for the Vector Potential A

We have shown that the magnetic induction $\mathbf{B}$ can always be calculated from the vector potential $\mathbf{A}$ through Eq. *5-56:*

$$\mathbf{B} = \boldsymbol{\nabla} \times \mathbf{A}. \tag{5-109}$$

We shall now show that

$$\boldsymbol{\nabla} \times \mathbf{B} = \mu_0 \left(\mathbf{J} + \frac{\partial\mathbf{D}}{\partial t}\right). \tag{5-110}$$

We have

$$\boldsymbol{\nabla} \times \mathbf{B} = \boldsymbol{\nabla} \times (\boldsymbol{\nabla} \times \mathbf{A}), \tag{5-111}$$

or, from Problem 1-24,

$$\boldsymbol{\nabla} \times \mathbf{B} = \boldsymbol{\nabla}(\boldsymbol{\nabla}\cdot\mathbf{A}) - \nabla^2\mathbf{A} \tag{5-112}$$

in Cartesian coordinates only. Let us first consider the first term on the right. From Eq. *5-107*,

$$\boldsymbol{\nabla}(\boldsymbol{\nabla}\cdot\mathbf{A}) = -K_e\epsilon_0\mu_0\boldsymbol{\nabla} \frac{\partial}{\partial t} V, \tag{5-113}$$

$$= -K_e\epsilon_0\mu_0 \frac{\partial}{\partial t} \boldsymbol{\nabla}V, \tag{5-114}$$

$$= \mu_0 \frac{\partial\mathbf{D}}{\partial t}. \tag{5-115}$$

For the second term, we have from the definition of $\mathbf{A}$ that

$$\nabla^2\mathbf{A} = \frac{\mu_0}{4\pi} \int_\tau \nabla^2 \frac{\mathbf{J}}{r} \, d\tau', \tag{5-116}$$

where we have interchanged the order of differentiation and integration.

The meaning of this equation can be understood by referring to Figure 5-10. At the field point $P(x, y, z)$, where we wish to compute $\nabla^2\mathbf{A}$, we form the vector $\mathbf{J}\,d\tau'/r$, where $\mathbf{J}$ and $d\tau'$ are respectively the current density and the volume element at the source point P' and where r is the distance from P' to P. We compute the Laplacian of this vector at P by taking the appropriate derivatives with respect to the coordinates x, y, and z of P. We then sum the contributions from all such sources in the volume τ', which includes all points at which J exists. The volume τ' may include the field point P, where $r = 0$, as will be shown below.

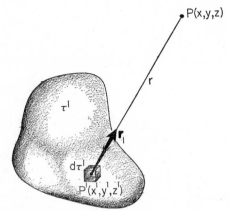

Figure 5-10

Source point P' and field point P for the calculation of $\nabla \times$ **B**.

Since **J** is not a function of the coordinates of P, we can write the integral as

$$\nabla^2 \mathbf{A} = \frac{\mu_0}{4\pi} \int_{\tau'} \mathbf{J}\, \nabla^2 \left(\frac{1}{r}\right) d\tau'. \tag{5-117}$$

Now, by differentiation of

$$\frac{1}{r} = \frac{1}{[(x - x')^2 + (y - y')^2 + (z - z')^2]^{1/2}}, \tag{5-118}$$

we find that $\nabla^2(1/r) = 0$ if $r \neq 0$. There can thus be no contribution to the integral from any element $d\tau'$, except possibly at the point P itself, where $r = 0$.

To investigate the integral at $r = 0$, let us consider a small volume enclosing P. We take the volume so small that **J** does not change appreciably within it, and so **J** may then be removed from the integral:

$$\nabla^2 \mathbf{A} = \frac{\mu_0 \mathbf{J}}{4\pi} \int_{\tau' \to 0} \nabla^2 \left(\frac{1}{r}\right) d\tau'. \tag{5-119}$$

Now

$$\int_{\tau' \to 0} \nabla^2 \left(\frac{1}{r}\right) d\tau' = \int_{\tau' \to 0} \nabla \cdot \nabla \left(\frac{1}{r}\right) d\tau', \tag{5-120}$$

$$= \int_{S' \to 0} \nabla \left(\frac{1}{r}\right) \cdot \mathbf{da}, \tag{5-121}$$

from the divergence theorem, and, from Problem 1-21,

$$\nabla \left(\frac{1}{r}\right) = +\frac{\mathbf{r}_1}{r^2}, \tag{5-122}$$

where $\mathbf{r}_1$ is the unit vector from the source point to the field point. In this case $\mathbf{r}_1$ points inward toward the point P. Thus

$$\int_{\tau' \to 0} \nabla^2 \left(\frac{1}{r} \right) d\tau' = \int_{S' \to 0} \frac{\mathbf{r}_1}{r^2} \cdot \mathbf{da}, \tag{5-123}$$

$$= -\int_{S' \to 0} d\Omega, \tag{5-124}$$

where $d\Omega$ is the element of solid angle subtended at the point P by the element of area $\mathbf{da}$. Since the surface S' completely surrounds P,

$$\int_{\tau' \to 0} \nabla^2 \left(\frac{1}{r} \right) d\tau' = -4\pi. \tag{5-125}$$

Then, from Eqs. *5-112, 5-107, 5-119,* and *5-125,*

$$\nabla \times \mathbf{B} = \mu_0 \left(\mathbf{J} + \frac{\partial \mathbf{D}}{\partial t} \right), \tag{5-126}$$

where $\mathbf{J}$ is the current density and $\partial\mathbf{D}/\partial t$ is the *displacement current density.* When $\mathbf{J} \gg \partial\mathbf{D}/\partial t$,

$$\nabla \times \mathbf{B} = \mu_0 \mathbf{J}, \tag{5-127}$$

and the current is said to be *quasi-stationary.* For a field of circular frequency ω, the current is quasi-stationary if (Appendix F)

$$J = \sigma E \gg \omega K_e \epsilon_0 E, \tag{5-128}$$

or if

$$\frac{1}{\omega} \gg \frac{K_e \epsilon_0}{\sigma},$$

$$\frac{T}{2\pi} \gg \frac{K_e \epsilon_0}{\sigma}.$$

That is, the current is quasi-stationary if the period is much larger than 2π times the relaxation time (Section 5.8).

We have assumed in the above discussion that $\mathbf{B}$ is produced only by the current $\mathbf{J}$ according to the Biot-Savart law. This assumption is well founded as long as we deal with nonmagnetic materials such as copper, silver, or aluminum, which are the ordinary conductors. However, in magnetic materials such as iron, polarization processes can produce equivalent currents which also contribute to the magnetic induction. Equation *5-127* is therefore of restricted applicability. We shall generalize it in Chapter 7, which deals with magnetic materials.

Returning to Eqs. *5-117* and *5-125,* the first of which is valid only in Cartesian coordinates, we can now write that

$$\nabla^2 \mathbf{A} = -\mu_0 \mathbf{J}. \tag{5-129}$$

This is the *Poisson equation for the vector potential A.*

5.11. Ampere's Circuital Law

Let us put Eq. *5-127* into integral form by integrating the normal component of $\nabla \times \mathbf{B}$ over an arbitrary surface S:

$$\int_S (\nabla \times \mathbf{B}) \cdot \mathbf{da} = \mu_0 \int_S \mathbf{J} \cdot \mathbf{da}. \qquad (5\text{-}130)$$

Using Stokes's theorem, we may transform the left side of this equation into a line integral around the closed path which bounds the surface:

$$\oint \mathbf{B} \cdot \mathbf{dl} = \mu_0 \int_S \mathbf{J} \cdot \mathbf{da}. \qquad (5\text{-}131)$$

This is *Ampere's circuital law:* the line integral of $\mathbf{B}$ around a closed path is equal to μ_0 times the total current crossing any surface bounded by the line integral path. Again, we are limited to nonmagnetic materials and to quasi-stationary currents.

The same current frequently crosses the surface bounded by the integration path several times, as in a solenoid, for which the integration path follows the axis and returns outside the solenoid. In this case the total current crossing the surface is the current in each turn multiplied by the number of turns, or the number of *ampere-turns.*

The circuital law can be used to compute the magnetic induction for cases in which, by symmetry, $\mathbf{B}$ is constant along some integration path of interest. It is thus somewhat similar to Gauss's law which is used to compute the electrostatic field intensity $\mathbf{E}$ when it is constant over a closed surface.

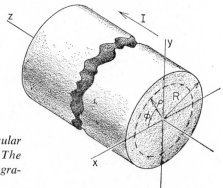

Figure 5-11

*Long cylindrical conductor of circular cross section carrying a current I. The circle of radius ρ is a path of integration for calculating **B** inside.*

5.11.1. Long Cylindrical Conductor. Let us investigate the magnitude and direction of the magnetic induction $\mathbf{B}$ and of the vector potential $\mathbf{A}$ in the interior of a long, straight cylindrical conductor carrying a current I uniformly distributed over its cross section with density

$$J = \frac{I}{\pi R^2}. \qquad (5\text{-}132)$$

Outside the conductor, **B** is azimuthal, and, from the circuital law,

$$B = \frac{\mu_0 I}{2\pi \rho}. \qquad (5\text{-}133)$$

Inside the conductor, **B** is also in the azimuthal direction and is independent of ϕ. For a circular path of radius ρ, as in Figure 5-11,

$$B\, 2\pi\rho = \mu_0 J \pi \rho^2, \qquad (5\text{-}134)$$

or

$$B = \frac{\mu_0 I \rho}{2\pi R^2}. \qquad (5\text{-}135)$$

The magnetic induction **B** therefore increases linearly with ρ inside the conductor. Outside the conductor, **B** decreases as $1/\rho$. The curve of B as a function of ρ is shown in Figure 5-12.

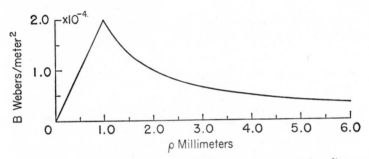

Figure 5-12. *The magnetic induction B as a function of radius for a wire of 1 millimeter radius carrying a current of 1 ampere.*

To compute the vector potential **A** at a point within the conductor, we cannot use Eq. 5-57, which yields an infinite value for **A**, as it did for a single infinite wire; instead we apply Eq. 5-83 to a path lying in a radial plane, as in Figure 5-13. The path follows the surface of the conductor parallel to the axis and

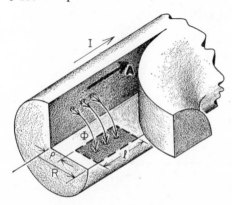

Figure 5-13

*Long cylindrical conductor of circular cross section carrying a current I. Part of the wire is removed to show the magnetic flux Φ and the path of integration for calculating **A** inside.*

returns at a distance ρ from the axis. Since the vector potential must be parallel to the current density **J**, it is everywhere parallel to the axis, and, for a long conductor, it is independent of position in the axial direction. Hence, from Eq. 5-83,

$$A(R)l - A(\rho)l = \Phi, \tag{5-136}$$

where $A(R)$ is the magnitude of A at radius R, $A(\rho)$ is the magnitude at ρ, and Φ is the flux through the radial plane surface enclosed by the path. Thus

$$\Phi = \int_{\rho}^{R} \frac{\mu_0 I \rho}{2\pi R^2} l \, d\rho, \tag{5-137}$$

$$= \frac{\mu_0 I \, l}{4\pi R^2} (R^2 - \rho^2). \tag{5-138}$$

The function $A(R)$ for the region outside the conductor was found in Eq. 5-62. Taking $\rho = R$ in this equation, we obtain

$$A(R) = \frac{\mu_0 I}{4\pi} \ln \left(1 + \frac{4L^2}{R^2} \right), \tag{5-139}$$

where L is the half length of the conductor. Then, from Eq. 5-136,

$$A(\rho) = \frac{\mu_0 I}{4\pi} \left[\ln \left(1 + \frac{4L^2}{R^2} \right) - 1 + \frac{\rho^2}{R^2} \right] \qquad (\rho \leqq R). \tag{5-140}$$

The first term is constant for a given wire and for a given current, whereas the third term shows that A increases as the square of the radius ρ inside the conductor. Figure 5-14 shows the value of A both inside and outside a wire 1 millimeter in diameter and 1 meter long carrying a current of 1 ampere.

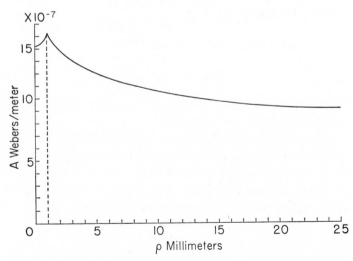

Figure 5-14. *The vector potential A for a length of wire 1 meter long and 1 millimeter in diameter carrying a current of 1 ampere.*

We have assumed that the conductor has the same magnetic properties as free space, which is an excellent approximation for ordinary conductors such as copper.

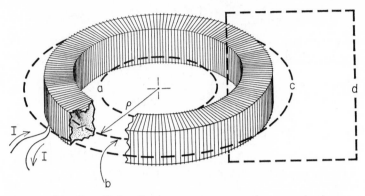

Figure 5-15. *Toroidal coil of square cross section carrying a current I. The figures shown by broken lines are paths of integration for* **B**.

5.11.2. The Toroid. As a second example, consider a toroidal coil of square cross section, as in Figure 5-15, carrying a current I.

Along the path a, the line integral of **B** must be equal to zero, since there is no current linking this path. Then the azimuthal B is zero in this region. The same applies to c and to any similar circular path outside the toroid. Then the azimuthal B is zero everywhere outside.

Inside, along path b,

$$2\pi\rho B = \mu_0 NI, \tag{5-141}$$

where N is the total number of turns. Thus

$$B = \mu_0 \frac{N}{2\pi\rho} I. \tag{5-142}$$

The magnetic induction is fairly constant throughout the cross section if the toroid is thin in the radial direction.

It is instructive to examine the nonazimuthal components of the magnetic induction **B** both inside and outside the toroid. For any closed path outside, the line integral of **B·dl** is equal to zero, since no current is linked. However, for a path such as d in Figure 5-15, the area bounded by the path is crossed by the current in the toroidal winding at one point, and

$$\oint \mathbf{B} \cdot \mathbf{dl} = \mu_0 I, \tag{5-143}$$

which is only $1/N'$ as large as the tangential component of **B** inside the toroid, where N' is the number of turns per meter around the toroid. We can assume that B_r and B_z will be of the order of $1/N'$ times the tangential component. In fact, at a distance large compared to the outer radius of the toroid, the magnetic induction **B** is that of a single turn along the mean radius.

It is interesting to notice that, although the magnetic field outside the toroid is essentially zero, the vector potential **A** is not. This will be evident if one remembers that **A** is a constant times the integral of $I\,d\mathbf{l}/r$, where r is the distance between the element **dl** and the point at which **A** is calculated. Outside the toroid and close to the winding, **A** is due mostly to the nearby turns and is parallel to the current. It is not zero.

The vector potential **A** can therefore exist in a region where there is no field. This simply means that we can have at the same time $\mathbf{A} \neq 0$ and $\nabla \times \mathbf{A} = 0$, which is entirely plausible. For example, $\mathbf{A} = K\mathbf{i}$, where K is a constant, satisfies this condition. We are already familiar with a similar situation in electrostatics in which the electrostatic potential can have any uniform value in a region where $\mathbf{E} = -\nabla V = 0$.

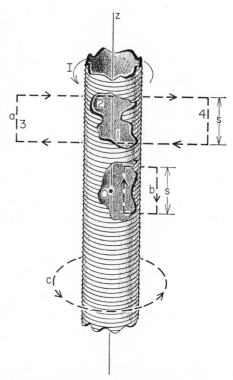

Figure 5-16. *Long Solenoid carrying a current I. The figures shown by broken lines are paths of integration for* **B**.

5.11.3. The Long Solenoid.
As another example, let us calculate **B** inside the long solenoid of Figure 5-16.

We shall assume that there are no end effects. This condition is satisfied approximately if the length of the solenoid is much greater than its diameter. We shall also assume that the pitch of the winding is infinitely small. We choose cylindrical coordinates with the z-axis coinciding with the axis of symmetry of the solenoid.

By symmetry, **B** is neither a function of z nor of ϕ. Moreover, $B_r = 0$, since by symmetry it should be neither positive nor negative. For the same reason, $B_\phi = 0$, the pitch of the winding being infinitely small. The magnetic induction **B** is therefore parallel to the axis of the solenoid and independent of both z and ϕ. By substituting these conditions in $\nabla \cdot \mathbf{B}$, expressed in cylindrical coordinates, we find that this quantity is identically equal to zero.

We also have $\nabla \times \mathbf{B} = 0$ at every point except inside the wire. Then

$$\frac{\partial B_z}{\partial r} = 0, \tag{5-144}$$

since $B_r = 0$ and $B_\phi = 0$. The axial magnetic induction B_z is therefore also independent of r. Inside the solenoid, B_z has some finite value, which we shall determine below. There is presumably a discontinuity in B_z at the position of the winding, and B_z takes on some other value outside.

To determine the value of B_z outside the solenoid, consider the path a shown in Figure 5-16. The net current linking this path is zero, and the line integral of $\mathbf{B} \cdot d\mathbf{r}$ around it is therefore also zero. Now the line integrals of $\mathbf{B}$ along sides 1 and 2 must be zero, since, by symmetry, $\mathbf{B}$ has no radial component. The line integrals of $\mathbf{B} \cdot d\mathbf{r}$ along the other two sides, 3 and 4, must therefore cancel. Now the sides 3 and 4 can each be situated at any distance from the solenoid, and B_z must therefore be zero along them. Then B_z is zero everywhere outside.

We can also arrive at the same conclusion in an intuitive way by recalling that the lines of flux have neither beginning nor end and that the total return flux in the infinite space outside must equal the finite flux inside the solenoid, hence $\mathbf{B}$ can be expected to be infinitely small everywhere outside.

For the rectangular path b shown in Figure 5-16, Ampere's law gives

$$Bs = \mu_0 N' s I, \tag{5-145}$$

where N' is the number of turns per meter along the solenoid. Then

$$B = \mu_0 N' I. \tag{5-146}$$

The magnetic induction inside a long solenoid in the region remote from the ends is therefore uniform and equal to μ_0 times the number of ampere-turns/meter.

Let us now take into account the pitch of the winding. A circular path c perpendicular to the axis of the solenoid is linked by the current I, and $\mathbf{B}$ at some distance outside the solenoid is $\mu_0 I$. This is just the field which would be produced by a current I along the axis of the solenoid. This field is N' times less than the axial field inside and can usually be neglected.

As for the toroid, $\mathbf{A}$ is not zero outside, despite the fact that $\mathbf{B}$ is negligible. We shall return to this point in Section 6.3.7.

5.12. The Magnetic Scalar Potential V_m

We shall now express the Biot-Savart law, Eq. 5-9, in a form such that, under some circumstances, the magnetic induction $\mathbf{B}$ becomes the gradient of a scalar potential function. This is a useful technique because it casts magnetic field calculations into the same form as the electrostatic field calculations with which we are already familiar.

Figure 5-17 shows a closed circuit carrying a current *I*. We wish to know the magnetic induction **B** at a point *P*. From the Biot-Savart law,

$$\mathbf{B} = \frac{\mu_0 I}{4\pi} \oint \frac{d\mathbf{l} \times \mathbf{r}_1}{r^2}. \qquad (5\text{-}147)$$

Let us calculate the quantity **B**·**dr** corresponding to an infinitesimal displacement **dr** of the point *P*:

$$\mathbf{B} \cdot d\mathbf{r} = \frac{\mu_0 I}{4\pi} \left(\oint \frac{d\mathbf{l} \times \mathbf{r}_1}{r^2} \right) \cdot d\mathbf{r}. \qquad (5\text{-}148)$$

It makes no difference whether we calculate the vector $\oint d\mathbf{l} \times \mathbf{r}_1/r^2$ at *P* and then take the scalar product with **dr** or whether we take the scalar product of the elementary vector $d\mathbf{l} \times \mathbf{r}_1/r^2$ with **dr** and then sum the resultant scalar quantities around

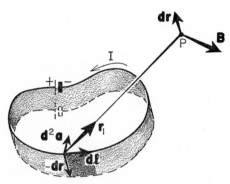

Figure 5-17. *The current I produces a magnetic induction* **B** *at the point P. The solid curve shows the original position of the circuit; the broken curve shows its position after an infinitesimal displacement* −**dr** *of all its points.*

the whole circuit. We can therefore place **dr** under the integral sign; then

$$\mathbf{B} \cdot d\mathbf{r} = \frac{\mu_0 I}{4\pi} \oint \frac{d\mathbf{l} \times \mathbf{r}_1 \cdot d\mathbf{r}}{r^2}. \qquad (5\text{-}149)$$

From Problem 1-7, cyclic permutation of the vectors in a triple product of the type under the integral sign changes neither the sign nor the magnitude of the resultant scalar quantity. However, if the vectors are permuted in noncyclic order, the sign is changed. Thus

$$d\mathbf{l} \times \mathbf{r}_1 \cdot d\mathbf{r} = -d\mathbf{l} \times d\mathbf{r} \cdot \mathbf{r}_1 = d\mathbf{l} \times (-d\mathbf{r}) \cdot \mathbf{r}_1. \qquad (5\text{-}150)$$

Let us investigate the meaning of this triple product in the permuted order. When the point *P* is displaced by an amount **dr**, the solid angle Ω subtended by the circuit at *P* changes by *d*Ω. If, instead of displacing the point *P* by **dr**, we hold *P* fixed and displace each point of the circuit by −**dr**, the change in solid angle is the same and is easier to calculate. Figure 5-17 shows the ribbon surface generated by such a displacement of the circuit.

The vector product

$$d\mathbf{l} \times (-d\mathbf{r}) = d^2\mathbf{a} \qquad (5\text{-}151)$$

is an element of the ribbon area traced out by the circuit element **dl** in the displacement −**dr**. It is written **d²a**, since it is a second order differential. Then $d\mathbf{l} \times (-d\mathbf{r}) \cdot \mathbf{r}_1 = d^2\mathbf{a} \cdot \mathbf{r}_1$ is the projection of the area **d²a** on a plane perpendicular to $\mathbf{r}_1$, and

$$\left| \frac{d^2\mathbf{a} \cdot \mathbf{r}_1}{r^2} \right| = |d^2\Omega| \qquad (5\text{-}152)$$

is the element of solid angle subtended at point P by the element of area $\mathbf{d^2a}$. We have taken the absolute values on both sides of the equation because we have as yet no convention for selecting the sign of Ω.

Integrating over the complete circuit, we obtain the solid angle subtended at P by the entire ribbon area:

$$\left| \oint \frac{\mathbf{dl} \times (-\mathbf{dr}) \cdot \mathbf{r_1}}{r^2} \right| = |d\Omega|. \qquad (5\text{-}153)$$

Now, as for any scalar function,

$$|d\Omega| = |\nabla\Omega \cdot dr|, \qquad (5\text{-}154)$$

as in Section 1-3. Altogether,

$$|\mathbf{B} \cdot \mathbf{dr}| = \frac{\mu_0 I}{4\pi} |\nabla\Omega \cdot \mathbf{dr}|, \qquad (5\text{-}155)$$

or, since this equation is true for any arbitrary displacement $\mathbf{dr}$,

$$|\mathbf{B}| = \frac{\mu_0 I}{4\pi} |\nabla\Omega|, \qquad (5\text{-}156)$$

$$= \left| \nabla \frac{\mu_0 I \Omega}{4\pi} \right|, \qquad (5\text{-}157)$$

$$= |\nabla V_m|. \qquad (5\text{-}158)$$

The scalar function V_m, where

$$|V_m| = \left| \frac{\mu_0}{4\pi} I\Omega \right|, \qquad (5\text{-}159)$$

is called the *magnetic scalar potential*, Ω being the solid angle subtended by the circuit at the field point where we wish to compute $\mathbf{B}$.

To assure the correct direction for $\mathbf{B}$ from this calculation, we must have a convention defining the sign of the solid angle Ω. When current flows in a *counter*clockwise direction as viewed from the point in question, the solid angle is taken to be *positive*. Then

$$\mathbf{B} = -\nabla V_m, \qquad (5\text{-}160)$$

and

$$V_m = \frac{\mu_0}{4\pi} I\Omega. \qquad (5\text{-}161)$$

With this convention, $\mathbf{B}$ is expressed in the same form as $\mathbf{E}$ in electrostatics:

$$\mathbf{E} = -\nabla V. \qquad (5\text{-}162)$$

This is the only reason for selecting the above convention.

The magnetic scalar potential is not single valued, since the solid angle Ω is not itself single valued: for any position P, we can add $4n\pi$ to Ω, where n is any integer. The difference in scalar potential between two points is also undefined, unless the path followed between the two points is specified. This is because each time the path links the circuit, the solid angle along the path is changed by 4π, and the difference in magnetic scalar potential is changed by $\mu_0 I$. We can even add *any* constant to V_m without affecting the value of **B**, just as we can add any constant to the electrostatic potential V without affecting the electric field intensity **E**.

As a rule, the method is used only for conductors of negligible cross section. It cannot be used for points within the conductors themselves.

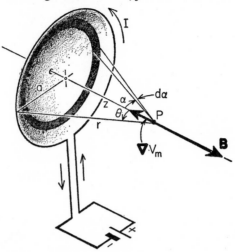

5.12.1. The Circular Loop. Point on the Axis. To illustrate the use of the scalar magnetic potential, let us calculate the magnetic induction **B** at a point on the axis of a circular loop carrying a current I. We have already calculated this **B** in Section 5.2.3 from the Biot-Savart law.

With the above sign convention for Ω, the solid angle subtended by the circuit is positive at

Figure 5-18. *A circular loop of radius a carrying a current I. The solid angle subtended by the loop at P is the same as that of the spherical cap with its center at P. The magnetic induction* **B** *and the gradient of the magnetic scalar potential* ∇V_m *at P are as shown.*

the point P in Figure 5-18, and $\nabla\Omega$ is along the axis, since that is the direction of most rapid change of solid angle with distance. Moreover, $\nabla\Omega$ and ∇V_m are in the direction of increasing Ω, which is toward the loop, and **B** is in the opposite direction as indicated in the figure.

The solid angle Ω is the area of the spherical cap drawn through the loop and centered on P, divided by the square of the radius of the cap:

$$\Omega = \frac{1}{r^2} \int_0^\theta 2\pi r^2 \sin\alpha \, d\alpha, \qquad\qquad (5\text{-}163)$$

$$= 2\pi(1 - \cos\theta), \qquad\qquad (5\text{-}164)$$

$$= 2\pi\left[1 - \frac{z}{(a^2 + z^2)^{1/2}}\right]. \qquad\qquad (5\text{-}165)$$

The magnetic scalar potential V_m is shown in Figure 5-19. The discontinuity of 4π in the plane of the loop arises from our definition of Ω. The same situation arises with plane angles, where an angle $+\pi$ is really equal to an angle $-\pi$: the addition of 4π to a solid angle corresponds to the addition of 2π to a plane angle. There is no discontinuity in **B** in the plane of the loop, as can be seen by

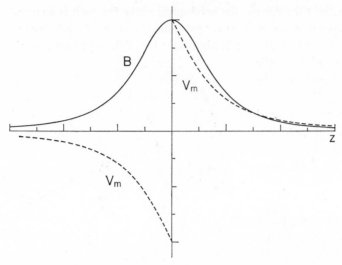

Figure 5-19. *The magnetic scalar potential V_m and the magnetic induction B on the axis of a circular loop.*

considering a small flat volume element on this plane: since $\nabla \cdot \mathbf{B} = 0$, the flux must be the same through both faces of the box, and **B** must therefore be continuous.

Then

$$\nabla \Omega = \frac{\partial \Omega}{\partial z} \mathbf{k} = -\frac{2\pi a^2}{(a^2 + z^2)^{3/2}} \mathbf{k}, \tag{5-166}$$

and

$$\mathbf{B} = \frac{\mu_0 I}{4\pi} \nabla \Omega = \frac{\mu_0 I a^2}{2(a^2 + z^2)^{3/2}} \mathbf{k}. \tag{5-167}$$

This result is the same as in Section 5.2.3.

5.12.2. Laplace's Equation for the Magnetic Scalar Potential. In regions of space where the scalar magnetic potential is defined, that is, in regions where the current density $\mathbf{J} = 0$,

$$\mathbf{B} = -\nabla V_m. \tag{5-168}$$

However, under any condition,

$$\nabla \cdot \mathbf{B} = 0. \tag{5-169}$$

Then

$$\nabla^2 V_m = 0. \tag{5-170}$$

The scalar potential therefore satisfies Laplace's equation in current-free regions, just as the electrostatic potential V satisfies it in charge-free regions, and all the techniques which we have developed for solving this equation in the electrostatic case are applicable here.

5.12.3. The Circular Loop. Point Off the Axis.*

Let us calculate the magnetic induction **B** at an arbitrary point P off the axis of a circular current loop by using Laplace's equation for the magnetic scalar potential. This problem is closely analogous to that of finding the electrostatic potential of a uniformly charged ring, as in Section 4.6.3.

The symmetry suggests spherical polar coordinates r and θ, with the origin of coordinates at the center of the loop, as in Figure 5-20. By symmetry, **B** is independent of the azimuth angle ϕ.

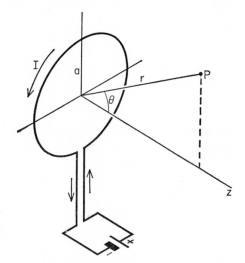

Figure 5-20

A circular loop carrying a current I with a point P (r, θ) off the axis of symmetry.

We require a solution of Laplace's equation which satisfies the boundary conditions. Then, from Section 4.6, the magnetic scalar potential must be of the form

$$V_m = A_0 P_0(\cos\theta) + A_1 r P_1(\cos\theta) + A_2 r^2 P_2(\cos\theta) + \cdots$$

$$+ \frac{B_0}{r} + \frac{B_1 P_1(\cos\theta)}{r^2} + \frac{B_2 P_2(\cos\theta)}{r^3} + \cdots, \qquad (5\text{-}171)$$

where the A's and B's are constant coefficients and where the P's are Legendre polynomials.

We can evaluate the coefficients from the value of Ω given in Eq. *5-165* for a point on the axis:

$$V_m = \frac{\mu_0 I}{2}\left[1 - \frac{z}{(a^2 + z^2)^{1/2}}\right] \qquad (\theta = 0), \qquad (5\text{-}172)$$

or, expanding as a power series in a/z,

$$V_m = \frac{\mu_0 I}{2}\left(\frac{a^2}{2z^2} - \frac{3a^4}{8z^4} + \frac{5a^6}{16z^6} - \cdots\right) \qquad (\theta = 0, z \geqq a). \quad (5\text{-}173)$$

* This section may be omitted without losing continuity.

This is for positive values of z; for negative values, V_m changes sign as in Figure 5-19. This series converges and is valid, except for sign, for any z greater than or equal to a.

In the region far away from the ring, where r is large, all of the A's in Eq. 5-171 must be zero, since $V_m \longrightarrow 0$ as $r \longrightarrow \infty$. Moreover, on the axis, $\theta = 0$, $r = z$, thus

$$V_m = \frac{B}{z} + \frac{B_1}{z^2} + \frac{B_2}{z^3} + \cdots \qquad (\theta = 0, z \geq a). \qquad (5\text{-}174)$$

The two expressions for V_m must be equal for all $z \geq a$; thus, matching coefficients, we have

$$B_0 = 0, \qquad\qquad\qquad (5\text{-}175)$$

$$B_1 = \frac{\mu_0 I a^2}{4}, \qquad\qquad (5\text{-}176)$$

$$B_2 = 0, \qquad\qquad\qquad (5\text{-}177)$$

$$B_3 = -\frac{3\mu_0 I a^4}{16}, \qquad\qquad (5\text{-}178)$$

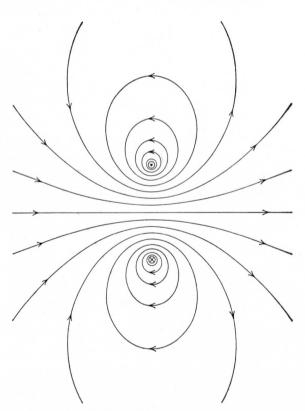

Figure 5-21. *The lines of* **B** *for a circular current loop.*

and so forth. Thus

$$V_m = \frac{\mu_0 I}{2}\left[\frac{a^2\cos\theta}{2r^2} - \frac{3a^4}{16r^4}(5\cos^3\theta - 3\cos\theta) + \cdots\right] \qquad (r \geqq a). \quad (5\text{-}179)$$

This expression does give the correct value and the correct sign for V_m along the axis, both along $\theta = 0$ and $\theta = \pi$ radians.

Then

$$B_r = -\frac{\partial V_m}{\partial r}, \qquad\qquad (5\text{-}180)$$

$$= \frac{\mu_0 I}{2a}\left[\frac{a^3\cos\theta}{r^3} - \frac{3}{4}\frac{a^5}{r^5}(5\cos^3\theta - 3\cos\theta) + \cdots\right] \qquad (r \geqq a), \quad (5\text{-}181)$$

$$B_\theta = -\frac{1}{r}\frac{\partial V_m}{\partial\theta}, \qquad\qquad (5\text{-}182)$$

$$= \frac{\mu_0 I}{2a}\left[\frac{a^3\sin\theta}{2r^3} - \frac{9}{16}\frac{a^5}{r^5}(5\cos^2\theta - 1)\sin\theta + \cdots\right] \qquad (r \geqq a), \quad (5\text{-}183)$$

$$B_\phi = -\frac{1}{r\sin\theta}\frac{\partial V_m}{\partial\phi} = 0 \qquad (r \geqq a). \qquad (5\text{-}184)$$

The calculation of **B** for $r \leqq a$ is made similarly, although it is somewhat more complex. This will be left as a problem at the end of the chapter.

The lines of **B** and the magnetic equipotentials $V_m = $ constant are shown in Figure 5-21.

5.13. The Magnetic Dipole Moment of a Current Loop

For a current loop, if the point P at which we wish to know **B** is far enough away such that

$$\frac{a^4}{r^4} \ll \frac{a^2}{r^2},$$

or

$$\frac{a^2}{r^2} \ll 1, \qquad\qquad (5\text{-}185)$$

we may neglect all but the first term in the series for the magnetic potential for $r \geqq a$; therefore

$$V_m = \frac{\mu_0}{4\pi} I\frac{\pi a^2\cos\theta}{r^2}. \qquad\qquad (5\text{-}186)$$

We could also have arrived at this result directly from the definition of V_m given in Eq. *5-161*, since $(\pi a^2\cos\theta)/r^2$ is simply the solid angle subtended by the circuit at a remote point $P(r, \theta)$. Regrouping the terms, we have

$$V_m = \frac{\mu_0}{4\pi}(\pi a^2 I)\frac{\cos\theta}{r^2}. \qquad\qquad (5\text{-}187)$$

This potential is closely analogous to that of the electrostatic dipole, Section 2.8. We set

$$\mathbf{m} = I\mathbf{S} \qquad (5\text{-}188)$$

as the dipole moment of the current loop, where $\mathbf{S}$ is a vector whose magnitude is equal to the area of the loop. It is perpendicular to the loop, and its direction is related to that of the current by the right-hand screw rule. Then

$$V_m = \frac{\mu_0}{4\pi} m \frac{\cos\theta}{r^2}, \qquad (5\text{-}189)$$

$$= \frac{\mu_0}{4\pi} \frac{\mathbf{m} \cdot \mathbf{r}_1}{r^2}. \qquad (5\text{-}190)$$

The loop is referred to as a dipole because the magnetic potential which it produces has the same mathematical form as the electrostatic potential of an electrostatic dipole.

The magnetic induction $\mathbf{B}$ of a current loop for $r \gg a$ is obtained from Eqs. 5-181, 5-183, and 5-184:

$$B_r = \frac{\mu_0}{4\pi} \frac{2m}{r^3} \cos\theta \qquad (r^2 \gg a^2), \qquad (5\text{-}191)$$

$$B_\theta = \frac{\mu_0}{4\pi} \frac{m}{r^3} \sin\theta \qquad (r^2 \gg a^2), \qquad (5\text{-}192)$$

$$B_\phi = 0. \qquad (5\text{-}193)$$

It is interesting to note the close analogy between the above result and Eqs. 2-73 to 2-75, which apply to the electric dipole.

We shall calculate the vector potential $\mathbf{A}$ for a circular loop in Chapter 13 for the general case in which the current I has a circular frequency ω.

5.13.1. The Magnetic Dipole Moment of a Current Distribution.

It is possible to generalize the concept of magnetic dipole moment to any distribution of current in space in the following way. The vector $\mathbf{m}$ of Eq. 5-188 can be rewritten in a more general form as

$$\mathbf{m} = \frac{1}{2} \oint \mathbf{r} \times I\, d\mathbf{l}, \qquad (5\text{-}194)$$

where the integral is evaluated over the loop. This expression is more general than the previous one because it can be applied to any loop, whether it is planar or not. It can be further generalized to a tube of current of section da and current density $\mathbf{J}$. Then, for a current distribution $\mathbf{J}$ in a volume τ,

$$\mathbf{m} = \frac{1}{2} \int_\tau \mathbf{r} \times \mathbf{J}\, da\, dl, \qquad (5\text{-}195)$$

$$= \frac{1}{2} \int_\tau \mathbf{r} \times \mathbf{J}\, d\tau. \qquad (5\text{-}196)$$

This expression should be compared with that for the electric dipole moment of a charge distribution as stated in Eq. *2-97*.

5.14. Ampere's Circuital Law and the Scalar Potential

It is possible to deduce Ampere's circuital law from the scalar potential. To do so, let us return to Eq. *5-155* and examine further the quantity $\mathbf{B} \cdot \mathbf{dr}$:

$$\mathbf{B} \cdot \mathbf{dr} = -\frac{\mu_0}{4\pi} I \nabla\Omega \cdot \mathbf{dr} = -\frac{\mu_0}{4\pi} I \, d\Omega. \qquad (5\text{-}197)$$

The line integral of $\mathbf{B} \cdot \mathbf{dr}$ between two points a and b is

$$\int_a^b \mathbf{B} \cdot \mathbf{dr} = -\frac{\mu_0 I}{4\pi} \int_a^b d\Omega, \qquad (5\text{-}198)$$

and so it depends on the change in solid angle between the two points.

This can be illustrated for the circular loop (Figure 5-18) carrying a current I. If the closed path does not link the current, then $\Delta\Omega = 0$, and the line integral of $\mathbf{B} \cdot \mathbf{dr}$ is zero. This is always true if it is possible to draw a surface which is bounded by the circuit carrying the current, and which is not crossed by the integration path. The situation is quite different, however, when it is impossible to draw such a surface, in which case the integration path *links* the current.

For the integration path which starts at $-\infty$, proceeds along the axis through the circuit to $+\infty$, and returns to the starting point along a path at infinite distance, the solid angle varies as in Figure 5-19. It decreases by 2π as P goes from $-\infty$ up to the plane of the loop and then decreases again by 2π as P goes further toward $+\infty$. The total change in solid angle is -4π, since the solid angle is zero for all parts of the return path at infinity, and

$$\oint \mathbf{B} \cdot \mathbf{dr} = \mu_0 I. \qquad (5\text{-}199)$$

This is Ampere's circuital law as given in Eq. *5-131*, except that we have considered here a less general case, with a single wire carrying a current I. No matter what the shape of the loop may be, the change in solid angle around a closed path which links the loop once is 4π steradians.

As in Section 5.11, the circuital law in this form is applicable only to non-magnetic materials.

5.15. Summary

It is a common laboratory experience that circuits carrying electric currents exert *magnetic* forces on each other. The force on the current in circuit a produced by the current in circuit b can be written

$$\mathbf{F}_{ab} = \frac{\mu_0}{4\pi} I_a I_b \oint_a \oint_b \frac{d\mathbf{l}_a \times (d\mathbf{l}_b \times \mathbf{r}_1)}{r^2}, \tag{5-1}$$

where $\mathbf{r}_1$ is the unit vector pointing from the element $d\mathbf{l}_b$ to the element $d\mathbf{l}_a$. The constant μ_0 is arbitrarily chosen to be exactly $4\pi \times 10^{-7}$ newton/ampere^2 in rationalized m.k.s. units. Equation 5-1 then provides the basis for defining the ampere as the current flowing in each of two long parallel wires separated by one meter when the force of interaction between the currents is 2×10^{-7} newton/meter.

The magnetic interaction is best thought of as an interaction between the current I_a in one circuit and a *magnetic induction field* $\mathbf{B}_b$ produced by a second current I_b. The magnetic induction field is then defined from Eq. *5-1:*

$$\mathbf{B}_b = \frac{\mu_0}{4\pi} I_b \oint_b \frac{d\mathbf{l}_b \times \mathbf{r}_1}{r^2}. \tag{5-9}$$

The vector $\mathbf{B}$ is measured in webers/meter^2, a weber being a volt-second. Equation 5-9 is known as the *Biot-Savart law*. If the current I_b is distributed with a density $\mathbf{J}$, the magnetic induction is given by

$$\mathbf{B} = \frac{\mu_0}{4\pi} \int_\tau \frac{\mathbf{J} \times \mathbf{r}_1}{r^2} \, d\tau. \tag{5-11}$$

As in electrostatics it is often convenient to think in terms of *lines* of magnetic induction which are everywhere tangent to the direction of the vector $\mathbf{B}$. It is also convenient to use the concept of magnetic *flux:*

$$\Phi = \int_S \mathbf{B} \cdot d\mathbf{a}. \tag{5-12}$$

The magnetic force acting on a charge Q moving with a velocity $\mathbf{u}$ in a magnetic field $\mathbf{B}$ can be deduced from Eq. *5-1:*

$$\mathbf{f} = Q(\mathbf{u} \times \mathbf{B}), \tag{5-28}$$

which is known as the *Lorentz force.*

Starting from the Biot-Savart law, we calculated the divergence of the magnetic induction $\mathbf{B}$ and showed that we always have

$$\boxed{\nabla \cdot \mathbf{B} = 0.} \tag{5-45}$$

This is the second of Maxwell's four fundamental equations for electromagnetic fields.

We also showed that the magnetic induction $\mathbf{B}$ can always be written as the curl of another vector $\mathbf{A}$, called the *vector potential:*

$$\mathbf{B} = \nabla \times \mathbf{A}, \tag{5-56}$$

where

$$\mathbf{A} = \frac{\mu_0 I}{4\pi} \oint \frac{d\mathbf{l}}{r}, \tag{5-57}$$

or, for distributed currents,

$$\mathbf{A} = \frac{\mu_0}{4\pi} \int_\tau \frac{\mathbf{J}\, d\tau}{r}. \tag{5-58}$$

The magnetic flux Φ through a surface S is given by

$$\Phi = \oint \mathbf{A} \cdot d\mathbf{l}, \tag{5-83}$$

where the line integral is calculated along the curve which bounds the surface S.

We showed that conservation of electric charge requires that we always have the *equation of continuity:*

$$\nabla \cdot \mathbf{J} = -\frac{\partial \rho}{\partial t}. \tag{5-86}$$

The *relaxation time* for the free charge density ρ in a conductor is $K_e \epsilon_0 / \sigma$. In good conductors this time is short even for optical frequencies, and both ρ and $\nabla \cdot \mathbf{J}$ can be taken as zero. Only surface charge densities can exist under these circumstances.

The vector potential $\mathbf{A}$ is related to the scalar electrostatic potential V through the *Lorentz condition*

$$\nabla \cdot \mathbf{A} = -\epsilon_0 K_e \mu_0 \frac{\partial V}{\partial t}, \tag{5-107}$$

and, for stationary currents,

$$\nabla \cdot \mathbf{A} = 0. \tag{5-108}$$

In free space, and in nonmagnetic materials,

$$\nabla \times \mathbf{B} = \mu_0 \mathbf{J} \tag{5-127}$$

for *quasi-stationary currents*, such that $\omega \ll \sigma / K_e \epsilon_0$. This leads to a *Poisson equation* (in Cartesian coordinates only) for the vector potential:

$$\nabla^2 \mathbf{A} = -\mu_0 \mathbf{J}, \tag{5-129}$$

again for quasi-stationary currents only.

Equation *5-127* also leads directly to *Ampere's circuital law*

$$\oint \mathbf{B} \cdot d\mathbf{l} = \mu_0 \int_S \mathbf{J} \cdot d\mathbf{a} \tag{5-131}$$

for quasi-stationary currents.

Going back to the Biot-Savart law, one can express the magnetic induction $\mathbf{B}$ in terms of a *magnetic scalar potential* V_m at points outside the conductor:

$$\mathbf{B} = -\nabla V_m \tag{5-160}$$

where

$$V_m = \frac{\mu_0}{4\pi} I\Omega, \qquad (5\text{-}161)$$

Ω being the solid angle subtended by the current-carrying circuit at the point where the induction **B** is to be calculated.

The definition of the scalar magnetic potential leads at once to a *Laplace's equation* for V_m in current-free regions:

$$\nabla^2 V_m = 0. \qquad (5\text{-}170)$$

Magnetic fields can therefore be calculated using the techniques appropriate for the solution of Laplace's equation in electrostatics.

At distances large compared to the size of a current loop, the scalar potential has a form identical to that of an electrostatic dipole. Consequently, we define its *magnetic dipole moment* as

$$\mathbf{m} = I\mathbf{S}, \qquad (5\text{-}188)$$

where S is the area of the loop. For a current distribution, the magnetic dipole moment is defined as

$$\mathbf{m} = \frac{1}{2} \int_\tau (\mathbf{r} \times \mathbf{J})\, d\tau. \qquad (5\text{-}196)$$

Problems

5-1. Show that the total force on a closed circuit carrying a current I in a uniform magnetic field is zero.

5-2. Calculate the force due to the earth's magnetic field on a wire 100 feet long carrying a current of 50 amperes due north (magnetic). Take the earth's magnetic field to be 0.5×10^{-4} weber/meter^2 at an angle of 70° with the horizontal.

5-3. Find the current density necessary to float a copper wire in the earth's magnetic field. Assume the experiment to be done at the earth's magnetic equator in a field of 10^{-4} weber/meter^2. The density of copper is 8.9 grams/centimeter^3.

Will the wire become hot? The resistivity of copper is 1.7×10^{-8} ohm-meter.

5-4. Use the Biot-Savart law to compute the magnetic induction **B** at the center of a square current loop carrying a current I.

5-5. A circuit carrying a current I forms a regular polygon of n sides inscribed in a circle of radius R. Calculate the magnetic induction **B** at the center of the circle, and show that **B** approaches that for a circular loop as the number of sides $n \longrightarrow \infty$.

5-6. Show that the axial component of the magnetic induction at the center of a helix of $2N$ turns, of radius R, and of length $2H$ carrying a current I is given by

$$B = \frac{\mu_0 IN}{(R^2 + H^2)^{1/2}}.$$

5-7. Find the magnetic induction **B** on the axis of a cylindrical solenoid of radius a, length L, and N turns carrying a current I. Assume that the winding is close enough such that the turns can be considered circular.

Draw a graph of B vs x, where x is the distance from the center of the solenoid. Do this for the following three cases: (a) $L \ll a$, (b) $L = 2a$, and (c) $L \gg a$.

5-8. A straight flat conductor of width $2a$ carries a current I. Show that

$$B_x = -\frac{\mu_0 I}{4\pi a} \alpha,$$

$$B_y = \frac{\mu_0 I}{4\pi a} \ln \frac{r_2}{r_1}$$

in the first quadrant when the coordinate axes are chosen such that the edges of the conductor are situated at $x = \pm a$ and when the current flows in the direction of the positive z-axis. The distance from the point where **B** is measured to the edge at $x = a$ is r_1. The angle α is that between r_1 and r_2 and is positive in the direction from r_1 to r_2.

Calculate B_x, B_y, and B at a distance of 26.0 centimeters from the axis of the conductor at an angle of 72.0 degrees from the x-axis in the first quadrant for a strip 10 centimeters wide carrying a current of 5.76 amperes.

Find the magnetic induction **B** at (a) an external point in the plane of the strip at a distance D from its axis and (b) an external point in the plane perpendicular to the strip and at the same distance D from its axis.

How do the results of (a) and (b) compare when $D \gg b$? Explain.

5-9. A pair of Helmholtz coils consists of two identical circular current loops placed coaxially so as to obtain uniformity of the magnetic induction **B** in the region midway between the loops. The loops have the same radius. Find the optimum separation of the loops, and investigate the uniformity of the field by calculating some derivatives of the components of **B** at the center.

5-10. A flat insulating disk of radius R carries a uniform charge density σ. The disk rotates with angular velocity ω about an axis through its center and perpendicular to its plane. Find the magnetic induction **B** at a point on the axis at a distance z from the disk.

5-11. Compute the period and radius of curvature of the path of an electron moving in a plane perpendicular to the earth's magnetic field. Assume

$$B = 10^{-4} \text{ weber/meter}^2,$$
$$e = 1.6 \times 10^{-19} \text{ coulomb},$$
$$m = 9.1 \times 10^{-31} \text{ kilogram},$$
$$\text{electron energy} = 3000 \text{ electron-volts},$$
$$\text{one electron volt} = 1.6 \times 10^{-19} \text{ joule.}$$

5-12. A circular magnetron consists of an electron-emitting filament at the center of a cylindrical anode situated in a uniform axial magnetic field. Electrons of charge e and mass m are emitted with negligible velocity from the filament. Find the minimum potential difference between filament and anode for electrons to reach the anode. Hint: Use the conservation of energy and Newton's second law in the form *Torque = Rate of Change of Angular Momentum.* Use polar coordinates

5-13. An ion beam carries ions of mass m and charge Q, the current density being assumed to be constant up to a radius R. The ions have a velocity u. Calculate the radial acceleration of an ion at the periphery, taking into account both the electric and the magnetic fields produced by the beam.

Neglecting relativistic effects, show that the net acceleration is proportional to $1 - (u^2/c^2)$, where $c = 1/(\epsilon_0\mu_0)^{1/2}$ is the velocity of light.

When the electrostatic repulsion is neutralized by the addition of electrons, the Lorentz force gives rise to the pinching effect used in thermonuclear experiments.

5-14. Find the magnetic induction $\mathbf{B}$ within a long straight wire of radius a carrying a uniform current density $\mathbf{J}$ parallel to the wire axis. Assuming that the charge carriers are electrons of charge e distributed with a density N/meter^3 and moving with a drift velocity u, find the direction and magnitude of the magnetic force on the moving charges.

Is the assumption of uniform current density realistic?

5-15. Calculate the electric polarization $\mathbf{P}$ in a long dielectric cylinder of radius a and dielectric constant K_e spinning with angular velocity ω about its axis in a uniform axial magnetic field. Calculate the bound charge densities ρ' and σ'.

5-16. Draw the curve of the magnitude of the vector potential $\mathbf{A}$ as a function of radius for a length of wire 1.00 meter long and 2.00 millimeters in diameter carrying a current of 1.00 ampere. Draw the curve for radii ranging from 0 to 10 centimeters.

5-17. Calculate the axial component of the vector potential $\mathbf{A}$ at the center of a helix of $2N$ turns, of radius R, and of length $2H$ carrying a current I.

Show that the result is the same as that for a single wire of length $2H$ along the side of the helix carrying a current I. Explain.

Is it possible to use this result to calculate the axial component of $\mathbf{B}$ at the center?

Show that the axial component of magnetic induction at the center of the above helix is given by

$$B_z = \frac{I\mu_0 N}{R(1 + 4\pi^2 N^2 \tan^2 \theta)^{1/2}},$$

where θ is the angle between the wire and a plane perpendicular to the axis of the helix.

5-18. A current I flows in a wire bent around a square form measuring $2a$ meters on a side. Calculate the vector potential $\mathbf{A}$ and the magnetic induction $\mathbf{B}$ along an axis passing through the center of the square and parallel to one of the sides.

Draw curves for $\mathbf{A}$ and for $\mathbf{B}$ vs distance from the center of the square when I is 1.00 ampere and a is 10.0 centimeters.

5-19. A circular loop whose axis is coincident with the z-axis carries a current I. Use the divergence and curl properties of the magnetic induction $\mathbf{B}$ to calculate (a) $\partial B_y/\partial y$ at a point on the axis, (b) B_y in the neighborhood of the axis, (c) $\partial B_z/\partial y$ at a point on the axis, and (d) B_z in the neighborhood of the axis.

5-20. A long straight conductor has a circular cross section of radius R and carries a current I. Inside the conductor, there is a cylindrical hole of radius a whose axis is parallel to the axis of the conductor and at a distance b from it. Show that the magnetic induction inside the hole is uniform and is given by

$$B = \frac{\mu_0 b I}{2\pi(R^2 - a^2)}.$$

Hint: Imagine that the hole is filled with a conductor carrying current of the same density. Use the circuital law to find **B**. Imagine that another current of the same density but of opposite direction is superposed in the space occupied by the hole. Superpose the two magnetic fields.

5-21. Show that the magnetic induction **B** inside a toroid of N turns carrying a current I is the same as that due to a current NI flowing in a wire on the axis of the toroid.

5-22. Show that the permeability of free space μ_0 can be defined as follows: if an infinitely long solenoid carries a current density of 1.0 ampere/meter, then the magnetic induction in webers/meter^2 inside the solenoid is numerically equal to μ_0.

5-23. The scalar magnetic potential V_m for a ring current was calculated in Section 5.12.3 for distances r which are larger than or equal to the ring radius a. Repeat the calculation for $r \leq a$, and show that

$$V_m = \frac{\mu_0 I}{2}\left[\left(\frac{3}{2} - \frac{r}{a}\right)\cos\theta - \left(\frac{7}{16} - \frac{r^3}{4a^3}\right)(5\cos^3\theta - 3\cos\theta) + \cdots\right],$$

where $r \leq a$. Show that this result agrees with Eq. *5-179* at $r = a$.

Caution: It will be found at first that V_m does *not* change sign when $\theta = \pi$ is substituted for $\theta = 0$ and that two slightly different series must be used, one for $0 \leq \theta \leq \pi/2$, and one for $\pi/2 \leq \theta \leq \pi$. It is possible to find a single series which is valid for all θ by using the series

$$\tfrac{3}{2}P_1(\cos\theta) - \tfrac{7}{8}P_3(\cos\theta) + \tfrac{11}{16}P_5(\cos\theta) - \cdots,$$

which is equal to $+1$ for $0 \leq \theta \leq \pi/2$ and equal to -1 for $\pi/2 \leq \theta \leq \pi$. Calculate B_r and B_θ.

5-24. Find the magnetic induction **B** at the center of a square current loop from $\mathbf{B} = -\nabla V_m$, where V_m is the magnetic scalar potential. Compare your result with those of Problems 5-4 and 5-18. Hint: It is not necessary to calculate the solid angle itself, since the $\Delta\Omega$ corresponding to a small displacement of the loop can be readily calculated.

5-25. A square circuit has one corner at the origin and two sides lying along the x- and y-axes. Show that the vector potential **A** at large distances from the circuit is given by

$$\mathbf{A} = \frac{\mu_0}{4\pi}\frac{\mathbf{m} \times \mathbf{r}_1}{r^2},$$

where **m** is the magnetic dipole moment of the circuit, $\mathbf{r}_1$ is a unit vector pointing from the origin to the point P where **A** is calculated, and r is the distance from the origin to P

Show that this result is also valid for a circular coil. Hint: Expand the reciprocal distance from a current element to a point in a Maclaurin's series about the origin.

5-26. Repeat the calculation of Problem 5-25 for a point near the center of the square. Using this result calculate the magnetic induction at the center of the square. Compare your result with those of Problems 5-4 and 5-18.

5-27. An electron revolves in a circular orbit with an angular momentum $\sqrt{2}(h/2\pi)$ about a fixed proton. The constant $h = 6.63 \times 10^{-34}$ joule second is Planck's constant. Calculate the magnetic moment in terms of h; evaluate the magnetic induction **B** at the proton. Is this a large or a small magnetic field?

5-28. An electron spins about its own axis with an angular momentum of $(\sqrt{3}/2)(h/2\pi)$. Find the magnetic moment associated with the spin (a) when the charge is uniformly distributed throughout the volume of the sphere and (b) when it is uniformly distributed over the surface of the sphere.

5-29. A conducting sphere of radius a is charged to a potential V and is rotated about a diameter at an angular velocity ω. Show that the resulting magnetic dipole moment is

$$\mathbf{m} = \tfrac{4}{3}\pi a^3 \epsilon_0 V \omega \mathbf{k},$$

where $\mathbf{k}$ is a unit vector along the axis and is related to the direction of rotation by the right-hand screw rule.

Calculate the dipole moment for a sphere 10.0 centimeters in diameter charged to 10,000 volts spinning at 30,000 turns/minute.

What current flowing through a loop 10.0 centimeters in diameter would give the same dipole moment?

In the case of the sphere, show that the magnetic induction is the same at all points on the axis. Show that it is the same everywhere within the spherical surface.

5-30. Show that the average magnetic induction produced over the volume of a sphere by a small current loop arbitrarily placed within the sphere is given by

$\bar{\mathbf{B}} = \dfrac{\mu_0 \mathbf{m}}{2\pi R^3}$, where $\mathbf{m}$ is the dipole moment of the loop and R is the radius of the sphere.

5-31. A single turn coil of radius a carries a current I. Show that

$$\mathbf{A} = \frac{\mu_0}{4\pi}\frac{I}{r^2}(\pi a^2)\sin\theta\,\mathbf{k}$$

$$= \frac{\mu_0}{4\pi}\frac{m}{r^2}\sin\theta\,\mathbf{k}$$

in polar coordinates. The origin is chosen to be at the center of the coil with the plane of the coil perpendicular to the polar axis. The direction of the current and the positive direction of the polar axis are related by the right-hand screw rule. Show that

$$\mathbf{B} = \frac{\mu_0}{4\pi}\frac{m}{r}(2\cos\theta\,\mathbf{i} \div \sin\theta\,\mathbf{j}).$$

CHAPTER 6

Induced
Electromotance and
Magnetic Energy

In the last chapter we discussed the production of magnetic fields by steady currents; we shall now extend the discussion to include time-dependent magnetic fields and the nonconservative electric fields which accompany them. We shall continue to restrict our discussion to nonmagnetic materials.

6.1. The Faraday Induction Law

We have seen in Section 2.3 that an electrostatic field is conservative. This property can be stated mathematically by the relation

$$\oint \mathbf{E} \cdot \mathbf{dl} = 0. \tag{6-1}$$

Thus the work performed by electrostatic forces is zero when a charge is moved around a closed path.

There are many other cases, however, in which the above line integral is not zero. Let us consider a particular one which involves the Lorentz force on charges moving in a magnetic field. This force was discussed in Section 5.3.

Figure 6-1 shows a closed rectangular circuit, one side of which can slide parallel to itself with a velocity $\mathbf{u}$ in a region of uniform magnetic induction $\mathbf{B}$. We shall assume, as in all our discussions of moving objects, that the velocity $\mathbf{u}$ is much smaller than the velocity of light. This will avoid complications from relativistic effects. A free charge Q in the moving wire then experiences a *Lorentz force* $\mathbf{f}$:

$$\mathbf{f} = Q(\mathbf{u} \times \mathbf{B}), \tag{6-2}$$

where the vector $\mathbf{u} \times \mathbf{B}$ is called the *induced electric field intensity*. This quantity is measured, as is the electrostatic field intensity, by the force exerted on a unit charge.

The line integral of the induced electric field intensity around the circuit is

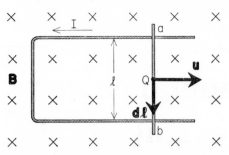

not zero. Taking the line integral in the clockwise direction, and $\mathbf{B}$ in the direction shown in the figure, we have

$$\oint \mathbf{E} \cdot d\mathbf{l} = \oint_a^b (\mathbf{u} \times \mathbf{B}) \cdot d\mathbf{l}, \quad (6\text{-}3)$$

$$= -luB. \quad (6\text{-}4)$$

Figure 6-1. *A conducting wire ab slides with a velocity* $\mathbf{u}$ *along conducting rails in a region of uniform magnetic induction* $\mathbf{B}$. *The Lorentz force on the electrons in the wire produces a current I in the circuit. The electronic charge is taken to be Q.*

The magnitude of the right-hand side is the product of the area swept by the wire per unit time and the magnetic induction B. It is thus the magnetic flux swept per unit time; hence

$$\oint \mathbf{E} \cdot d\mathbf{l} = -\frac{d\Phi}{dt}. \quad (6\text{-}5)$$

It is important to note that the direction in which the line integral is evaluated, and the direction in which the flux Φ is taken to be positive, are related according to the right-hand screw rule.

The line integral of $\mathbf{E} \cdot d\mathbf{l}$ around the circuit is called the *induced electromotance*,* where $\mathbf{E}$ is the induced electric field intensity. The current flowing through the circuit is equal to the induced electromotance divided by the resistance of the circuit at that moment, exactly as if the induced electromotance were replaced by a battery of the same voltage and polarity.

If we had assumed that two or more sides of the circuit moved in the magnetic field, the end result would have been the same; the induced electromotance is always given by $-d\Phi/dt$ in such cases.

This type of induced electromotance is known as *motional induced electromotance*. It is a direct consequence of the Lorentz force, which itself follows from the magnetic force law discussed at the beginning of the last chapter.

There is also another type of induced electromotance, called *transformer induced electromotance*, which is observed in a rigid, fixed circuit when it is linked by a variable magnetic flux. The distinction between motional and transformer electromotance is artificial, in some cases, in that different observers

---

* This quantity is usually called the *induced electromotive force*, or the induced EMF. The term force is not appropriate, however, since electromotance is definitely not a force. The simplest word to use is voltage, but this term has the disadvantage of referring to a particular unit, namely, the volt.

would identify them differently. They would always agree, however, on the electromotance. This will be shown in Appendix E.

The above equation can be rewritten as

$$\oint \mathbf{E} \cdot \mathbf{dl} = -\frac{d}{dt} \int_S \mathbf{B} \cdot \mathbf{da}, \qquad (6\text{-}6)$$

where S is any surface bounded by the path of integration chosen for the line integral. This path can be chosen at will, and it need not lie in conducting material. This is the *Faraday induction law*.

This law is correct, insofar as has been determined experimentally, no matter what the origin of the changing flux may be: the current producing the flux may change with time, it may move relative to the closed path around which the electromotance is calculated, or the path, or parts of it, may move relative to the flux-producing circuit. Care must be taken, however, in applying the Faraday law to nonfilamentary circuits when there is relative motion between different parts of the circuit. We shall discuss specific examples later on in this chapter and also in Appendix E.

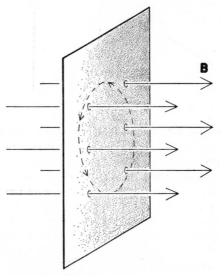

Figure 6-2. *The positive direction around an integration path in a magnetic field* **B**. *The positive direction around the path and the positive direction for* **B** *are related according to the right-hand screw rule.*

6.1.1. Lenz's Law. The negative sign in the Faraday law defines the sign of the induced electromotance relative to a positive direction around the integration path. It is illustrated in Figure 6-2, where a path of integration lies in a plane perpendicular to a uniform magnetic field **B**: the positive direction is chosen according to the right-hand screw rule. This choice of positive direction for **B** through the path of integration also makes the flux of **B** positive, since we also choose the normal to a surface bounded by the integration path in the right-hand sense.

If the flux Φ increases, $d\Phi/dt$ is positive, and the electromotance is negative, that is, the induced electric field intensity is in the negative direction. On the other hand, if Φ decreases, $d\Phi/dt$ is negative, and **E** is in the positive direction.

The direction of the induced current is always such that it produces a magnetic field which *opposes*, to a greater or lesser extent, the change in flux, depending on the resistance in the circuit. Thus, if Φ increases, the induced current produces an opposing flux. If Φ decreases, the induced current produces an aiding flux. This is *Lenz's law*. This law follows from the conservation of energy, for if the induced electric field acted in the direction to aid the change in flux, it would produce a current which would further increase the flux, which would in turn induce still more current, and energy would thus be created in the system.

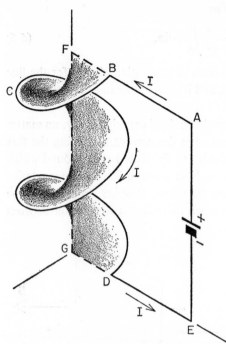

Lenz's law is a particular case of *Le Chatelier's principle*, which states that, whenever a stress is applied to a system in equilibrium, the equilibrium is displaced so as to reduce the effect of the stress.

Figure 6-3. *Solenoid connected to a source. The real circuit is ABCDE. To calculate the flux linkages, the real circuit is replaced by (a) ABFGDE, in which the current flows downward along the dotted part and by (b) BCDGFB, in which the current flows upward in the dotted part. The flux linkage for the real circuit is then the sum of the flux linkages through the spiral ramp and through the surface AFGE.*

6.1.2. Flux Linkage. The surface over which the magnetic induction must be integrated to obtain the flux Φ can be complicated. For example, let us consider a solenoid of N turns. The procedure in this case is illustrated in Figure 6-3.* If the lines of **B** are parallel to the axis of the solenoid, they cross the spiral ramp once for each turn of the solenoid. The total flux crossing the entire spiral surface is then N times the flux crossing the surface corresponding to a single turn. The lines of **B** are then said to *link* all N turns, and Faraday's law gives

$$\oint \mathbf{E} \cdot \mathbf{dl} = -N \frac{d\Phi}{dt}, \tag{6-7}$$

where Φ is the flux linking a single turn.

In general, not all the flux links all the turns, and the electromotance induced in the solenoid is

* See G. W. Carter, *The Electromagnetic Field and Its Engineering Applications* (Longmans, New York, 1954), p. 166.

$$\oint \mathbf{E} \cdot \mathbf{dl} = -\frac{d}{dt}(N\Phi), \tag{6-8}$$

where $N\Phi$ is the total flux linkage.

6.1.3. The Faraday Law in Differential Form.

The Faraday law as stated in Eq. *6-6* says nothing about the induced electric field intensity $\mathbf{E}$ itself. It only gives the electromotance in the complete circuit. Using Stokes's theorem to transform the line integral into a surface integral, we have

$$\int_S (\nabla \times \mathbf{E}) \cdot \mathbf{da} = -\frac{d}{dt} \int_S \mathbf{B} \cdot \mathbf{da}, \tag{6-9}$$

where S is any surface bounded by the closed integration path. For the case in which this path is fixed in space, we may interchange the order of differentiation and integration on the right-hand side. Then

$$\int_S (\nabla \times \mathbf{E}) \cdot \mathbf{da} = -\int_S \frac{\partial \mathbf{B}}{\partial t} \cdot \mathbf{da}, \tag{6-10}$$

where we have written the partial derivative of $\mathbf{B}$ because we now require the rate of change of $\mathbf{B}$ with time at a fixed point. In a later section we shall examine the more general case in which the path moves. The restriction to a fixed path means that the electric field intensity $\mathbf{E}$ and the magnetic induction vector $\mathbf{B}$ must be measured in the same coordinate system.

Since the above equation is valid for arbitrary surfaces, the integrands must be equal at every point, thus

$$\boxed{\nabla \times \mathbf{E} = -\frac{\partial \mathbf{B}}{\partial t}.} \tag{6-11}$$

This is the third of the four Maxwell equations. The other two which we have found so far are Eqs. *3-58* and *5-45*. Equation *6-11* is a differential equation which relates the space derivatives of the electric field intensity $\mathbf{E}$ at a particular point to the time rate of change of the magnetic induction $\mathbf{B}$ at the same point. The equation does not give $\mathbf{E}$ itself unless it can be integrated.

6.1.4. The Induced Electric Field Intensity E in Terms of the Vector Potential A.

The electric field intensity $\mathbf{E}$ induced by a changing magnetic field can be expected to be related to the vector potential $\mathbf{A}$ of Section 5.5. The relationship can be found as follows. Since

$$\mathbf{B} = \nabla \times \mathbf{A} \tag{6-12}$$

always, then, from Eq. *6-11*,

$$\nabla \times \mathbf{E} = -\frac{\partial}{\partial t}(\nabla \times \mathbf{A}), \tag{6-13}$$

or, interchanging the order of differentiation,

$$\nabla \times \mathbf{E} = -\nabla \times \frac{\partial \mathbf{A}}{\partial t}, \tag{6-14}$$

$$\nabla \times \left(\mathbf{E} + \frac{\partial \mathbf{A}}{\partial t}\right) = 0. \tag{6-15}$$

The term between parentheses must equal a quantity whose curl is zero. Thus

$$\mathbf{E} = -\frac{\partial \mathbf{A}}{\partial t} - \nabla V, \tag{6-16}$$

since any vector whose curl is zero can be represented as the gradient of a scalar function.

For steady currents, $\mathbf{A}$ is a constant, and Eq. *6-16* reduces to Eq. *2-10* of electrostatics:

$$\mathbf{E} = -\nabla V. \tag{6-17}$$

This $\mathbf{E}$ is the electrostatic field intensity, which, because it is of no interest to us at the moment, we shall disregard. We shall return to Eq. *6-16* for the general case in Chapter 13. Thus the *induced* electric field intensity at a point is given by

$$\mathbf{E} = -\frac{\partial \mathbf{A}}{\partial t}. \tag{6-18}$$

We could also have arrived at this same result in the following way. According to the Faraday induction law, the induced electromotance for any given path is given by

$$\oint \mathbf{E} \cdot d\mathbf{l} = -\frac{d\Phi}{dt}, \tag{6-19}$$

$$= -\frac{d}{dt} \oint \mathbf{A} \cdot d\mathbf{l}, \tag{6-20}$$

from Eq. *5-83*. Interchanging the order of differentiation and of integration on the right, which we may do, since we are considering fixed paths, we find that

$$\oint \mathbf{E} \cdot d\mathbf{l} = -\oint \frac{\partial \mathbf{A}}{\partial t} \cdot d\mathbf{l}. \tag{6-21}$$

We have used a partial derivative under the integral sign because the time derivative of $\mathbf{A}$ must be evaluated at a given point on the path. Since this equation must be valid for any arbitrary path,

$$\mathbf{E} = -\frac{\partial \mathbf{A}}{\partial t} \tag{6-22}$$

at each point, as long as $\mathbf{E}$ is an induced electric field intensity.

6.1.5. The Electromotance Induced in a Loop by a Pair of Long Parallel Wires Carrying a Variable Current *I*. As an illustration, let us consider Fig-

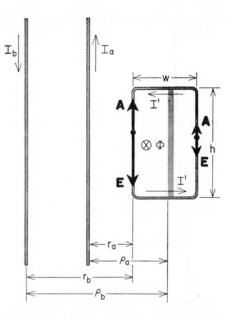

Figure 6-4

*Pair of parallel wires carrying a current I in opposite directions in the plane of a closed rectangular loop of wire. When the current I increases, the induced electromotance gives rise to a current I' in the direction shown. The vector potentials **A** and the induced electromotances −∂**A**/∂t are shown on the vertical wires. The induced current I' flows in the counterclockwise direction because **E** is larger on the left than on the right.*

ure 6-4. The wires carry a current I in opposite directions, and I increases at the rate dI/dt. We shall first calculate the induced electromotance from the Faraday induction law, Eq. 6-6, and then from Eq. 6-21.

The current I in wire a produces a magnetic induction in the azimuthal direction such that

$$B_a = \frac{\mu_0 I}{2\pi\rho_a}. \tag{6-23}$$

A similar relation exists for wire b. The flux through the loop is thus

$$\Phi = \frac{\mu_0 I}{2\pi}\left(\int_{r_a}^{r_a+w} \frac{h\,d\rho_a}{\rho_a} - \int_{r_b}^{r_b+w} \frac{h\,d\rho_b}{\rho_b}\right), \tag{6-24}$$

$$= \frac{\mu_0 h I}{2\pi} \ln\left[\frac{r_b(r_a+w)}{r_a(r_b+w)}\right], \tag{6-25}$$

and it points into the paper, as shown in Figure 6-4. The induced electromotance is given by

$$\oint \mathbf{E}\cdot d\mathbf{l} = -\frac{\mu_0 h}{2\pi}\frac{dI}{dt} \ln\left[\frac{r_b(r_a+w)}{r_a(r_b+w)}\right], \tag{6-26}$$

$$= \frac{\mu_0 h}{2\pi}\frac{dI}{dt} \ln\left[\frac{r_a(r_b+w)}{r_b(r_a+w)}\right]. \tag{6-27}$$

It is negative, and, from Lenz's law, produces a current I' in the direction shown in Figure 6-4.

Let us now use Eq. 6-21 to calculate this same induced electromotance from the time derivative of the vector potential **A**. From Section 5.5.2, **A** is parallel to the wires, and

$$A_L = \frac{\mu_0 I}{2\pi} \ln \frac{r_b}{r_a}, \tag{6-28}$$

$$A_R = -\frac{\mu_0}{2\pi} \ln \left(\frac{r_b + w}{r_a + w} \right) \tag{6-29}$$

along the left- and right-hand sides of the loop, respectively. The positive direction is taken to be upwards. Thus the induced electric field intensities are respectively

$$E_L = -\frac{\mu_0}{2\pi} \frac{dI}{dt} \ln \frac{r_b}{r_a}, \tag{6-30}$$

$$E_R = \frac{\mu_0}{2\pi} \frac{dI}{dt} \ln \left(\frac{r_b + w}{r_a + w} \right), \tag{6-31}$$

and the electromotance,

$$\oint \mathbf{E} \cdot \mathbf{dl} = \frac{\mu_0 h}{2\pi} \frac{dI}{dt} \ln \left[\frac{r_a(r_b + w)}{r_b(r_a + w)} \right], \tag{6-32}$$

produces a current I' in the direction shown in the figure, just as in Eq. *6-26.*

If we wish to find the electromotance induced by a changing current in a single conductor, we choose $r_b \gg w$, and then

$$\oint \mathbf{E} \cdot \mathbf{dl} = \frac{\mu_0 h}{2\pi} \frac{dI}{dt} \ln \left(\frac{r_a}{r_a + w} \right). \tag{6-33}$$

6.2. Induced Electromotance in a Moving System

Our differential form of the Faraday law, Eq. *6-11,* was limited to systems at rest. We shall now consider systems moving with velocities which are small compared to the velocity of light. This limitation in velocity is again made to avoid complications from relativistic effects.

We return to the integral form of the Faraday law, Eq. *6-6,* and consider

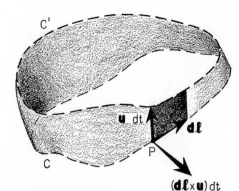

Figure 6-5

*A path of integration moves from C to C′ in the time dt. The displacement is general and involves a translation, a rotation, and a distortion. The point P is assumed to move with a velocity **u** in a region where the magnetic induction is **B**.*

the rate of change of magnetic flux through a surface bounded by a path C which moves in some arbitrary manner, as in Figure 6-5. A given point P on the path C moves with a velocity $\mathbf{u}$ through a region where the magnetic induction depends both on the coordinates and on time:

$$\mathbf{B} = \mathbf{B}(x, y, z, t). \tag{6-34}$$

The rate of change of flux through the circuit is

$$\frac{d\Phi}{dt} = \frac{\int_{S_b} \mathbf{B}_b(t + dt)\cdot \mathbf{da}_b - \int_{S_a} \mathbf{B}_a(t)\cdot \mathbf{da}_a}{dt}, \tag{6-35}$$

where $\mathbf{B}_b(t + dt)$ is the magnetic induction on the surface S_b at $t + dt$, and similarly for $\mathbf{B}_a(t)$.

Applying the divergence theorem *at time $t + dt$* to the volume swept out, we obtain

$$\int_{S_b} \mathbf{B}_b(t + dt)\cdot \mathbf{da}_b - \int_{S_a} \mathbf{B}_a(t + dt)\cdot \mathbf{da}_a$$

$$+ dt \oint_C \mathbf{B}\cdot(\mathbf{dl} \times \mathbf{u}) = \int_\tau \mathbf{\nabla}\cdot\mathbf{B}\, d\tau \tag{6-36}$$

$$= 0, \tag{6-37}$$

since the divergence of $\mathbf{B}$ is always zero. We have used $\mathbf{B}$ without an index for the magnetic induction along the path of integration C. Now

$$\int_{S_a} \mathbf{B}_a(t + dt)\cdot \mathbf{da}_a = \int_{S_a} \mathbf{B}_a(t)\cdot \mathbf{da}_a + \int_{S_a} \frac{\partial \mathbf{B}_a}{\partial t}\, dt\cdot \mathbf{da}_a, \tag{6-38}$$

and, from Stokes's theorem,

$$\oint_C \mathbf{B}\cdot(\mathbf{dl} \times \mathbf{u}) = \oint_C (\mathbf{u} \times \mathbf{B})\cdot \mathbf{dl}, \tag{6-39}$$

$$= \int_{S_a} \mathbf{\nabla} \times (\mathbf{u} \times \mathbf{B})\cdot \mathbf{da}_a. \tag{6-40}$$

Substituting these two equations in the preceding one, we have

$$\int_{S_b} \mathbf{B}_b(t + dt)\cdot \mathbf{da}_b - \int_{S_a} \mathbf{B}_a(t)\cdot \mathbf{da}_a - \int_{S_a} \frac{\partial \mathbf{B}_a}{\partial t}\, dt\cdot \mathbf{da}_a$$

$$+ dt \int_{S_a} \mathbf{\nabla} \times (\mathbf{u} \times \mathbf{B})\cdot \mathbf{da}_a = 0, \tag{6-41}$$

and, finally,

$$\frac{d\Phi}{dt} = -\int_S \mathbf{\nabla} \times (\mathbf{u} \times \mathbf{B})\cdot \mathbf{da} + \int_S \frac{\partial \mathbf{B}}{\partial t} \cdot \mathbf{da}. \tag{6-42}$$

The subscript on S is now unnecessary, since we have really calculated $\Delta\Phi/\Delta t$ in the limit $\Delta t \longrightarrow 0$. The two terms represent respectively: (a) the flux lost or gained through the sides of the volume traced out by the moving path, and (b) the change of flux by virtue of the change of **B** with time.

Thus, from the Faraday law,

$$\oint \mathbf{E} \cdot d\mathbf{l} = \int_S \left[\nabla \times (\mathbf{u} \times \mathbf{B}) - \frac{\partial \mathbf{B}}{\partial t} \right] \cdot d\mathbf{a}, \qquad (6\text{-}43)$$

or, using Stokes's theorem,

$$\int_S \nabla \times \mathbf{E} \cdot d\mathbf{a} = \int_S \left[\nabla \times (\mathbf{u} \times \mathbf{B}) - \frac{\partial \mathbf{B}}{\partial t} \right] \cdot d\mathbf{a}. \qquad (6\text{-}44)$$

Since this equation must be valid for any surface S bounded by any curve C, the integrands must be equal at every point, and

$$\nabla \times \mathbf{E} = -\frac{\partial \mathbf{B}}{\partial t} + \nabla \times (\mathbf{u} \times \mathbf{B}). \qquad (6\text{-}45)$$

In this equation, **E** is the induced electric field intensity as measured in a coordinate system moving with a velocity **u** relative to that in which the mag-

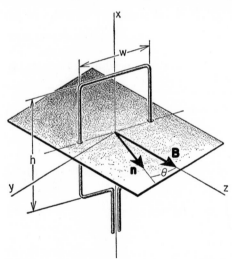

netic induction is measured as **B**. For example, if **E** is induced in a moving conductor, **u** is the velocity of the conductor relative to the laboratory; **B** is measured with an appropriate instrument which is fixed with respect to the laboratory. This does not exclude the use of a search coil and ballistic galvanometer in the usual way. As we saw at the beginning of this chapter, the electric field intensity **E** in the moving conductor is the force on a unit charge at rest with respect to the conductor.*

Figure 6-6. *Fixed loop in a time-dependent magnetic field* **B**. *The vector* **n** *is normal to the loop.*

6.2.1. The Electromotance Induced in a Fixed Loop in a Time-dependent Magnetic Field. To illustrate the above equation, we consider the square loop of Figure 6-6. Let us first suppose that the loop is at rest, its normal making an angle θ with the z-axis as indicated in the diagram. There is a uniform magnetic field **B** that is parallel to the z-axis and which varies with time:

$$\mathbf{B} = \mathbf{B}_0 \sin \omega t. \qquad (6\text{-}46)$$

* See Appendix E for a discussion of Eq. *6-45*.

Since the loop is at rest, $\mathbf{u} = 0$,

$$\nabla \times \mathbf{E} = -\frac{\partial \mathbf{B}}{\partial t}, \tag{6-47}$$

and

$$\oint \mathbf{E} \cdot \mathbf{dl} = \int_S (\nabla \times \mathbf{E}) \cdot \mathbf{da}, \tag{6-48}$$

$$= -\int_S \frac{\partial \mathbf{B}}{\partial t} \cdot \mathbf{da}, \tag{6-49}$$

$$= -B_0 \omega S \cos \theta \cos \omega t, \tag{6-50}$$

where $S = wh$ is the area of the loop.

For example, for a square loop 10×10 centimeters normal to a magnetic field varying at 60 cycles/second with a maximum value of 10^{-2} webers/meter^2 (100 gauss), the induced electromotance has a frequency of 60 cycles/second and a maximum value of about 38 millivolts/turn.

6.2.2. The Electromotance Induced in a Rotating Loop in a Fixed Magnetic Field.
Consider now the same loop of Figure 6-6 rotating with an angular velocity ω about the x-axis in a uniform, time-*in*dependent magnetic field $\mathbf{B}$ parallel to the z-axis. Then, from Eq. 6-45,

$$\nabla \times \mathbf{E} = \nabla \times (\mathbf{u} \times \mathbf{B}), \tag{6-51}$$

and

$$\mathbf{E} = \mathbf{u} \times \mathbf{B}, \tag{6-52}$$

as in Section 6.1. We have neglected any field due to the electrostatic potential V, as in Section 6.1.4. Thus

$$\oint \mathbf{E} \cdot \mathbf{dl} = \oint (\mathbf{u} \times \mathbf{B}) \cdot \mathbf{dl}, \tag{6-53}$$

$$= 2\omega \frac{w}{2} hB \sin \omega t. \tag{6-54}$$

The only contributions to the integral are on the vertical sides, $(\mathbf{u} \times \mathbf{B})$ being perpendicular to $\mathbf{dl}$ along the top and bottom parts of the integration path. Hence

$$\oint \mathbf{E} \cdot \mathbf{dl} = BS\omega \sin \omega t, \tag{6-55}$$

where S is again the area of the loop. The electromotance must go to zero when the plane of the loop is perpendicular to $\mathbf{B}$, since at this instant the free charges inside the wire are moving parallel to $\mathbf{B}$ and there is no force on them.

6.2.3. The Electromotance Induced in a Rotating Loop in a Time-dependent Magnetic Field.

Let us consider again the loop of Figure 6-6, letting **B** depend on time as in Eq. *6-46* and letting the loop rotate with angular velocity ω about the x-axis, its normal being parallel to the z-axis at $t = 0$. Then

$$\nabla \times \mathbf{E} = -\frac{\partial \mathbf{B}}{\partial t} + \nabla \times (\mathbf{u} \times \mathbf{B}). \qquad (6\text{-}56)$$

Integrating over the plane surface S bounded by the loop, we find that

$$\int_S (\nabla \times \mathbf{E}) \cdot \mathbf{da} = -\int_S \frac{\partial \mathbf{B}}{\partial t} \cdot \mathbf{da} + \int_S [\nabla \times (\mathbf{u} \times \mathbf{B})] \cdot \mathbf{da}, \qquad (6\text{-}57)$$

and, applying Stokes's theorem to the curl terms, we obtain

$$\oint \mathbf{E} \cdot \mathbf{dl} = -\int_S \frac{\partial \mathbf{B}}{\partial t} \cdot \mathbf{da} + \oint (\mathbf{u} \times \mathbf{B}) \cdot \mathbf{dl}, \qquad (6\text{-}58)$$

$$= B_0 S \omega (\sin^2 \omega t - \cos^2 \omega t), \qquad (6\text{-}59)$$

$$= -B_0 S \omega \cos 2\omega t. \qquad (6\text{-}60)$$

In this case the electromotance alternates at double the frequency $\omega/2\pi$.

We may also calculate this electromotance from the total rate of change of flux through the loop, according to Eq. *6-8*. The flux is given by

$$\Phi = BS', \qquad (6\text{-}61)$$

where

$$S' = S \cos \theta \qquad (6\text{-}62)$$

is the area of the loop projected on a plane normal to the direction of **B**. Then

$$\frac{d\Phi}{dt} = B \frac{dS'}{dt} + S' \frac{dB}{dt}. \qquad (6\text{-}63)$$

On evaluating these derivatives we find the same electromotance as above.

6.3. Inductance and Induced Electromotance

In computing the electromotance induced in one circuit when the current changes in another, it is convenient to calculate the flux through the first circuit in terms of: (a) the current in the second and (b) a purely geometrical factor involving both circuits. This factor is known as the mutual inductance. The same procedure can be used to relate the linking flux and the current for a single circuit, in which case the geometrical factor is known as the self-inductance.

6.3.1. Mutual Inductance.

Let us seek an expression for the magnetic flux which links one circuit but arises from the current in another. This flux is

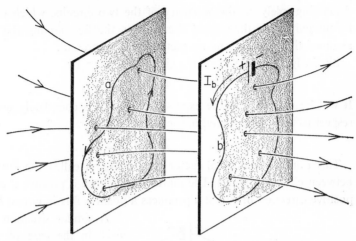

Figure 6-7. *Two circuits a and b. The flux Φ_{ab} shown linking a and originating in b is positive. This is because its direction is related by the right-hand screw rule to the direction chosen to be positive around a.*

required for the calculation of the induced electromotance in the linked circuit. The current I_b in a circuit b produces a magnetic flux Φ_{ab} linking a circuit a, as in Figure 6-7, thus

$$\Phi_{ab} = \int_{S_a} \mathbf{B}_b \cdot \mathbf{da}_a, \tag{6-64}$$

where $\mathbf{da}_a$ is an element of area on an arbitrary surface S_a bounded by circuit a and where $\mathbf{B}_b$ is the magnetic induction from current I_b at a point on S_a.

We can now calculate B_b from the vector potential $\mathbf{A}_b$ produced by I_b:

$$\Phi_{ab} = \int_{S_a} (\nabla \times \mathbf{A}_b) \cdot \mathbf{da}_a, \tag{6-65}$$

$$= \oint_a \mathbf{A}_b \cdot \mathbf{dl}_a, \tag{6-66}$$

$$= \oint_a \left(\frac{\mu_0 I_b}{4\pi} \oint_b \frac{\mathbf{dl}_b}{r} \right) \cdot \mathbf{dl}_a, \tag{6-67}$$

$$= \frac{\mu_0 I_b}{4\pi} \oint_a \oint_b \frac{\mathbf{dl}_b \cdot \mathbf{dl}_a}{r}, \tag{6-68}$$

$$= M_{ab} I_b, \tag{6-69}$$

where

$$M_{ab} = \frac{\mu_0}{4\pi} \oint_a \oint_b \frac{\mathbf{dl}_a \cdot \mathbf{dl}_b}{r}. \tag{6-70}$$

This is the *Neumann equation*. It is rather remarkable: M_{ab} is a quantity depending solely on the geometry of the two circuits, which when multiplied by the current in the second circuit gives the flux linking the first. We have assumed that there are no magnetic materials present.

Similarly, the flux Φ_{ba} linking circuit b is given by

$$\Phi_{ba} = M_{ba}I_a. \tag{6-71}$$

It will be noticed that the expression for M_{ab} is completely symmetrical with respect to the indices a and b, such that

$$M_{ab} = M_{ba}. \tag{6-72}$$

This purely geometrical factor $M_{ab} = M_{ba}$ is called the *mutual inductance* between circuits a and b. The mutual inductance is positive if a current in the positive direction in circuit a produces a positive flux in circuit b.

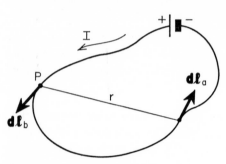

Figure 6-8. *Single circuit carrying a current I.*

A similar situation was found to exist in the case of capacitance in Section 2.13.1. It was shown there that the charge on a conductor is the product of its potential multiplied by a purely geometrical factor called the coefficient of capacitance.

The mutual inductance is the magnetic flux linking one circuit per unit of current in the other. In rationalized m.k.s. units, inductance is measured in webers/ampere, or in henrys. The mutual inductance between two circuits is one henry when a current of one ampere in one of the circuits produces a flux linkage of one weber-turn in the other.

6.3.2. Self-inductance. A single circuit is of course linked by its own flux. This flux can be computed in the same manner as above:

$$\Phi = \frac{\mu_0 I}{4\pi} \oint_a \left(\oint_b \frac{dl_a}{r} \right) \cdot dl_b, \tag{6-73}$$

where r is the distance between a fixed point P on the circuit and an element dl_a of the same circuit, as in Figure 6-8.

The double line integral is explained as follows. We form the elementary vector dl_a/r at a point P located at the position of another element dl_b of the same circuit. We then sum the elementary vectors corresponding to the elements dl_a around the circuit. This gives

$$\oint_a (dl_a/r)$$

at P. We then form the scalar product of this vector with $\mathbf{dl}_b$ at P, and, finally, we sum the resultant scalar quantities for all the $\mathbf{dl}_b$'s around the circuit.

As for mutual inductance, the total flux linkage is

$$\Phi = LI, \tag{6-74}$$

where

$$L = \frac{\mu_0}{4\pi} \oint_b \left(\oint_a \frac{\mathbf{dl}_a}{r} \right) \cdot \mathbf{dl}_b \tag{6-75}$$

is called the *self-inductance* of the circuit. It depends solely on the geometry of the circuit. Self-inductance, like mutual inductance, is measured in henrys. It is always positive. A circuit has a self-inductance of one henry if a current of one ampere produces a flux linkage of one weber-turn.

If the circuit is truly filamentary, that is, if the cross-sectional area of the conductor is infinitely small, the flux Φ and the inductance L become infinite, since $\mathbf{dl}_a/r \longrightarrow \infty$ as $\mathbf{dl}_a$ approaches the point P. The infinite flux and inductance can also be explained as follows. As the radius r of the conductor tends to zero, $\mathbf{B}$ tends to infinity in the immediate neighborhood of the wire. The region where $\mathbf{B}$ is infinitely large is itself infinitely small, but the flux tends to infinity logarithmically. This flux clings infinitely close to the wire. In practice, currents are found to be distributed over a finite cross section, thus the flux linkage, and therefore the inductance, does not in fact diverge.

We shall calculate self-inductance for two cases in which the currents are effectively distributed over a surface. Then both the flux and the inductance are finite. Volume distributions of current will be discussed in Section 6.5.

Circuits designed to possess self-inductance are called *inductors*, and pairs of circuits designed to possess mutual inductance are called *mutual inductors*.

We shall now use these concepts to calculate the self-inductance of a long solenoid, the self-inductance of a toroid, and the mutual inductance between two coaxial solenoids.

6.3.3. Self-inductance of a Long Solenoid.

It was shown in Section 5.11.3 that the magnetic induction inside a long solenoid, neglecting end effects, is constant and that

$$B = \mu_0 N'I, \tag{6-76}$$

where N' is the number of turns per meter. Thus we can write

$$\Phi = \frac{\mu_0 NI}{s} \pi R^2, \tag{6-77}$$

where N is the total number of turns, s is the length of the solenoid, and R is its radius. Then

$$L = \frac{N\Phi}{I}, \tag{6-78}$$

$$L = \frac{\mu_0 N^2}{s} \pi R^2, \qquad (6\text{-}79)$$

$$= \mu_0 N'^2 s \pi R^2. \qquad (6\text{-}80)$$

When end effects are taken into account, the inductance is reduced by a factor K which is a function of R/s. Representative values of K are shown in Table 6-1. The calculation for K is complex and will not be discussed.

TABLE 6-1.   Representative Values of K

Radius/Length	K
0	1.00
0.2	0.85
0.4	0.74
0.6	0.65
0.8	0.58
1.0	0.53
1.5	0.43
2.0	0.37
4.0	0.24
10.0	0.12

6.3.4. Self-inductance of a Toroid.

We consider a circuit in the form of a toroidal coil of N turns wound on a form of nonmagnetic material with a square cross section, as in Figure 6-9.

We shall calculate the flux Φ linking the coil when the current in the winding is I. The self-inductance L will then be given by the ratio $N\Phi/I$, since the circuit is linked N times by the flux.

Inside the toroid, on a radius ρ, we have, from the circuital law, or from Eq. 5-142,

$$B = \frac{\mu_0 NI}{2\pi\rho}. \qquad (6\text{-}81)$$

Thus

$$\Phi = \frac{\mu_0 NI}{2\pi} \int_{R-\frac{w}{2}}^{R+\frac{w}{2}} \frac{w\,d\rho}{\rho}, \qquad (6\text{-}82)$$

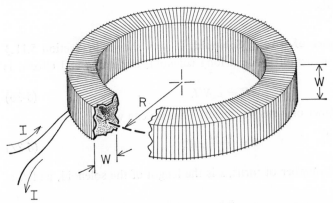

Figure 6-9. *Toroidal coil of square cross section and mean radius R.*

$$\Phi = \frac{\mu_0 NI}{2\pi} \, w \ln \left[\frac{2R + w}{2R - w} \right], \tag{6-83}$$

$$L = \frac{\mu_0 N^2 w}{2\pi} \ln \left[\frac{2R + w}{2R - w} \right]. \tag{6-84}$$

For the case in which $R \gg w$,

$$\frac{2R + w}{2R - w} \approx \left(1 + \frac{w}{2R} \right)\left(1 + \frac{w}{2R} \right), \tag{6-85}$$

$$\approx 1 + \frac{w}{r}, \tag{6-86}$$

$$\ln \left[\frac{2R + w}{2R - w} \right] \approx \frac{w}{R}, \tag{6-87}$$

and

$$L \approx \frac{\mu_0 N^2}{2\pi} \frac{w^2}{R} \qquad (R \gg w). \tag{6-88}$$

As with the solenoid, the self-inductance is proportional both to the square of the number of turns and to the cross-sectional area enclosed by the winding and is inversely proportional to the length of the winding. The two results are identical because we have assumed for the solenoid that end effects could be neglected and that **B** was uniform inside and zero outside.

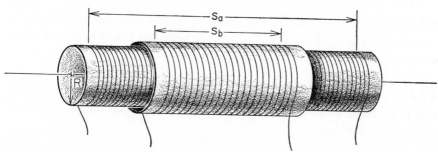

Figure 6-10. *Coaxial solenoids. The two radii are taken to be approximately equal.*

6.3.5. Mutual Inductance Between Two Coaxial Solenoids.
Let us now add a second winding over the solenoid as in Figure 6-10. We assume for simplicity that both windings are long with respect to the common diameter, in order that end effects can be neglected. We also assume that the pitches of the two windings are equal, with the result that

$$\frac{N_a}{s_a} = \frac{N_b}{s_b}. \tag{6-89}$$

To calculate the mutual inductance between the two coils, let us assume a current I_a in coil a (we do not use the Neumann equation, Eq. 6-70, because it would require a much more complicated calculation). Then the flux Φ_{ba} linking coil b and produced by I_a is

$$\Phi_{ba} = \frac{\mu_0 \pi R^2 N_a I_a}{s_a}, \tag{6-90}$$

and the mutual inductance is

$$M_{ba} = \frac{N_b \Phi_{ba}}{I_a}, \tag{6-91}$$

$$= \frac{\mu_0 \pi R^2 N_a N_b}{s_a}. \tag{6-92}$$

Let us now calculate the mutual inductance M_{ab} by assuming a current I_b in coil b. In this case

$$\Phi_{ab} = \frac{\mu_0 \pi R^2 N_b I_b}{s_b}. \tag{6-93}$$

This flux now links only N_b turns of coil a, since $\mathbf{B}$ falls rapidly to zero beyond the end of the solenoid, as we saw in Problem 5-7. Then,

$$M_{ab} = \frac{\mu_0 \pi R^2 N_b^2}{s_b}, \tag{6-94}$$

and

$$M_{ab} = \frac{\mu_0 \pi R^2 N_a N_b}{s_a} \tag{6-95}$$

from Eq. 6-89. Thus

$$M_{ab} = M_{ba}. \tag{6-96}$$

This is true even if we take the end effects of the two solenoids into account: a current of one ampere in coil a produces the same flux in coil b as a current of one ampere in coil b produces in coil a.

6.3.6. Coefficient of Coupling. Let us consider a coil a through which a current I_a produces a flux Φ_{aa} and a coil b arranged such that only a fraction k_a of Φ_{aa} passes through it:

$$\Phi_{ba} = k_a \Phi_{aa}. \tag{6-97}$$

We consider single-turn coils for simplicity. The self-inductance of coil a is

$$L_a = \frac{N_a \Phi_{aa}}{I_a}, \tag{6-98}$$

and the mutual inductance between the two coils is

$$M_{ba} = \frac{N_b k_a \Phi_{aa}}{I_a}. \tag{6-99}$$

Thus

$$M_{ba} = k_a \frac{N_b}{N_a} L_a. \tag{6-100}$$

Likewise,

$$M_{ab} = k_b \frac{N_a}{N_b} L_b. \tag{6-101}$$

Then, since $M_{ba} = M_{ab} = M$,

$$M^2 = k_a k_b L_a L_b, \qquad (6\text{-}102)$$

$$M = \pm k(L_a L_b)^{1/2}, \qquad (6\text{-}103)$$

where

$$k = \pm(k_a k_b)^{1/2} \qquad (6\text{-}104)$$

is called the *coefficient of coupling* between the two coils. It can have values ranging from -1 to 1. The maximum mutual inductance between two coils is thus the square root of the product of their self-inductances.

We have seen in Section 6.3.2 that the self-inductance of a circuit tends to infinity as the wire radius r tends to zero. The mutual inductance, however, does *not* tend to infinity if one or both of the circuits is filamentary, since the magnetic induction at some distance from a wire is hardly sensitive to r. This can be seen from the integral for **B** in the general case, Eq. *5-9*. We have also seen that **B** outside a long straight wire depends only on the current flowing through it. The intense flux very close to a thin wire does not link another circuit some distance away. That is, as $r \longrightarrow 0$, $L \longrightarrow \infty$, $k \longrightarrow 0$, and the mutual inductance remains about the same.

6.3.7. Inductance and Induced Electromotance. We return to the Faraday law and express the induced electromotance in terms of inductance. Consider a current I_b in circuit b producting a flux Φ_{ab} through circuit a. If I_b changes, there is a corresponding change in Φ_{ab}, and the induced electromotance in circuit a is

$$\oint_a \mathbf{E} \cdot d\mathbf{l} = -\frac{d\Phi_{ab}}{dt}, \qquad (6\text{-}105)$$

$$= -M_{ab}\frac{dI_b}{dt}, \qquad (6\text{-}106)$$

where the minus sign comes from Lenz's law, the sign of the mutual inductance being determined as in Section 6.3.1.

This equation is convenient for computing the induced electromotance, since it involves only the mutual inductance M and dI_b/dt, both of which can be measured.

If the current changes in a circuit, the induced electromotance within the same circuit is

$$\oint \mathbf{E} \cdot d\mathbf{l} = -\frac{d\Phi}{dt}, \qquad (6\text{-}107)$$

$$= -L\frac{dI}{dt}, \qquad (6\text{-}108)$$

where L is the self-inductance of the circuit. This induced electromotance adds to whatever other voltages are present.

These equations can be used to define both mutual and self-inductance. In the single circuit, for example, the self-inductance L is 1 henry if a current changing at the rate of 1 ampere/second induces an electromotance of 1 volt.

We have calculated (Section 6.3.5) the mutual inductance between coaxial solenoids. It is paradoxical that a varying current in the *inner* solenoid should induce an electromotance in the *outer* one, since we have shown in Section 5.11.3 that the magnetic induction outside a long solenoid is zero! The explanation is that the induced electric field intensity at any given point is equal to the negative time derivative of the *vector potential* at that point and that the vector potential $\mathbf{A}$ does *not* vanish outside an infinite solenoid, despite the fact that $\mathbf{B} = \nabla \times \mathbf{A}$ does.

We can actually calculate the vector potential at the surface of the inner solenoid from the mutual inductance found earlier. If we consider the direction of the current I_a in the primary as positive, then the electromotance induced in the secondary is

$$\mathcal{V} = -M \frac{dI_a}{dt}, \tag{6-109}$$

where the negative sign comes from Lenz's law. Then

$$\mathcal{V}_b = -\frac{\mu_0 \pi R^2 N_a N_b}{s_a} \frac{dI_a}{dt}, \tag{6-110}$$

and the induced electric field intensity is

$$\frac{\mathcal{V}_b}{2\pi R N_b} = -\frac{\mu_0 R N_a}{2 s_a} \frac{dI_a}{dt}, \tag{6-111}$$

$$= -\frac{\partial A}{\partial t} \tag{6-112}$$

at $\rho = R$. Integrating this expression, we obtain

$$A_{\rho=R} = \frac{\mu_0 R N_a}{2 s_a} I_a \tag{6-113}$$

in the azimuthal direction at the surface of the solenoid. This can be shown to be correct. In fact, at any radius ρ outside the solenoid, $\mathbf{A}$ is azimuthal and is given by

$$A = \frac{\mu_0 R^2}{2\rho} \frac{N_a}{s_a} I_a. \tag{6-114}$$

This can be found by calculating $\mathbf{A}$ for a single turn and integrating over the length of the solenoid. But since this calculation involves elliptic integrals, it will not be given here. However, it is easy to verify that $\mathbf{B} = \nabla \times \mathbf{A} = 0$ in this case.

6.4. Energy Stored in a Magnetic Field

To calculate the work which must be done to establish a magnetic field, we shall calculate the energy supplied by a source to an isolated circuit when the current density increases from zero to some value **J**.

At a given point in the conducting medium, which we assume to be non-magnetic, there is a current density **J** and a corresponding electric field intensity

$$\mathbf{E} = \frac{\mathbf{J}}{\sigma}, \qquad (6\text{-}115)$$

where σ is the electrical conductivity in mhos/meter at the point considered. This equation is *always* true, whatever the origin of **E**. It states that, under the action of an electric field intensity **E**, the electrons drift through the conductor at such a velocity that the resulting current density is $\mathbf{J}/\sigma$ This is Ohm's law (Eq. *5-87*).

The electric field intensity results from (a) the field $-\nabla V$ produced by accumulations of charge on the terminals of the source and on the surfaces of the conductor and from (b) the field $-\partial\mathbf{A}/\partial t$ induced by the vector potential **A** in the conductor, if it is time dependent. It will be remembered from Section 5.8 that the net charge density ρ can be set equal to zero inside a conductor. In a wire, ∇V adjusts itself such that the total field intensity **E** is along the axis.

Inside a source, we also have a third electric field which comes from the local generation of energy. This field can be written as $\mathbf{E}_s$; for example, inside a battery,

$$\mathbf{J}/\sigma = \mathbf{E} + \mathbf{E}_s. \qquad (6\text{-}116)$$

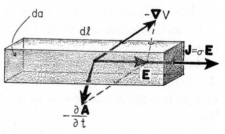

Figure 6-11. *Rectangular parallelepiped parallel to the current density vector* **J** *in a conductor. The electric field intensity* **E** *is the sum of* $-\nabla V$ *and* $-\partial\mathbf{A}/\partial t$.

The work done per unit time and per unit volume on the moving charges at any point outside the source can be calculated as follows. Consider an element of volume having the form of a rectangular parallelepiped oriented such that one set of sides is parallel to the total current density **J**, as in Figure 6-11. In one second, a charge $J\,da$ goes in through the left-hand face and a similar charge comes out at the other end. The source which maintains a difference in potential of $\nabla V \cdot d\mathbf{l}$ across these faces supplies to the element of volume $d\tau$ an amount of power given by

$$\frac{dW}{dt} = (-\nabla V) \cdot d\mathbf{l}\, J\, da, \qquad (6\text{-}117)$$

$$\frac{dW}{dt} = (-\nabla V)\cdot \mathbf{J}\, d\tau, \tag{6-118}$$

$$= \left(\mathbf{E} + \frac{\partial \mathbf{A}}{\partial t}\right) \cdot \mathbf{J}\, d\tau, \tag{6-119}$$

and the integral of this expression over the volume τ, including all the current in the system, gives the total power spent by the source:

$$\frac{dW}{dt} = \int_\tau \frac{J^2}{\sigma}\, d\tau + \int_\tau \frac{\partial \mathbf{A}}{\partial t} \cdot \mathbf{J}\, d\tau. \tag{6-120}$$

The first term on the right gives the total power spent in ohmic or Joule losses; the second gives the rate at which work is done by the source against the induced electromotance. This latter work is that which must be done to establish the magnetic field, and it is the one which concerns us here. We shall disregard Joule losses and write W_m for the energy stored in the magnetic field. Then

$$\frac{dW_m}{dt} = \int_\tau \frac{\partial \mathbf{A}}{\partial t} \cdot \mathbf{J}\, d\tau. \tag{6-121}$$

This expression is always true, even if there are magnetic materials such as iron present in the field. We shall now find other expressions for W_m, but those will not be as general as the one above.

6.4.1. The Magnetic Energy in Terms of the Magnetic Induction B. It is possible to express the magnetic energy W_m in terms of the magnetic induction B, just as the electrostatic energy was expressed in terms of the electrostatic field intensity E in Section 2.14.1.

We shall now restrict our discussion in two different ways. We shall assume that (a) there are no magnetic materials present and that (b) the displacement current is negligible compared to the conduction current, as in Section 5.10. Then

$$\mathbf{J} = \frac{1}{\mu_0}(\nabla \times \mathbf{B}), \tag{6-122}$$

and

$$\frac{dW_m}{dt} = -\frac{1}{\mu_0}\int_\tau [\mathbf{E}_i\cdot(\nabla \times \mathbf{B})]\, d\tau, \tag{6-123}$$

$$= \frac{1}{\mu_0}\int_\tau [\nabla\cdot(\mathbf{E}_i \times \mathbf{B})]\, d\tau - \frac{1}{\mu_0}\int_\tau [\mathbf{B}\cdot(\nabla \times \mathbf{E}_i)]\, d\tau, \tag{6-124}$$

where $\mathbf{E}_i$ is the induced electric field intensity. Using the divergence theorem to transform the first term into a surface integral, and using the Maxwell equation 6-11 $\nabla \times \mathbf{E} = -\partial \mathbf{B}/\partial t$ in the second term, we obtain

$$\frac{dW_m}{dt} = \frac{1}{\mu_0}\int_S (\mathbf{E}_i \times \mathbf{B})\cdot \mathbf{da} + \frac{1}{\mu_0}\int_\tau \left(\mathbf{B} \cdot \frac{\partial \mathbf{B}}{dt}\right)d\tau, \tag{6-125}$$

the volume τ being any volume which includes all points where the current density **J** is not zero, and S being the corresponding surface.

As in the corresponding electrostatic case, Eq. *6-125* becomes simple if we choose τ to include all space, in which case the surface S is at infinity. The magnetic induction **B** falls off as $1/r^3$ at large distances. This was shown for the case of a current loop in Eqs. *5-191* and *5-192*. The induced electric field intensity $\mathbf{E}_i$ also falls off as $1/r^2$, as was shown in Problem 5-25, where we found that the vector potential **A**, and therefore $\mathbf{E}_i$, falls off as $1/r^2$ at large distances from a current loop. Since the surface area S increases only as r^2, the surface integral decreases as $1/r^3$ and vanishes as the surface of integration becomes infinite. Thus

$$\frac{dW_m}{dt} = \frac{1}{\mu_0} \int_\infty \left(\mathbf{B} \cdot \frac{\partial \mathbf{B}}{\partial t} \right) d\tau, \tag{6-126}$$

$$= \frac{1}{2\mu_0} \frac{d}{dt} \int_\infty B^2 \, d\tau. \tag{6-127}$$

Setting $W_m = 0$ when $B = 0$, we have

$$W_m = \frac{1}{2\mu_0} \int_\infty B^2 \, d\tau. \tag{6-128}$$

The quantity W_m is the total work which must be done to establish a magnetic field in terms of the magnetic induction B either in free space or in nonmagnetic matter.

It should be noted that the magnetic energy varies as the *square* of the magnetic induction B. If several fields are superposed, the total energy is therefore *not* just the sum of the energies calculated for each separate field.

Just as in electrostatics, Section 2.14.1, we may define an energy density

$$\frac{dW_m}{d\tau} = \frac{B^2}{2\mu_0} \tag{6-129}$$

associated with each point in space. This matter will be discussed further in the next section.

6.4.2. The Magnetic Energy in Terms of the Current Density J and of the Vector Potential A.
It will be recalled from Sections 2.14 and 2.14.1 that we expressed the energy density in an electrostatic field either in the form $\epsilon_0 E^2/2$ or as $\rho V/2$. We have already expressed the magnetic energy density as $B^2/2\mu_0$; we shall now express it in terms of the current density **J** and of the vector potential **A**.

We rewrite Eq. *6-128* as follows:

$$W_m = \frac{1}{2\mu_0} \int_\infty (\mathbf{B} \cdot \boldsymbol{\nabla} \times \mathbf{A}) \, d\tau. \tag{6-130}$$

Using the vector identity of Problem 1-23 and the divergence theorem, we obtain

$$W = \frac{1}{2\mu_0} \int_\infty \mathbf{A} \cdot (\nabla \times \mathbf{B}) \, d\tau - \frac{1}{2\mu_0} \int_\infty (\mathbf{A} \times \mathbf{B}) \cdot d\mathbf{a}. \qquad (6\text{-}131)$$

The surface integral vanishes again as in Eq. 6-125, and when $\nabla \times \mathbf{B} = \mu_0 \mathbf{J}$ (Section 5.10),

$$W_m = \frac{1}{2} \int_\tau (\mathbf{J} \cdot \mathbf{A}) \, d\tau, \qquad (6\text{-}132)$$

where τ is any volume which includes all regions where $\mathbf{J}$ is not zero.

It is convenient to assign an energy density

$$\frac{dW_m}{d\tau} = \frac{1}{2} (\mathbf{J} \cdot \mathbf{A}) \qquad (6\text{-}133)$$

to conductors carrying a current density $\mathbf{J}$.

Again as in electrostatics, the assignment of an energy density to a point in space is quite arbitrary and meaningless, except as a means of computing the overall magnetic energy W_m. Equations 6-129 and 6-133 are clearly contradictory in that the former assigns a finite energy density to all points where $B \neq 0$, whereas the latter makes the energy density zero wherever there is zero current density. Does the energy reside in the field, or does it reside in the current? These are meaningless questions, even though the "densities" we have found do provide convenient methods for computing the total energy stored in a magnetic field.

6.4.3. The Magnetic Energy in Terms of the Current *I* and of the Flux Φ.

For a filamentary circuit, we may also express the field energy in terms of the current and of the flux linking the circuit. If we replace $\mathbf{J} \, d\tau$ by $I \, d\mathbf{l}$ in Eq. 6-132, $d\mathbf{l}$ being an element of the circuit which carries the current I, then

$$W_m = \frac{1}{2} I \oint \mathbf{A} \cdot d\mathbf{l}. \qquad (6\text{-}134)$$

With real conductors the current is not truly filamentary but is distributed over a small but finite area. We can then use the mean value of $\mathbf{A}$ over the cross section.

Since, from Eq. 5-83, the integral gives the flux Φ linking the circuit,

$$W_m = \frac{1}{2} I\Phi. \qquad (6\text{-}135)$$

The directions in which I and Φ are taken to be positive are related as in the right-hand screw rule.

6.4.4. The Magnetic Energy in Terms of the Currents and of the Inductances.

It is possible to express the energy stored in a magnetic field in still another way, in terms of the currents and of the inductances. In the above equation, the magnetic flux Φ can be replaced by the product of the self-inductance L and the current I, from Section 6.3.2. Then

$$W_m = \frac{1}{2} LI^2. \tag{6-136}$$

For two circuits carrying currents I_a and I_b,

$$W_m = \frac{1}{2} I_a \Phi_a + \frac{1}{2} I_b \Phi_b, \tag{6-137}$$

where Φ_a and Φ_b are the total fluxes linking circuits a and b respectively. The total fluxes consist of contributions from both circuits:

$$\Phi_a = \Phi_{aa} + \Phi_{ab}, \tag{6-138}$$
$$\Phi_b = \Phi_{ba} + \Phi_{bb}. \tag{6-139}$$

Thus

$$W_m = \frac{1}{2} I_a \Phi_{aa} + \frac{1}{2} I_b \Phi_{bb} + \frac{1}{2} I_a \Phi_{ab} + \frac{1}{2} I_b \Phi_{ba}, \tag{6-140}$$

$$= \frac{1}{2} I_a \Phi_{aa} + \frac{1}{2} I_b \Phi_{bb} + I_a \Phi_{ab}, \tag{6-141}$$

$$= \frac{1}{2} I_a \Phi_{aa} + \frac{1}{2} I_b \Phi_{bb} + I_b \Phi_{ba}, \tag{6-142}$$

or, from the definition of self- and mutual inductance,

$$\Phi_a = L_a I_a + M I_b, \tag{6-143}$$
$$\Phi_b = L_b I_b + M I_a, \tag{6-144}$$

and so

$$W_m = \frac{1}{2} L_a I_a^2 + \frac{1}{2} L_b I_b^2 + M I_a I_b. \tag{6-145}$$

The first two terms on the right are self-energies arising from the interaction of each current with its own field, whereas the third term is an interaction energy arising from the mutual inductance.

To sum up, we have found four ways to calculate the magnetic energy associated with a current. We have expressed magnetic energy (1) in terms of the magnetic induction B in Eq. *6-128*, (2) in terms of the current density $\mathbf{J}$ and the vector potential $\mathbf{A}$ in Eq. *6-132*, (3) in terms of the current I and the flux Φ linking the circuit in Eq. *6-135*, and (4) in terms of the currents I and the self- and mutual inductances of a pair of circuits in Eq. *6-145*.

6.4.5. The Magnetic Energy for a Solenoid Carrying a Current *I*. We shall consider again the relatively simple case of the long solenoid of length s and radius R with negligible end effects and calculate W_m by each of the four methods given above.

(1) We have found in Section 5.11.3 that, neglecting end effects, the magnetic induction is uniform throughout the interior of the solenoid and that

$$B = \mu_0 N'I, \tag{6-146}$$

where N' is the number of turns per meter. The magnetic induction is zero everywhere outside. Then

$$W_m = \frac{1}{2\mu_0} \int B^2 \, d\tau, \tag{6-147}$$

$$= \frac{\pi}{2} \mu_0 I^2 N'^2 s R^2. \tag{6-148}$$

(2) Also,

$$W_m = \frac{1}{2} \int \mathbf{J} \cdot \mathbf{A} \, d\tau. \tag{6-149}$$

In this case the current can be taken to be distributed, not over a volume, but over the surface of the solenoid with a density

$$\lambda = N'I. \tag{6-150}$$

The vector potential $\mathbf{A}$ is parallel to I and is given by Eq. 6-114. Then

$$W_m = \frac{1}{2} \int \lambda A \, da, \tag{6-151}$$

$$= \frac{\pi}{2} \mu_0 I^2 N'^2 s R^2 \tag{6-152}$$

as before.

(3) Using still another method, we find that

$$W_m = \frac{1}{2} I\Phi, \tag{6-153}$$

$$= \frac{1}{2} IB(\pi R^2 s), \tag{6-154}$$

$$= \frac{\pi}{2} \mu_0 I^2 N'^2 s R^2. \tag{6-155}$$

(4) Finally,

$$W_m = \frac{1}{2} LI^2, \tag{6-156}$$

and, from the value of L given in Eq. 6-80, we again find that

$$W_m = \frac{\pi}{2} \mu_0 I^2 N'^2 s R^2. \tag{6-157}$$

6.5. Self-inductance for a Volume Distribution of Current

The self-inductance of a circuit comprising currents distributed over a finite volume is defined from the energy stored in the system:

$$W_m = \frac{1}{2\mu_0} \int_\infty B^2 \, d\tau = \frac{1}{2} L I^2. \tag{6-158}$$

Then the self-inductance L is given by

$$L = \frac{1}{\mu_0 I^2} \int_\infty B^2 \, d\tau, \tag{6-159}$$

where the integral is evaluated over all space.

6.5.1. Self-inductance of a Coaxial Line.
The coaxial line of Figure 6-12 is a good example for the calculation of self-inductance of conductors of finite dimensions. We assume that the frequency is low, such that the currents are distributed uniformly throughout the cross sections of the conductors, and again neglect end effects for simplicity.

We shall calculate successively the magnetic energies per unit length of line in regions 1, 2, 3, and 4 as in Figure 6-12, and then set the sum of these energies equal to $(1/2)LI^2$. This will give us the inductance L per unit length.

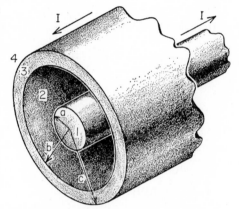

Figure 6-12. *Coaxial line of radii a, b, and c carrying currents I in opposite directions in the inner and outer conductors.*

In region 1, from the circuital law,

$$2\pi\rho B = \mu_0 I \frac{\pi\rho^2}{\pi a^2}, \tag{6-160}$$

and

$$W_{m1} = \frac{1}{2\mu_0} \int_0^{R_1} \left(\frac{\mu_0 I \rho}{2\pi a^2}\right)^2 2\pi\rho \, d\rho, \tag{6-161}$$

$$= \frac{\mu_0 I^2}{16\pi}. \tag{6-162}$$

In region 2,

$$B = \frac{\mu_0 I}{2\pi\rho}, \tag{6-163}$$

$$W_{m2} = \frac{\mu_0 I^2}{4\pi} \ln \frac{b}{a}. \tag{6-164}$$

In region 3, the current within a circular path of radius ρ is that in the center conductor, namely I, less that part of the current in the outer conductor which lies between the radii b and ρ. Thus

$$B = \frac{\mu_0}{2\pi\rho} \left[I - I \left(\frac{\rho^2 - b^2}{c^2 - b^2} \right) \right], \tag{6-165}$$

$$= \frac{\mu_0 I}{2\pi\rho} \left(\frac{c^2 - \rho^2}{c^2 - b^2} \right), \tag{6-166}$$

and

$$W_{m3} = \frac{\mu_0 I^2}{4\pi} \left[\frac{c^4}{(c^2 - b^2)^2} \ln \frac{c}{b} - \frac{(3c^2 - b^2)}{4(c^2 - b^2)} \right]. \tag{6-167}$$

In region 4, $B = 0$ and $W_{m4} = 0$. The inductance L is now given by

$$L = \frac{2(W_{m1} + W_{m2} + W_{m3} + W_{m4})}{I^2}, \tag{6-168}$$

$$= \mu_0 \left\{ \frac{1}{8\pi} + \frac{1}{2\pi} \ln \frac{b}{a} + \frac{1}{2\pi} \left[\frac{c^4}{(c^2 - b^2)^2} \ln \frac{c}{b} - \frac{3c^2 - b^2}{4(c^2 - b^2)} \right] \right\}. \tag{6-169}$$

The second term within the braces is normally the most important; it gives the magnetic energy in the annular region between the conductors.

6.6. Magnetic Force

The magnetic force acting between two current-carrying circuits was stated in Eq. 5-1, and later in Eq. 5-6, in the form of double line integrals. Although the magnetic force law was the starting point for all of Chapter 5, we did not really use it to calculate forces because of the difficulty in evaluating the line integrals.

It is now possible at this stage to find other more convenient expressions for this force. We shall be able to find the force in terms of the mutual inductance between the two circuits. This is experimentally quite satisfactory, since mutual inductance can be measured with accuracy. Its numerical value is not easily calculated, however, even in the simplest cases. This should be obvious from the Neumann equation, Eq. 6-70.

We shall proceed as we did in Section 2.15 where we discussed electrostatic forces on conductors. We shall assume a small virtual displacement of one coil parallel to itself, without any rotation, and then apply the principle of the conservation of energy:

Work done by sources = Increase in magnetic energy

+ Mechanical work done.   *(6-170)*

For simplicity we disregard Joule losses and assume that the displacements are made infinitely slowly, such that kinetic energy is not involved.

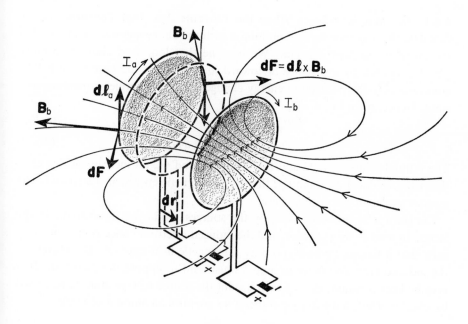

Figure 6-13. *The two loops shown with solid lines carry currents I_a and I_b. Typical lines of induction originating in b are shown linking a. Observe that the elementary forces **dF** have a component in the direction of coil b, with the result that the total force **F** is attractive. To calculate **F**, coil a is assumed to be displaced parallel to itself by a distance **dr** into the position shown by the broken line, and the mechanical work done, **F·dr**, is found from the principle of conservation of energy.*

We consider two loops carrying currents I_a and I_b in the same direction as in Figure 6-13. The elementary forces shown in the figure indicate that the loops tend to move toward each other, thus the coils can be kept fixed in space only if the magnetic forces are balanced by equal and opposite mechanical forces.

The virtual displacement can be made in any convenient way: we may, for example, assume that either the currents or the flux linkages are kept constant. Whatever be the assumption, the result must be the same, since the force acting between two fixed circuits obviously has some single definite value. We had a similar situation in Section 2.15.1, where we found the force on a capacitor plate from the conservation of energy, assuming first that the plates were insulated, and then assuming that they were connected to a battery. The force was found to be the same in both cases.

6.6.1. The Magnetic Force When the Currents Are Kept Constant.

Let us calculate the magnetic force F on loop a with the above method, assuming that the currents are kept constant. We imagine that loop a is allowed to move parallel to itself by a distance dr toward loop b. Since the currents are kept constant, only the interaction energy changes, the self-energies remaining constant. Hence, from Eq. 6-145,

$$dW_m = I_a I_b \, dM, \tag{6-171}$$

$$= I_a \, d\Phi_{ab} = I_b \, d\Phi_{ba}. \tag{6-172}$$

The mutual inductance M and the fluxes Φ_{ab} and Φ_{ba} all increase in this case, thus dW_m is a positive quantity; the stored magnetic energy also *increases*. The mutual inductance is positive here.

Consider next the work done by the sources producing the currents in the loops. In loop b, Φ_{ba} increases, and the induced electromotance is in a direction such that it would, by itself, produce a magnetic field opposing $\mathbf{B}_a$. Therefore, the induced electromotance in loop b must tend to oppose the current I_b. If I_b is to be kept constant, then at each instant the source voltage must be *increased* by $d\Phi_{ba}/dt$. The source in loop b therefore supplies an amount of work

$$dW_{sb} = I_b \frac{d\Phi_{ba}}{dt} \, dt, \tag{6-173}$$

$$= I_b \, d\Phi_{ba}, \tag{6-174}$$

$$= I_b I_a \, dM. \tag{6-175}$$

By symmetry, the work supplied by the source in loop a is the same, and the total work supplied by the sources is

$$dW_s = 2I_a I_b \, dM, \tag{6-176}$$

which is exactly twice the increase in magnetic energy. The remainder has gone into mechanical work. In other words, the mechanical work done is accompanied by an *increase* of magnetic energy, both being supplied by the sources.

The mechanical work done is

$$\mathbf{F}_{ab} \cdot \mathbf{dr} = I_a I_b \, dM, \tag{6-177}$$

$$= (dW_m)_I, \tag{6-178}$$

where F_{ab} is the force exerted *on a by b*. The index I indicates that the currents are kept constant.

Since the quantity on the right is positive in the present case, the scalar product $\mathbf{F}_{ab}\cdot \mathbf{dr}$ must be positive, and the force $\mathbf{F}_{ab}$ must point toward coil b, like $\mathbf{dr}$. This is correct, since we found at the beginning that the coils tend to move closer to each other. It is important to note that we would have obtained the wrong sign if we had neglected the work done by the sources.

In the general case, the x-component of $\mathbf{F}_{ab}$ can thus be expressed as

$$F_{abx} = I_a I_b \frac{\partial M}{\partial x}, \qquad (6\text{-}179)$$

where the increment of x is the x-component of $\mathbf{dr}$. We also have

$$F_{abx} = I_a \left(\frac{\partial \Phi_{ab}}{\partial x}\right)_I \qquad (6\text{-}180)$$

$$= \left(\frac{\partial W_m}{\partial x}\right)_I. \qquad (6\text{-}181)$$

The partial derivatives are to be evaluated for constant currents.

Although we have been considering a system comprising only two circuits, the procedure remains the same for any number. The only difference is that the expression for the force F_{abx} must then be replaced by a sum of such terms. Stated in another way, the component of force in a given direction on the ith circuit is the product of its current by the space rate of change of flux linking it when it is displaced in the specified direction, all the currents in the system being held constant.

Let us return to Eq. *6-177* and substitute for M the Neumann formula stated in Eq. *6-70*. Then

$$\mathbf{F}_{ab}\cdot \mathbf{dr} = \frac{\mu_0}{4\pi} I_a I_b \, d\left(\oint_a \oint_b \frac{\mathbf{dl}_a\cdot \mathbf{dl}_b}{r}\right). \qquad (6\text{-}182)$$

It is to be understood that the differential of the term within the parentheses on the right-hand side must correspond to the displacement $\mathbf{dr}$ of the coil a as in Figure 6-13. Now it is permissible to interchange the order of the d operator and of the line integrals, so that

$$\mathbf{F}_{ab}\cdot \mathbf{dr} = \frac{\mu_0}{4\pi} I_a I_b \oint_a \oint_b d\frac{\mathbf{dl}_a\cdot \mathbf{dl}_b}{r}. \qquad (6\text{-}183)$$

In the process of moving coil a parallel to itself by a distance dr, both $\mathbf{dl}_a$ and $\mathbf{dl}_b$ remain unaffected, and the first d under the integral signs therefore operates only on the $1/r$ factor. If we now define $\mathbf{r}_1$ as a unit vector pointing *from* $\mathbf{dl}_b$ *to* $\mathbf{dl}_a$,

$$d\left(\frac{1}{r}\right) = -\frac{dr}{r^2} = -\frac{\mathbf{r}_1\cdot \mathbf{dr}}{r^2}, \qquad (6\text{-}184)$$

and

$$\mathbf{F}_{ab}\cdot d\mathbf{r} = -\frac{\mu_0}{4\pi} I_a I_b \oint_a \oint_b \frac{d\mathbf{l}_a \cdot d\mathbf{l}_b}{r^2} \mathbf{r}_1 \cdot d\mathbf{r}. \qquad (6\text{-}185)$$

Since the term $d\mathbf{r}$ on the right is independent of both $d\mathbf{l}_a$ and $d\mathbf{l}_b$, it can be removed from under the integral sign, and, finally,

$$\mathbf{F}_{ab} = -\frac{\mu_0}{4\pi} I_a I_b \oint_a \oint_b \frac{\mathbf{r}_1(d\mathbf{l}_a \cdot d\mathbf{l}_b)}{r^2}, \qquad (6\text{-}186)$$

which is exactly Eq. *5-6*. Referring back to Chapter 5, we will find that this is an alternative form of the magnetic force law stated in Eq. *5-1*. We have therefore rediscovered the law which was the starting point for our entire discussion of magnetic fields.

6.6.2. The Magnetic Force When the Fluxes Are Kept Constant.
We can imagine making the virtual displacement $d\mathbf{r}$ while adjusting the currents so as to keep the flux linkages constant. There are then no induced electromotances in the circuits, and the sources supply no energy to the system, except for the Joule losses, which we are neglecting. Then

$$\mathbf{F}_{ab}\cdot d\mathbf{r} = -(dW_m)_\Phi. \qquad (6\text{-}187)$$

In this case the mechanical work is accompanied by a corresponding *decrease* of magnetic energy. It will be shown in Problem 6-19 that the above result is really the same as that found previously in Eq. *6-177*.

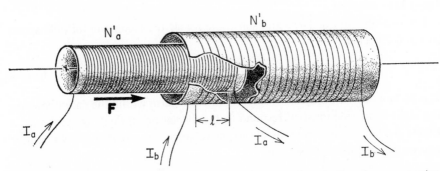

Figure 6-14. *Two coaxial solenoids of different sizes, the smaller one penetrating a distance l inside the other. There is an axial attractive force* **F** *when the two currents I_a and I_b are in the same direction. The number of turns per meter on each solenoid is N_a' and N_b'.*

6.6.3. Force Between Two Coaxial Solenoids.
The case of two long solenoids, one of which extends a distance *l* within the other as in Figure 6-14, will serve as an example. We must again neglect end effects, for otherwise the

calculation would be vastly more complex. We therefore assume that the solenoids are long and thin.

Let us first calculate the force from the rate of change of the mutual inductance, using Eq. *6-179*. By symmetry, **F** is along the common axis of the solenoids. Setting S to be the cross-sectional area of the smaller solenoid,

$$M = \frac{(N_a'l)\Phi_{ab}}{I_b} = \frac{(N_b'l)\Phi_{ba}}{I_a}, \tag{6-188}$$

where N_a' and N_b' are the number of turns per meter on the two solenoids. Thus

$$M = \frac{\mu_0 N_b' N_a' I_b S l}{I_b} = \frac{\mu_0 N_a' N_b' I_a S l}{I_a}, \tag{6-189}$$

$$= \mu_0 N_a' N_b' l S, \tag{6-190}$$

$$\frac{\partial M}{\partial l} = \mu_0 N_a' N_b' S, \tag{6-191}$$

and

$$F = \mu_0 N_a' N_b' S I_a I_b. \tag{6-192}$$

The force is attractive, since M increases with l.

It is interesting to repeat the calculation by using the rate of change of the
magnetic energy when the currents are kept constant, as in Eq. *6-181*. We have,
from Eq. *6-128*,

$$W_m = \frac{1}{2\mu_0} \int_\infty B^2 \, d\tau, \tag{6-193}$$

hence

$$W_m = \frac{1}{2\mu_0} [B_a^2(\tau_a - Sl) + B_b^2(\tau_b - Sl) + (B_a + B_b)^2 Sl], \tag{6-194}$$

$$= \frac{1}{2\mu_0} (B_a^2 \tau_a + B_b^2 \tau_b + 2B_a B_b Sl), \tag{6-195}$$

where $B_a = \mu_0 N_a' I_a$ is the magnetic induction originating in solenoid a and,
similarly, where B_b is the magnetic induction originating in solenoid b. These
are constants, since the currents I_a and I_b are again assumed to be constant. Then

$$dW_m = F \, dl = \frac{B_a B_b S}{\mu_0} \, dl, \tag{6-196}$$

and

$$F = \mu_0 N_a' N_b' S I_a I_b, \tag{6-197}$$

as in Eq. *6-192*.

Note that the magnetic energy W_m is a function of l because the magnetic
energy density depends on the *square* of the magnetic induction B. If it depended
on the first power of B, W_m would not be a function of l, and the force **F** would
be *zero*.

6.7. Magnetic Torque

In many cases a circuit is submitted to a torque, and not to a single force. The moving coil of a galvanometer is an obvious example. The same procedure can then be used to calculate the torque, and Eqs. *6-179* to *6-181* become

$$M_\theta = I_a I_b \frac{\partial M}{\partial \theta}, \qquad (6\text{-}198)$$

$$= I \left(\frac{\partial \Phi}{\partial \theta} \right)_I, \qquad (6\text{-}199)$$

$$= \left(\frac{\partial W_m}{\partial \theta} \right)_I, \qquad (6\text{-}200)$$

where Φ is the flux linking the circuit.

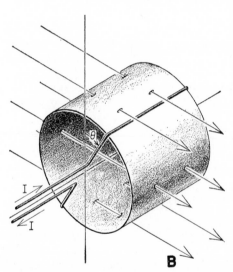

For example, the torque on a loop, such as that shown in Figure 6-15, carrying a current I and set at an angle θ in a uniform magnetic field B is

$$M_\theta = I \frac{\partial}{\partial \theta} (\Phi - BS \cos \theta), \quad (6\text{-}201)$$

where Φ is the flux produced by the current I in the loop and S is the area of the loop. The flux $BS \cos \theta$ is negative because it links the loop in the negative direction with respect to the current I. Thus

$$M = IBS \sin \theta, \qquad (6\text{-}202)$$

and the torque is positive, or is in the direction of increasing θ, for $0 < \theta < \pi$. This result can be easily verified from the direction of the elementary forces $I(\mathbf{dl} \times \mathbf{B})$ on a rectangular coil.

Figure 6-15. *Loop carrying a current I in a uniform magnetic field* **B**. *With the current in the direction shown, the loop is subjected to a torque tending to increase the angle θ.*

6.8. Summary

This chapter is concerned with (a) the nonconservative electric fields associated with time-dependent magnetic fields, (b) the energy stored in magnetic fields, and (c) the forces and torques exerted on current-carrying circuits situated in magnetic fields.

If a conductor is moved with a velocity **u** with respect to a magnetic field **B**, its electrons of charge Q experience a *Lorentz force* **f** given by

$$\mathbf{f} = Q(\mathbf{u} \times \mathbf{B}), \tag{6-2}$$

where $\mathbf{u} \times \mathbf{B}$ is called the *induced electric field intensity*. For a closed circuit,

$$\oint \mathbf{E} \cdot d\mathbf{l} = -\frac{d\Phi}{dt}. \tag{6-5}$$

The directions in which the line integral and Φ are taken to be positive are related according to the right-hand screw rule. The above line integral is the *induced electromotance*.

Induced electromotance can arise as above from the relative motion of a circuit and a magnetic field. It is also observed when a fixed circuit is linked by a variable flux, as in a transformer.

The *Faraday induction law* is

$$\oint \mathbf{E} \cdot d\mathbf{l} = -\frac{d}{dt} \int_S \mathbf{B} \cdot d\mathbf{a}, \tag{6-6}$$

which is really the same as Eq. 6-5. The negative sign means that the induced electromotance tends to oppose changes in the flux linking the circuit. This is *Lenz's law*.

In differential form,

$$\boxed{\nabla \times \mathbf{E} = -\frac{\partial \mathbf{B}}{\partial t}.} \tag{6-11}$$

This is *one of Maxwell's fundamental equations of electromagnetism*. It leads to the general expression for the electric field intensity **E**:

$$\mathbf{E} = -\frac{\partial \mathbf{A}}{\partial t} - \nabla V, \tag{6-16}$$

where the first term is the electric field intensity induced by a changing magnetic field and where ∇V is the electric field intensity produced by accumulations of charge, as in electrostatics.

For a conductor moving with a velocity **u** in a magnetic field **B**, Eq. 6-11 becomes

$$\nabla \times \mathbf{E} = -\frac{\partial \mathbf{B}}{\partial t} + \nabla \times (\mathbf{u} \times \mathbf{B}) \tag{6-45}$$

when **E** is measured with respect to a coordinate system moving with a velocity **u** relative to that in which the magnetic induction is measured as **B**.

The *mutual inductance M* between two circuits is equal to the magnetic flux linking one circuit per unit current flowing in the other:

$$\Phi_{ab} = M_{ab}I_b, \tag{6-69}$$

where Φ_{ab} is the flux linking circuit a and originating in circuit b. It is found that

$$M_{ab} = \frac{\mu_0}{4\pi} \oint_a \oint_b \frac{d\mathbf{l}_a \cdot d\mathbf{l}_b}{r}. \qquad (6\text{-}70)$$

This is the *Neumann equation*. It shows that M depends solely on the geometry of the two circuits, if there are no magnetic materials present. By symmetry,

$$M_{ab} = M_{ba}. \qquad (6\text{-}72)$$

Self-inductance L is a similar quantity, but which applies to a single circuit:

$$\Phi = LI, \qquad (6\text{-}74)$$

and

$$L = \frac{\mu_0}{4\pi} \oint_b \left(\oint_a \frac{d\mathbf{l}_a}{r} \right) \cdot d\mathbf{l}_b. \qquad (6\text{-}75)$$

The *coefficient of coupling* k between two circuits is defined by

$$M = \pm k(L_a L_b)^{1/2}. \qquad (6\text{-}103)$$

It can have values ranging from -1 to $+1$. It is zero if none of the flux of one circuit links the other.

In terms of inductance, the induced electromotance is given by

$$\oint \mathbf{E} \cdot d\mathbf{l} = -L \frac{dI}{dt}; \qquad (6\text{-}108)$$

a similar relation applies to mutual inductance.

A magnetic field involves energy, as does an electric field. This energy is equal to that required to establish the field, and we find that the energy supplied to an element of volume $d\tau$ of conductor per unit time is

$$\frac{dW_m}{dt} = \int_\tau \frac{\partial \mathbf{A}}{\partial t} \cdot \mathbf{J} \, d\tau. \qquad (6\text{-}121)$$

If there are no magnetic materials present, and if the displacement current is negligible compared to the conduction current, then

$$W_m = \frac{1}{2\mu_0} \int_\infty B^2 \, d\tau \qquad (6\text{-}128)$$

or

$$W_m = \frac{1}{2} \int_\tau (\mathbf{J} \cdot \mathbf{A}) \, d\tau, \qquad (6\text{-}132)$$

where τ is any volume which includes all regions in which $\mathbf{J}$ is not zero. We also find that

$$W_m = \frac{1}{2} I\Phi, \qquad (6\text{-}135)$$

where Φ is the flux linking the current I. As usual, the positive directions for I and Φ are related according to the right-hand screw rule. In terms of the self-inductance L,

$$W_m = \frac{1}{2} LI^2. \qquad (6\text{-}136)$$

The self-inductance of a volume distribution of current follows from the above. It is defined as

$$L = \frac{1}{\mu_0 I^2} \int_\infty B^2 \, d\tau. \qquad (6\text{-}159)$$

The *magnetic force* on a current-carrying circuit can be calculated from the principle of conservation of energy applied to a virtual displacement of the circuit. The x-component of the force F_{ab} exerted on a by b is found to be

$$F_{abx} = I_a I_b \frac{\partial M}{\partial x}, \qquad (6\text{-}179)$$

$$= I_a \left(\frac{\partial \Phi_{ab}}{\partial x} \right)_I, \qquad (6\text{-}180)$$

$$= \left(\frac{\partial W_m}{\partial x} \right)_I, \qquad (6\text{-}181)$$

the index I indicating that the currents are kept constant. This leads us back to Eq. *5-6*, which is an alternative form of the magnetic force law stated in Eq. *5-1* and which was the starting point for our entire discussion of magnetic fields.

Magnetic torque is given similarly by

$$M_\theta = \left(\frac{dW_m}{d\theta} \right)_I. \qquad (6\text{-}200)$$

Problems

6-1. A conducting bar slides with a constant velocity **u** along conducting rails in a region of uniform magnetic induction **B**, as in Figure 6-1. The total resistance in the circuit is R. What current flows in the circuit?

How much power is required to move the bar?

How does this power compare with the rate at which Joule heat is developed in the circuit?

6-2. Compute the magnitude and direction of the electromotance induced in a square loop of side a moving in the magnetic field of a long straight wire carrying a steady current I. The loop and the wire lie in the same plane, and the loop moves toward the wire with a velocity **u**.

6-3. An electron is at rest in vacuum at a distance r from the axis of a wire $1 \gg r$ meters long carrying a current I. If the current increases at the rate dI/dt, what is the magnitude and direction of the force on the electron? Disregard the field due to the rest of the circuit.

6-4. In the betatron, electrons are held in a circular orbit in a vacuum chamber by a magnetic field **B**. The electrons are accelerated by increasing the magnetic flux linking the orbit. Show that the average magnetic induction over the plane of the orbit must be twice the induction at the orbit if the orbit radius is to remain fixed as the electron's energy is increased. Hint: Relate the centripetal acceleration to the magnetic force acting on the electron, and then find the condition which lets the linear momentum of the electron increase with fixed orbit radius. Use Newton's second law with the tangential force on the electron given by the Faraday induction law.

6-5. An electron revolves with angular momentum $h/2\pi$ in an orbit about a proton, and an external magnetic field $\mathbf{B}$ is applied in a direction perpendicular to the plane of the orbit. What happens to the motion of the electron by virtue of the electromotance induced as the magnetic field is established?

Calculate the change in the electron's angular frequency, assuming that its radius remains fixed.

What is the change in the electron's orbital magnetic moment? In which direction is this change? This is the phenomenon of diamagnetism. Hint: The total centripetal force acting on the electron after the magnetic field is established consists of both electrostatic and magnetic forces. Equate the change in centripetal force to the magnetic force.

6-6. A conducting rod of length L rotates with angular frequency ω about an axis perpendicular to the rod and through one end in a uniform magnetic field $\mathbf{B}$ parallel to the axis. What is the electromotance developed between the ends of the rod?

What happens to the conduction electrons in the rod? What forces hold them in equilibrium?

6-7. A magnetic field is described by $B_x = B_0 \sin \dfrac{2\pi y}{\lambda} \sin \omega t$. In this field a square loop of side $\lambda/4$ lies in the yz-plane with its sides parallel to the y- and z-axes. The loop moves in the positive y direction with a constant velocity $\mathbf{u}$. Compute the electromotance induced in the loop as a function of time if the trailing edge of the loop is at $y = 0$ at $t = 0$. Assume $\omega = 2\pi u/\lambda$.

6-8. A thin flat conducting disk of thickness h, diameter D, and resistivity ρ is placed in a uniform alternating magnetic field $B = B_0 \sin \omega t$ parallel to the axis of the disk. Find the induced current density as a function of distance from the axis of the disk. What is the direction of this current?

6-9. Show that both the normal and tangential components of the vector potential $\mathbf{A}$ must be continuous across the interface between two media if the currents are constant.

6-10. Two long parallel wires of radius a are separated by a distance D and carry a current I in the same direction. Calculate the magnetic induction $\mathbf{B}$ at a point that is located between the wires and which lies in the plane containing the two wires.

What is the magnetic flux per unit length linking the wires?

What is the flux per unit length when the currents flow in opposite directions in the two wires?

Calculate the inductance per unit length for a parallel wire transmission line.

What effect does the flux within the conductors have on the inductance?

6-11. Show that the self-inductance of a close-wound toroidal coil of radii R and r is given by

$$L = \mu_0 n(R - \sqrt{R^2 - r^2}),$$

where n is the number of turns.

6-12. It is known that high frequency currents do not penetrate into a conductor as do low frequency currents. This is called the skin effect. Would you expect the self-inductance of a coaxial line to increase or to decrease with increasing frequency? What would you expect the approximate percentage change to be between very low and very high frequencies?

6-13. The coefficient of coupling k between two coils was defined in Eq. *6-104*, where k_a and k_b are defined as in Eq. *6-97*. Show that

$$\frac{k_a}{k_b} = \frac{L_b}{L_a},$$

so that $k_a \neq k_b$, in general.

6-14. Two long parallel rectangular loops lying in the same plane have lengths l_1 and l_2 and widths w_1 and w_2, respectively. The loops do not overlap, and the distance between the near sides is s.

Show that the mutual inductance between the loops is given by

$$M = \frac{\mu_0 l_2}{2\pi} \ln \frac{s + w_2}{s\left(1 + \dfrac{w_2}{s + w_1}\right)}$$

if $l_2 < l_1$, and if the loops have but a single turn. Neglect end effects.

6-15. A wire bent in the form of a circle of radius R is placed so that its center is at a distance $D = 2R$ from a long straight wire, the two being in the same plane. Show that the mutual inductance is

$$M = 0.268\mu_0 R.$$

What is the mutual inductance in microhenrys when $R = 10.0$ centimeters?

6-16. Compute the mutual inductance between two single-turn circular loops of radii R and r, where $R \gg r$, when the small loop is on the axis of the large one at a distance x from its center, with the planes of the loops parallel.

Find how the mutual inductance varies as a function of the angle between the normals to the two planes.

6-17. Find the vector potential **A** just outside a close-wound toroidal coil. Hint: Proceed as in Section 6.3.7.

6-18. Compare the energies per unit volume in (a) a magnetic field of 1.0 weber/meter² and (b) an electrostatic field of 10^6 volts/meter.

6-19. It was shown in Eqs. *6-177* and *6-187* that the mechanical work $\mathbf{F} \cdot \mathbf{dr}$ done when one circuit is displaced a distance $\mathbf{dr}$ with respect to another is either $I_a I_b \, dM$ or $-dW_m$, depending on whether the currents or the fluxes are assumed to remain constant during the virtual displacement. Show that these two expressions are equal.

6-20. Consider a general system of n rigid fixed circuits in which the ith circuit carries a current I_i. Show that the magnetic energy associated with the system can be written as a sum of self-energy terms of the form $(1/2)L_i I_i^2$, plus a sum of mutual energy terms of the form $M_{ij} I_i I_j$, each pair of currents appearing once.

6-21. Starting with the definition of self-inductance in terms of energy, find the self-inductance per unit length for a long straight conductor of radius a carrying a uniform current density.

Is this likely to be a major contribution to the inductance per unit length of a transmission line consisting of two parallel wires? See Problem 6-10.

6-22. From the computation of the mutual inductance between two single-turn current loops in Problem 6-16, find the magnetic force acting on the small coil when I_1 flows in the large coil and I_2 in the small one. Compare this result with a direct calculation from the force law (Eq. 5-8), assuming that the induction at the position of the small coil due to the current in the large coil is uniform and of the same magnitude as on the axis.

CHAPTER 7

Magnetic Materials

Thus, far, our discussion of magnetic phenomena has been limited to free space and to nonmagnetic materials, that is, to magnetic fields arising solely from conduction currents. Now, on the atomic scale, all bodies contain electrons which move in orbits, thereby constituting currents in the usual sense, and which spin about an axis. These moving electrons produce magnetic fields which add to those produced by the conduction currents. For example, the electron spin is believed to be responsible for ferromagnetic effects.

Our purpose in this chapter is to examine the magnetic fields of such atomic currents and to express these fields in macroscopic terms.

The situation in magnetic materials is quite similar to that in dielectrics. Individual charges or systems of charges possess magnetic moments, and these moments can be oriented to produce a resultant magnetic moment in a finite volume. When there is a net orientation of this sort the material is said to be magnetically *polarized*.

The polarization process by which the dipoles are oriented is beyond the scope of this book and will not be discussed here.

7.1. The Magnetic Polarization Vector **M**

In discussing the fields of the magnetic dipoles associated with atomic systems we shall follow much the same pattern as for dielectrics. We saw in Section 5.13 that, at distances which are large compared to the size of the loop, the magnetic induction **B** of a circular current loop has the form of a dipole field. The dipole moment is the current multiplied by the area of the loop. This concept of magnetic dipole moment can be extended to loops of arbitrary shape, and we can always associate a magnetic dipole moment **m**, measured in ampere-meters^2, with a current loop. *Although a magnetic dipole produces a magnetic field which, at large distances, is identical in form to the electrostatic dipole field, the existence of magnetic charges is not implied.* There is compelling evidence that all magnetic effects arise from moving electric charges. The analogy with the electrostatic dipole extends only to the mathematical similarity of the two fields.

The magnetic polarization **M** is the magnetic dipole moment per unit volume, and, if **m** is the *average magnetic dipole moment per atom* and N is the number of atoms per unit volume, then

$$\mathbf{M} = N\mathbf{m}. \qquad\qquad (7\text{-}1)$$

The vector **M** is measured in amperes/meter. Later we shall express the magnetic induction **B** due to the atomic dipoles entirely in terms of **M**, but, just as for dielectrics, this procedure must be justified by first examining the phenomenon from a molecular point of view.

The above definition of **M** is subject to the same limitations as is the corresponding quantity **P** (Section 3.1) for dielectrics. The volume τ in which **M** is defined must be large enough such that there is no significant statistical fluctuation in **M** from one τ to a neighboring one, or from one instant to the next. On the other hand, the volume τ must not be so large that we make significant errors in using the smoothed-over, macroscopic distribution **M** rather than the discrete distribution of elementary dipoles **m**. As for dielectrics, the smallness of atomic dimensions ensures the validity of the macroscopic approach.

7.2. The Magnetic Induction from Polarized Magnetic Material at an External Point

Let us calculate the magnetic induction **B** at a point **P** external to a magnetic core polarized by a conduction current I, as in the solenoid wound around the core shown in Figure 7-1.

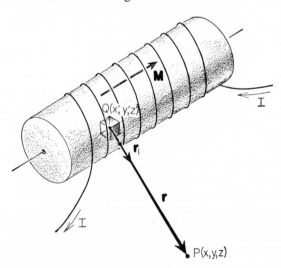

Figure 7-1

A coil carrying a current I polarizes a core of magnetic material. The vector **M** *is the magnetic dipole moment per unit volume; P is a point outside the core.*

The current I and the polarization $\mathbf{M}$ both contribute to the magnetic induction $\mathbf{B}$ at the external point P, hence

$$\mathbf{B} = \mathbf{B}_I + \mathbf{B}_M. \tag{7-2}$$

We shall be concerned here only with $\mathbf{B}_M$, the magnetic induction produced by the polarized material, but we must remember that $\mathbf{B}_I$, the contribution from the conduction currents in the system, must always be taken into account to find the *total* magnetic induction $\mathbf{B}$.

7.2.1. The Magnetic Pole Formalism. The magnetic induction $\mathbf{B}_M$ due to the polarized material can be calculated by starting either from the scalar magnetic potential V_m (Section 5.12), which leads to the concept of *magnetic poles*, or from the vector potential $\mathbf{A}$ (Section 5.5), which leads to the concept of *equivalent currents*. Let us first calculate $\mathbf{B}_M$ by using the scalar magnetic potential. Since the point P is relatively far removed from the dipoles, $\mathbf{B}_M$ at P is adequately represented by the dipole approximation such that, as in Section 5.13, the scalar potential is

$$V_M = \frac{\mu_0}{4\pi} \int_\tau \frac{\mathbf{M} \cdot \mathbf{r}_1}{r^2} \, d\tau, \tag{7-3}$$

since the dipole moment in a small volume $d\tau$ is $\mathbf{M} \, d\tau$. It is convenient to write V_M in the equivalent form

$$V_M = \frac{\mu_0}{4\pi} \int_\tau \left[\mathbf{M} \cdot \nabla \left(\frac{1}{r} \right) \right] d\tau, \tag{7-4}$$

where $\nabla \left(\dfrac{1}{r} \right)$ is calculated at the position of the dipole.

As in Section 3.2 on dielectrics, this equation can be put in a form which facilitates physical interpretation by using the vector identity of Problem 1-14:

$$\nabla \cdot f\mathbf{C} = \mathbf{C} \cdot \nabla f + f(\nabla \cdot \mathbf{C}), \tag{7-5}$$

where f is an arbitrary scalar function and $\mathbf{C}$ is an arbitrary vector function. If we let $1/r$ be the scalar and $\mathbf{M}$ the vector function, then

$$V_M = \frac{\mu_0}{4\pi} \int_\tau \left(\nabla \cdot \frac{\mathbf{M}}{r} \right) d\tau - \frac{\mu_0}{4\pi} \int_\tau \left(\frac{\nabla \cdot \mathbf{M}}{r} \right) d\tau. \tag{7-6}$$

Applying the divergence theorem to the first term on the right, we have

$$V_M = \frac{\mu_0}{4\pi} \int_S \frac{\mathbf{M}}{r} \cdot d\mathbf{a} - \frac{\mu_0}{4\pi} \int_\tau \left(\frac{\nabla \cdot \mathbf{M}}{r} \right) d\tau, \tag{7-7}$$

where S is the surface of the volume τ. Writing V_M in this form is neither more nor less correct than writing it in the form of Eq. 7-3. Both statements are equivalent, and both are correct, but Eq. 7-7 facilitates qualitative interpretation.

Both terms in this equation vary as $1/r$, and the scalar magnetic potential V_M in this case is therefore exactly of the same form as the electrostatic potential due to surface and volume distributions of electrostatic charge. The quantity

$$\sigma'_m = \mathbf{M} \cdot \mathbf{n}, \tag{7-8}$$

which is the normal component of the polarization vector $\mathbf{M}$ at a point on the surface, is called the *surface magnetic pole density*, and

$$\rho'_m = -\nabla \cdot \mathbf{M} \tag{7-9}$$

is the *volume magnetic pole density*. It is important to remember that magnetic charges do *not* exist. The term magnetic pole has no more significance than that associated with the definitions of σ'_m and ρ'_m. Thus

$$V_M = \frac{\mu_0}{4\pi} \int_S \frac{\sigma'_m}{r} \, da + \frac{\mu_0}{4\pi} \int_\tau \frac{\rho'_m}{r} \, d\tau. \tag{7-10}$$

Since $\mathbf{B} = -\nabla V_M$, from Eq. 5-160, and since $\nabla\left(\dfrac{1}{r}\right) = \mathbf{r}_1/r^2$,

$$\mathbf{B}_M = \frac{\mu_0}{4\pi} \int_S \frac{\sigma'_m \, da}{r^2} \mathbf{r}_1 + \frac{\mu_0}{4\pi} \int_\tau \frac{\rho'_m \, d\tau}{r^2} \mathbf{r}_1 \tag{7-11}$$

where $\mathbf{r}_1$ is the unit vector from the source point to the field point, as in Figure 7-1.

We can thus find the magnetic pole densities σ'_m and ρ'_m from the polarization vector $\mathbf{M}$, and from these we can calculate $\mathbf{B}_M$. In terms of the poles, $\mathbf{B}_M$ varies as $1/r^2$, as does the electrostatic field intensity $\mathbf{E}$.

7.2.2. The Equivalent Current Formalism.

It is also possible to calculate the magnetic induction $\mathbf{B}_M$ at the external point P starting with the vector potential $\mathbf{A}$. From Problem 5-25, the vector potential for a current loop is

$$\mathbf{A} = \frac{\mu_0}{4\pi} \frac{\mathbf{m} \times \mathbf{r}_1}{r^2}, \tag{7-12}$$

where $\mathbf{m}$ is the magnetic dipole moment of the loop and where r, the distance from the loop to P, is large compared to the size of the loop. In this case the element of dipole moment $\mathbf{M} \, d\tau$ gives

$$d\mathbf{A}_M = \frac{\mu_0}{4\pi} \left(\frac{\mathbf{M} \times \mathbf{r}_1}{r^2}\right) d\tau \tag{7-13}$$

at P, and

$$\mathbf{A}_M = \frac{\mu_0}{4\pi} \int_\tau \left(\frac{\mathbf{M} \times \mathbf{r}_1}{r^2}\right) d\tau, \tag{7-14}$$

$$= \frac{\mu_0}{4\pi} \int_\tau \left[\mathbf{M} \times \nabla\left(\frac{1}{r}\right)\right] d\tau. \tag{7-15}$$

This equation can also be put in a form more amenable to physical interpretation through the vector identity of Problem 1-22:

$$\nabla \times f\mathbf{C} = \nabla f \times \mathbf{C} + f(\nabla \times \mathbf{C}), \tag{7-16}$$

where f is an arbitrary scalar function and $\mathbf{C}$ is an arbitrary vector function. Taking $f = 1/r$ and $\mathbf{C} = \mathbf{M}$, we obtain

$$\mathbf{A}_M = -\frac{\mu_0}{4\pi} \int_\tau \left(\nabla \times \frac{\mathbf{M}}{r}\right) d\tau + \frac{\mu_0}{4\pi} \int_\tau \left(\frac{\nabla \times \mathbf{M}}{r}\right) d\tau. \qquad (7\text{-}17)$$

The first term on the right can be further modified through the use of another vector transformation (see Problem 1-25) which states that

$$\int_\tau \left(\nabla \times \frac{\mathbf{M}}{r}\right) d\tau = -\int_S \left(\frac{\mathbf{M}}{r} \times d\mathbf{a}\right). \qquad (7\text{-}18)$$

Thus, finally,

$$\mathbf{A}_M = \frac{\mu_0}{4\pi} \int_S \left(\frac{\mathbf{M}}{r} \times \mathbf{n}\right) da + \frac{\mu_0}{4\pi} \int_\tau \left(\frac{\nabla \times \mathbf{M}}{r}\right) d\tau. \qquad (7\text{-}19)$$

Again, the various expressions for $\mathbf{A}_M$ are all equivalent, but Eq. *7-19* lends itself to simple physical interpretation: both integrands have the form of the vector potential calculations already familiar to us (from Section 5.5), provided both numerators represent a current density—a surface current density in the first term and a volume current density in the second term. We therefore define an *equivalent surface current density* $\boldsymbol{\lambda}'$ such that

$$\boldsymbol{\lambda}' = \mathbf{M} \times \mathbf{n} \qquad (7\text{-}20)$$

and an *equivalent volume current density* $\mathbf{J}'$ such that

$$\mathbf{J}' = \nabla \times \mathbf{M}, \qquad (7\text{-}21)$$

$\boldsymbol{\lambda}'$ being expressed in amperes/meter and $\mathbf{J}'$ in amperes/meter². In these terms the vector potential at the point P due to the polarized material is

$$\mathbf{A}_M = \frac{\mu_0}{4\pi} \int_S \frac{\boldsymbol{\lambda}'}{r} da + \frac{\mu_0}{4\pi} \int_\tau \frac{\mathbf{J}'}{r} d\tau. \qquad (7\text{-}22)$$

These equivalent current densities $\boldsymbol{\lambda}'$ and $\mathbf{J}'$ are *not* conduction currents. They are fictitious currents which enable us to calculate the vector potential, and therefore the magnetic induction, just as we would for conduction currents. They provide a convenient method of visualizing the magnetic induction due to the polarized material, since they may be treated as if they were ordinary currents. The equivalent surface current $\boldsymbol{\lambda}'$ for a uniformly polarized rod is indicated in Figure 7-2.

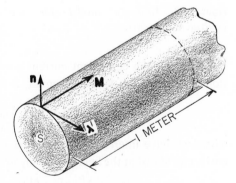

Figure 7-2. *Equivalent surface current density* $\boldsymbol{\lambda}'$ *for a uniformly polarized rod. The current is* λ' *amperes per meter of length.*

The physical nature of the equivalent or *Amperian currents* can be understood from a model due to Ampere. Consider Figure 7-3, and imagine currents λ' flowing around square cells in a piece of material whose length in the direction perpendicular to the plane of the paper is one meter. The current in one cell is nullified by the currents in the adjoining cells, except at the periphery of the material. The net current density on the surface of the rod is thus λ'. Equating the magnetic moment of the current λ' around the periphery to the sum of the magnetic moments of the current in the cells, we have

$$\lambda'S = MS, \qquad (7\text{-}23)$$

where S is the cross-sectional area of the rod and M is the magnetic moment per unit volume of the material, or

$$\lambda' = M. \qquad (7\text{-}24)$$

The origin of the equivalent surface current density λ' can now be understood by extending this model to currents on the atomic scale.

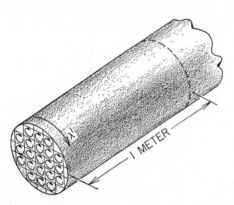

The volume current density arises when currents in adjacent cells are unequal. Note that, since the equivalent volume current density $\mathbf{J}'$ is equal to $\boldsymbol{\nabla} \times \mathbf{M}$, $\boldsymbol{\nabla} \cdot \mathbf{J}'$ is identically equal to zero, thus charge cannot accumulate at a point by virtue of the equivalent volume current density $\mathbf{J}'$. Furthermore, the equivalent currents do not dissipate energy and therefore do not produce heating, since equivalent currents do not involve electron drift and scattering processes of the type associated with conduction currents.

Figure 7-3. *Ampere's model for the equivalent currents.*

Let us use the equivalent current concept to calculate the magnetic induction $\mathbf{B}_M$. Since $\mathbf{B}_M = \boldsymbol{\nabla} \times \mathbf{A}_M$ from Eq. 5-56, where $\mathbf{A}_M$ is given by Eq. 7-22, then

$$\mathbf{B}_M = \frac{\mu_0}{4\pi} \int_S \left(\boldsymbol{\nabla} \times \frac{\lambda'}{r} \right) da + \frac{\mu_0}{4\pi} \int_\tau \boldsymbol{\nabla} \times \frac{\mathbf{J}'}{r}\, d\tau, \qquad (7\text{-}25)$$

where we have interchanged the order of differentiation and integration. The curl is calculated at the field point P by uring the vector identity of Problem 1-22,

$$\boldsymbol{\nabla} \times \frac{\lambda'}{r} = \left[\boldsymbol{\nabla}\left(\frac{1}{r}\right) \times \lambda' \right] + \frac{1}{r}(\boldsymbol{\nabla} \times \lambda'). \qquad (7\text{-}26)$$

The second term on the right is zero, since the curl involves derivatives with respect to x, y, and z, whereas λ' is a function of x', y', and z'. Finally, setting

$$\nabla \left(\frac{1}{r} \right) = -\frac{\mathbf{r}_1}{r^2}, \qquad (7\text{-}27)$$

we obtain

$$\mathbf{B}_M = \frac{\mu_0}{4\pi} \int_S \left(\frac{\lambda' \times \mathbf{r}_1}{r^2} \right) da + \frac{\mu_0}{4\pi} \int_\tau \left(\frac{\mathbf{J}' \times \mathbf{r}_1}{r^2} \right) d\tau. \qquad (7\text{-}28)$$

It will be observed that we could have written this equation directly from the Biot-Savart law on the assumption that $\mathbf{B}_M$ is produced by the surface current density λ' and by the volume current density $\mathbf{J}'$. Thus, if we know the polarization vector $\mathbf{M}$, we can find the equivalent current densities and then treat them as conduction current densities for calculating the magnetic induction $\mathbf{B}_M$.

In practice we never know the magnetic polarization $\mathbf{M}$ *a priori*, and we must eventually find a practical way of dealing with magnetic problems. This will require the concept of magnetic circuits discussed at the end of this chapter.

7.3. The Magnetic Induction from Polarized Magnetic Material at an Internal Point

We must now calculate the macroscopic magnetic induction, that is, the space and time average of the magnetic induction on the molecular scale at an internal point in the polarized magnetic material. We shall see that the magnetic poles alone do not give $\mathbf{B}_M$ at an internal point, whereas the equivalent currents do.

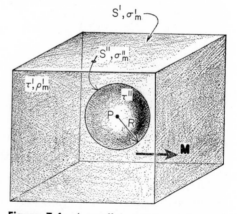

7.3.1. Calculation of $\mathbf{B}_M$ at an Internal Point Using the Pole Formalism.

We shall proceed exactly as with dielectrics and divide the material into two regions, one near the point P and one farther away. The near region is the volume τ'' within a small sphere of radius R, as in Figure 7-4, and the far region includes all the volume τ' of the material outside this sphere.

Thus, at P,

Figure 7-4. *A small imaginary sphere of radius R, surface S", surface pole density σ''_m, and volume τ'' centered at P within a magnetic material. The remaining volume τ' has a volume pole density ρ'_m and a surface pole density σ'_m on its outer surface S'.*

$$\mathbf{B}_M = \mathbf{B}'_M + \mathbf{B}''_M, \qquad (7\text{-}29)$$

where $\mathbf{B}_M$ is the total magnetic induction caused by the magnetic material, $\mathbf{B}'_M$ is the part contributed by the polarized material in the volume τ', and $\mathbf{B}''_M$ is the part contributed by the material in τ''. The radius R is taken large enough such that, for all the dipoles outside the spherical surface S'', the point P is an external point.

Using the pole formalism, we have

$$\mathbf{B}_M = \frac{\mu_0}{4\pi} \int_{\tau'} \frac{\rho'_m \, d\tau}{r^2} \mathbf{r}_1 + \frac{\mu_0}{4\pi} \int_{S'} \frac{\sigma'_m \, da}{r^2} \mathbf{r}_1 + \frac{\mu_0}{4\pi} \int_{S''} \frac{\sigma''_m \, da}{r^2} \mathbf{r}_1 + \mathbf{B}''_M, \quad (7\text{-}30)$$

where ρ'_m is the volume pole density in τ', σ'_m is the surface pole density on the external surface S', and σ''_m is the surface pole density on the imaginary spherical surface S''.

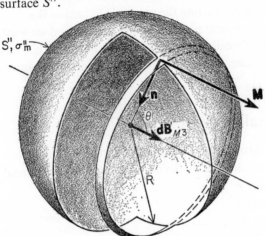

Figure 7-5

The small imaginary sphere of Figure 7-4 is shown here in greater detail for the calculation of the induction B'_{M3} due to the poles on the surface S''. The surface charge density σ''_m is equal to $\mathbf{M} \cdot \mathbf{n}$.

Let us first evaluate the third term on the right:

$$\mathbf{B}'_{M3} = \frac{\mu_0}{4\pi} \int_{S''} \frac{\sigma''_m}{r^2} \, da \, \mathbf{r}_1. \quad (7\text{-}31)$$

From Figure 7-5, the surface pole density is

$$\sigma''_m = \mathbf{M} \cdot \mathbf{n},$$

and an element of area da contributes at the center of the sphere an element of induction

$$d\mathbf{B}'_{M3} = \frac{\mu_0}{4\pi} \frac{\mathbf{M} \cdot \mathbf{n}}{R^2} \, da \, \mathbf{n}. \quad (7\text{-}32)$$

By symmetry, all the poles on the strip of width $R \, d\theta$ shown in Figure 7-5 will contribute a resultant induction in the axial direction, and

$$\mathbf{B}'_{M3} = \frac{\mu_0}{4\pi} \int_0^\pi \frac{\mathbf{M} \cos \theta}{R^2} 2\pi R^2 \sin \theta \cos \theta \, d\theta, \quad (7\text{-}33)$$

$$= \frac{\mu_0 \mathbf{M}}{3} \quad (7\text{-}34)$$

in the same direction as $\mathbf{M}$.

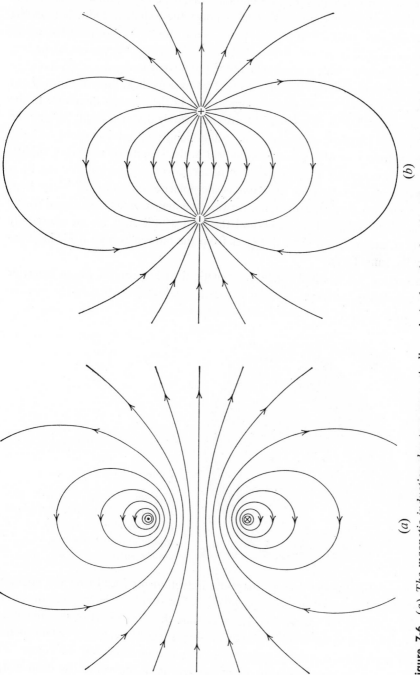

(b)

(a)

Figure 7-6. (a) *The magnetic induction due to a magnetically polarized molecule.* (b) *The electric field intensity due to an electrically polarized molecule.*

We must also calculate $\mathbf{B}_M''$, which is the magnetic induction at P due to the near dipoles. Furthermore, we must average the magnetic induction on the molecular scale over a volume containing many atomic systems in order to find the macroscopic induction. For dielectrics we made this calculation by finding the average field inside a sphere containing polarized molecules, each having a resultant dipole moment (Section 2.12). This average field intensity turned out to be proportional to the dipole moment and in the *opposite* direction. In the magnetic case, the same calculation gives an entirely different result because the form of the magnetic induction field in the vicinity of a current loop is quite different from that of the electrostatic field in the vicinity of an electric dipole. In fact, the average magnetic field produced over a spherical volume by a current loop is in the *same* direction as the polarization vector $\mathbf{M}$, as we shall see. Figure 7-6 shows the difference between the magnetic field associated with a magnetically polarized molecule and the electrostatic field for an electrically polarized molecule. At large distances from the molecules both fields have exactly the same form.

In Section 7.4 we shall define a magnetic field intensity $\mathbf{H}$ whose behavior in magnetically polarized material is strictly analogous to that of the electrostatic field intensity $\mathbf{E}$ in electrically polarized matter.

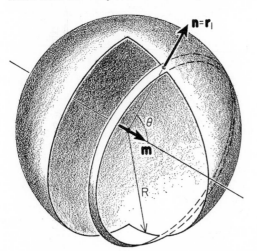

Figure 7-7

Current loop of magnetic moment $\mathbf{m}$ at the center of a sphere of radius R large enough for the dipole approximation to be valid on the surface.

Let us compute the average magnetic induction produced over the volume of a sphere by a small current loop within it. For simplicity let us place the loop at the center of the sphere, and let us assume that the radius of the sphere is large compared to the size of the loop. At the surface of the sphere the magnetic induction is then accurately given by the dipole approximation. In Figure 7-7 the loop is represented by a dipole of moment $\mathbf{m}$ at the center. By definition, the average field in the sphere is

$$\bar{\mathbf{B}} = \frac{1}{\tau} \int_\tau \mathbf{B} \, d\tau, \tag{7-35}$$

$$= \frac{1}{\tau} \int_\tau (\nabla \times \mathbf{A}) \, d\tau, \tag{7-36}$$

where τ is the volume of the sphere. We do not know $\mathbf{A}$ in the immediate vicinity of the loop, but, on the surface of the sphere, where the dipole approximation is valid, we have, from Problem 5-25,

$$\mathbf{A} = \frac{\mu_0}{4\pi} \frac{\mathbf{m} \times \mathbf{r}_1}{r^2}. \tag{7-37}$$

But, from Problem 1-25,

$$\int_\tau (\nabla \times \mathbf{A}) \, d\tau = \int_S (\mathbf{n} \times \mathbf{A}) \, da, \tag{7-38}$$

where S is the surface bounding the volume τ and $\mathbf{n}$ is the outward drawn normal to S. The volume integral can thus be evaluated without $\mathbf{A}$ being known within the volume, provided it is known at all points of the surface. In this case, therefore,

$$\int_\tau \mathbf{B} \, d\tau = \frac{\mu_0}{4\pi} \int_S \left(\mathbf{n} \times \frac{\mathbf{m} \times \mathbf{r}_1}{R^2} \right) da. \tag{7-39}$$

Expanding the triple vector product according to Problem 1-9,

$$\int_\tau \mathbf{B} \, d\tau = \frac{\mu_0}{4\pi} \int_S \mathbf{m} \left(\mathbf{n} \cdot \frac{\mathbf{r}_1}{R^2} \right) da - \int_S \frac{\mathbf{r}_1}{R^2} (\mathbf{n} \cdot \mathbf{m}) \, da. \tag{7-40}$$

We have taken the component of the elementary vector along the axis, that is, in the direction of $\mathbf{m}$, by virtue of the symmetry. Or

$$\int_\tau \mathbf{B} \, d\tau = \frac{\mu_0}{4\pi} \int_S \mathbf{m} \left(\frac{\mathbf{n} \cdot \mathbf{n}}{R^2} \right) da - \int_0^\pi \frac{\mathbf{m} \cos \theta}{R^2} 2\pi R^2 \sin \theta \cos \theta \, d\theta, \tag{7-41}$$

$$= \frac{\mu_0}{4\pi} \left(4\pi \mathbf{m} - \frac{4\pi}{3} \mathbf{m} \right), \tag{7-42}$$

$$= \frac{2}{3} \mu_0 \mathbf{m}, \tag{7-43}$$

and the average magnetic induction inside the sphere is

$$\bar{\mathbf{B}} = \frac{1}{\tau} \int_\tau \mathbf{B} \, d\tau, \tag{7-44}$$

$$= \frac{(2/3)\mu_0 \mathbf{m}}{(4/3)\pi R^3}, \tag{7-45}$$

$$= \frac{\mu_0 \mathbf{m}}{2\pi R^3}. \tag{7-46}$$

If the current loop is not centered in the volume, $\bar{\mathbf{B}}$ has the same magnitude and direction as above. This will be shown in Problem 7-2. Thus the average induction over the volume of the sphere depends only on the magnitude and direction of the loop producing the field, and not on its position inside the sphere.

If there are many small current loops within the volume, each one produces an average field as above, hence

$$\bar{\mathbf{B}} = \frac{2}{3}\mu_0\mathbf{M}, \tag{7-47}$$

since

$$\mathbf{M} = N\mathbf{m}, \tag{7-48}$$

where N is the number of molecules per unit volume, $\mathbf{m}$ is the average magnetic dipole moment of each molecule, and $\mathbf{M}$ is the magnetic dipole moment per unit volume. The resultant total dipole moment of all the molecules within the sphere is

$$\mathbf{P}_M = \mathbf{M}(4/3)\pi R^3. \tag{7-49}$$

The above result is open to question because some of the loops will be too close to the spherical surface for the dipole approximation of Eq. 7-37 to be valid. However, the error introduced from this source can be made arbitrarily small by increasing the size of the sphere. Molecules are so small that it is easy to choose a sphere which is large enough to make this error negligible but which will still be macroscopically small. This type of problem was encountered previously in Section 3.3.

We still have to average the field on the molecular scale over a volume containing a large number of molecules. This average is calculated exactly as it was for dielectrics in Section 3.3. As the point at the center of the sphere moves about, taking the sphere with it, the contribution from the far dipoles does not change significantly for small displacements. The average induction produced by the near dipoles has already been calculated. Consequently we need make no further calculation to obtain the space average of the magnetic induction on the molecular scale.

Finally, then, with the third term $\mathbf{B}'_{M3}$ of Eq. 7-30 evaluated, and with $\mathbf{B}''_M$ calculated and averaged over the volume τ'', we have

$$\mathbf{B}_M = \frac{\mu_0}{4\pi} \int_{\tau'} \frac{\rho'_m \, d\tau}{r^2} \mathbf{r}_1 + \frac{\mu_0}{4\pi} \int_{S'} \frac{\sigma'_m \, da}{r^2} \mathbf{r}_1 + \frac{\mu_0\mathbf{M}}{3} + \frac{2}{3}\mu_0\mathbf{M}. \tag{7-50}$$

The volume integral is to be taken only over the volume τ' of Figure 7-4. Again, as for dielectrics (Section 3.3.2), it makes no difference if we include the volume τ'' in the integration. Thus, substituting τ for τ', and writing S for the real surface of the material, we obtain

$$\mathbf{B}_M = \frac{\mu_0}{4\pi} \int_{\tau} \frac{\rho'_m \, d\tau}{r^2} \mathbf{r}_1 + \frac{\mu_0}{4\pi} \int_{S} \frac{\sigma'_m \, da}{r^2} \mathbf{r}_1 + \mu_0\mathbf{M}. \tag{7-51}$$

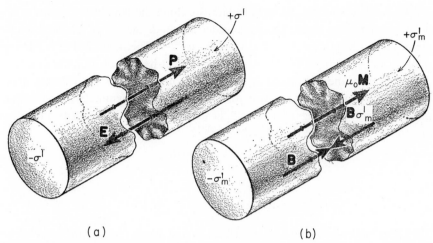

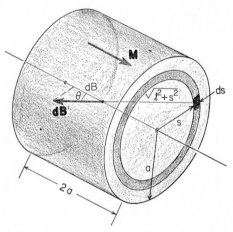

Figure 7-8. (*a*) *The field inside a permanently polarized dielectric.* (*b*) *The field inside a permanently polarized magnetic material.*

Only the first two terms represent the contribution of the magnetic poles to $\mathbf{B}_M$. The poles therefore do *not* give the correct value of $\mathbf{B}_M$ *inside* the polarized material, but only $\mathbf{B}_M - \mu_0\mathbf{M}$.

To illustrate this fact, and to indicate the contrast with dielectrics, let us consider uniformly polarized blocks of dielectric and of magnetic material, as in Figure 7-8. Let us assume that these blocks are permanently polarized such that the polarization is not caused by an external field. Since the polarization is uniform, both the volume distribution of bound electric charge ρ' and the volume distribution of magnetic poles ρ'_m are zero. The macroscopic electric field $\mathbf{E}$ of the dielectric arises only from the bound charges and is thus in the direction *opposite* to the polarization vector $\mathbf{P}$. In the magnetic material, the poles contribute an induction in the direction opposite to $\mathbf{M}$, but

Figure 7-9. *Permanently polarized rod of magnetic material. The surface poles on the shaded element of area produce a magnetic induction dB on the axis.*

$\mu_0\mathbf{M}$ must be added to this in order to find the total induction $\mathbf{B}_M$. The resultant induction is in the *same* direction as the polarization vector.

As a further example, let us calculate $\mathbf{B}_M$ along the length of the uniformly polarized magnetic block. Let us consider a cylindrical rod of material whose diameter and length are both $2a$, as in Figure 7-9. The pole density is $\mathbf{M} \cdot \mathbf{n} = +M$ on the right-hand face and $-M$ on the left-hand face. On the axis, at a distance l from the right-hand face, the poles of magnitude $M\,da$ on the small shaded area produce an induction $\mathbf{dB}'$ as indicated. By symmetry, the resultant induction must be along the axis, as indicated by dB, and the magnetic induction due to the poles on the right-hand face is

$$B_{\sigma'_m} = \frac{\mu_0}{4\pi} \int_0^a \frac{Ml2\pi s\,ds}{(s^2 + l^2)^{3/2}}, \tag{7-52}$$

$$= \frac{\mu_0 M}{2}\left(1 - \frac{l}{\sqrt{a^2 + l^2}}\right). \tag{7-53}$$

The poles on the left-hand face contribute in like manner and in the same direction. The induction $B_{\sigma'_m}$ due to both sets of poles is plotted in the negative direction in Figure 7-10, which also shows the total induction, that is, the magnetic induction due to the poles plus the quantity $\mu_0 M$.

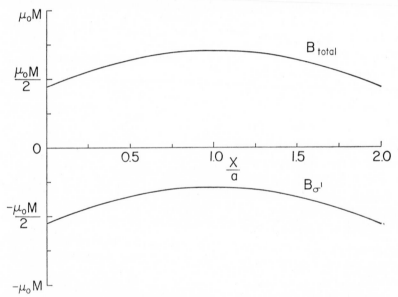

Figure 7-10. *The magnetic induction due to the poles, and the total magnetic induction in a permanent magnet.*

Let us return to the comparison with dielectric materials. When the polarization results from the action of an external field, the electric field intensity $\mathbf{E}$ inside the dielectric is weakened by the bound charge field which is in the opposite direction to that of the external field. In magnetic materials, on the other hand, the magnetic induction **B** produced by the polarized material is in the same direction as the external field and adds to it.

7.3.2. Gauss's Law for the Magnetic Induction B_P.

In discussing the magnetic pole formalism it is useful to derive a Gauss's law for poles. Consider Figure 7-11, where $\rho'_m\,d\tau$ is an element of magnetic charge at a point where the volume density of poles is ρ'_m. At a point on the surface S enclosing the volume τ, these poles contribute an element of induction $\mathbf{dB}_P$ given by

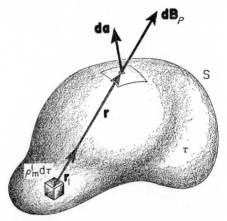

$$\mathbf{dB}_P = \frac{\mu_0}{4\pi}\frac{\rho'_m\,d\tau}{r^2}\,\mathbf{r}_1, \qquad (7\text{-}54)$$

according to Eq. *7-11*. The flux of $\mathbf{B}_P$ through an element $\mathbf{da}$ of the surface is

$$\mathbf{dB}_P\cdot\mathbf{da} = \frac{\mu_0}{4\pi}\,\rho'_m\,d\tau\,\frac{\mathbf{r}_1\cdot\mathbf{da}}{r^2}, \quad (7\text{-}55)$$

Figure 7-11. *An element of magnetic charge $\rho'_m\,d\tau$ inside a closed surface S.*

$$= \frac{\mu_0}{4\pi}\,\rho'_m\,d\tau\,d\Omega, \qquad (7\text{-}56)$$

which is exactly analogous to the electrostatic Gauss's law of Section 2.4. Integrating the flux over the whole surface S, we have

$$\int_S \mathbf{dB}_P\cdot\mathbf{da} = \mu_0\rho'_m\,d\tau, \qquad (7\text{-}57)$$

and for all the poles enclosed within the surface S,

$$\int \mathbf{B}_P\cdot\mathbf{da} = \mu_0\int_\tau \rho'_m\,d\tau. \qquad (7\text{-}58)$$

As an illustration, consider an infinite plane with a magnetic pole density σ'_m, as in Figure 7-12. Symmetry considerations require the magnetic induction $\mathbf{B}_{\sigma'_m}$ contributed by the poles to be perpendicular to the plane. If we take a cylindrical Gaussian surface as shown, then the only flux is through the ends, and

$$B_{\sigma'_m} = \frac{\mu_0\sigma'_m}{2}. \qquad (7\text{-}59)$$

On the end faces of the rod in Figure 7-9, $\sigma'_m = M$, thus if we consider the surface to be an infinite plane,

$$B_{\sigma'_m} = \frac{\mu_0 M}{2} \qquad (7\text{-}60)$$

at points close to the face. The contribution of the poles on the other face is

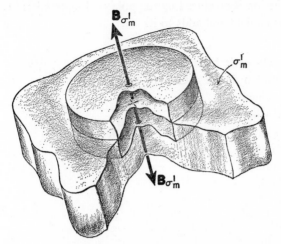

smaller and cannot be calculated in this way, since they are relatively far away. To get the total $\mathbf{B}_M$, we must add $\mu_0\mathbf{M}$ to $\mathbf{B}_{\sigma'_m}$ at every point.

It is important to understand clearly that this Gauss's law applies only to that part of the magnetic induction which is associated with the fictitious poles. The divergence of the total magnetic induction is always zero and the *total* flux of **B** through any closed surface is always zero.

7.3.3. Calculation of $\mathbf{B}_M$ at an Internal Point Using the Equivalent Current Formalism.

Let us also investigate the macroscopic induction at a point in the interior of a magnetic material in terms of the equivalent currents, starting with the vector potential **A**. As in Section 7.3.1, we consider a block of magnetic material and divide it into two parts separated by an imaginary sphere of radius R. This radius is again chosen large enough such that, at the center of the sphere, the magnetic induction due to atomic current loops in the outer volume τ' is adequately given by the dipole approximation. If we use the same notation as in Figure 7-4, and if we use Eq. *7-28* for the magnetic induction produced by the dipoles in the outer volume τ', we find that, at the center of the sphere,

$$\mathbf{B}_M = \frac{\mu_0}{4\pi} \int_{\tau'} \frac{\mathbf{J}' \times \mathbf{r}_1}{r^2} \, d\tau + \frac{\mu_0}{4\pi} \int_{S'} \frac{\boldsymbol{\lambda}' \times \mathbf{r}_1}{r^2} \, d\tau + \frac{\mu_0}{4\pi} \int_{S''} \frac{\boldsymbol{\lambda}' \times \mathbf{r}_1}{r^2} \, da + \mathbf{B}_M''. \quad (7\text{-}61)$$

Let us again leave the first two terms as they are for the moment and evaluate the third. The equivalent current on the imaginary surface S'' is $\boldsymbol{\lambda}'' = \mathbf{M} \times \mathbf{n}$ and is in the direction indicated in Figure 7-13. This current produces a magnetic induction at the center of the sphere which is in the direction opposite to **M**, and

$$\boldsymbol{\lambda}'' = |\mathbf{M} \times \mathbf{n}| = M \sin\theta \quad (7\text{-}62)$$

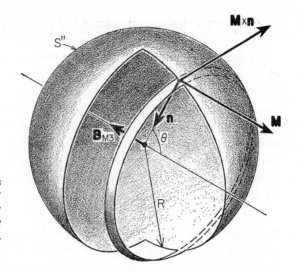

Figure 7-13

The magnetic induction B_{M3} at the center of the imaginary sphere of Figure 7-4 can be calculated from the equivalent currents flowing on its surface.

is the current per unit length on the surface. Then the current dI'' on a strip of width $R\,d\theta$ is

$$dI'' = M \sin \theta\, R\, d\theta. \tag{7-63}$$

From the Biot-Savart law, the induction B_{M3} produced by this current is, in the direction opposite to $\mathbf{M}$,

$$\mathbf{B}_{M3} = -\frac{\mu_0}{4\pi} \int_0^\pi \mathbf{M} \sin \theta\, R\, d\theta \frac{2\pi R \sin \theta}{R^2} \sin \theta, \tag{7-64}$$

$$= -\frac{2}{3} \mu_0 \mathbf{M}. \tag{7-65}$$

The contribution $\mathbf{B}_M''$ from the current loops within the small sphere of radius R can be calculated in exactly the same way as in Section 7.3.1. Finally,

$$\mathbf{B}_M = \frac{\mu_0}{4\pi} \int_{\tau'} \frac{\mathbf{J}' \times \mathbf{r}_1}{r^2} \, d\tau + \frac{\mu_0}{4\pi} \int_{S'} \frac{\mathbf{\lambda}' \times \mathbf{r}_1}{r^2} \, da - \frac{2}{3} \mu_0 \mathbf{M} + \frac{2}{3} \mu_0 \mathbf{M}. \tag{7-66}$$

If we take the volume integral over the whole volume and write S to indicate the real surfaces of the material, then

$$\mathbf{B}_M = \frac{\mu_0}{4\pi} \int_{\tau} \frac{\mathbf{J}' \times \mathbf{r}_1}{r^2} \, d\tau + \frac{\mu_0}{4\pi} \int_{S} \frac{\mathbf{\lambda}' \times \mathbf{r}_1}{r^2} \, da, \tag{7-67}$$

where $\mathbf{J}' = \nabla \times \mathbf{M}$ and $\mathbf{\lambda}' = \mathbf{M} \times \mathbf{n}$. The equivalent currents therefore give the correct value for the magnetic induction at points inside the polarized material as well as outside.

The magnetic induction on the axis of the uniformly polarized cylinder of Figure 7-9 is thus the same as inside a short solenoid, and the result is identical with that shown in Figure 7-10.

7.4. The Magnetic Field Intensity **H**

We are now in a position to calculate the macroscopic magnetic induction **B**, either inside magnetic material or outside, for any distribution of conduction currents and of magnetic materials, provided that the polarization vector **M** is known at all points in the magnetic material. So far we have no way of finding **M**. We could, in principle, determine **M** by measuring the total flux through each unit cross section of the system, but the experiment would be impossibly complicated and wholly impractical. Our discussion is therefore not yet satisfactory.

In developing magnetic concepts for free space and nonmagnetic materials, we found in Eq. *5-127* that

$$\nabla \times \mathbf{B} = \mu_0 \mathbf{J} \qquad (7\text{-}68)$$

for quasi-stationary currents. In this chapter we have seen that magnetically polarized materials can always be replaced by equivalent currents and that these currents produce magnetic inductions in exactly the same manner as do conduction currents, both inside and outside magnetic materials. Consequently the above equation should be rewritten as

$$\nabla \times \mathbf{B} = \mu_0(\mathbf{J} + \mathbf{J}') \qquad (7\text{-}69)$$

to account for the presence of magnetically polarized material, $\mathbf{J}'$ including both surface and volume equivalent current densities.

Now, since

$$\mathbf{J}' = \nabla \times \mathbf{M}, \qquad (7\text{-}70)$$

then

$$\nabla \times \mathbf{B} = \mu_0\mathbf{J} + \mu_0(\nabla \times \mathbf{M}), \qquad (7\text{-}71)$$

or

$$\nabla \times \left(\frac{\mathbf{B}}{\mu_0} - \mathbf{M}\right) = \mathbf{J}. \qquad (7\text{-}72)$$

The vector in the parentheses is such that its curl depends only on the *conduction* current density **J** at the point, and not on the equivalent currents. This is the *magnetic field intensity* vector:

$$\mathbf{H} = \frac{\mathbf{B}}{\mu_0} - \mathbf{M}. \qquad (7\text{-}73)$$

The vector **H** has the same units as **M**:

$$\frac{\text{Dipole moment}}{\text{Volume}} = \frac{\text{Ampere turns} \times \text{Area}}{\text{Volume}}, \qquad (7\text{-}74)$$

$$= \frac{\text{Ampere turns}}{\text{Meter}}. \qquad (7\text{-}75)$$

Thus

$$\nabla \times \mathbf{H} = \mathbf{J} \qquad (7\text{-}76)$$

for quasi-stationary currents, regardless of whether magnetic materials are present or not. The magnetic field intensity **H** itself can be found only when this differential equation can be solved, but even then the magnetic induction **B** remains unknown. A more general expression for $\nabla \times \mathbf{H}$ will be found in Section 7.10.

7.4.1. Gauss's Law for the Magnetic Field Intensity H.

Before proceeding with a general method of calculating **H**, let us derive a Gauss's law for **H**, as we have already done for **B** in Section 7.3.2. We have

$$\mathbf{B} = \mu_0\mathbf{H} + \mu_0\mathbf{M} \tag{7-77}$$

and

$$\nabla \cdot \mathbf{B} = \mu_0\nabla \cdot \mathbf{H} + \mu_0\nabla \cdot \mathbf{M}, \tag{7-78}$$

but, from Eq. *5-45*, $\nabla \cdot \mathbf{B} = 0$, and

$$\nabla \cdot \mathbf{H} = -\nabla \cdot \mathbf{M}. \tag{7-79}$$

From the definition of pole density in Eq. *7-9*,

$$\nabla \cdot \mathbf{H} = \rho'_m, \tag{7-80}$$

or, integrating over a volume τ bounded by a surface S, we have

$$\int_\tau \nabla \cdot \mathbf{H}\, d\tau = \int_\tau \rho'_m\, d\tau, \tag{7-81}$$

and, using the divergence theorem, we find

$$\int_S \mathbf{H} \cdot \mathbf{da} = \int_\tau \rho'_m\, d\tau. \tag{7-82}$$

Thus Gauss's law for **H** is analogous to the corresponding law for **E** in electrostatics.

7.4.2. Calculation of the Magnetic Field Intensity H.

Let us concentrate for the moment on the calculation of **H**. On integrating $\nabla \times \mathbf{H}$ of Eq. *7-76* over a surface S, for quasi-stationary currents,

$$\int_S (\nabla \times \mathbf{H}) \cdot \mathbf{da} = \int_S \mathbf{J} \cdot \mathbf{da}, \tag{7-83}$$

or, if we use Stokes's theorem,

$$\oint \mathbf{H} \cdot \mathbf{dl} = I, \tag{7-84}$$

where the line integral is to be evaluated around the curve which bounds the surface S. The line integral of $\mathbf{H} \cdot \mathbf{dl}$ is called the *magnetomotance*, and Eq. *7-84* is *Ampere's circuital law* (Section 5.11) in its more general form for quasi-stationary currents. This equation is applicable in the presence of magnetic materials. It can be used to calculate $\mathbf{H}$, at least for simple current distributions.

Using the pole formalism for expressing the magnetic induction as in Eq. 7-51, and taking into account both volume and surface distributions $\mathbf{J}$ and λ of *conduction* currents, we have from Eq. 7-73 that

$$\mathbf{H} = \frac{1}{4\pi} \int_\tau \frac{\rho_m' \, d\tau}{r^2} \mathbf{r}_1 + \frac{1}{4\pi} \int_S \frac{\sigma_m' \, da}{r^2} \mathbf{r}_1 + \frac{1}{4\pi} \int_\tau \frac{\mathbf{J} \times \mathbf{r}_1}{r^2} d\tau + \frac{1}{4\pi} \int_S \frac{\lambda \times \mathbf{r}_1}{r^2} da. \quad (7\text{-}85)$$

Thus $\mathbf{H}$ depends only on the poles and on the conduction currents. The contribution from the poles is calculated just as one would calculate an electrostatic field from electrostatic charges, except that the constant multiplying the integrals is $1/4\pi$ rather than $1/4\pi\epsilon_0$. The contribution from the conduction currents is calculated just as one would calculate the magnetic induction from conduction currents using the Biot-Savart law, except that again the constant is $1/4\pi$ rather than $\mu_0/4\pi$.

In terms of equivalent currents, Eqs. 7-67 and 7-73 give

$$\mathbf{H} = \frac{1}{4\pi} \int_\tau \frac{(\mathbf{J} + \mathbf{J}') \times \mathbf{r}_1}{r^2} d\tau + \frac{1}{4\pi} \int_S \frac{(\lambda + \lambda') \times \mathbf{r}_1}{r^2} da - \mathbf{M}, \quad (7\text{-}86)$$

where we have included the conduction as well as the equivalent currents. Thus, from Eqs. 7-85 and 7-86, the vector $\mathbf{H}$ depends on (a) the conduction currents and the poles if we use the pole formalism, or (b) on the conduction currents, the equivalent currents, and the magnetic polarization vector $\mathbf{M}$ if we use the equivalent current formalism. For some purposes it is simpler to think in terms of poles, whereas for other purposes it is preferable to use the equivalent currents.

7.4.3. Magnetic Susceptibility χ_m and Relative Permeability K_m. Again, as for dielectrics, it is convenient to define a *magnetic susceptibility* χ_m such that

$$\mathbf{M} = \chi_m \mathbf{H}, \quad (7\text{-}87)$$

where χ_m is a dimensionless number, $\mathbf{M}$ and $\mathbf{H}$ having the same dimensions. This equation holds only if the polarization $\mathbf{M}$ and the magnetic field intensity $\mathbf{H}$ are in the same direction, that is, if the material is isotropic. Many magnetic materials which are interesting from an engineering point of view are not isotropic and must be dealt with by considering the individual components of $\mathbf{B}$ and of $\mathbf{H}$, as for dielectrics (Section 3.12). In permanent magnets $\mathbf{B}$, $\mathbf{M}$, and $\mathbf{H}$ may all be in different directions.

There is one important distinction to be made between magnetic and dielectric materials: many interesting dielectrics are linear, hence the electric susceptibility χ_e is a constant, whereas most interesting magnetic materials are nonlinear, thus χ_m is *not* a constant but depends on $\mathbf{H}$. The magnetic susceptibility is nonetheless a useful quantity.

From Eq. *7-73*,

$$\mathbf{B} = \mu_0\mathbf{H} + \mu_0\mathbf{M}, \tag{7-88}$$

$$= \mu_0(1 + \chi_m)\mathbf{H}, \tag{7-89}$$

$$= K_m\mu_0\mathbf{H}, \tag{7-90}$$

where

$$K_m = 1 + \chi_m \tag{7-91}$$

is another dimensionless quantity called the *relative permeability*. In general, K_m is not a constant but is a function of **H**.

If a given material can have a magnetic polarization **M** different from zero, it must consist of atomic systems which possess magnetic moments capable of orientation. In terms of the magnetic susceptibility or the relative permeability we may place magnetic materials into the following three classes.

PARAMAGNETIC MATERIALS. In most atoms the magnetic moments arising from the orbital and spinning motions of the electrons cancel. In some, however, the cancellation is not complete, and there exists a residual permanent magnetic dipole moment. The so-called transition elements, such as manganese, are examples of this. When such atoms are placed in a magnetic field, they are subject to a torque which tends to align them, but thermal agitation tends to destroy this alignment. This phenomenon is entirely analogous to the alignment of polar molecules in dielectrics (Section 3.9).

Consider a gas or liquid with N atoms or molecules per unit volume, each with a magnetic dipole moment **m**. The fraction dN/N of the atoms or molecules which have their moments lying in the angular interval between θ and $\theta + d\theta$ is

$$\frac{dN}{N} = \frac{\sin\theta\, d\theta}{2} \tag{7-92}$$

in the absence of an external field, as in Eq. *3-122*. If, however, the magnetic dipoles are placed in an external field with a magnetic induction **B**, the solid angle elements are no longer equally probable, and

$$dN = C \exp[\mathbf{m}\cdot\mathbf{B}/kT] \sin\theta\, d\theta, \tag{7-93}$$

as in Eq. *3-123*. The normalizing constant C is chosen so that the total number of atoms or molecules per unit volume is N. Then, just as in Section 3.9.1, the resultant magnetic dipole moment per unit volume is

$$M = Nm \left(\coth\frac{mB}{kT} - \frac{kT}{mB} \right). \tag{7-94}$$

As for dielectrics, the magnetic energy $mB \ll kT$. The elementary dipole moment is approximately 10^{-23} ampere-meter^2, thus in a field of one weber/meter^2, $(mB/kT) \approx 2.5 \times 10^{-3}$. Expanding the exponentials as in Section 3.9.1, we find that

$$M \approx \frac{Nm^2}{3kT} B \tag{7-95}$$

and that

$$\chi_m \approx \mu_0 \frac{M}{B} = \frac{\mu_0 Nm^2}{3kT}. \tag{7-96}$$

The magnetic susceptibility χ_m is small compared to unity and varies inversely with the absolute temperature. Table 7-1 shows typical values of χ_m.

DIAMAGNETIC MATERIALS. In these materials the elementary moments are not permanent but are induced according to the Faraday law. The resultant polarization is in the direction *opposite* to the external field; the relative permeability is *less* than unity and is independent of temperature. All materials are diamagnetic, but orientational polarization may predominate, in which case the resultant permeability is greater than unity.

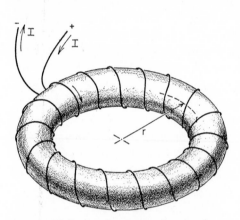

Figure 7-14. *Rowland ring for the determination of the magnetic properties of a ferromagnetic material.*

FERROMAGNETIC MATERIALS. In these materials there is a strong magnetic polarization, and the relative permeability can be large compared to unity, reaching magnitudes of many thousands in some materials. Such large polarizations are the result of group phenomena in the material, in which all the elementary moments in a small region, known as a *domain*, are aligned. The resultant polarization in one domain may be oriented at random with respect to the polarization in a neighboring domain. The large polarizations characteristic of ferromagnetic materials are the result of the orientation of whole domains. The phenomenon is complex and will not be discussed further here.*

7.5. Measurement of Magnetic Properties. The Rowland Ring

To determine the properties of a particular ferromagnetic material it is convenient to use a torus of the material on which a coil is wound, as in Figure 7-14. The lines of **B** and **H** are nearly azimuthal if the turns are closely spaced. If the

* See, for example, Kittel, *Introduction to Solid State Physics* (Wiley, New York, 1956), 2nd ed., p. 402 ff.

material is isotropic, the polarization **M** is also azimuthal, and there are no surface poles.

Let us examine the polarization **M** on a cross section of the torus. This will show whether or not there exists a volume distribution of poles. From the circuital law,

$$\oint \mathbf{H} \cdot \mathbf{dl} = NI \tag{7-97}$$

along a path of radius r, as in Figure 7-14, and, by symmetry, **H** is everywhere the same on this path. Thus

$$H = \frac{NI}{2\pi r}, \tag{7-98}$$

and

$$M = \chi_m H, \tag{7-99}$$

$$M = \chi_m \frac{NI}{2\pi r}. \tag{7-100}$$

Then

$$\rho'_m = -\boldsymbol{\nabla} \cdot \mathbf{M}. \tag{7-101}$$

Since there is cylindrical symmetry with no dependence on the ϕ- or z-coordinates, and if we assume for the moment that χ_m is a constant, then

$$\rho'_m = \frac{1}{r}\frac{\partial}{\partial r}\left(r \frac{\chi_m NI}{2\pi r}\right) = 0. \tag{7-102}$$

Thus the volume density of poles is also zero, provided that χ_m is constant. However, χ_m depends on **H** in ferromagnetic materials and then ρ'_m does not vanish. However, if the radius of the torus is large compared to the cross-sectional radius, ρ'_m can be arbitrarily small, and for practical purposes we may consider the volume pole density to be zero.

Equation 7-85 shows that, in the absence of poles, **H** depends only on the conduction currents. Inside the torus,

$$\mathbf{B} = \mathbf{B}_I + \mathbf{B}_M = \mathbf{B}_I + \mu_0\mathbf{M}, \tag{7-103}$$

from Eq. 7-51, $\mathbf{B}_I$ being the induction due to the current in the coil. Thus

$$B = B_I + \mu_0\chi_m H, \tag{7-104}$$

$$= B_I + \frac{\mu_0(K_m - 1)NI}{2\pi r}, \tag{7-105}$$

$$= B_I + B_M, \tag{7-106}$$

where B_M is the extra induction inside the core due to the polarization. The terms B and B_I can be measured from the total flux linking the coil with and without the core present. This gives B_M, and thus K_m, from Eq. 7-105.

7.6. Hysteresis

Using the Rowland ring, it is observed that the relative permeability K_m is not constant but that it depends both on H and on the previous history of the

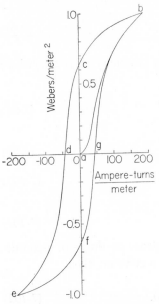

Figure 7-15. *Magnetization curve ab and hysteresis loop bcdefg. Adapted from data provided in United States Steel Engineering Manual for USS Transformer grade 72, 29-gauge electrical steel sheets.*

sample. For example, if we start with an unmagnetized sample of iron and increase the current in the coil to some specified magnitude, the magnetic induction increases along a curve such as *ab* in Figure 7-15. This curve is known as the *magnetization curve.* If the current in the winding is reduced to zero, the magnetic induction B does not fall to zero along the same curve but decreases along *bc.* The magnitude of the magnetic induction at *c* is the *remanence* or the *retentivity* for the particular sample of material. If the current is then reversed in direction and increased, B reaches a point *d* where it is reduced to zero. The magnitude of the magnetic field intensity H at this point is known as the *coercive force.* On further increasing the current in the same direction a point *e*, symmetrical to point *b*, is reached. If the current is now reduced, reversed, and increased, the point *b* is again reached. The closed curve *bcdefgb* is known as a *hysteresis* loop. If, at any point on the hysteresis cycle, the current is varied in a smaller cycle, a small hysteresis loop is described.

A characteristic feature of the hysteresis cycle is the *saturation* induction which is reached if the intensity H is increased beyond a certain magnitude. Maximum alignment of the domains is achieved, and further increase in H increases B only as the contribution from the conduction current increases. The saturation induction is characteristically in the range from 1 to 2 webers/meter^2.

7.6.1. Energy Dissipated in a Hysteresis Cycle. Energy is required to describe a hysteresis cycle in a magnetic substance as above. This can be shown by considering a Rowland ring connected to a source as in Figure 7-14. When the current is in the direction indicated and is increasing, the electromotance induced in the winding will tend to oppose the increase in current according to Lenz's law (Section 6.1.1). Thus the generator S is taking charges at low potential

energy and raising them to higher potential energy at this instant, and so it is
doing work at a rate

$$\frac{dW}{dt} = I\left(N\frac{d\Phi}{dt}\right), \tag{7-107}$$

$$= INS\frac{dB}{dt}, \tag{7-108}$$

where S is the cross-sectional area of the ring,
N is the number of turns, and B is the mean
magnetic induction in the core. We can rewrite
Eq. *7-108* in the form

$$\frac{dW}{dt} = \frac{INSl}{l}\frac{dB}{dt} = H\tau\frac{dB}{dt}, \tag{7-109}$$

where l is the mean circumference of the ring,
$\tau = Sl$ is its volume, and $H = NI/l$ as in Eq.
7-98. Thus

$$W_1 = \tau \int_g^b H\,dB \tag{7-110}$$

is the energy supplied by the source in going
from the point g to the point b in Figure 7-16.
This integral corresponds to the crosshatched
area in the figure and is equal to the energy
supplied per unit volume of the magnetic core.

When the current is in the same direction
but is decreasing, the polarity of the induced
electromotance is reversed according to Lenz's
law, with the result that charges enter the generator at high potential energy and leave it
at low potential energy, thus energy is returned
to the source. This energy is

$$W_2 = \tau \int_b^c H\,dB. \tag{7-111}$$

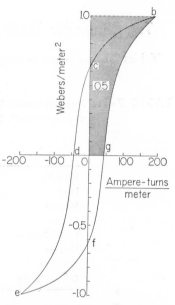

Figure 7-16. *The shaded area
gives the energy required, per
unit volume, in going from g
to b on the hysteresis loop. The
total energy per unit volume
required to describe a complete
hysteresis loop is equal to the
area enclosed by the loop.*

Finally, for the whole loop, the total energy supplied by the source is

$$W = \tau \oint H\,dB, \tag{7-112}$$

where the integral is to be evaluated around the hysteresis loop. With H in
ampere turns/meter, B in webers/meter² and τ in meters³, the energy W is in
joules. The area of the hysteresis loop in weber-ampere-turns/meter therefore
gives the energy dissipated per unit volume and per cycle in the core.

7.6.2. Relative Permeability. The relative permeability K_m can be defined in various ways. The differential permeability is the slope of the hysteresis curve:

$$K_m = \frac{1}{\mu_0} \frac{dB}{dH}; \qquad (7\text{-}113)$$

a more usual measure of K_m is simply the ratio of B/μ_0 to H:

$$K_m = \frac{1}{\mu_0} \frac{B}{H}. \qquad (7\text{-}114)$$

7.7. Magnetic Data for Various Materials

Tables 7-1 and 7-2 show magnetic data for some common substances.

TABLE 7-1. Magnetic Susceptibilities of Common Diamagnetic and Paramagnetic Substances

Substance	Magnetic Susceptibility
Bismuth	-1.7×10^{-4}
Lead	-1.7×10^{-5}
Mercury	-3.2×10^{-5}
Copper	-9.4×10^{-6}
Liquid Oxygen	3.5×10^{-3}
Platinum	2.9×10^{-4}
Aluminum	2.1×10^{-5}
Oxygen (NTP)	1.8×10^{-6}

TABLE 7-2. Magnetic Characteristics of Common Ferromagnetic Substances

Substance	Maximum Relative Permeability	Saturation Induction (webers/meter²)	Coercive Force (ampere turns/meter)	Remanence (webers/meter²)
Cold-rolled steel	2×10^3	2.1	1.4×10^2	
4% Silicon iron	7×10^3	2.0	0.4×10^2	
78 Permalloy	10^5	1.1	0.04×10^4	
Supermalloy	10^6	0.8	0.2	
Alnico V			6×10^4	1.3
Remalloy			3×10^4	1.0

Figure 7-17 shows magnetization data for several different kinds of iron, with lines of constant relative permeability indicated. The detailed shape of the magnetization curve and the maximum permeability achieved with a given

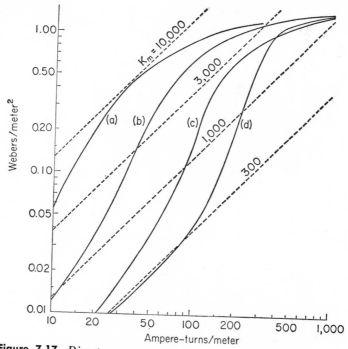

Figure 7-17. *Direct current magnetization curves for various grades of iron. Data adapted from USS Electrical Steel Sheets Engineering Manual. (a) Transformer grade 52, 29 gauge. (b) USS motor steel, 26 gauge. (c) Pure iron sheet. (d) Hot-rolled sheet.*

sample of iron depend on the purity, on the method of annealing, and on the thickness of the sheets, as well as on other particular characteristics of the sample.

7.8. Boundary Conditions

Let us examine the continuity conditions which must exist at the interface between two magnetic media. We shall proceed in much the same way as in Section 4.1 and discover that the normal component of **B** and the tangential component of **H** must both be continuous.

Consider a short cylindrical volume as in Figure 7-18a. The top and bottom faces are taken to be parallel to, and infinitely close to, the interface. There is thus no flux through the cylindrical surface, and the flux through the top face must be equal to that through the bottom, since $\nabla \cdot \mathbf{B} = 0$. Thus

$$B_{1n} = B_{2n}. \qquad (7\text{-}115)$$

The normal component of **B** is therefore continuous across the interface.

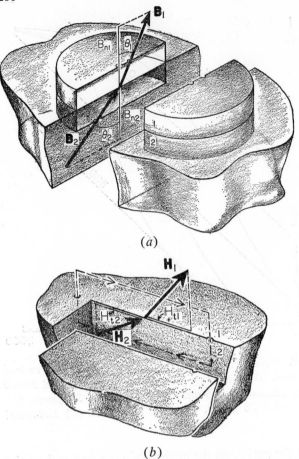

(a)

(b)

Figure 7-18. (a) *Gaussian surface at the interface between two different media.* (b) *Closed path crossing the interface between two media.*

Consider now Figure 7-18b. The closed path has two sides parallel to the interface and infinitely close to it. From the circuital law,

$$\oint \mathbf{H} \cdot \mathbf{dl} = I, \qquad (7\text{-}116)$$

and if there is no conduction current flowing on the interface, the integral vanishes. Since the parts of the path perpendicular to the boundary are arbitrarily short, we must have

$$H_{t_1} = H_{t_2}, \qquad (7\text{-}117)$$

and the tangential component of **H** must be continuous across the interface, unless it carries a current.

If both media are isotropic, that is, if **H** and **B** are in the same direction such that $\mathbf{B} = K_m\mu_0\mathbf{H}$, then the lines of $\mathbf{B}$ or of $\mathbf{H}$ are bent at the boundary in such a way that

$$K_{m_1}\mu_0\, H_1 \cos \theta_1 = K_{m_2}\mu_0\, H_2 \cos \theta_2, \qquad (7\text{-}118)$$

from Eq. *7-115* for $\mathbf{B}$, and

$$H_1 \sin \theta_1 = H_2 \sin \theta_2, \qquad (7\text{-}119)$$

from Eq. *7-117* for $\mathbf{H}$. Dividing the second equation by the first, we obtain

$$\frac{\tan \theta_1}{\tan \theta_2} = \frac{K_{m_1}}{K_{m_2}}. \qquad (7\text{-}120)$$

The lines of $\mathbf{B}$ or of $\mathbf{H}$ are farthest away from the normal in the medium having the larger relative permeability K_m.

There are many materials in which $\mathbf{B}$ and $\mathbf{H}$ are not in the same direction, and this simple bending of the lines of $\mathbf{B}$ and $\mathbf{H}$ at a boundary is then inapplicable. The case of the permanent magnet discussed below is an example.

7.9. Magnetic Field Calculations

We are now in a position to approach the calculation of the magnetic induction $\mathbf{B}$ for specified distributions of conduction currents and specified geometrical arrangements of specified magnetic materials. We shall approach such problems from the magnetic circuit point of view, using the concept of relative permeability and making appropriate approximations. Before developing this

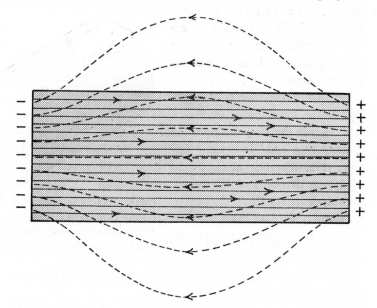

Figure 7-19. *Lines of* $\mathbf{M}$ *(solid) and of* $\mathbf{H}$ *(broken) in an idealized bar magnet.*

subject, however, it is instructive to examine the qualitative relationships between the vectors **B**, **H** and **M** in some simple cases.

7.9.1. The Permanent Bar Magnet. Let us first consider the uniformly magnetized bar magnet which we have already discussed in Section 7.3.1. It is

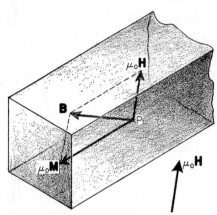

assumed that the magnet has a magnetic polarization **M** which is everywhere constant, both in magnitude and direction as in Figure 7-19. This is a hypothetical condition which is *not* realizable in practice, but it will serve to illustrate the principles. There are uniform pole densities $\sigma'_m = \pm \mathbf{M} \cdot \mathbf{n}$ induced at the ends. These poles produce the magnetic field intensity **H** shown in Figure 7-19, exactly like the electrostatic field of similarly distributed electrostatic charges. This magnetic field intensity **H** satisfies the boundary condition which requires

Figure 7-20. B *and* H *at the surface of a bar magnet.*

continuity of its tangential component at the surface of the magnet, but the lines of **H** are not bent at the pole-free surfaces. We have seen in Section 7.4.2 that one can calculate the magnetic field intensity **H** due to the polarized material from the magnetic poles by treating it as an electrostatic problem.

Let us first consider **H**. According to the lower curve in Figure 7-10, **H** is in the direction opposite to **M**. At the ends, **H** has a maximum value of somewhat more than $M/2$; near the center of the magnet, the values are smaller.

From Eq. *7-73* we have

$$\mathbf{B} = \mu_0(\mathbf{H} + \mathbf{M}). \quad (7\text{-}121)$$

On the axis, **B** is thus everywhere

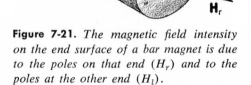

Figure 7-21. *The magnetic field intensity on the end surface of a bar magnet is due to the poles on that end (H_r) and to the poles at the other end (H_l).*

parallel to **M**, and its magnitude varies from somewhat less than $\mu_0 M/2$ at the ends to a maximum at the center.

Just inside the surface of the magnet, $\mu_0\mathbf{M}$ adds to $\mu_0\mathbf{H}$, as indicated in Figure 7-20, to produce a resultant **B** as shown. Just outside the surface, $\mathbf{B} = \mu_0\mathbf{H}$, since **M** = 0 outside the magnet. There is a discontinuity in the direction of **B** at the surface, but continuity of the normal component of **B** is maintained.

Next consider the ends of the magnet, where the poles are located. On the axis, **M** and **H** are both discontinuous as they pass through the end surface of the magnet. The polarization **M** goes from its full magnitude just inside the surface to zero just outside. The magnetic field intensity **H**, however, has two components which arise from the poles on both end faces of the magnet, as indicated in Figure 7-21. Just inside the right-hand surface, $H_r = M/2$ toward the left, and just outside, $H_r = M/2$ toward the right. However, H_l is continuous across the boundary, and so the discontinuity in **H** as it passes through the surface is

$$\Delta H = M. \tag{7-122}$$

Thus, just inside the right-hand surface,

$$\mathbf{B}_i = \mu_0\mathbf{H}_r + \mu_0\mathbf{H}_l + \mu_0\mathbf{M}, \tag{7-123}$$

$$= -\frac{\mu_0\mathbf{M}}{2} + \mu_0\mathbf{H}_l + \mu_0\mathbf{M}, \tag{7-124}$$

$$= \frac{\mu_0\mathbf{M}}{2} + \mu_0\mathbf{H}_l, \tag{7-125}$$

whereas just outside,

$$\mathbf{B}_0 = \mu_0\mathbf{H}_r + \mu_0\mathbf{H}_l, \tag{7-126}$$

$$= \frac{\mu_0\mathbf{M}}{2} + \mu_0\mathbf{H}_l, \tag{7-127}$$

and **B** is continuous at the end, at least on the axis.

Let us now consider a point off the axis on the right-hand end face, as in Figure 7-22. If we assume that the poles are uniformly distributed on the face,

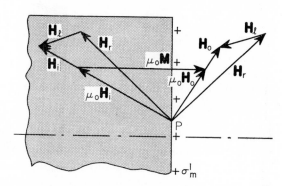

Figure 7-22

Field vectors at a point P off the axis on an end face of a permanent bar magnet.

then **H** is perpendicular to the face only on the axis. In Figure 7-22, H_r is the magnetic field intensity arising from the poles on the right-hand face of the magnet. On the right side of the surface, it points to the right, as indicated;

on the left side, to the left. However, $\mathbf{H}_l$, the contribution of the poles on the left face, is the same outside as it is inside, and it adds to $\mathbf{H}_r$ as indicated to produce $\mathbf{H}_0$ outside the magnet and $\mathbf{H}_i$ inside. It is clear from the diagram that the tangential component of $\mathbf{H}$ is continuous across the boundary.

We now multiply $\mathbf{H}$ by μ_0 and add $\mu_0\mathbf{M}$ to find the magnetic induction $\mathbf{B}$. Since $\mathbf{M} = 0$ outside the magnet, $\mathbf{B}_0 = \mu_0\mathbf{H}_0$; adding $\mu_0\mathbf{M}$ to $\mu_0\mathbf{H}_i$ must result in this same vector, since the normal component of $\mathbf{B}$ must be continuous across the boundary. Thus

$$\mu_0\mathbf{H}_i + \mu_0\mathbf{M} = \mu_0\mathbf{H}_0 \qquad\qquad (7\text{-}128)$$

or

$$\mathbf{B}_i = \mathbf{B}_0, \qquad\qquad (7\text{-}129)$$

and so $\mathbf{B}$ itself is continuous across the boundary.

On drawing the lines of $\mathbf{B}$ and $\mathbf{H}$ for the whole magnet we obtain the result indicated in Figure 7-23.

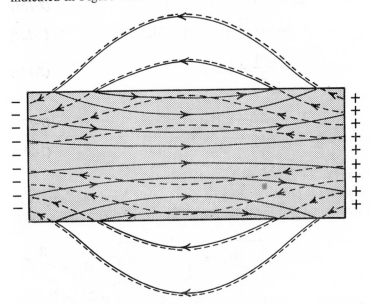

Figure 7-23. *Lines of* $\mathbf{B}$ *(solid) and of* $\mathbf{H}$ *(broken) in an idealized permanent bar magnet.*

7.9.2. Toroid with a Concentrated Winding. Let us return now to the common type of magnetic engineering problem in which we have a ferromagnetic core of known permeability around which is wound a coil carrying a current I. Suppose we wish to determine the magnetic induction $\mathbf{B}$ at some point or the flux Φ through some cross section. In problems of this sort the core is usually isotropic, thus $\mathbf{B}$ and $\mathbf{H}$ are in the same direction and $\mathbf{B} = \mu_0 K_m \mathbf{H}$. In devices of practical interest, K_m is not constant, and the problem is nonlinear, hence

we must resort to approximate methods. Engineers designing magnetic structures often resort to model measurements for more precision, although approximations and "rules of thumb" can yield reasonably accurate results.

Let us consider a toroid of magnetic material with a localized
winding, as in Figure 7-24, and let
us calculate the magnetic induction
B at a point within the iron on the
side of the toroid opposite the
winding. Figure 7-24 indicates the
lines of **B** in the absence of the
core. It might appear at first sight
that **B** is much greater in the iron
within the winding than it is on
the opposite side. This is not the
case, however, and **B** is of the same
order of magnitude at all points

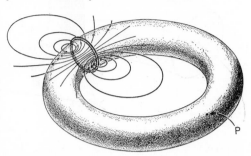

Figure 7-24. *Iron toroid with concentrated
winding. The lines of force shown are in the
plane of the toroid and are similar to those
of Figure 5-21. They apply only when there
is no iron present.*

within the iron. This can be understood in terms of the magnetic field intensity
H which is produced by the current I and by the poles, the former contributing
the same **H** as for the coreless solenoid. The *leakage flux*, that is, the flux of **B**
which leaves the core, produces poles on the surface in the manner discussed
below, and these poles contribute an intensity **H** within the iron, which keeps
H, and therefore **B**, nearly uniform all around the toroid.

To see how this comes about, let us make a rough calculation* of the magnetic
induction **B** due to the surface poles at a point in the toroid opposite the winding.
Figure 7-25 shows two bands symmetrically located at a distance d from the
point P and of width s equal to the radius of the cross section. Let us assume
that the normal component of **B** all around the band is

$$B_n = fB, \qquad (7\text{-}130)$$

where f is some small fraction and B is the total induction at the point, as indicated in Figure 7-25. Let us draw a cylindrical Gaussian surface around the
toroidal surface, but with slightly greater radius, and then apply Gauss's law
for **H** as in Eq. *7-82.*

The vectors **H** and **B** are everywhere in the same direction, and in the space
outside the toroid $H_n = B_n/\mu_0$. Then, from Gauss's law,

$$H_n 2\pi s^2 = \int_S \sigma'_m \, da, \qquad (7\text{-}131)$$

where $S = 2\pi s^2$ is the cylindrical area of the Gaussian surface, there being no

---

* See Moulin, *Principles of Electro-Magnetism* (Clarendon Press, Oxford, 1955), 3rd Edition,
p. 167.

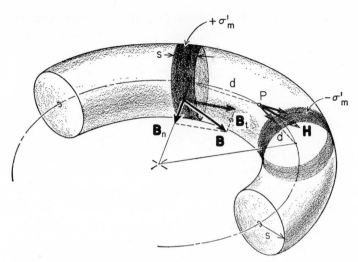

Figure 7-25. *Section of the toroid illustrated in Figure 7-24. The point P is opposite the winding as in Figure 7-24.*

contribution to the flux from the tangential component of **H** through the flat end surfaces, and where σ'_m is the density of induced poles on the cylindrical surface. The total pole strength is then

$$\int_S \sigma'_m \, da = \frac{fB2\pi s^2}{\mu_0}. \tag{7-132}$$

The positive poles on the upper band and the negative poles on the lower band then contribute a magnetic field intensity **H** at P according to the inverse square law. Thus if we neglect the fact that **H** from these sets of poles is not quite azimuthal,

$$H = \frac{2}{4\pi} \frac{fB2\pi s^2}{\mu_0 d^2}, \tag{7-133}$$

$$= \frac{fB}{\mu_0} \frac{s^2}{d^2}. \tag{7-134}$$

If the winding is far enough from P such that its **H** is negligible, then this **H** from the poles alone must produce a magnetic induction **B** such that

$$B = K_m \mu_0 H, \tag{7-135}$$

$$= K_m \mu_0 \frac{fB}{\mu_0} \frac{s^2}{d^2} \tag{7-136}$$

or

$$f = \frac{d^2}{s^2} \frac{1}{K_m}. \tag{7-137}$$

For example, if the relative permeability $K_m = 1000$ and if $(d^2/s^2) = 10$, the leakage magnetic induction need only be 1% of the total to maintain the induction in the ring. Furthermore, all the poles, and not only those on the two bands, contribute to the **H** at *P*, with the result that *f* is in fact smaller than the above calculation indicates. The calculation is at best approximate, but it illustrates the effect of the surface poles in confining the flux to the core. The high permeability makes it possible for a small **H** to produce a large **B** in the iron.

The effect of the leakage flux can be seen by imagining that the winding is at first uniformly distributed around the toroid and is then gradually compressed to occupy only a short section. At first **B** and **H** are uniform around the ring, but as the winding is compressed, the flux begins to leave the ring, producing surface poles. Those poles produce an **H** and a **B** in the part of the ring where there is no winding. As the winding is more and more compressed, the leakage flux increases, but, as we have seen, only a small amount suffices to maintain **B** and **H** nearly uniform, provided the relative permeability K_m is high.

For a closed path around the toroid linking the winding, the circuital law requires that

$$\oint \mathbf{H} \cdot \mathbf{dl} = NI, \tag{7-138}$$

or that

$$H = \frac{NI}{2\pi R}, \tag{7-139}$$

if **H** is uniformly distributed around the toroid, thus

$$B = K_m \mu_0 \frac{NI}{2\pi R}. \tag{7-140}$$

The magnetic induction varies inversely with *R*, but we may assume without risking much error that the total flux is the product of the cross section times the value of *B* at the average radius.

Let us finally investigate the magnitude of the intensity **H** at a point in the core within the winding. The magnetic field intensity **H** arises both from the current in the winding and from the poles. When the winding is distributed uniformly, there are no poles, and **H** has the magnitude given in Eq. *7-139* above. When the same winding is concentrated, the **H** due to the winding current is given approximately by

$$H_c = \frac{NI}{2s}. \tag{7-141}$$

This H_c is much larger than the *total* intensity $H_c = NI/2\pi R$ for the distributed coil. With the concentrated winding,

$$\mathbf{H}_{tot} = \mathbf{H}_c + \mathbf{H}_{\sigma'_m}, \tag{7-142}$$

where $\mathbf{H}_{\sigma'_m}$ is produced by the poles and is in the direction opposite to $\mathbf{H}_c$, as we can see from an approximate calculation of the type made above for the point opposite the winding. We can see how large $H_{\sigma'_m}$ must be from Eq. *7-142* if we assume that H_{tot} is the same as in the case of the distributed winding. We have

$$H_{\sigma'_m} = \frac{NI}{2\pi R} - \frac{NI}{2s}, \qquad (7\text{-}143)$$

$$= \frac{NI}{2}\left(\frac{1}{\pi R} - \frac{1}{s}\right). \qquad (7\text{-}144)$$

If $R \gg s$, then $H_{\sigma'_m}$ and H_c are nearly equal in magnitude but opposite in direction, and H_{tot} is small compared to either.

At other parts of the toroid H_c and $H_{\sigma'_m}$ have different magnitudes, but they add to produce nearly the same H_{tot} everywhere.

7.9.3. Toroid with a Gap.

Let us now examine the case of a toroid with a concentrated winding and a small gap g in the core, as in Figure 7-26.

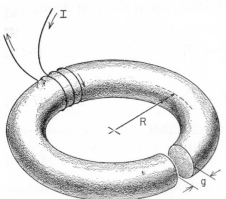

Figure 7-26. *Toroid with a concentrated winding and a small gap g in the core.*

It would appear, at first sight, that the poles on the gap faces cannot have much importance, since they have opposite signs on the two faces and thus tend to cancel each other's field. In other words, the gap acts as a magnetic dipole whose H falls off inversely as the cube of the distance from the gap. On the contrary, both H and B are greatly reduced by its presence, the reason being that H_{tot} is the difference between two larger quantities, H_c and $H_{\sigma'_m}$.

We can understand the situation qualitatively as follows. It was shown in the previous section that the poles on the toroidal surface tend to keep the total intensity uniform at all points in the toroid. The poles on the gap produce a demagnetizing intensity in the core which is opposite to H_{tot}. If H decreases, then B must also decrease; but the B at a given point can decrease only if there is more leakage flux, or if B is decreased everywhere. If there is more leakage flux, the associated surface poles tend to maintain a nearly uniform B. Thus the only way to decrease B at one point is to decrease it everywhere. At a point in the core within the winding, the surface poles at the gap produce a large reduction in H_{tot}, since $H_{\sigma'_m}$ is much larger than H_{tot}. For example, if $H_{\sigma'_m} = 0.9 H_c$ in the direction opposite to H_c in the toroid without a gap, then

$$H_{\text{tot}} = H_c - H_{\sigma'_m}, \qquad (7\text{-}145)$$

$$H_{\text{tot}} = 0.1H_c. \tag{7-146}$$

If now we cut a gap in the toroid, such that $H_{\sigma'_m}$ increases slightly in magnitude to $0.95H_c$, then

$$H_{\text{tot}} = 0.05H_c. \tag{7-147}$$

In both cases H_c is the same, provided the winding and the current are the same. Thus an increase of about 5% in the surface pole strength changes H_{tot} by a factor of two.

This calculation can be put on a quantitative basis as follows. The magnetic field intensity in the core is taken to be uniform, since the surface poles will maintain a nearly constant field intensity as long as the relative permeability of the material is high. Since the normal component of **B** must be continuous at the gap, **B** must be the same in the gap as it is in the iron. Since the relative permeability of the gap is unity, **H** must increase discontinuously in passing from the iron through the core surface into the gap. This is to be expected from Gauss's law for magnetic poles (Section 7.4.1).

Applying the circuital law to a path around the toroid and through the gap,

$$H_{Fe}l + H_g g = NI, \tag{7-148}$$

where H_{Fe} and H_g are the magnitudes of **H** in the iron and in the gap, respectively, and where l and g are the lengths of the iron path and of the gap. Since **B** has the same magnitude in the iron and in the gap,

$$\frac{Bl}{K_m\mu_0} + \frac{B_g}{\mu_0} = NI, \tag{7-149}$$

or

$$B = \frac{K_m\mu_0 NI}{l + gK_m}. \tag{7-150}$$

Comparison of this result with Eq. *7-140* for the toroid without the gap shows that the gap reduces **B** as if it were filled with iron and K_m times longer.

7.9.4. Magnetic Circuits. It is now possible to transform our calculations of magnetic inductions and fluxes into a form suitable for engineering through the concept of magnetic circuit. We must make the following simplifying assumptions based on the above discussion.

(1) **H** and **B** are either tangential or perpendicular to all the ferromagnetic surfaces.

(2) **H** and **B** are uniform through any cross section of the material.

(3) The relative permeability is a constant throughout each type of material in the circuit.

With these assumptions, let us return to the toroid with the air gap and calculate the flux through the core. From the circuital law,

$$\oint \mathbf{H \cdot dl} = NI \tag{7-151}$$

or

$$H_{Fe}l + H_g g = NI, \tag{7-152}$$

and

$$B = \frac{NI}{(l/K_m\mu_0) + (g/\mu_0)}, \tag{7-153}$$

as we found previously. If S is the cross-sectional area of the core, then

$$\Phi = SB, \tag{7-154}$$

$$= \frac{NI}{(l/K_m\mu_0 S) + (g/\mu_0 S)}. \tag{7-155}$$

The flux is proportional to the ampere-turns NI and to the cross-sectional area S, and inversely proportional to the length of the gap g.

Equation 7-155 is similar to Ohm's law for an electric circuit, with the flux corresponding to the current, whereas the magnetomotance (Section 7.4.2).

$$\oint \mathbf{H \cdot dl} = NI \tag{7-156}$$

corresponds to the electromotance, and the *reluctance*

$$R = \sum_i \frac{l_i}{K_{mi}\mu_0 S_i} \tag{7-157}$$

of the magnetic circuit corresponds to the resistance. The magnetic flux Φ is thus given by

$$\Phi = \frac{NI}{R}. \tag{7-158}$$

For example, the flux in a toroidal core, with a mean diameter of 20 centimeters, a cross-sectional area of 10 centimeters^2, and a relative permeability of 1000, wound with 100 turns carrying a current of 100 milliamperes is

$$\Phi = \frac{100 \times 10^{-1}}{\pi \times 0.2} \times 1000 \times 4\pi \times 10^{-7} \times 10^{-3}, \tag{7-159}$$

$$= 2.0 \times 10^{-5} \text{ weber}, \tag{7-160}$$

and the self-inductance

$$L = \frac{N\Phi}{I} = \frac{100 \times 2 \times 10^{-5}}{10^{-1}} = 2.0 \times 10^{-2} \text{ henry}. \tag{7-161}$$

If the ring has a 1.0-millimeter gap cut in it, the length of the iron path is still approximately 0.20π meter,

$$\Phi = \frac{100 \times 10^{-1} \times 4\pi \times 10^{-7} \times 10^{-3}}{(0.2\pi/1000) + 10^{-3}}, \tag{7-162}$$

$$= 7.7 \times 10^{-6} \text{ weber}, \tag{7-163}$$

and

$$L = \frac{100 \times 7.7 \times 10^{-6}}{10^{-1}} = 7.7 \times 10^{-3} \text{ henry}. \qquad (7\text{-}164)$$

The 1.0-mm gap has therefore decreased the flux and the inductance by a factor greater than two.

7.10. Maxwell's Fourth Equation

Although we have introduced the magnetic field intensity **H** as an aid in computing the induction in magnetic materials, its usefulness is of much broader scope. Let us examine Eq. *5-126* for $\nabla \times \mathbf{B}$. We have

$$\nabla \times \mathbf{B} = \mu_0 \mathbf{J} + \mu_0 \frac{\partial \mathbf{D}}{\partial t}. \qquad (7\text{-}165)$$

For this equation to be completely general, such that it applies to fields in dielectrics and magnetic materials as well as in free space and in nonmagnetic materials, **J** must include all forms of current.

It must include not only the usual conduction current but also convection currents such as are found in a vacuum diode or in an electrolytic cell. We shall call this current density (conduction plus convection) $\mathbf{J}_c$. The current density **J** must also include dielectric polarization currents $\mathbf{J}_p$ and equivalent magnetic currents $\mathbf{J}_M$. The dielectric polarization current density is given by $\partial \mathbf{P}/\partial t$ (see Problem 7-16), and we have already seen in Eq. *7-21* that the equivalent magnetic current is given by $\nabla \times \mathbf{M}$. Thus

$$\nabla \times \mathbf{B} = \mu_0 \left(\mathbf{J}_c + \frac{\partial \mathbf{P}}{\partial t} + \nabla \times \mathbf{M} \right) + \mu_0 \frac{\partial \mathbf{D}}{\partial t}, \qquad (7\text{-}166)$$

$$\nabla \times \left(\frac{\mathbf{B}}{\mu_0} - \mathbf{M} \right) = \mathbf{J}_c + \frac{\partial}{\partial t} (\epsilon_0 \mathbf{E} + \mathbf{P}). \qquad (7\text{-}167)$$

In terms of the magnetic field intensity **H** and the electric displacement **D** we have

$$\boxed{\nabla \times \mathbf{H} = \mathbf{J} + \frac{\partial \mathbf{D}}{\partial t},} \qquad (7\text{-}168)$$

where we have dropped the subscript from **J**, which from now on will always represent conduction plus convection current density. *This is the fourth and last of the Maxwell equations.* The term $\partial \mathbf{D}/\partial t$ is the displacement current density and is expressed in amperes/meter^2 (Section 5.10).

The displacement current obviously does not correspond to current in the usual sense of the word. For example, $\partial \mathbf{D}/\partial t$ can have a finite value in a perfect vacuum, where there are no charges of any kind. It serves to make the total current continuous across discontinuities in conduction current. For example, consider a current charging a capacitor, as in Figure 7-27. The current produces a magnetic field, and for the path indicated we have, from Ampère's circuital law (Eq. *7-84*),

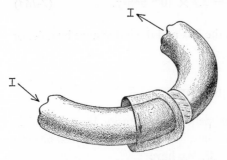

$$\oint \mathbf{H} \cdot \mathbf{dl} = I \qquad (7\text{-}169)$$

Figure 7-27. *Current I flowing through a conductor and charging the capacitance at the gap. The displacement current through the gap is equal to the conduction current through the conductor, and the line integral of* **H·dl** *around the path shown is equal to I even if the surface limited by the path is chosen to pass through the gap.*

where I is the current crossing any surface whose boundary is the path of integration. If we choose the surface such that it passes through the gap, then the conduction current through the surface is zero. However, if we compute the displacement current in this case (see Problem 7-17) we find that it is just equal to I. Thus, if the circuital law is written

$$\oint \mathbf{H} \cdot \mathbf{dl} = I + \int_S \frac{\partial \mathbf{D}}{\partial t} \cdot \mathbf{da} \qquad (7\text{-}170)$$

the result is independent of which surface S we choose.

It is instructive to estimate the ratio of displacement current density $\partial \mathbf{D}/\partial t$ to conduction current density $\mathbf{J}$ in a conductor. For an alternating field $E_0 \cos \omega t$ within a conductor of conductivity σ, the conduction current density is

$$\mathbf{J} = \sigma \mathbf{E}_0 \cos \omega t, \qquad (7\text{-}171)$$

whereas the displacement current density is

$$\frac{\partial \mathbf{D}}{\partial t} = \omega K_e \epsilon_0 \mathbf{E}_0 \sin \omega t, \qquad (7\text{-}172)$$

where K_e is the dielectric coefficient of the conducting material. Thus

$$\left| \frac{\frac{\partial D}{\partial t}}{J} \right| = \frac{\omega K_e \epsilon_0}{\sigma}. \qquad (7\text{-}173)$$

The dielectric coefficient K_e for a conductor is not readily measured, since any polarization effect is completely overshadowed by conduction. However, the atoms of the material are polarizable, and, for purposes of estimation, we may take $K_e \approx 1$. Setting $\sigma \approx 10^7$ mhos/meter for a good conductor, we have

$$\left| \frac{\partial D}{\partial t} \right| \approx 10^{-17} f, \qquad (7\text{-}174)$$

where $f = \omega/2\pi$. Thus the displacement current in a good conductor is completely negligible compared to the conduction current at any frequency lower than optical frequencies, where $f \approx 10^{15}/second$.

It is interesting to note that, although the conduction current is in phase with the electric field intensity, the displacement current leads the electric field by $\pi/2$ radians.

In free space $\sigma = 0$, and there is no conduction current—only displacement current.

7.11. Summary

Electron motions within atoms produce atomic magnetic moments. A material possessing a resultant moment is said to be magnetically *polarized,* and the *polarization vector* **M** is the magnetic dipole moment per unit volume. The total magnetic induction **B** in or near polarized magnetic material is the sum of the induction produced by the currents and that produced by the oriented dipoles of the material.

The magnetic induction contributed by the polarized material may be calculated by using either the *magnetic pole formalism* or the *equivalent current formalism.* The former is based on the scalar magnetic potential V_m and the latter on the vector potential **A**.

At a point outside the polarized material the induction due to the material is

$$\mathbf{B}_M = \frac{\mu_0}{4\pi} \int_S \frac{\sigma_m' \, da}{r^2} \mathbf{r}_1 + \frac{\mu_0}{4\pi} \int_\tau \frac{\rho_m' \, d\tau}{r^2} \mathbf{r}_1, \tag{7-11}$$

where

$$\sigma_m' = \mathbf{M} \cdot \mathbf{n} \tag{7-8}$$

and

$$\rho_m' = -\nabla \cdot \mathbf{M} \tag{7-9}$$

are the *surface* and *volume pole densities*, respectively. Using the poles, we calculate the induction $\mathbf{B}_M$ at an external point exactly as we would calculate an electrostatic field intensity from electric charge densities.

At the same external point the induction can also be written

$$\mathbf{B}_M = \frac{\mu_0}{4\pi} \int_S \left(\frac{\lambda' \times \mathbf{r}_1}{r^2} \right) da + \frac{\mu_0}{4\pi} \int_\tau \left(\frac{\mathbf{J}' \times \mathbf{r}_1}{r^2} \right) d\tau, \tag{7-28}$$

where

$$\lambda' = \mathbf{M} \times \mathbf{n} \tag{7-20}$$

and

$$\mathbf{J}' = \nabla \times \mathbf{M} \tag{7-21}$$

are the *equivalent surface current density* and the *equivalent volume current density*, respectively. Using these equivalent currents, we calculate the induction exactly as we would for conduction currents—from the Biot-Savart law.

At an internal point the poles by themselves do not give the induction $\mathbf{B}_M$; instead, they give $\mathbf{B}_M - \mu_0\mathbf{M}$. The equivalent currents give the correct value of the induction $\mathbf{B}_M$ at an internal point.

A *Gauss's law* for magnetic poles can be written for the magnetic induction $\mathbf{B}$:

$$\int_S \mathbf{B}_P \cdot \mathbf{da} = \mu_0 \int_\tau \rho_m' \, d\tau. \tag{7-58}$$

However, the induction $\mathbf{B}_P$ in this equation is only that part of the induction associated with the poles. The *total* flux of $\mathbf{B}$ through any surface bounding a volume is always zero.

Since equivalent currents produce magnetic fields in the same manner as do conduction currents,

$$\nabla \times \mathbf{B} = \mu_0(\mathbf{J} + \mathbf{J}') \tag{7-69}$$

for steady currents. This leads to the definition of the *magnetic field intensity:*

$$\mathbf{H} = \frac{\mathbf{B}}{\mu_0} - \mathbf{M}, \tag{7-73}$$

whose curl depends only on the conduction current:

$$\nabla \times \mathbf{H} = \mathbf{J}. \tag{7-76}$$

The corresponding integral statement,

$$\oint \mathbf{H} \cdot \mathbf{dl} = I, \tag{7-84}$$

is *Ampere's circuital law.*

We can also write a *Gauss's law* for magnetic poles in terms of $\mathbf{H}$:

$$\int_S \mathbf{H} \cdot \mathbf{da} = \int_\tau \rho_m' \, d\tau, \tag{7-82}$$

which is always true.

The magnetic field intensity $\mathbf{H}$ can be written in terms of poles and conduction currents:

$$\mathbf{H} = \frac{1}{4\pi} \int_\tau \frac{\rho_m' \, d\tau}{r^2} \mathbf{r}_1 + \frac{1}{4\pi} \int_S \frac{\sigma_m' \, da}{r^2} \mathbf{r}_1 + \frac{1}{4\pi} \int_\tau \frac{\mathbf{J} \times \mathbf{r}_1}{r^2} d\tau + \frac{1}{4\pi} \int_S \frac{\lambda \times \mathbf{r}_1}{r^2} da, \tag{7-85}$$

or in terms of conduction currents, equivalent currents, and $\mathbf{M}$:

$$\mathbf{H} = \frac{1}{4\pi} \int_\tau \frac{(\mathbf{J} + \mathbf{J}') \times \mathbf{r}_1}{r^2} d\tau + \frac{1}{4\pi} \int_S \frac{(\lambda + \lambda') \times \mathbf{r}_1}{r^2} da - \mathbf{M}. \tag{7-86}$$

In many magnetic materials $\mathbf{B}$ and $\mathbf{H}$ are in the same direction, and $\mathbf{M}$ is proportional to $\mathbf{H}$, thus

$$\mathbf{M} = \chi_m\mathbf{H}, \tag{7-87}$$

and

$$\mathbf{B} = \mu_0(1 + \chi_m)\mathbf{H}, \tag{7-89}$$

$$= K_m\mu_0\mathbf{H}, \tag{7-90}$$

where χ_m is the *magnetic susceptibility* and K_m is the *relative permeability*. Both χ_m and K_m are dimensionless numbers.

Materials fall into three general classes: (a) *diamagnetic materials*, whose susceptibility χ_m is slightly less than unity, (b) *paramagnetic materials*, whose susceptibility is slightly greater than unity, and (c) *ferromagnetic materials*, whose susceptibility is large compared to unity.

In ferromagnetic materials $\mathbf{B}$ depends not only on $\mathbf{H}$ but also on previous values of $\mathbf{H}$, and the B vs H curves are loops. This phenomenon is called *hysteresis*. When a sample of such material is subjected to a cyclic variation in $\mathbf{H}$ and $\mathbf{B}$, the energy dissipated is

$$W = \tau \oint H \, dB. \tag{7-112}$$

For a unit volume and for one cycle this energy is equal to the area enclosed by the hysteresis loop.

At an interface between two magnetic media the *tangential component* of $\mathbf{H}$ and the *normal component* of $\mathbf{B}$ *are continuous*.

To find the magnetic induction $\mathbf{B}$ in magnetic materials one can, in principle, calculate the magnetic field intensity $\mathbf{H}$ from either Eq. *7-85* or *7-86* and then, knowing the relative permeability for the material, find $\mathbf{B}$. In practice, however, to find the induction $\mathbf{B}$ at some point, or to find the flux Φ through some cross section, we resort to the magnetic circuit concept. We assume (a) that $\mathbf{H}$ and $\mathbf{B}$ are either tangential or perpendicular to all the ferromagnetic surfaces, (b) that $\mathbf{H}$ and $\mathbf{B}$ are uniform over any cross section of the material, and (c) that the relative permeability is constant throughout each type of material in the circuit.

The effects of magnetic poles on the surfaces of the material help make these assumptions generally valid. In such a magnetic circuit

$$\Phi = \frac{NI}{R}, \tag{7-158}$$

where NI is called the *magnetomotance* and where

$$R = \sum_i \frac{l_i}{K_{mi}\mu_0 S_i} \tag{7-157}$$

is the *reluctance* of the circuit.

The utility of the magnetic field intensity vector $\mathbf{H}$ is not limited to the calculation of the induction in magnetic materials. When we write the general equation for $\nabla \times \mathbf{B}$ (Eq. *5-126*) and include dielectric polarization currents and equivalent magnetic currents we find that

$$\boxed{\nabla \times \mathbf{H} = \mathbf{J} + \frac{\partial \mathbf{D}}{\partial t},} \tag{7-168}$$

where $\partial \mathbf{D}/\partial t$ is the displacement current density. This is the *fourth and last Maxwell equation*.

Problems

7-1. Two magnetic dipoles of moments $\mathbf{m}_1$ and $\mathbf{m}_2$ are separated by a distance D. If the dipoles are aligned along the line joining them, what is the force of interaction?

If $\mathbf{m}_1$ lies along the line and $\mathbf{m}_2$ is perpendicular to the line, what is the force exerted by each on the other?

What about Newton's third law?

7-2. A small current loop of moment $\mathbf{m}$ is arbitrarily oriented at an off-center point within a spherical surface of radius R. What is the mean value of the induction $\bar{\mathbf{B}}$ within the sphere?

7-3. An iron rod is magnetized in the azimuthal direction (that is, $\mathbf{M}$ is always perpendicular to the radius and to the axis of the rod). What dependence on distance from the axis can $\mathbf{M}$ have in order that there be no net magnetic charge in the system?

7-4. The magnetic polarization of iron can contribute as much as 2 webers/meter² to the magnetic induction in iron. If each electron can contribute a magnetic moment of 0.927×10^{-23} ampere-meter² (one Bohr magneton), how many electrons per atom, on the average, contribute to the polarization?

7-5. A steel sphere of radius R has a uniform magnetization $\mathbf{M}$ parallel to the z-axis. What is the total magnetic moment of the sphere?

Calculate the magnetic induction $\mathbf{B}$ and the magnetic field intensity $\mathbf{H}$ at the center of the sphere.

How would you find $\mathbf{B}$ at points outside the sphere at a distance large compared to R? How does $\mathbf{B}$ depend on the distance to the sphere?

7-6. A thin disk of iron of radius r and thickness t is permanently magnetized with a magnetic dipole moment per unit volume $\mathbf{M}$ parallel to the axis of the disk. Calculate $\mathbf{H}$ in the iron at a point on the axis.

Calculate $\mathbf{B}$ at the same point and at a point on the axis outside the disk at a distance D from the center of the disk.

If the disk was magnetized by carrying it around a hysteresis loop, at what point on the loop was it left after the magnetizing current was removed?

7-7. A permanent horseshoe magnet has its poles connected with a "keeper" of soft iron when it is not in use. What is the effect of the keeper?

7-8. A permanent magnet consists of a ring of iron of mean radius a, with a small gap of height d cut out. If the iron is magnetized uniformly with magnetic moment $\mathbf{M}$ per unit volume, calculate the magnetic field intensity $\mathbf{H}$ in the gap and in the iron.

7-9. A permanent magnet (consider a torus with a gap cut out) operates at a point in the second quadrant of its hysteresis curve—the curve in the second quadrant portion being known as the demagnetization curve—since the poles produce a demagnetizing H. The B_0 and H_0 in the iron at the operating point can be adjusted by varying the relative lengths of the iron and of the gap in the magnetic circuit. Show that a minimum volume of iron is required to produce a given $\mathbf{B}_g$ in the gap if the operating point is selected to make the so-called energy product B_0H_0 a maximum. Assume that the flux in the iron is the same as that in the gap.

7-10. A long wire of radius a carries a current I and is surrounded coaxially by a long hollow iron cylinder of relative permeability K_m. The inner radius of the cylinder is b and the outer radius c. Compute the total flux of $\mathbf{B}$ inside a section of the cylinder l meters long.

Find the equivalent current density on the inner and outer iron surfaces, and find the direction of the equivalent currents relative to the current in the wire.

Find the equivalent current density inside the iron.

Find $\mathbf{B}$ at distances $r > c$ from the wire. How would this value be affected if the iron cylinder were removed?

7-11. A toroidal solenoid has a mean radius R, has a cross section of radius r, is wound with N turns, and carries a current I. Calculate the magnetic flux through the solenoid by integrating the induction $\mathbf{B}$ over a cross section.

Calculate the magnetic flux by finding a mean value of $\mathbf{B}$ and multiplying by the cross-sectional area. At what radius does $\mathbf{B}$ have its mean value?

7-12. An iron rod of square cross section and of relative permeability K_m is bent to form a ring, and its ends are welded together. Wire is wound toroidally around the ring to form a coil of N turns. Compute the total flux of B in the ring when the current in the wire is I amperes, taking into account the variation of B over the cross section of the iron.

Calculate the inductance of the coil.

7-13. A coil of 300 turns is wound on an iron ring ($K_m = 500$) of 40 centimeters mean diameter and 10 centimeters² in cross section. Calculate the magnetic flux in the ring when the current in the coil is one ampere.

Calculate the flux when there is a gap of 1.0 millimeter in the ring.

7-14. Show that the energy stored in a magnetic circuit can be written as

$$W = \tfrac{1}{2}\Phi^2 R,$$

where Φ is the flux and R is the reluctance of the circuit.

7-15. A region of space may be "shielded" from magnetic fields by surrounding it with high permeability iron. Show this for a magnetic field $\mathbf{B}$ perpendicular to the axis of an iron cylinder of inner and outer radii a and b, respectively, and of relative permeability K_m.

Solve Laplace's equation for the magnetic potential outside the iron, in the iron, and in the enclosed space. Use the cylindrical harmonics of Problem 4-16 in a suitable combination to match the boundary conditions.

By how large a factor can the field in the inner region be reduced with this technique?

7-16. Show that a time-dependent dielectric polarization vector $\mathbf{P}$ is accompanied by an effective electric current whose density is $\partial\mathbf{P}/\partial t$. This is the *polarization current density*.

7-17. A constant current charges a capacitor as in Figure 7-27. Show that the displacement current is equal to the charging current.

CHAPTER 8

Maxwell's Equations

We have established at this stage the four basic principles of electromagnetic theory which are stated in mathematical form as the four equations of Maxwell. Our object in this chapter is to re-examine these four equations as a group and to draw from them several conclusions of fundamental importance.

8.1. Maxwell's Equations

Let us group the four equations of Maxwell which we found successively as Eqs. *3-58*, *5-45*, *6-11*, and *7-168*:

$$\boldsymbol{\nabla} \cdot \mathbf{D} = \rho, \tag{8-1}$$

$$\boldsymbol{\nabla} \cdot \mathbf{B} = 0, \tag{8-2}$$

$$\boldsymbol{\nabla} \times \mathbf{E} + \frac{\partial \mathbf{B}}{\partial t} = 0, \tag{8-3}$$

$$\boldsymbol{\nabla} \times \mathbf{H} - \frac{\partial \mathbf{D}}{\partial t} = \mathbf{J}. \tag{8-4}$$

As usual,

$\mathbf{D}$ is the electric displacement in coulombs/meter²,
$\mathbf{B}$ is the magnetic induction in webers/meter²,
$\mathbf{E}$ is the electric field intensity in volts/meter,
$\mathbf{H}$ is the magnetic field intensity in amperes/meter,
ρ is the free charge density in coulombs/meter³, and
$\mathbf{J}$ is the current density in amperes/meter².

The current density $\mathbf{J}$ is meant to include both conduction and convection currents (Section 7.10). For points outside the sources, and for conductors obeying Ohm's law,

$$\mathbf{J} = \sigma \mathbf{E}, \tag{8-5}$$

where σ is the conductivity of the medium in mhos/meter. Inside a source such as a battery, there is also another electric field intensity $\mathbf{E}_s$ due to the local generation of energy, and

$$\mathbf{J} = \sigma(\mathbf{E} + \mathbf{E}_s). \tag{8-6}$$

Maxwell's equations are partial differential equations involving space derivatives of the four *field vectors* $\mathbf{E}$, $\mathbf{D}$, $\mathbf{B}$, and $\mathbf{H}$, the time derivatives of $\mathbf{B}$ and of $\mathbf{D}$, the free charge density ρ, and the current density $\mathbf{J}$. They do not, of course, yield the values of the field vectors directly, but only after integrating with the boundary conditions appropriate to the field under consideration.

Since these equations are linear, each charge or current distribution produces its own field independently; for example, the resulting $\mathbf{E}$ vector at a given point is the vector sum of the $\mathbf{E}$ vectors produced at that point by the various sources. This is the *principle of superposition* (Section 2.2).

These are the four fundamental equations of electromagnetism. They are completely general and apply to all electromagnetic phenomena in media which are at rest with respect to the coordinate system used. They are valid for nonhomogeneous, nonlinear and even for nonisotropic media. All of the remaining chapters will be based on them.

It is worthwhile to rewrite Maxwell's equations in scalar form for Cartesian coordinates:

$$\frac{\partial D_x}{\partial x} + \frac{\partial D_y}{\partial y} + \frac{\partial D_z}{\partial z} = \rho, \tag{8-7}$$

$$\frac{\partial B_x}{\partial x} + \frac{\partial B_y}{\partial y} + \frac{\partial B_z}{\partial z} = 0, \tag{8-8}$$

$$\frac{\partial E_z}{\partial y} - \frac{\partial E_y}{\partial z} + \frac{\partial B_x}{\partial t} = 0, \tag{8-9}$$

$$\frac{\partial E_x}{\partial z} - \frac{\partial E_z}{\partial x} + \frac{\partial B_y}{\partial t} = 0, \tag{8-10}$$

$$\frac{\partial E_y}{\partial x} - \frac{\partial E_x}{\partial y} + \frac{\partial B_z}{\partial t} = 0, \tag{8-11}$$

$$\frac{\partial H_z}{\partial y} - \frac{\partial H_y}{\partial z} - \frac{\partial D_x}{\partial t} = J_x, \tag{8-12}$$

$$\frac{\partial H_x}{\partial z} - \frac{\partial H_z}{\partial x} - \frac{\partial D_y}{\partial t} = J_y, \tag{8-13}$$

$$\frac{\partial H_y}{\partial x} - \frac{\partial H_x}{\partial y} - \frac{\partial D_z}{\partial t} = J_z. \tag{8-14}$$

Maxwell's equations, Eqs. *8-1* to *8-4*, are not all independent of each other. If we take the divergence of Eq. *8-3*, recalling that the divergence of the curl of any vector is zero, then

$$\nabla \cdot \frac{\partial \mathbf{B}}{\partial t} = 0, \tag{8-15}$$

or, inverting the order of the operations,

$$\frac{\partial}{\partial t}(\nabla \cdot \mathbf{B}) = 0. \tag{8-16}$$

The quantity $\nabla \cdot \mathbf{B}$ is therefore independent of the time at any point in space. We can set the divergence of $\mathbf{B}$ equal to zero everywhere if we assume that, for each point of space, it becomes equal to zero at any time, either in the past or in the future. Under this assumption, Eq. *8-2* can thus be deduced from Eq. *8-3*. Equations *8-2* and *8-3* are sometimes called *the first pair of Maxwell's equations*.

Similarly, taking the divergence of Eq. *8-4*, we have

$$\nabla \cdot \frac{\partial \mathbf{D}}{\partial t} = -\nabla \cdot \mathbf{J}. \tag{8-17}$$

If we assume that there is conservation of charge, as we did in Eq. *5-86*, then

$$\nabla \cdot \frac{\partial \mathbf{D}}{\partial t} = \frac{\partial \rho}{\partial t}, \tag{8-18}$$

where ρ is the charge density, and

$$\nabla \cdot \mathbf{D} = \rho + C, \tag{8-19}$$

where C is some quantity which can be a function of the coordinates, but which is independent of the time. If we further assume that, at every point of space, at some time either in the past or in the future, both $\nabla \cdot \mathbf{D}$ and ρ become equal to zero, then the constant of integration C must be zero, and we are left with Eq. *8-1*. Under these two assumptions, Eqs. *8-1* and *8-4* are therefore not independent. They form *the second pair of Maxwell's equations*.

It is possible to eliminate the vectors $\mathbf{D}$ and $\mathbf{H}$ from Maxwell's equations by substituting for these quantities the values given in Eqs. *3-57* and *7-73*:

$$\mathbf{D} = \epsilon_0 \mathbf{E} + \mathbf{P}, \tag{8-20}$$

$$\mathbf{H} = \frac{\mathbf{B}}{\mu_0} - \mathbf{M}, \tag{8-21}$$

where $\mathbf{P}$ is the polarization vector in a dielectric in coulombs/meter², and $\mathbf{M}$ is the magnetization vector in a magnetic medium in ampere-turns/meter. These two quantities account for the presence of matter at the point considered. Then Maxwell's equations take the following form:

$$\nabla \cdot \mathbf{E} = \frac{1}{\epsilon_0}(\rho - \nabla \cdot \mathbf{P}), \tag{8-22}$$

$$\nabla \cdot \mathbf{B} = 0, \tag{8-23}$$

$$\nabla \times \mathbf{E} + \frac{\partial \mathbf{B}}{\partial t} = 0, \tag{8-24}$$

$$\nabla \times \mathbf{B} - \epsilon_0 \mu_0 \frac{\partial \mathbf{E}}{\partial t} = \mu_0 \left(\mathbf{J} + \frac{\partial \mathbf{P}}{\partial t} + \nabla \times \mathbf{M} \right). \tag{8-25}$$

The above are again Maxwell's equations in completely general form, but expressed in such a way as to stress the contributions of the medium. It will be observed that the presence of matter has the effect of adding the bound charge density $-\nabla \cdot \mathbf{P}$ (Section 3.2.1), the polarization current density $\partial \mathbf{P}/\partial t$ (Problem 7-16), and the equivalent current density $\nabla \times \mathbf{M}$ (Section 7.2.2.).

Usually, in linear isotropic media,

and

$$\mathbf{D} = K_e \epsilon_0 \mathbf{E}, \tag{8-26}$$

$$\mathbf{H} = \frac{\mathbf{B}}{K_m \mu_0}, \tag{8-27}$$

where K_e is the dielectric coefficient and K_m is the relative permeability. Then, in terms of $\mathbf{E}$ and $\mathbf{H}$, Maxwell's equations become

$$\nabla \cdot \mathbf{E} = \frac{\rho}{K_e \epsilon_0}, \tag{8-28}$$

$$\nabla \cdot \mathbf{H} = 0, \tag{8-29}$$

$$\nabla \times \mathbf{E} + K_m \mu_0 \frac{\partial \mathbf{H}}{\partial t} = 0, \tag{8-30}$$

$$\nabla \times \mathbf{H} - K_e \epsilon_0 \frac{\partial \mathbf{E}}{\partial t} = \mathbf{J}. \tag{8-31}$$

In the remaining chapters we shall be concerned mostly with phenomena in which the field vectors are sinusoidal functions of time. Then, instead of differentiating with respect to time, we can multiply by $j\omega$, according to Appendix F, and Maxwell's equations can then be rewritten as

$$\nabla \cdot \mathbf{D} = \rho, \tag{8-32}$$
$$\nabla \cdot \mathbf{B} = 0, \tag{8-33}$$
$$\nabla \times \mathbf{E} + j\omega \mathbf{B} = 0, \tag{8-34}$$
$$\nabla \times \mathbf{H} - j\omega \mathbf{D} = \mathbf{J}. \tag{8-35}$$

8.2. Maxwell's Equations in Integral Form

We have stated Maxwell's equations in differential form; let us now state them in their integral form in order that we may arrive at a better understanding of their physical meaning.

Integrating Eq. *8-1* over a volume τ, we obtain

$$\int_\tau \nabla \cdot \mathbf{D} \, d\tau = \int_\tau \rho \, d\tau, \tag{8-36}$$

or, from the divergence theorem,

$$\int_S \mathbf{D} \cdot d\mathbf{a} = \int_\tau \rho \, d\tau = Q, \tag{8-37}$$

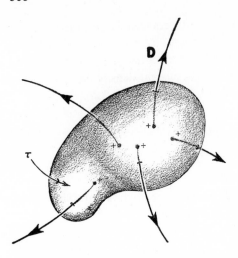

Figure 8-1

*Lines of **D** emerging from a volume τ, containing a net charge Q. The outward flux of **D** is equal to Q.*

where S is the surface bounding the volume τ and where Q is the net charge contained within τ. The outward flux of the electric displacement **D** through any closed surface S is therefore equal to the net charge inside, as illustrated in Figure 8-1. This is Gauss's law (Section 2.4).

Integrating Eq. *8-2* in a similar manner, we find that the outward flux of the magnetic induction **B** through any closed surface S is equal to zero. This is shown in Figure 8-2.

Equation *8-3* can be integrated over a surface S bounded by a curve C:

$$\int_S \nabla \times \mathbf{E} \cdot \mathbf{da} = -\int_S \frac{\partial \mathbf{B}}{\partial t} \cdot \mathbf{da}, \qquad (8\text{-}38)$$

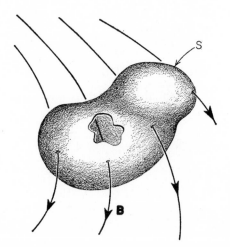

Figure 8-2

*Lines of **B** through a closed surface S. The net outward flux of **B** is equal to zero.*

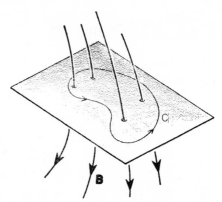

Figure 8-3.

The direction of the electromotance induced around C is indicated by an arrow for the case where the magnetic induction **B** *is in the direction shown and increases. The electromotance is in the same direction if* **B** *is upward and decreases.*

or, if we use Stokes's theorem on the left and invert the operations on the right, we have

$$\oint_C \mathbf{E} \cdot \mathbf{dl} = -\frac{\partial}{\partial t} \int_S \mathbf{B} \cdot \mathbf{da}. \qquad (8\text{-}39)$$

Then the electromotance induced around the curve C is equal to minus the rate of change of the magnetic flux linking the curve C, as in Figure 8-3. The positive directions for **B** and around C are related according to the right-hand screw rule.

Finally, if we also integrate Eq. *8-4* over an area S bounded by a curve C, we find that

$$\oint_C \mathbf{H} \cdot \mathbf{dl} = \int_S \left(\mathbf{J} + \frac{\partial \mathbf{D}}{\partial t} \right) \cdot \mathbf{da}, \qquad (8\text{-}40)$$

and the magnetomotance around the curve C is equal to the total current linking the curve C, $\partial \mathbf{D}/\partial t$ being the displacement current density. This is illustrated in Figure 8-4. The positive directions are again related by the right-hand screw rule.

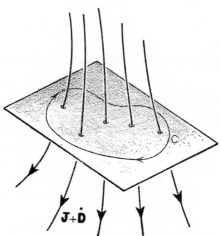

Figure 8-4

The direction of the magnetomotance around C is indicated by an arrow for the case where the total current **J** $+$ *($\partial \mathbf{D}/\partial t$) is in the direction shown. The displacement current is downward if ($\partial \mathbf{D}/\partial t$) is downward and increases, or if it is upward and decreases.*

8.3. E-H Symmetry

In a linear isotropic medium where the charge density ρ and the conductivity σ are both zero, Maxwell's equations reduce to

$$\nabla \cdot \mathbf{E} = 0, \tag{8-41}$$

$$\nabla \cdot \mathbf{H} = 0, \tag{8-42}$$

$$\nabla \times \mathbf{E} + K_m \mu_0 \frac{\partial \mathbf{H}}{\partial t} = 0, \tag{8-43}$$

$$\nabla \times \mathbf{H} - K_e \epsilon_0 \frac{\partial \mathbf{E}}{\partial t} = 0. \tag{8-44}$$

Let us consider one field where the electric field intensity is $\mathbf{E}$ and the magnetic field intensity is $\mathbf{H}$. Then the above equations are necessarily satisfied. Let us now consider another *different* field $\mathbf{E}'$, $\mathbf{H}'$, in which

$$\mathbf{E}' = -\alpha K_m \mu_0 \mathbf{H} = -\alpha \mathbf{B}, \tag{8-45}$$

$$\mathbf{H}' = \alpha K_e \epsilon_0 \mathbf{E} = \alpha \mathbf{D}, \tag{8-46}$$

where the constant of proportionality α has the dimensions of a velocity. Substituting $\mathbf{E}'$ and $\mathbf{H}'$ for $\mathbf{E}$ and $\mathbf{H}$ in the above Maxwell's equations, we find that the Maxwell equations also apply to the primed field:

$$\nabla \cdot \mathbf{E}' = 0, \tag{8-47}$$

$$\nabla \cdot \mathbf{H}' = 0, \tag{8-48}$$

$$\nabla \times \mathbf{E}' + K_m \mu_0 \frac{\partial \mathbf{H}'}{\partial t} = 0, \tag{8-49}$$

$$\nabla \times \mathbf{H}' - K_e \epsilon_0 \frac{\partial \mathbf{E}'}{\partial t} = 0. \tag{8-50}$$

We shall again have occasion to find such pairs of fields in Chapter 13.

8.4. Lorentz's Lemma

Let us consider a region of space where there are no sources, that is, no externally applied electric fields. The medium is assumed to be linear and isotropic, but not necessarily homogeneous, with dielectric coefficient K_e, permeability K_m, and conductivity σ.

We consider two distinct fields, one with field vectors $\mathbf{E}_a$, $\mathbf{D}_a$, $\mathbf{B}_a$, and $\mathbf{H}_a$, and another with vectors $\mathbf{E}_b$, $\mathbf{D}_b$, $\mathbf{B}_b$, and $\mathbf{H}_b$. From the principle of superposition, these two fields can either exist separately or be superposed without disturbing each other, the net field being then described by $\mathbf{E}_a + \mathbf{E}_b$, $\mathbf{D}_a + \mathbf{D}_b$, and so on.

For these two fields we have the following vector identity:

$$\nabla \cdot (\mathbf{E}_a \times \mathbf{H}_b - \mathbf{E}_b \times \mathbf{H}_a)$$
$$= \mathbf{H}_b \cdot \nabla \times \mathbf{E}_a - \mathbf{E}_a \cdot \nabla \times \mathbf{H}_b - \mathbf{H}_a \cdot \nabla \times \mathbf{E}_b + \mathbf{E}_b \cdot \nabla \times \mathbf{H}_a, \quad (8\text{-}51)$$

or, from the Maxwell equations *8-3* and *8-4*,

$$\nabla \cdot (\mathbf{E}_a \times \mathbf{H}_b - \mathbf{E}_b \times \mathbf{H}_a)$$
$$= -\mathbf{H}_b \cdot \frac{\partial \mathbf{B}_a}{\partial t} - \mathbf{E}_a \cdot \left(\mathbf{J}_b + \frac{\partial \mathbf{D}_b}{\partial t} \right) + \mathbf{H}_a \cdot \frac{\partial \mathbf{B}_b}{\partial t} + \mathbf{E}_b \cdot \left(\mathbf{J}_a + \frac{\partial \mathbf{D}_a}{\partial t} \right). \quad (8\text{-}52)$$

Now if there are no sources, that is, no externally applied electric fields at the point considered, the current densities $\mathbf{J}_a$ and $\mathbf{J}_b$ are simply $\sigma \mathbf{E}_a$ and $\sigma \mathbf{E}_b$, as explained in Section 8.1, and the two terms involving the $\mathbf{J}$'s cancel. If the two fields are also harmonic in time and of the same frequency, the $\partial/\partial t$ operators can be replaced by $j\omega$ (Appendix F), and

$$\nabla \cdot (\mathbf{E}_a \times \mathbf{H}_b - \mathbf{E}_b \times \mathbf{H}_a) = 0. \quad (8\text{-}53)$$

Therefore, at any point where these conditions are satisfied, the two different fields must satisfy the relation

$$\nabla \cdot (\mathbf{E}_a \times \mathbf{H}_b) = \nabla \cdot (\mathbf{E}_b \times \mathbf{H}_a). \quad (8\text{-}54)$$

This result is known as *Lorentz's lemma*. It is remarkable in that it relates *any* two electromagnetic fields, provided they are of the same frequency at any point outside the sources and in any linear isotropic medium. The fields must of course obey Maxwell's equations.

The more general case which applies to any point, including the region within the sources, will be considered in Section 13.9 and will lead to an important theorem.

8.5. Summary

The equations of Maxwell are the four fundamental equations of electromagnetism:

$$\nabla \cdot \mathbf{D} = \rho, \quad (8\text{-}1)$$

$$\nabla \cdot \mathbf{B} = 0, \quad (8\text{-}2)$$

$$\nabla \times \mathbf{E} + \frac{\partial \mathbf{B}}{\partial t} = 0, \quad (8\text{-}3)$$

$$\nabla \times \mathbf{H} - \frac{\partial \mathbf{D}}{\partial t} = \mathbf{J}. \quad (8\text{-}4)$$

They are valid under all conditions, with one exception: they do not apply to media which move with respect to the system of coordinates.

Equation *8-2* can be deduced from Eq. *8-3* on the single assumption that, for each point in space, $\nabla \cdot \mathbf{B}$ becomes equal to zero at some time, either in the past or in the future. Similarly, Eq. *8-1* can be deduced from Eq. *8-4* if we assume (a) that charge is conserved and (b) that, for each point in space, $\nabla \cdot \mathbf{D}$ and ρ both become equal to zero at some time.

As a rule, the medium is linear and isotropic, thus

$$\nabla \cdot \mathbf{E} = \frac{\rho}{K_e \epsilon_0}, \tag{8-28}$$

$$\nabla \cdot \mathbf{H} = 0, \tag{8-29}$$

$$\nabla \times \mathbf{E} + K_m \mu_0 \frac{\partial \mathbf{H}}{\partial t} = 0, \tag{8-30}$$

$$\nabla \times \mathbf{H} - K_e \epsilon_0 \frac{\partial \mathbf{E}}{\partial t} = \mathbf{J}. \tag{8-31}$$

There exists a symmetry between the $\mathbf{E}$ and $\mathbf{H}$ vectors in linear and isotropic media ($\mathbf{D} = K_e \epsilon_0 \mathbf{E}$, $\mathbf{H} = \mathbf{B}/K_m \mu_0$) in which the charge density ρ and the conductivity σ are both zero. To any field $\mathbf{E}$, $\mathbf{H}$ there corresponds another possible field $\mathbf{E}'$, $\mathbf{H}'$, such that

$$\mathbf{E}' = -\alpha \mathbf{B} \tag{8-45}$$

and

$$\mathbf{H}' = \alpha \mathbf{D}. \tag{8-46}$$

Lorentz's lemma applies to any two fields $\mathbf{E}_a$, $\mathbf{H}_a$ and $\mathbf{E}_b$, $\mathbf{H}_b$ of the same frequency in a linear isotropic medium and outside the sources. It states that

$$\nabla \cdot (\mathbf{E}_a \times \mathbf{H}_b) = \nabla \cdot (\mathbf{E}_b \times \mathbf{H}_a). \tag{8-54}$$

Problems

8-1. Deduce Eq. *2-3* for the electric field intensity due to a point charge Q, starting from Maxwell's equations.

8-2. A large flat plate carries a current of I amperes/meter of width. Show that the magnetic field intensity outside is everywhere equal to $I/2$, neglecting end effects.

Calculate the magnetic field intensity inside and outside the plate if the current density J decreases linearly with depth z inside the plate such that $J = J_0(1 - az)$. The plate thickness is $1/a$.

8-3. Write out Maxwell's equations in terms of $\mathbf{E}$ and $\mathbf{H}$ only for a nonhomogeneous medium in which K_e and K_m are functions of the coordinates.

8-4. We have seen in Eq. *6-16* that the electric field intensity can be written as

$$\mathbf{E} = -\nabla V - \frac{\partial \mathbf{A}}{\partial t},$$

and, in Eq. *5-56*, that

$$\mathbf{B} = \nabla \times \mathbf{A},$$

where V and $\mathbf{A}$ are the scalar and vector potentials, respectively. Rewrite Maxwell's equations in terms of these potentials, for linear homogeneous media.

8-5. Ohm's law states that

$$\mathbf{J} = \sigma \mathbf{E},$$

where $\mathbf{J}$ is the conduction current density, σ is the electrical conductivity, and $\mathbf{E}$ is the electric field intensity. Show that the charge density ρ is equal to zero under steady-state conditions inside a homogeneous conductor obeying Ohm's law.

8-6. A parallel-plate capacitor is formed of two long rectangular plates and is connected at one end to a source whose voltage increases slowly and linearly with time. Find the currents flowing through the plates.

Use the Lorentz condition (Eq. *5-108*) to find an expression for the vector potential $\mathbf{A}$ both between the capacitor plates and outside.

Show that $\nabla \times \mathbf{H} = \partial \mathbf{D}/\partial t$ inside and outside. Hint: The Laplacian of $\mathbf{A}$ is equal to zero in this case.

Draw a sketch showing $\mathbf{A}$, $\mathbf{H}$, $\nabla \times \mathbf{H}$, $\mathbf{D}$, $\partial \mathbf{D}/\partial t$ and the manner in which these quantities change along the length of the capacitor, both inside and outside.

8-7. The space between the plates of a parallel-plate capacitor is filled with a slightly conducting medium. The plates are charged to a potential V_0 and then allowed to discharge through the medium. Show that the sum of the conduction and displacement currents is zero if the discharge takes place so slowly that $\partial \mathbf{A}/\partial t$ is negligible compared to ∇V and if the space charge density in the medium is zero.

8-8. Two plane parallel electrodes are separated by a distance s with a medium whose conductivity σ varies linearly from σ_0 near the positive plate to $\sigma_0 + a$ near the negative plate. Calculate the space charge density ρ when the current density is J.

Calculate ρ near both plates for $\sigma_0 = 1.00 \times 10^7$ mhos/meter, $\sigma_0 + a = 2.00 \times 10^7$ mhos/meter, $J = 1.00$ ampere/meter^2, $K_e = 1$, $s = 1$ centimeter.

8-9. At very high frequencies, currents are limited to the region close to the surface of a conductor, and there is essentially zero electric and magnetic field in the interior.

Setting E and B to be the tangential electric field intensity and magnetic induction in the conductor, show that

$$\frac{\partial E}{\partial z} = \frac{\partial B}{\partial t},$$

where the z-axis is normal to the surface of the conductor and points outward, E is taken to be positive in the direction of the x-axis, and B is in the direction of the y-axis.

Show that $\mathbf{H}$ and $\mathbf{B}$ are tangential to the surface outside the conductor.

Show that $\mathbf{H}$ is related to the surface current density $\boldsymbol{\lambda}$ by the equations

$$\mathbf{H} = \boldsymbol{\lambda} \times \mathbf{n}$$

and

$$H = \lambda,$$

where $\mathbf{n}$ is a unit vector normal to the surface of the conductor and pointing outward. Does this result depend on the way in which the current varies with depth inside the conductor?

Can there be a normal component of $\mathbf{E}$ outside?

8-10. A point charge Q moves at a constant velocity u in the positive direction along the z-axis, and its position z' is given by ut.

Calculate the flux of $\mathbf{D}$ through a circle of radius ρ perpendicular to the z-axis at $z = 0$, and plot a graph of this flux as a function of time.

Calculate the time derivative of this flux, and show it on the above graph.

Calculate the magnetomotance around the circle, and show that the magnetic field intensity at the point (ρ, ϕ, z) is given by

$$H_\phi = \frac{Qu\rho}{4\pi[\rho^2 + (z' - z)^2]^{3/2}}.$$

Show that the time integral of the magnetomotance from $t = -\infty$ to $t = +\infty$ is equal to Q.

8-11. A point charge Q moves as in the preceding problem.

Calculate $\partial \mathbf{D}/\partial t$ and $\boldsymbol{\nabla} \times \mathbf{H}$ at a position (ρ, ϕ, z) expressed in cylindrical coordinates. Show that H_ϕ is given by the above expression.

This result is valid only for $u^2 \ll c^2$, where c is the velocity of light. The more general case will be done in Problem 14-4.

8-12. Starting from an electromagnetic field characterized by the field vectors $\mathbf{E}$ and $\mathbf{H}$, utilize the symmetry between $\mathbf{E}$ and $\mathbf{H}$ four times to find successively the fields $\mathbf{E}^i$, $\mathbf{H}^i$; $\mathbf{E}^{ii}$, $\mathbf{H}^{ii}$, $\mathbf{E}^{iii}$, $\mathbf{H}^{iii}$; and $\mathbf{E}^{iv}$, $\mathbf{H}^{iv}$.

Assuming that $\mathbf{E}$ and $\mathbf{H}$ are respectively parallel to the x- and y-axes, show the 10 vectors on 5 separate diagrams. Compare the fields when the constant of proportionality is equal to the velocity of light in the medium, that is, $1/(\epsilon_0 K_e \mu_0 K_m)^{1/2}$.

8-13. Imagine various pairs of electromagnetic fields in free space, and verify whether Lorentz's lemma applies. Suggestions: Try a capacitor in a magnetic field; the fields of the electric and magnetic dipoles; the electric and magnetic fields in a cylindrical magnetron; and so forth.

CHAPTER 9

Plane Electromagnetic Waves in Free Space

We shall study in this chapter the basic aspects of plane electromagnetic waves in free space, that is, in a vacuum infinitely remote from matter. Wave propagation in dielectrics, in conductors, and in ionized gases will be treated in the next chapter; reflection and refraction will be treated in Chapter 11. Waveguides will be studied in Chapter 12. No mention will be made in this chapter of the manner in which electromagnetic waves can be generated; this subject will be left for Chapter 13.

At this stage, the student would be well advised to work through Appendixes F and G, unless he is quite familiar with (a) the exponential notation for representing the cosine function and (b) wave propagation. The next five chapters require a thorough knowledge of the material contained in these two Appendixes.

9.1. Electromagnetic Waves in Free Space

We shall restrict our discussion to phenomena occurring in a vacuum infinitely remote from matter. This will have the advantage of simplifying the theory, while conserving many of its basic aspects. We therefore set

$$K_e = 1,$$
$$\rho = 0,$$
$$K_m = 1,$$
$$\sigma = 0,$$

(9-1)

thus Maxwell's equations, Eqs. 8-1, 8-2, 8-3, and 8-4, reduce to

$$\nabla \cdot \mathbf{D} = 0,$$

(9-2)

$$\nabla \cdot \mathbf{B} = 0, \tag{9-3}$$

$$\nabla \times \mathbf{E} + \frac{\partial \mathbf{B}}{\partial t} = 0, \tag{9-4}$$

$$\nabla \times \mathbf{H} - \frac{\partial \mathbf{D}}{\partial t} = 0, \tag{9-5}$$

where

$$\mathbf{D} = \epsilon_0 \mathbf{E}$$

and

$$\mathbf{H} = \frac{\mathbf{B}}{\mu_0}. \tag{9-6}$$

To find an equation for $\mathbf{E}$, we take the curl of Eq. *9-4:*

$$\nabla \times (\nabla \times \mathbf{E}) + \nabla \times \frac{\partial \mathbf{B}}{\partial t} = 0. \tag{9-7}$$

Then, from Equation *1-30,*

$$\nabla(\nabla \cdot \mathbf{E}) - \nabla^2 \mathbf{E} + \nabla \times \frac{\partial \mathbf{B}}{\partial t} = 0, \tag{9-8}$$

and, from Eqs. *9-2* and *9-5,*

$$\nabla^2 \mathbf{E} = \epsilon_0 \mu_0 \frac{\partial^2 \mathbf{E}}{\partial t^2}. \tag{9-9}$$

Starting with Equation *9-5,* we find, in a similar manner, an identical equation for $\mathbf{H}$:

$$\nabla^2 \mathbf{H} = \epsilon_0 \mu_0 \frac{\partial^2 \mathbf{H}}{\partial t^2}. \tag{9-10}$$

The equations for $\mathbf{D}$ and for $\mathbf{B}$ are again identical. They can be obtained from Eqs. *9-9* and *9-10* simply by multiplying the first by ϵ_0 and the second by μ_0.

Equation *9-9* is equivalent to the following set

$$\left(\frac{\partial^2}{\partial x^2} + \frac{\partial^2}{\partial y^2} + \frac{\partial^2}{\partial z^2} \right) E_x = \epsilon_0 \mu_0 \frac{\partial^2 E_x}{\partial t^2}, \tag{9-11}$$

$$\left(\frac{\partial^2}{\partial x^2} + \frac{\partial^2}{\partial y^2} + \frac{\partial^2}{\partial z^2} \right) E_y = \epsilon_0 \mu_0 \frac{\partial^2 E_y}{\partial t^2}, \tag{9-12}$$

$$\left(\frac{\partial^2}{\partial x^2} + \frac{\partial^2}{\partial y^2} + \frac{\partial^2}{\partial z^2} \right) E_z = \epsilon_0 \mu_0 \frac{\partial^2 E_z}{\partial t^2}. \tag{9-13}$$

There are four such families of equations for the four field vectors $\mathbf{E}$, $\mathbf{D}$, $\mathbf{B}$, and $\mathbf{H}$.

These differential equations are identical in form to Eq. *G-28* of Appendix G for an unattenuated wave traveling at a velocity u, except that the coefficient $1/u^2$ is here replaced by $\epsilon_0\mu_0$. *It follows that the field vectors can be propagated as waves in free space. It also follows that the velocity of propagation is*

$$c = \frac{1}{(\epsilon_0 \mu_0)^{1/2}}. \qquad (9\text{-}14)$$

These are two most remarkable results. We have deduced from our investigation of the basic electromagnetic phenomena: (a) the possibility of the existence of electromagnetic waves and (b) the velocity of such waves in free space.

The above expression for the velocity c of an electromagnetic wave in free space is in itself remarkable. It links three basic constants of electromagnetism: the velocity of an electromagnetic wave c, the permittivity of free space ϵ_0, which we first met in Section 2.1 while discussing Coulomb's law, and the permeability of free space μ_0, which enters into the magnetic force law of Section 5.1.

It will be remembered from Section 5.1 that the constant μ_0 was *defined* arbitrarily to be *exactly* $4\pi \times 10^{-7}$ henrys/meter. The constant ϵ_0 can thus be deduced from the measured value for the velocity of electromagnetic waves:

$$c = 2.9979 \times 10^8 \text{ meters/second}, \qquad (9\text{-}15)$$

thus

$$\epsilon_0 = \frac{1}{c^2 \mu_0} = 8.8542 \times 10^{-12} \text{ farad/meter}. \qquad (9\text{-}16)$$

The permittivity of free space ϵ_0 can also be determined directly from measurements involving electrostatic phenomena. The measurements lead to the above value within experimental error, thereby confirming the theory.

9.1.1. Plane Electromagnetic Waves in Free Space.

Let us consider the relatively simple case of plane waves propagating along the z-axis. The electric field intensity $\mathbf{E}$ then varies only in the direction of z, that is, $\mathbf{E}$ is a function of z and of t only:

$$\mathbf{E} = \mathbf{E}(z, t), \qquad (9\text{-}17)$$

hence

$$\frac{\partial \mathbf{E}}{\partial x} = 0, \quad \frac{\partial \mathbf{E}}{\partial y} = 0. \qquad (9\text{-}18)$$

Then the divergence of $\mathbf{E}$ reduces to $\partial E_z/\partial z$, and

$$\mathbf{\nabla \cdot E} = \frac{\partial E_z}{\partial z} = 0. \qquad (9\text{-}19)$$

Thus E_z cannot be a function of z. We shall set

$$E_z = 0, \qquad (9\text{-}20)$$

since we are interested in waves and not in uniform fields.

Under the assumption of Eq. 9-17 the vector $\mathbf{E}$ of an electromagnetic wave can thus have only x- and y-components, that is, it has no longitudinal component—only transverse components.

For simplicity, we choose our system of axes such that the x-axis is parallel to the vector $\mathbf{E}$:

$$\mathbf{E} = \mathbf{i}E_x(z, t). \tag{9-21}$$

Substituting the above value of $\mathbf{E}$ in Eq. 9-4, we find that

$$\begin{aligned} B_x &= 0, \\ H_x &= 0, \\ B_z &= 0, \\ H_z &= 0, \end{aligned} \tag{9-22}$$

and that

$$\frac{\partial E_x}{\partial z} = -\frac{\partial B_y}{\partial t}. \tag{9-23}$$

From Eqs. 9-20 and 9-22, it can be seen that a plane electromagnetic wave propagating in free space is *transverse*. To further simplify the calculations, we can consider only the wave traveling in the positive direction of the z-axis. The velocity of the wave being c, as we found above, we therefore have

$$E_x = E_{x0} \cos\left[\omega\left(t - \frac{z}{c}\right) + \theta\right], \tag{9-24}$$

θ being the phase angle at $t = 0$ and $z = 0$. With the exponential notation described in Appendix F, we write that

$$E_x = E_{x0} \exp\left[j\omega\left(t - \frac{z}{c}\right) + \theta\right], \tag{9-25}$$

where it is tacitly understood that we must use only the real part of the right-

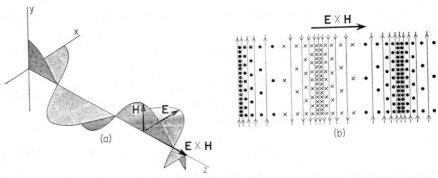

Figure 9-1. *The $\mathbf{E}$ and $\mathbf{H}$ vectors for a plane electromagnetic wave traveling in the positive direction along the z-axis. (a) The variation of $\mathbf{E}$ and $\mathbf{H}$ with z at a particular moment. The two quantities are in phase, but perpendicular to each other. (b) The corresponding lines of force as seen when looking down on the xz-plane. The lines represent the electric field. The dots represent magnetic lines of force coming out of the paper, and the crosses represent magnetic lines of force going into the paper. The vector $\mathbf{E} \times \mathbf{H}$ gives the direction of propagation.*

hand side. The displacement D_x is given by $\epsilon_0 E_x$. Similar expressions apply to B_y and H_y.

Then Eq. *9-23* can be rewritten as

$$j\frac{\omega}{c}E_x = j\omega B_y. \tag{9-26}$$

Thus

$$\frac{E_x}{B_y} = c = 3.00 \times 10^8 \text{ meters/second}, \tag{9-27}$$

and

$$\frac{E_x}{H_y} = \mu_0 c = \left(\frac{\mu_0}{\epsilon_0}\right)^{1/2} = 377 \text{ ohms}. \tag{9-28}$$

The **E** and **H** vectors are therefore mutually perpendicular and are oriented such that their vector product **E** $\times$ **H** points in the direction of propagation as in Figure 9-1. The **E** and **H** vectors are in phase, since the quantity E_x/H_y is real, and they have the same relative magnitudes at all points at all times.

The electric and magnetic energy densities are in phase and are equal, since

$$\frac{\frac{1}{2}\epsilon_0 E^2}{\frac{1}{2}\mu_0 H^2} = \epsilon_0\mu_0 c^2 = 1. \tag{9-29}$$

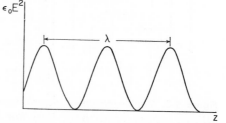

Figure 9-2. *The energy density* $\varepsilon_0 E^2 = \mu_0 H^2$ *as a function of z for a plane electromagnetic wave traveling along the z-axis.*

At any instant, the total energy density is therefore distributed as in Figure 9-2.

9.1.2. The Spectrum of Electromagnetic Waves.

Maxwell's equations impose no limit on either the frequency or the wavelength of electromagnetic waves. To date, the spectrum which has been investigated experimentally extends continuously from the long radio waves to the very high energy gamma rays observed in cosmic radiation or produced by large electron synchrotrons. In the former, the frequencies are about 10^4 cycles/second, and the wavelengths are about 3×10^4 meters; in the latter, the frequencies are of the order of 10^{24} cycles/second, and the wavelengths are of the order of 3×10^{-16} meter. The known spectrum thus covers a range of 20 orders of magnitude. Radio, radar, light, and heat waves, X-rays and gamma rays are all electromagnetic waves, as shown in Figure 9-3, although the sources and the detectors, as well as the modes of interaction with matter, vary widely as the frequency changes by orders of magnitude.

The fundamental identity of all these types of waves is demonstrated by series of experiments in overlapping parts of the spectrum. It is also demonstrated by

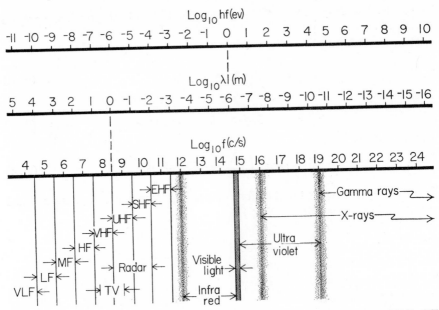

Figure 9-3. *The spectrum of electromagnetic waves. The abbreviations VLF, LF, MF, . . . mean, respectively, Very low frequency, Low frequency, Medium frequency, High frequency, Very high frequency, Ultrahigh frequency, Super high frequency, and Extremely high frequency. The limits indicated by the shaded regions are approximate. The energy hf, where h is Planck's constant (6.63×10^{-34} joule-second) and f is the frequency, is that of a photon or quantum of radiation.*

the fact that in free space they are all transverse waves with a common velocity of propagation c given by Eq. *9-14.*

9.1.3. Polarization. We have considered in the previous section a type of wave in which the **E** and **H** vectors always point in the same directions perpendicular to each other. Assuming that the **E** vector is always parallel to the *x*-axis, we have found that the **H** vector is then parallel to the *y*-axis. Such waves are said to be *plane-polarized.* The *plane of polarization* was originally taken to be the plane containing the direction of propagation and the **H** vector. In modern treatises it is common either to avoid the use of the term *plane of polarization* entirely or to use the term *plane*

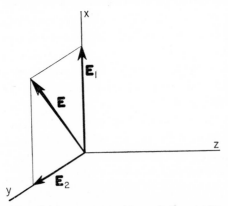

Figure 9-4. *Decomposition of the vector* **E** *into two components* **E**$_1$ *and* **E**$_2$.

of vibration, which is defined to be the plane containing the direction of propagation and the **E** vector. Radio engineers say that a wave is polarized in the direction of its **E** vector.

Any plane-polarized wave can be considered to be the sum of two components which are plane-polarized in perpendicular directions and in phase. For example, in Figure 9-4, the vector **E** can be resolved into two mutually perpendicular components $\mathbf{E}_1$ and $\mathbf{E}_2$.

One can also add two plane-polarized waves which differ in phase. Then, at a given point, the maxima of $\mathbf{E}_1$ and of $\mathbf{E}_2$ do not occur at the same time and the sum vector **E** describes an ellipse about the z-axis. We then have an *elliptically polarized wave*.

If $\mathbf{E}_1$ and $\mathbf{E}_2$ have equal amplitudes but are $\pi/2$ out of phase, the ellipse becomes a circle and the wave is said to be *circularly polarized*. The polarization is said to be right- or left-handed according to whether the vectors **E** and **H** rotate clockwise or counterclockwise for an observer looking toward the *source*.

9.2. The Poynting Vector in Free Space

It was found in Section 9.1.1 that the direction of propagation of a plane electromagnetic wave in free space is that of the vector $\mathbf{E} \times \mathbf{H}$. Let us calculate the divergence of this vector for any electromagnetic field in free space:

$$\nabla \cdot (\mathbf{E} \times \mathbf{H}) = -\mathbf{E} \cdot (\nabla \times \mathbf{H}) + \mathbf{H} \cdot (\nabla \times \mathbf{E}), \tag{9-30}$$

$$= -\left(\mathbf{E} \cdot \frac{\partial \mathbf{D}}{\partial t}\right) - \left(\mathbf{H} \cdot \frac{\partial \mathbf{B}}{\partial t}\right), \tag{9-31}$$

$$= -\frac{\partial}{\partial t}\left[\frac{\epsilon_0 E^2}{2} + \frac{\mu_0 H^2}{2}\right]. \tag{9-32}$$

Integrating over a volume τ bounded by a surface S, and using the divergence theorem, we have

$$\int_S (\mathbf{E} \times \mathbf{H}) \cdot d\mathbf{a} = -\frac{\partial}{\partial t} \int_\tau \left(\frac{\epsilon_0 E^2}{2} + \frac{\mu_0 H^2}{2}\right) d\tau. \tag{9-33}$$

The integral on the right-hand side is the sum of the electric and magnetic energies, according to Sections 2.14.1 and 6.4.1. The right-hand side is thus the energy lost per unit time by the volume τ, and the left-hand side must be the total outward flux of energy in watts over the surface S bounding τ.

The quantity

$$\mathbf{S} = \mathbf{E} \times \mathbf{H} \quad \text{(watts/meter}^2\text{)} \tag{9-34}$$

is called the *Poynting vector*. When integrated over a closed surface, it gives the total outward flow of energy per unit time. It will be noticed that the vector **S** points in the direction of propagation of the wave.

It is convenient to consider Poynting's vector as representing a flow of energy.

Although this interpretation is usually correc', it is not rigorous, as can be seen by superposing arbitrary static and magnetic fields. One can imagine, for example, the field due to an electrically charged bar magnet. In such a field, $\mathbf{E} \times \mathbf{H} = 0$ only on the axis, despite the fact that there is, of course, zero energy flow everywhere.

The situation here is similar to that which we encountered in discussing electric energy density in Section 2.14.1. Equation 9-33 is rigorously correct and applies to any electromagnetic field, as long as $K_e = 1$, $K_m = 1$, $\rho = 0$, and $\sigma = 0$. It does *not* follow, however, that the vector product $\mathbf{E} \times \mathbf{H}$ at a given point in space corresponds to an actual energy flow at that point.

The instantaneous value of the Poynting vector at a given point in space is $\mathbf{E} \times \mathbf{H}$, or, according to Eq. 9-28,

$$\mathbf{S} = \frac{1}{\mu_0 c} E^2 \mathbf{k}, \tag{9-35}$$

$$= c\epsilon_0 E^2 \mathbf{k}. \tag{9-36}$$

For a plane wave of circular frequency ω, the average value of $\mathbf{S}$ is given by

$$\mathbf{S}_{\text{av.}} = c\epsilon_0 E_{\text{rms}}^2 \mathbf{k} = \frac{1}{2} c\epsilon_0 E_0^2 \mathbf{k}. \tag{9-37}$$

$$= 2.65 \times 10^{-3} E_{\text{rms}}^2 \mathbf{k} \text{ watts/meter}^2. \tag{9-38}$$

The energy can thus be considered to travel with an average density

$$\frac{1}{2} \epsilon_0 E_{\text{rms}}^2 + \frac{1}{2} \mu_0 H_{\text{rms}}^2 = \epsilon_0 E_{\text{rms}}^2 = \frac{1}{2} \epsilon_0 E_0^2$$

at the velocity of propagation $c\mathbf{k}$.

It is worth noting that we have used the vector $\mathbf{H}$ rather than $\mathbf{B}$ in discussing electromagnetic waves, in spite of the fact that we had previously used $\mathbf{H}$ only for the study of magnetic materials, in Chapter 7. There are two reasons for using $\mathbf{H}$ instead of $\mathbf{B}$ in dealing with electromagnetic waves. One reason is that $\mathbf{E} \times \mathbf{H}$ is an energy flux density; the other is that E/H has the dimensions of an impedance (Eq. 9-28). Both of these concepts prove to be of great value.

9.2.1. The Energy Flow Due to a Plane Wave Through an Imaginary Cylinder.

Equation 9-33 can be illustrated by considering a plane electromagnetic wave going through an imaginary cylindrical volume, as in Figure 9-5. If the amplitude of the wave is constant, the electric and magnetic energy densities averaged over one period are constant, and the net outward energy flow is zero. However, if the electromagnetic wave decreases in amplitude, the average energy density decreases with time, and there must be a net outward flux of energy.

The instantaneous value of $\mathbf{E}$ for a *plane* wave traveling in the positive direction along the z-axis is the same as that near the source at a previous time

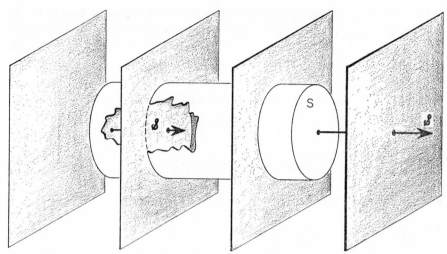

Figure 9-5. *The planes shown represent wave fronts for a plane electromagnetic wave traveling to the right. The amplitude gradually decreases at the source and the intensity is thus larger on the right than on the left. The wave sweeps through the imaginary cylinder shown; the arrows represent the Poynting vectors on the two end faces.*

$\left(t - \dfrac{z}{c}\right)$ (Appendix G). For a source whose amplitude decreases linearly with time, we can write that, near the source,

$$\mathbf{E} = \mathbf{E}_0(1 - at)e^{j\omega t}, \tag{9-39}$$

whereas at a distance z,

$$\mathbf{E} = \mathbf{E}_0\left[1 - a\left(t - \frac{z}{c}\right)\right]\exp\left[j\omega\left(t - \frac{z}{c}\right)\right]. \tag{9-40}$$

At any given time t, the wave then has the general shape shown in Figure 9-6.

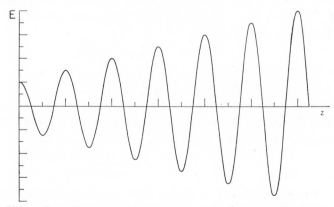

Figure 9-6. *Sine wave from a source whose amplitude decreases linearly with time.*

Let us now calculate the rate at which the electromagnetic energy in the cylindrical volume decreases with time. We assume that the constant a is small enough such that the amplitude of $\mathbf{E}$ changes only slightly during a period $1/f$, thus averages can be evaluated as above.

The net average outward energy flow is obtained by evaluating the surface integral of $(\mathbf{E} \times \mathbf{H})$ over the two ends of the cylinder:

$$\int_S (\mathbf{E} \times \mathbf{H}) \cdot d\mathbf{a} = \frac{1}{2} c\epsilon_0 S E_0^2 \left\{ \left[1 - at + \frac{a(z_0 + L)}{c} \right]^2 - \left(1 - at + \frac{az_0}{c} \right)^2 \right\}, \quad (9\text{-}41)$$

$$= \frac{\epsilon_0 S E_0^2}{2} \left[2a(1 - at)L + \frac{a^2}{c}(2z_0 + L)L \right], \quad (9\text{-}42)$$

whereas the average energy enclosed at a time t is given by

$$W = \int_{z_0}^{z_0 + L} \frac{\epsilon_0}{2} E_0^2 \left(1 - at + \frac{az}{c} \right)^2 S \, dz, \quad (9\text{-}43)$$

$$= \frac{\epsilon_0 S E_0^2}{2} \left[(1 - at)^2 L + \frac{a^2}{3c^2}(L^3 + 3z_0 L^2 + 3z_0^2 L) + \frac{a}{c}(1 - at)(2z_0 + L)L \right]. \quad (9\text{-}44)$$

Then

$$-\frac{dW}{dt} = \frac{\epsilon_0 S E_0^2}{2} \left[2a(1 - at)L + \frac{a^2}{c}(2z_0 + L)L \right]. \quad (9\text{-}45)$$

The net average outward energy flow per unit time is thus equal to the rate at which the enclosed energy decreases with time, as expected.

9.3. Summary

We began our discussion of electromagnetic waves by considering the simplest case, namely, that of plane waves propagating in a vacuum. Then $K_e = 1$, $K_m = 1$, $\rho = 0$, $\sigma = 0$, and Maxwell's equations led directly to the wave equations for $\mathbf{E}$ and for $\mathbf{H}$:

$$\nabla^2 \mathbf{E} = \epsilon_0 \mu_0 \frac{\partial^2 \mathbf{E}}{\partial t^2}, \quad (9\text{-}9)$$

$$\nabla^2 \mathbf{H} = \epsilon_0 \mu_0 \frac{\partial^2 \mathbf{H}}{\partial t^2}. \quad (9\text{-}10)$$

This shows that the velocity of propagation of a plane electromagnetic wave in a vacuum is, in meters/second,

$$c = \frac{1}{(\epsilon_0 \mu_0)^{1/2}}. \quad (9\text{-}14)$$

We find, from $\nabla \cdot \mathbf{E} = 0$, that there can be no longitudinal component of $\mathbf{E}$, and similarly for $\mathbf{H}$. Plane electromagnetic waves in free space are therefore transverse. We also find that $\mathbf{E}$ and $\mathbf{H}$ are orthogonal, that they are oriented in such a way that their vector product $\mathbf{E} \times \mathbf{H}$ points in the direction of propagation, and that their magnitudes are related to give equal electric and magnetic energy densities:

$$\frac{E_x}{H_y} = \left(\frac{\mu_0}{\epsilon_0}\right)^{1/2} = 377 \text{ ohms.} \tag{9-28}$$

The quantity $\mathbf{S} = \mathbf{E} \times \mathbf{H}$ is called the Poynting vector. It plays a fundamental role in electromagnetic theory. When its normal component is integrated over a closed surface it gives the rate of energy loss within the surface. For a plane wave, $\mathbf{S}$ is the energy flow in watts/meter², and it is the product of the energy density $\epsilon_0 E^2$ and the wave velocity c.

Problems

9-1. Show that the wave equation can be written in the form

$$(\nabla^2 + k^2)\mathbf{E} = 0,$$

where k is the wave number and is equal to $1/\lambda = 2\pi/\lambda$.

9-2. A plane electromagnetic wave of circular frequency ω propagates in free space in the direction of the unit vector $\mathbf{n}_1$. Setting $\mathbf{k} = k\mathbf{n}_1$, show that

$$\mathbf{k} \cdot \mathbf{D} = 0, \qquad \mathbf{k} \times \mathbf{E} - \omega\mathbf{B} = 0,$$
$$\mathbf{k} \cdot \mathbf{B} = 0, \qquad \mathbf{k} \times \mathbf{H} + \omega\mathbf{D} = j\mathbf{J}.$$

9-3. An electromagnetic wave in which the rms value of E is 20 volts/meter falls normally on an absorbing mass of 10^{-3} gram/centimeter² and of specific heat 0.1 calorie/gram-°C. Assuming that no heat is lost, calculate the rate at which the temperature of the absorber rises.

9-4. Calculate the electric field intensity due to radiation at the surface of the sun from the following data: power radiated by the sun, 3.8×10^{26} watts; radius of the sun, 7.0×10^8 meters.

What is the electric field intensity due to solar radiation at the surface of the earth? The average distance between the sun and the earth is 1.5×10^{11} meters. Show that the average solar energy incident on the earth is 2 calories/centimeter²-minute.

9-5. Calculate the value of the Poynting vector $\mathbf{E} \times \mathbf{H}$ for a field produced by a magnetic dipole and a point charge Q at the origin. The magnetic moment $\mathbf{m}$ of the dipole can be taken to be $\mathbf{m} = I a \mathbf{k}$, where I is the current, a is the area enclosed by a circular wire in the xy-plane carrying the current I, and $\mathbf{k}$ is the unit vector along the z-axis.

Show $\mathbf{E}$, $\mathbf{H}$, and $\mathbf{E} \times \mathbf{H}$ on a diagram. Is there a real flux of energy?

9-6. A coaxial line has an inner diameter of 0.500 centimeter and an outer diameter of 2.00 centimeters. The outer conductor is grounded; the inner conductor is held at +220 volts. The current is 10.0 amperes. Integrate the Poynting vector over the annular region between the conductors, and compare with the power 220×10.0 watts.

Propagation of Plane Electromagnetic Waves in Matter

We now go on to the propagation of plane electromagnetic waves in homogeneous, isotropic, linear, and stationary media. A medium is *homogeneous* if its properties do not vary from point to point; it is *isotropic* if its properties are the same in all directions from any given point. It is both *isotropic* and *linear* if the following relations hold

$$\mathbf{D} = K_e \epsilon_0 \mathbf{E} = \epsilon \mathbf{E}, \tag{10-1}$$

$$\mathbf{H} = \frac{\mathbf{B}}{K_m \mu_0} = \frac{\mathbf{B}}{\mu}, \tag{10-2}$$

$$\mathbf{J} = \sigma \mathbf{E}, \tag{10-3}$$

where the dielectric coefficient K_e, the relative permeability K_m, and the conductivity σ are constants independent of the field intensities and independent of direction. Crystalline media are usually *anisotropic*. Since the medium is assumed to be homogeneous, K_e, K_m, and σ are also independent of the coordinates. *To simplify the notation, from now on we shall write ϵ instead of $K_e\epsilon_0$ and μ for $K_m\mu_0$. The quantities ϵ and μ are, respectively, the permittivity and the permeability of the medium. We shall call a medium stationary if it is at rest with respect to the coordinate system used.*

We shall assume that the medium of propagation is infinite in extent and that its properties do not vary from point to point. We shall also assume that there are no sources in the region under consideration, such that $\mathbf{E}_s = 0$ in Eq. *8-6*.

This will avoid reflection and refraction; these phenomena will be treated in the next chapter. In this chapter we shall consider successively three types of media: nonconductors, conductors, and ionized gases.

10.1. The Wave Equations for the Field Vectors E, D, B, and H for Homogeneous Isotropic, Linear, Stationary Media

In Section 9.1 we deduced the wave equations for the field vectors in free space; we shall proceed similarly for the more general case of homogeneous, isotropic, linear, and s'a ionary media.

We start again from Maxwell's equations:

$$\nabla \cdot \mathbf{D} = \rho, \qquad (10\text{-}4)$$

$$\nabla \cdot \mathbf{B} = 0, \qquad (10\text{-}5)$$

$$\nabla \times \mathbf{E} + \frac{\partial \mathbf{B}}{\partial t} = 0, \qquad (10\text{-}6)$$

$$\nabla \times \mathbf{H} - \frac{\partial \mathbf{D}}{\partial t} = \mathbf{J}. \qquad (10\text{-}7)$$

Taking the curl of Eq. *10-6* and using Eq. *10-7*, we obtain

$$\nabla \times (\nabla \times \mathbf{E}) + \epsilon\mu \frac{\partial^2 \mathbf{E}}{\partial t^2} + \sigma\mu \frac{\partial \mathbf{E}}{\partial t} = 0, \qquad (10\text{-}8)$$

or, from Equation *1-30*,

$$\nabla(\nabla \cdot \mathbf{E}) - \nabla^2 \mathbf{E} + \epsilon\mu \frac{\partial^2 \mathbf{E}}{\partial t^2} + \sigma\mu \frac{\partial \mathbf{E}}{\partial t} = 0. \qquad (10\text{-}9)$$

Using now Eq. *10-4*,

$$\nabla^2 \mathbf{E} = \epsilon\mu \frac{\partial^2 \mathbf{E}}{\partial t^2} + \sigma\mu \frac{\partial \mathbf{E}}{\partial t} + \nabla\left(\frac{\rho}{\epsilon}\right), \qquad (10\text{-}10)$$

where the first term on the right comes from the displacement current density $\partial \mathbf{D}/\partial t$, whereas the second comes from the conduction current density $\sigma \mathbf{E}$.

Similarly, we can obtain an equation for the magnetic field intensity **H** by taking the curl of Eq. *10-7* and using Eqs. *10-6* and *10-5:*

$$\nabla^2 \mathbf{H} = \epsilon\mu \frac{\partial^2 \mathbf{H}}{\partial t^2} + \sigma\mu \frac{\partial \mathbf{H}}{\partial t}. \qquad (10\text{-}11)$$

Again, the first term on the right comes from the displacement current; the second, from the conduction current. This equation is identical to that for **E**, except that we now have only two terms on the right, since there is no magnetic equivalent of free electric charges. On comparing this with Eq. *G-78* (Appendix G) we find that the differential equation for **H** is exactly that for an attenuated wave.

10.1.1. The Relative Orientations of the E and H Vectors in a Plane Wave.
Let us first dispose of the charge density which appears in Eq. *10-10*. We consider
a plane wave propagating in the positive direction along the z-axis such that all
derivatives with respect to x and to y are zero. Then, from the Maxwell equation *10-4*,

$$\mathbf{\nabla} \cdot \mathbf{E} = \frac{\partial}{\partial z} E_z = \frac{\rho}{\epsilon}, \tag{10-12}$$

and

$$\frac{\partial}{\partial z} \left(\frac{\rho}{\epsilon} \right) \mathbf{k} = \frac{\partial^2}{\partial z^2} E_z \mathbf{k}, \tag{10-13}$$

and the wave equation for **E** (Eq. *10-10*) becomes

$$\frac{\partial^2}{\partial z^2} (E_x \mathbf{i} + E_y \mathbf{j}) = \mu \left(\epsilon \frac{\partial^2}{\partial t^2} + \sigma \frac{\partial}{\partial t} \right)(E_x \mathbf{i} + E_y \mathbf{j} + E_z \mathbf{k}). \tag{10-14}$$

The longitudinal component E_z of the electric field intensity must therefore
satisfy the equation

$$\epsilon \frac{\partial^2 E_z}{\partial t^2} + \sigma \frac{\partial E_z}{\partial t} = 0, \tag{10-15}$$

with the result that E_z, if it exists, must be of the form

$$E_z = a + b e^{-\sigma t / \epsilon}, \tag{10-16}$$

where a and b are constants of integration independent of t. Thus E_z must
decrease exponentially with time, there is thus no E_z wave, hence we may set

$$E_z = 0, \tag{10-17}$$

since we are concerned solely with wave propagation. Then, from Eq. *10-12*,
we may set

$$\rho = 0 \tag{10-18}$$

for a plane wave in a conducting medium.

In a nonconductor, $\sigma = 0$, thus from Eq. *10-16*, E_z is at most a function of z,
and the wave again has no longitudinal component of **E**.

We have therefore found that, for plane electromagnetic waves, (a) we may
set $\rho = 0$ in Eq. *10-10*, and (b) the **E** vector is transverse.

It is easy to show that the **H** vector is also transverse: the divergence of **H**
being equal to zero, we must have

$$\frac{\partial H_z}{\partial z} = 0, \tag{10-19}$$

because the derivatives with respect to x and to y are both zero, by hypothesis.
Then H_z is not a function of z, and, if we consider only waves, we may set

$$H_z = 0. \tag{10-20}$$

Then the **H** vector is also transverse. *Plane electromagnetic waves are therefore
transverse in any homogeneous, isotropic, linear and stationary medium.*

Now that we have shown that **E** and **H** are transverse, let us investigate their relative orientations. From the Maxwell equation *10-6* for $\nabla \times \mathbf{E}$,

$$\begin{vmatrix} \mathbf{i} & \mathbf{j} & \mathbf{k} \\ 0 & 0 & \dfrac{\partial}{\partial z} \\ E_x & E_y & 0 \end{vmatrix} = -j\omega B_x \mathbf{i} - j\omega B_y \mathbf{j}. \tag{10-21}$$

The operator $\partial/\partial z$ in the determinant can be replaced by $-jk$, since any wave of angular frequency ω propagating in the positive direction of the z-axis must involve the exponential function

$$e^{j(\omega t - kz)},$$

where the wave number k is in general complex. Then

$$jkE_y = -j\omega\mu H_x, \tag{10-22}$$
$$-jkE_x = -j\omega\mu H_y, \tag{10-23}$$

and

$$-\frac{E_y}{H_x} = \frac{E_x}{H_y} = \frac{\omega\mu}{k}. \tag{10-24}$$

The **E** *and* **H** *vectors are therefore mutually perpendicular.* For example, if **E** is along the x-axis ($E_y = 0$), then **H** is along the y-axis ($H_x = 0$). They are not necessarily in phase because the wave number can be complex. *The* **E** *and* **H** *vectors are oriented such that their vector product* **E** $\times$ **H** *points in the direction of propagation.*

10.2. Propagation of Plane Electromagnetic Waves in Nonconductors

The case of nonconductors is relatively simple, since their conductivity σ is zero. Then the wave equations *10-10* and *10-11* reduce to

$$\nabla^2 \mathbf{E} = \epsilon\mu \frac{\partial^2 \mathbf{E}}{\partial t^2} \tag{10-25}$$

and

$$\nabla^2 \mathbf{H} = \epsilon\mu \frac{\partial^2 \mathbf{H}}{\partial t^2}. \tag{10-26}$$

These differential equations correspond to an unattenuated wave having a phase velocity

$$u = \frac{1}{(\epsilon\mu)^{1/2}} = \frac{1}{(K_e K_m)^{1/2}} \frac{1}{(\epsilon_0\mu_0)^{1/2}} = \frac{c}{(K_e K_m)^{1/2}}. \tag{10-27}$$

The wave velocity is thus *less* than in free space, and the index of refraction is

$$n = \frac{c}{u} = (K_e K_m)^{1/2}. \tag{10-28}$$

In a nonmagnetic medium, $K_m = 1$, and

$$n = K_e^{1/2}. \tag{10-29}$$

We thus have a simple relation between the index of refraction n and the dielectric coefficient K_e of a nonmagnetic nonconductor. We must keep in mind, however, that K_e, and therefore n, are functions of the frequency (Section 3.10). The variation of n with frequency gives rise to the well-known phenomenon of dispersion in optics. Tables of the index of refraction n are usually compiled for optical frequencies, whereas K_e is measured at much lower frequencies. Such pairs of values cannot, therefore, be expected to correspond.

For a plane wave propagating in the positive direction of the z-axis, both $\mathbf{E}$ and $\mathbf{H}$ are independent of x and of y, with the result that

$$\frac{\partial^2 \mathbf{E}}{\partial z^2} = \epsilon\mu \frac{\partial^2 \mathbf{E}}{\partial t^2}. \tag{10-30}$$

A similar relation exists for $\mathbf{H}$. For a sine wave of angular frequency ω,

$$\mathbf{E} = \mathbf{E}_0 e^{j(\omega t - kz)}, \tag{10-31}$$

where the wave number k is given by

$$k = \frac{1}{\lambda} = \frac{n}{\lambda_0} = \frac{(K_e K_m)^{1/2}}{\lambda_0}, \tag{10-32}$$

$$= \frac{\omega}{u} = \omega(\epsilon\mu)^{1/2}. \tag{10-33}$$

In a nonconductor, k is real, and there is no attenuation. From Eq. *10-24*, we have

$$-\frac{E_y}{H_x} = \frac{E_x}{H_y} = \frac{\omega\mu}{k} = \left(\frac{\mu}{\epsilon}\right)^{1/2}. \tag{10-34}$$

If we choose the x-axis to be parallel to $\mathbf{E}$, then

$$\mathbf{E} = E_0 e^{j(\omega t - kz)} \, \mathbf{i}, \tag{10-35}$$

$$\mathbf{H} = H_0 e^{j(\omega t - kz)} \, \mathbf{j}, \tag{10-36}$$

$$= \left(\frac{\epsilon}{\mu}\right)^{1/2} E_0 e^{j(\omega t - kz)} \, \mathbf{j}. \tag{10-37}$$

The vectors $\mathbf{E}$ and $\mathbf{H}$ are in phase and the electric and magnetic energy densities are equal:

$$\frac{1}{2}\epsilon E^2 = \frac{1}{2}\mu H^2. \tag{10-38}$$

The total instantaneous energy density is thus ϵE^2 or μH^2; the average total energy density is one-half of this, or $\epsilon E_{\text{rms}}^2 = \mu H_{\text{rms}}^2$.

The average value of the Poynting vector is

$$\mathbf{S}_{av.} = \frac{1}{2} E_0 H_0 \mathbf{k}, \tag{10-39}$$

$$= \frac{1}{2} \left(\frac{\epsilon}{\mu}\right)^{1/2} E_0^2 \, \mathbf{k}, \tag{10-40}$$

$$= \left(\frac{\epsilon}{\mu}\right)^{1/2} E_{rms}^2 \, \mathbf{k}, \tag{10-41}$$

$$= \frac{1}{(\epsilon\mu)^{1/2}} \epsilon E_{rms}^2 \, \mathbf{k}. \tag{10-42}$$

This is the phase velocity multiplied by the average total energy density. We also have

$$\mathbf{S}_{av.} = 2.65 \times 10^{-3} \left(\frac{K_e}{K_m}\right)^{1/2} E_{rms}^2 \text{ watts/meter}^2. \tag{10-43}$$

10.3. Propagation of Plane Electromagnetic Waves in Conducting Media

We must now solve the two wave equations *10-10* and *10-11* for a wave traveling along the z-axis, with $\rho = 0$ (Section 10.1.1). We therefore have two identical equations for **E** and for **H**:

$$\frac{\partial^2 \mathbf{E}}{\partial z^2} = \epsilon\mu \frac{\partial^2 \mathbf{E}}{\partial t^2} + \sigma\mu \frac{\partial \mathbf{E}}{\partial t}, \tag{10-44}$$

$$\frac{\partial^2 \mathbf{H}}{\partial z^2} = \epsilon\mu \frac{\partial^2 \mathbf{H}}{\partial t^2} + \sigma\mu \frac{\partial \mathbf{H}}{\partial t}. \tag{10-45}$$

Let us solve the equation for **E**. We have

$$\frac{\partial^2 \mathbf{E}}{\partial z^2} = (-\omega^2 \epsilon\mu + j\omega\sigma\mu) \, \mathbf{E}, \tag{10-46}$$

$$= -\frac{K_e K_m}{\lambda_0^2} \left(1 - j \frac{\sigma}{\omega\epsilon}\right) \mathbf{E}, \tag{10-47}$$

where

$$\lambda_0 = \frac{c}{\omega} = \frac{\lambda_0}{2\pi} \tag{10-48}$$

is the radian length for a wave of angular frequency ω propagating in free space.

The quantity $j\omega\epsilon/\sigma$ is the ratio of the displacement current density $\partial D/\partial t$ to the conduction current density σE (Section 7.10). We shall call the modulus of this ratio the Q of the medium:

$$Q = \left|\frac{\frac{\partial D}{\partial t}}{\sigma E}\right| = \frac{\omega\epsilon}{\sigma}, \tag{10-49}$$

$$\varrho = \frac{K_e}{60\sigma\lambda_0}. \qquad (10\text{-}50)$$

For nonconductors, $\varrho \longrightarrow \infty$. For common types of conductors, σ is of the order of 10^7 mhos/meter (5.8×10^7 for copper), and we can set $K_e \approx 1$ (Section 7.10). The ratio ϱ is thus very *small* for the usual conductors, even down to wavelengths corresponding to the near ultraviolet ($\lambda_0 \approx 10^{-7}$ meters, from Figure 9-3).

In terms of ϱ,

$$\frac{\partial^2 \mathbf{E}}{\partial z^2} = -\frac{K_e K_m}{\lambda_0^2}\left(1 - \frac{j}{\varrho}\right)\mathbf{E}. \qquad (10\text{-}51)$$

It is shown in Appendix G that the above partial differential equation corresponds to a pair of attenuated waves traveling in opposite directions along the z-axis, the wave traveling in the positive direction being given by

$$\mathbf{E} = \mathbf{E}_0 e^{j(\omega t - kz)}, \qquad (10\text{-}52)$$

where the wave number k is complex:

$$k = k_r - jk_i. \qquad (10\text{-}53)$$

Both k_r and k_i are positive, and

$$k^2 = \frac{K_e K_m}{\lambda_0^2}\left(1 - \frac{j}{\varrho}\right), \qquad (10\text{-}54)$$

$$= \frac{K_e K_m}{\lambda_0^2}\left(1 - \frac{j\sigma}{\omega\epsilon}\right), \qquad (10\text{-}55)$$

or

$$k_r = \frac{1}{\lambda_0}\left(\frac{K_e K_m}{2}\right)^{1/2}\left[\left(1 + \frac{1}{\varrho^2}\right)^{1/2} + 1\right]^{1/2}, \qquad (10\text{-}56)$$

$$k_i = \frac{1}{\lambda_0}\left(\frac{K_e K_m}{2}\right)^{1/2}\left[\left(1 + \frac{1}{\varrho^2}\right)^{1/2} - 1\right]^{1/2}, \qquad (10\text{-}57)$$

$$k = \frac{(K_e K_m)^{1/2}}{\lambda_0}\left(1 + \frac{1}{\varrho^2}\right)^{1/4}\exp\left\{-j\text{ arc tan}\left[\frac{\left(1 + \frac{1}{\varrho^2}\right)^{1/2} - 1}{\left(1 + \frac{1}{\varrho^2}\right)^{1/2} + 1}\right]^{1/2}\right\}. \qquad (10\text{-}58)$$

Our expression for the arc tan function is correct, since k_r is a positive quantity. In a vacuum, $k_r = 1/\lambda_0$, and $k_i = 0$.

The real part k_r of the wave number is always $1/\lambda = 2\pi/\lambda$, where λ is the wavelength in the medium; the imaginary part k_i is the reciprocal of the distance δ over which the wave amplitude is attenuated by a factor of e.

Again from Appendix G, the phase of the wave travels with a velocity

$$u = \frac{\omega}{k_r}, \qquad (10\text{-}59)$$

$$= \frac{c}{\left(\frac{K_e K_m}{2}\right)^{1/2}\left[\left(1 + \frac{1}{\varrho^2}\right)^{1/2} + 1\right]^{1/2}}, \qquad (10\text{-}60)$$

corresponding to an index of refraction (defined as the ratio of the phase velocity in free space to the phase velocity in the medium) of

$$n = \frac{c}{u} = \frac{\lambda_0}{\lambda} = \lambda_0 k_r,$$

(10-61)

$$= \left(\frac{K_e K_m}{2}\right)^{1/2} \left[\left(1 + \frac{1}{Q^2}\right)^{1/2} + 1\right]^{1/2}.$$

(10-62)

The amplitude of the wave is attenuated by a factor of $1/e = 0.368$ in a distance

$$\delta = \frac{1}{k_i},$$

(10-63)

and

$$\frac{\delta}{\lambda_0} = \frac{1}{\left(\frac{K_e K_m}{2}\right)^{1/2} \left[\left(1 + \frac{1}{Q^2}\right)^{1/2} - 1\right]^{1/2}},$$

(10-64)

$$\frac{\delta}{\lambda} = \frac{k_r}{k_i} = \frac{\left[\left(1 + \frac{1}{Q^2}\right)^{1/2} + 1\right]^{1/2}}{\left[\left(1 + \frac{1}{Q^2}\right)^{1/2} - 1\right]^{1/2}}.$$

(10-65)

The ratio E/H is again given by Eq. *10-24*:

$$\frac{E}{H} = \frac{\omega\mu}{k},$$

(10-66)

$$= \left(\frac{\mu}{\epsilon}\right)^{1/2} \frac{1}{\left(1 + \frac{1}{Q^2}\right)^{1/4}} \exp\left[j \arctan (k_i/k_r)\right],$$

(10-67)

where the coefficient of j in the exponent gives the phase of E with respect to H. The quantities Q, k, k_r, and k_i are defined as in Eqs. *10-50, 10-53, 10-56,* and *10-57,* respectively.

Setting **E** to be parallel to the x-axis, we have

$$\mathbf{E} = E_0 \exp\left[j(\omega t - k_r z) - k_i z\right] \mathbf{i},$$

(10-68)

and then

$$\mathbf{H} = \left(\frac{\epsilon}{\mu}\right)^{1/2} \left(1 + \frac{1}{Q^2}\right)^{1/4} E_0 \exp\left\{j[\omega t - k_r z - \arctan (k_i/k_r)] - k_i z\right\} \mathbf{j},$$

(10-69)

$$= H_0 \exp\left[j(\omega t - k_r z - \theta) - k_i z\right] \mathbf{j},$$

(10-70)

where

$$\frac{E_0}{H_0} = \left(\frac{\mu}{\epsilon}\right)^{1/2} \frac{1}{\left(1 + \frac{1}{Q^2}\right)^{1/4}}$$

(10-71)

and

$$\theta = \arctan \frac{k_i}{k_r}.$$

(10-72)

The ratio of the electric and magnetic energy densities is

$$\left| \frac{\frac{1}{2} \epsilon E^2}{\frac{1}{2} \mu H^2} \right| = \frac{1}{\left(1 + \dfrac{1}{\varrho^2}\right)^{1/2}}, \tag{10-73}$$

The *average* total energy density is

$$\frac{1}{2}\left(\frac{1}{2}\epsilon E_0^2 + \frac{1}{2}\mu H_0^2\right)e^{-2k_i z} = \frac{1}{4}\epsilon E_0^2\left[1 + \left(1 + \frac{1}{\varrho^2}\right)^{1/2}\right]e^{-2k_i z}, \tag{10-74}$$

$$= \frac{1}{2}\epsilon E_{\text{rms}}^2\left[1 + \left(1 + \frac{1}{\varrho^2}\right)^{1/2}\right]e^{-2k_i z}, \tag{10-75}$$

where E_{rms} is the rms value of E at $z = 0$: $E_{\text{rms}}^2 = (1/2)E_0^2$.

10.3.1. The Poynting Vector in Conducting Media.

The Poynting vector

$$\mathbf{S} = \mathbf{E} \times \mathbf{H} \tag{10-76}$$

was discussed in Section 9.2 for a wave propagating in free space. We shall now re-examine this vector for the more general case in which $\mathbf{E}$ and $\mathbf{H}$ are not in phase.

We again have the vector identity

$$\mathbf{\nabla} \cdot (\mathbf{E} \times \mathbf{H}) = \mathbf{H} \cdot (\mathbf{\nabla} \times \mathbf{E}) - \mathbf{E} \cdot (\mathbf{\nabla} \times \mathbf{H}). \tag{10-77}$$

Now, from Eqs. *10-6* and *10-7*,

$$\mathbf{\nabla} \cdot (\mathbf{E} \times \mathbf{H}) = -\mathbf{H} \cdot \frac{\partial \mathbf{B}}{\partial t} - \mathbf{E} \cdot \left(\frac{\partial \mathbf{D}}{\partial t} + \mathbf{J}\right), \tag{10-78}$$

$$= -\frac{\partial}{\partial t}\left(\frac{1}{2}\mu H^2 + \frac{1}{2}\epsilon E^2\right) - \mathbf{E} \cdot \mathbf{J}. \tag{10-79}$$

Integrating over a volume τ and using the divergence theorem on the left-hand side,

$$\int_S (\mathbf{E} \times \mathbf{H}) \cdot \mathbf{da} = -\frac{\partial}{\partial t}\int_\tau \left(\frac{1}{2}\epsilon E^2 + \frac{1}{2}\mu H^2\right) d\tau - \int_\tau \mathbf{E} \cdot \mathbf{J}\, d\tau, \tag{10-80}$$

where S is the closed surface bounding the volume τ. The first integral on the right represents the loss of electric and magnetic energy in the volume τ in one second; the second integral is the electromagnetic energy removed from the same volume through Joule heating in one second.

The Poynting vector $\mathbf{E} \times \mathbf{H}$ thus appears to represent a flux of energy, just as in the case of free space which was discussed in Section 9.2. Although this concept is convenient, again it must not be taken too literally. Although the above equation is rigorously true for any linear, isotropic, stationary medium, it does *not* follow necessarily that $\mathbf{E} \times \mathbf{H}$ represents an actual flow of energy at any given point in space.

We shall now evaluate the time average of the vector product $\mathbf{E} \times \mathbf{H}$ for the general case in which $\mathbf{E}$ and $\mathbf{H}$ are not in phase. Since these two vectors are mutually perpendicular, from Section 10.1.1, the magnitude of their vector product is simply EH.

Since we wish to evaluate the *product* EH, we must avoid the exponential notation and revert to the cosine function (Appendix F). Then, instead of Eqs. *10-68* and *10-70* for $\mathbf{E}$ and for $\mathbf{H}$, we write

$$E = E_0 e^{-k_i z} \cos (\omega t - k_r z), \qquad (10\text{-}81)$$

$$H = H_0 e^{-k_i z} \cos (\omega t - k_r z - \theta), \qquad (10\text{-}82)$$

and

$$EH = E_0 H_0 e^{-2k_i z} \cos (\omega t - k_r z) \cos (\omega t - k_r z - \theta), \qquad (10\text{-}83)$$

$$= E_0 H_0 e^{-2k_i z} [\cos^2 (\omega t - k_r z) \cos \theta \qquad (10\text{-}84)$$
$$+ \cos (\omega t - k_r z) \sin (\omega t - k_r z) \sin \theta].$$

Since the average value of $\cos^2 (\omega t - k_r z)$ is $1/2$, whereas the average of $\cos (\omega t - k_r z) \sin (\omega t - k_r z)$ is zero, we have

$$S_{\text{av.}} = \frac{1}{2} E_0 H_0 e^{-2k_i z} \cos \theta, \qquad (10\text{-}85)$$

$$= \frac{1}{2^{3/2}} \left(\frac{\epsilon}{\mu}\right)^{1/2} \left[\left(1 + \frac{1}{Q^2}\right)^{1/2} + 1\right]^{1/2} e^{-2k_i z} E_0^2, \qquad (10\text{-}86)$$

$$= \frac{1}{2^{1/2}} \left(\frac{\epsilon}{\mu}\right)^{1/2} \left[\left(1 + \frac{1}{Q^2}\right)^{1/2} + 1\right]^{1/2} e^{-2k_i z} E_{\text{rms}}^2. \qquad (10\text{-}87)$$

The average value of the Poynting vector is thus proportional to the square of the amplitude of the wave.

Using the exponential expressions for $\mathbf{E}$ and $\mathbf{H}$ given in Eqs. *10-68* and *10-70*, we find that

$$S_{\text{av.}} = \frac{1}{2} \text{Re} (\mathbf{E} \times \mathbf{H}^*), \qquad (10\text{-}88)$$

where $\mathbf{H}^*$ is the complex conjugate of $\mathbf{H}$. *This is the most convenient expression for calculating* $S_{\text{av.}}$.

If we now calculate the product of the average energy density given by Eq. *10-75* by the phase velocity of Eq. *10-60*, we find that it is equal to the average value of the Poynting vector:

$$S_{\text{av.}} = (\text{Average energy density}) \times (\text{Phase velocity}). \qquad (10\text{-}89)$$

We can thus consider again, in this general case, that the average energy density is propagated at the phase velocity $\mathbf{u}$.

10.4. Propagation of Plane Electromagnetic Waves in Good Conductors

Let us return to the values of k_r and k_i for conducting media as given in Eqs. *10-56* and *10-57*. They can be simplified considerably for good conductors because Q is then much smaller than unity. Then

$$\left[\left(1 + \frac{1}{Q^2}\right)^{1/2} \pm 1\right]^{1/2} \approx \left(\frac{1}{Q}\right)^{1/2}\left[1 + \frac{Q^2}{2} \pm Q\right]^{1/2}, \tag{10-90}$$

$$\approx \left(\frac{1}{Q}\right)^{1/2}\left(1 \pm \frac{Q}{2}\right), \tag{10-91}$$

$$\approx \left(\frac{1}{Q}\right)^{1/2}, \tag{10-92}$$

within 1% for

$$Q = \frac{\omega\epsilon}{\sigma} \leq \frac{1}{50}. \tag{10-93}$$

It will be observed that this inequality means that the conduction current σE must be at least 50 times as large as the displacement current $\partial D/\partial t$.

Good conductors will be defined as those for which the above condition is satisfied. According to this definition, copper is a "good" conductor up to frequencies of about 3×10^{15} cycles/second, or to the near ultraviolet. In fact, the theory breaks down at considerably lower frequencies due to atomic phenomena which we shall disregard.

For good conductors, the wave equation *10-51* simplifies to

$$\frac{\partial^2 E}{\partial z^2} = j\frac{\omega^2}{c^2}\frac{K_e K_m}{Q}E, \tag{10-94}$$

$$= j\omega\sigma\mu E, \tag{10-95}$$

and the wave number is

$$k = (-j\omega\sigma\mu)^{1/2}, \tag{10-96}$$

$$= \left(\frac{\omega\sigma\mu}{2}\right)^{1/2}(1 - j), \tag{10-97}$$

$$= \frac{(\sigma K_m f)^{1/2}}{504}(1 - j) \text{ meter}^{-1}, \tag{10-98}$$

$$= (\omega\sigma\mu)^{1/2}e^{-j\pi/4}, \tag{10-99}$$

$$= \frac{(\sigma K_m f)^{1/2}}{356}e^{-j\pi/4} \text{ meter}^{-1}. \tag{10-100}$$

Since the real and the imaginary parts of the wave number are equal,

$$k = \frac{1 - j}{\delta}, \tag{10-101}$$

and the attenuation distance is

$$\delta = \lambda = \left(\frac{2}{\omega\sigma\mu}\right)^{1/2},$$ (10-102)

$$= \frac{504}{(\sigma K_m f)^{1/2}} \text{ meters.}$$ (10-103)

From Eq. *10-24*, we have

$$\frac{E}{H} = \frac{\omega\mu}{k},$$ (10-104)

$$= \left(\frac{\omega\mu}{\sigma}\right)^{1/2} e^{j\pi/4},$$ (10-105)

$$= \frac{1}{356}\left[\frac{K_m f}{\sigma}\right]^{1/2} e^{j\pi/4} \text{ ohms.}$$ (10-106)

The electric field intensity **E** leads the magnetic field intensity **H** by $\pi/4$ radian in good conductors. This comes from the fact that the current which gives rise to **H** in conductors is the conduction current, and not the displacement current as in nonconductors.

The relative amplitudes of **E** and of **H** depend on the frequency, but **E** tends to be numerically small compared to **H**. For example, at a frequency of 1 megacycle/second, E/H is about 10^{-3} in copper, whereas it is 377 in air, from Eq. *9-28*.

From Eqs. *10-101* and *10-105*, we obtain

$$\mathbf{E} = E_0 \exp\left[j\left(\omega t - \frac{z}{\delta}\right) - \frac{z}{\delta}\right]\mathbf{i},$$ (10-107)

$$\mathbf{H} = \left(\frac{\sigma}{\omega\mu}\right)^{1/2} E_0 \exp\left[j\left(\omega t - \frac{z}{\delta} - \frac{\pi}{4}\right) - \frac{z}{\delta}\right]\mathbf{j},$$ (10-108)

or, in terms of cosine functions,

$$\mathbf{E} = E_0 e^{-z/\delta} \cos\left(\omega t - \frac{z}{\delta}\right)\mathbf{i},$$ (10-109)

$$\mathbf{H} = \left(\frac{\sigma}{\omega\mu}\right)^{1/2} E_0 e^{-z/\delta} \cos\left(\omega t - \frac{z}{\delta} - \frac{\pi}{4}\right)\mathbf{j},$$ (10-110)

$$= H_0 e^{-z/\delta} \cos\left(\omega t - \frac{z + \frac{\lambda}{8}}{\delta}\right)\mathbf{j}.$$ (10-111)

Figure 10-1 shows the curves of E/E_0 and of H/H_0 for $t = 0$.

The wave is attenuated by a factor of $1/e = 0.368$ in amplitude in one radian length λ, and by a factor of $(1/e)^{2\pi} \approx 2 \times 10^{-3}$ in one wavelength λ, whereas the Poynting vector is attenuated by $(1/e)^2 = 0.135$ in λ and by $(1/e)^{4\pi} \approx 4 \times 10^{-6}$ in λ. The attenuation is therefore extremely rapid. The attenuation

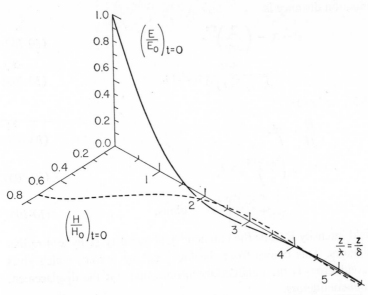

Figure 10-1. *The ratios* $E/E_o = e^{-z/\delta} \cos [\omega t - (z/\delta)]$ *and* H/H_o
$= e^{-z/\delta} \cos [\omega t - (z/\delta) - (\pi/4)]$ *at* $t = 0$ *as functions of* z/λ *for
an electromagnetic wave propagating in the positive direction of the
z-axis in a good conductor.*

distance δ in conductors is usually called the *skin depth* or *depth of penetration.*
The skin depth *decreases* if either the conductivity σ, the permeability K_m, or
the frequency f *increases.* Good conductors are therefore always highly opaque
to light, except when in the form of extremely thin films. It does *not* follow,
however, that substances which are nonconducting at low frequencies are
necessarily transparent at optical frequencies.

Table 10-1 shows the skin depth δ for various conductors at four typical
frequencies. Note that the attenuation in iron is much larger than in silver,
despite the fact that the former is a relatively poor conductor.

The phase velocity

$$u = \frac{\omega}{k_r} = \left(\frac{2\omega}{\sigma\mu}\right)^{1/2}, \qquad (10\text{-}112)$$

$$= 3.16 \times 10^8 \left(\frac{f}{\sigma K_m}\right)^{1/2} \text{ meters/second}, \qquad (10\text{-}113)$$

and

$$\frac{\lambda}{\lambda_0} = 1.05 \times 10^{-5} \left(\frac{f}{\sigma K_m}\right)^{1/2}. \qquad (10\text{-}114)$$

A striking feature of this expression is the strong dispersion which occurs in
good conductors: the wave velocity varies as the square root of the frequency.

TABLE 10-1. Skin Depths δ for Conductors*

Conductor	Conductivity σ (mhos/meter)	Relative Permeability K_m †	$\delta f^{1/2}$ (meters/second$^{1/2}$)	Skin Depth δ			
				60 cps (centimeters)	1000 cps (millimeters)	1 Mcs (millimeters)	3000 Mcs (microns)
Aluminum	3.54×10^7	1.00	0.085	1.1	2.7	0.085	1.6
Brass (65.8 Cu, 34.2 Zn)	1.59×10^7	1.00	0.126	1.63	3.98	0.126	2.30
Chromium	3.8×10^7	1.00	0.081	1.0	2.6	0.081	1.5
Copper	5.80×10^7	1.00	0.066	0.85	2.1	0.066	1.2
Gold	4.50×10^7	1.00	0.075	0.97	2.38	0.075	1.4
Graphite	1.0×10^5	1.00	1.59	20.5	50.3	1.59	29.0
Magnetic iron	1.0×10^7	2×10^2	0.011	0.14	0.35	0.011	0.20
Mumetal (75 Ni, 2 Cr, 5 Cu, 18 Fe)	0.16×10^7	2×10^4	0.0029	0.037	0.092	0.0029	0.053
Nickel	1.3×10^7	1×10^2	0.014	0.18	4.4	0.014	0.26
Sea water	5.0	1.00	2×10^2	3×10^3	7×10^3	2×10^2	**
Silver	6.15×10^7	1.00	0.064	0.83	2.03	0.064	1.2
Tin	0.870×10^7	1.00	0.171	2.21	5.41	0.171	3.12
Zinc	1.86×10^7	1.00	0.117	1.51	3.70	0.117	2.14

* Adapted from the *American Institute of Physics Handbook* (McGraw-Hill, New York, 1957), Section 5, p. 90.
† At $B = 0.002$ weber/meter^2.
** At this frequency φ is about 2, and sea water is not a "good" conductor ($K_e \approx 70$).

The velocity is also low, at least as long as Q is small, as required by our calculation. For example, at a frequency of 1 megacycle/second in copper, the velocity turns out to be about 500 meters/second and the index of refraction c/u about 7×10^5. The wavelength in the copper is only about 0.5 millimeter, whereas it is 300 meters in air. Within the limits of our approximation, that is, for $Q \leqq \frac{1}{50}$, the wavelength in the conductor is always much shorter than in free space. For copper,

$$\frac{\lambda}{\lambda_0} = 1.4 \times 10^{-9} f^{1/2}. \qquad (10\text{-}115)$$

The ratio of the electric to the magnetic energy density is

$$\frac{\frac{1}{2} \epsilon E_0^2}{\frac{1}{2} \mu H_0^2} = \frac{\omega \epsilon}{\sigma} = Q, \qquad (10\text{-}116)$$

$$\leqq \frac{1}{50}, \qquad (10\text{-}117)$$

and the energy is essentially all in the magnetic form. This results from the large conductivity σ, which causes E/J to be small. The electric field intensity is thus weak, but the current density, and hence H, are relatively large.

10.4.1. Joule Heating in a Good Conductor. From Eqs. *10-107* and *10-108*, the average value of the Poynting vector is

$$\mathbf{S}_{\text{av.}} = \frac{1}{2} \operatorname{Re} (\mathbf{E} \times \mathbf{H}^*), \qquad (10\text{-}118)$$

$$= \frac{1}{2} \left(\frac{\sigma}{2\omega\mu}\right)^{1/2} e^{-2z/\delta} E_0^2 \, \mathbf{k}, \qquad (10\text{-}119)$$

$$= \left(\frac{\sigma}{2\omega\mu}\right)^{1/2} e^{-2z/\delta} E_{\text{rms}}^2 \, \mathbf{k}, \qquad (10\text{-}120)$$

$$= 252 \left(\frac{\sigma}{K_m f}\right)^{1/2} e^{-2z/\delta} E_{\text{rms}}^2 \, \mathbf{k} \text{ watts/meter}^2. \qquad (10\text{-}121)$$

Since the electric field intensity decreases with z as $e^{-z/\delta}$, the Poynting vector decreases as $e^{-2z/\delta}$. The wave energy is thus continuously dissipated by Joule heating of the conducting medium.

Let us compare the energy lost by the wave and that gained by the medium through Joule heating. We consider a thin sheet of the conductor, perpendicular to the direction of propagation, ab square meters in area, and of thickness Δz,

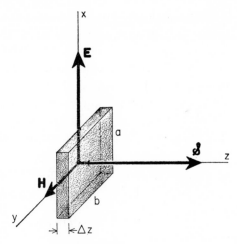

Figure 10-2

Element of volume ab meters² in area and Δz meters thick, normal to the direction of propagation in a conducting medium.

as in Figure 10-2. If the rms value of E on the left-hand face is $E_{\rm rms}$, then, on the right-hand face it is

$$E_{\rm rms}e^{-\Delta z/\delta},$$

and $S_{\rm av.}$ thus decreases from

$$\left(\frac{\sigma}{2\omega\mu}\right)^{1/2}E_{\rm rms}^2 \qquad \text{to} \qquad \left(\frac{\sigma}{2\omega\mu}\right)^{1/2}E_{\rm rms}^2 e^{-2\,\Delta z/\delta}$$

within the sheet. Then the average energy lost by the wave per second in the sheet is

$$ab\left(\frac{\sigma}{2\omega\mu}\right)^{1/2}E_{\rm rms}^2(1-e^{-2\,\Delta z/\delta}) = ab\left(\frac{\sigma}{2\omega\mu}\right)^{1/2}E_{\rm rms}^2\frac{2\,\Delta z}{\delta}, \qquad (10\text{-}122)$$

$$= ab\sigma\,\Delta z E_{\rm rms}^2 \text{ watts/second}, \qquad (10\text{-}123)$$

if we assume that Δz is small with respect to δ. We could also have arrived at this result by calculating $(dS_{\rm av.}/dz)\,\Delta z$.

We now wish to know the average energy lost per second by Joule heating in the sheet. The voltage across the sheet is $aE_{\rm rms}$ and the resistance in the direction of current flow is $a/\sigma b\,\Delta z$. Then Joule heating produces an average of $\sigma ab\,\Delta z E_{\rm rms}^2$ watts/second, which is exactly the energy lost by the wave in one second.

10.5. Propagation of Plane Electromagnetic Waves in Ionized Gases

We have studied nonconductors, in which the current is entirely of the displacement type, and good conductors, in which current of the conduction type is predominant; we shall now study ionized gases, in which the current arises from the presence of free electrons and ions in the electric and magnetic fields of the incident electromagnetic wave. The phenomena here are very different from those occurring in a metal in which the conduction electrons suffer large numbers of collisions with the crystal lattice in the process of diffusing under the action of the electric field. We shall assume here that the pressure is low enough such that there are essentially no collisions, and hence no energy losses.

Let us consider a plane electromagnetic wave traveling in the positive direction along the z-axis with the $\mathbf{E}$ and $\mathbf{H}$ vectors respectively parallel to the x- and the y-axes. An ion of charge Q, of mass m, and of velocity $\mathbf{u}$ is subjected to a force $\mathbf{f}$ given by the Coulomb force plus the Lorentz force as in Eq. 5-29:

$$\mathbf{f} = Q[\mathbf{E} + (\mathbf{u} \times \mathbf{B})], \qquad (10\text{-}124)$$

$$= Q\left(E\mathbf{i} - B\frac{\partial \zeta}{\partial t}\mathbf{i} + B\frac{\partial \xi}{\partial t}\mathbf{k}\right), \qquad (10\text{-}125)$$

the ion being situated at (ξ, η, ζ), with respect to its average position $\xi = 0$, $\eta = 0$, $\zeta = 0$. Then

$$\frac{\partial^2 \xi}{\partial t^2} = Q\left(\frac{E}{m} - \frac{B}{m}\frac{\partial \zeta}{\partial t}\right), \qquad (10\text{-}126)$$

$$= Q\frac{E}{m}\left(1 - \frac{1}{c}\frac{\partial \zeta}{\partial t}\right), \qquad (10\text{-}127)$$

where we have used the free-space relationship between E and B: $E = cB$ (Eq. 9-27). As we shall see later on in Section 10.5.3, the magnetic induction is smaller relative to the electric field intensity than in free space, thus we are overestimating the magnetic force. We also have

$$\frac{\partial^2 \eta}{\partial t^2} = 0 \qquad (10\text{-}128)$$

and

$$\frac{\partial^2 \zeta}{\partial t^2} = Q\frac{E}{mc}\frac{\partial \xi}{\partial t}. \qquad (10\text{-}129)$$

We can neglect thermal agitation, which contributes random velocities, and hence zero net current.

Let us assume that the intensity of the wave is low enough such that the velocity of the ion along the z-axis is, due to the action of the electromagnetic wave, much smaller than the velocity of light:

$$\frac{1}{c}\frac{\partial \zeta}{\partial t} \ll 1. \qquad (10\text{-}130)$$

We shall justify this assumption later on. Then, along the x-axis, the magnetic force is negligible compared to the electric force, and Eq. 10-127 reduces to

$$\frac{\partial^2 \xi}{\partial t^2} = \frac{Q}{m}E = \frac{Q}{m}E_0 \cos \omega t. \qquad (10\text{-}131)$$

We must *not* use the exponential notation here because we shall have to solve Eq. *10-129*, which involves the product of the two variables E and $\partial \xi / \partial t$.

Thus

$$\xi = -\frac{1}{\omega^2} \frac{Q}{m} E_0 \cos \omega t, \tag{10-132}$$

and

$$\frac{\partial \xi}{\partial t} = \frac{1}{\omega} \frac{Q}{m} E_0 \sin \omega t. \tag{10-133}$$

Substituting in Eq. *10-129*, we obtain

$$\frac{\partial^2 \zeta}{\partial t^2} = \frac{Q^2 E_0^2}{2\omega m^2 c} \sin 2\omega t, \tag{10-134}$$

$$\frac{\partial \zeta}{\partial t} = -\frac{Q^2 E_0^2}{4\omega^2 m^2 c} \cos 2\omega t, \tag{10-135}$$

and

$$\zeta = -\frac{Q^2 E_0^2}{8\omega^3 m^2 c} \sin 2\omega t. \tag{10-136}$$

We have set the constants of integration equal to zero so that the average values of ξ and ζ can be zero, as we assumed at the beginning.

Before proceeding further, let us find the conditions under which the inequality expressed in Eq. *10-130* is satisfied. We expect that the ion velocity will remain low either if the field is not intense or if the frequency is high and the time available for acceleration is small. We have

$$\frac{1}{c} \left(\frac{\partial \zeta}{\partial t} \right)_{max} = \frac{Q^2 E_0^2}{4\omega^2 m^2 c^2}. \tag{10-137}$$

For an electron, $Q = 1.60 \times 10^{-19}$ coulomb, $m = 9.11 \times 10^{-31}$ kilogram, and

$$\frac{1}{c} \left(\frac{\partial \zeta}{\partial t} \right)_{max} = \frac{2.17 \times 10^3}{f^2} E_0^2. \tag{10-138}$$

Let us assume that the Poynting vector is calculated as in free space (Eq. *9-38*):

$$S_{av.} = 2.65 \times 10^{-3} \frac{E_0^2}{2}. \tag{10-139}$$

We shall see later on that this is correct only at high frequencies. Then

$$\frac{1}{c} \left(\frac{\partial \zeta}{\partial t} \right)_{max} = 1.64 \times 10^6 \frac{S_{av.}}{f^2}. \tag{10-140}$$

The velocity $\partial \zeta / \partial t$ along the z-axis is thus proportional to the average flux of energy $S_{av.}$ and is inversely proportional to the square of the frequency. The above equation seems to indicate that it is possible for $(\partial z / \partial t)_{max}$ to exceed the velocity of light c. This is because we have neglected relativistic effects in our calculation.

As a rough indication of orders of magnitude, the ratio $(\partial \zeta / \partial t)/c$ is about

10^{-8} at 1 kilometer from an antenna radiating 50 kilowatts of power isotropically at a frequency of 1 megacycle per second. Much higher peak power densities are common in the field of microwaves, but the frequencies are then of the order of 3000 megacycles per second, and $(\partial z/\partial t)/c$ is small even then. Our assumption of Eq. *10-130* is therefore well justified for electrons; it is even better justified for heavy ions, since $(\partial \zeta/\partial t)/c$ is proportional to Q^2/m^2.

The ratio

$$\frac{\zeta_{\max}}{\xi_{\max}} = \frac{QE_0}{8\omega mc} \qquad (10\text{-}141)$$

is about 10^{-5} for the above example and much smaller in the case of microwaves. We also find that $\xi_{\max}$ is about 1 centimeter, $\zeta_{\max}$ about 10^{-5} centimeter and that $\partial \zeta/\partial t$ is about 6×10^5 meters/second. This velocity corresponds to an energy of about 1 electron volt, E_0 being 3 volts/meter.

The ion motion is thus due almost exclusively to the electric field, the effect of the magnetic field being negligible. Then the space charge density remains unaffected by the ion motion, since ions of a given type move as a group in a plane perpendicular to the direction of propagation.

10.5.1. The Conductivity σ of an Ionized Gas. Since the ion drift velocity can be ascribed almost exclusively to the electric field intensity E, we can consider the ionized gas as having a conductivity σ such that

$$\sigma E = J, \qquad (10\text{-}142)$$

$$= \sum_i N_i Q_i \left(\frac{\partial \xi}{\partial t}\right)_i, \qquad (10\text{-}143)$$

where the summation is taken over the electrons and the various types of ions present in the gas, N_i is the number of ions or electrons of a given type per cubic meter, Q_i is the charge per ion or electron in coulombs, and $(\partial \xi/\partial t)_i$ is the drift velocity found above. Thus

$$\sigma E_0 \cos \omega t = \sum_i \frac{N_i Q_i^2 E_0}{\omega m_i} \sin \omega t, \qquad (10\text{-}144)$$

or, in exponential notation,

$$\sigma E_0 e^{j\omega t} = \sum_i \frac{N_i Q_i^2}{\omega m_i} E_0 e^{j(\omega t - \pi/2)}, \qquad (10\text{-}145)$$

and

$$\sigma = -\frac{j}{\omega} \sum_i \frac{N_i Q_i^2}{m_i}. \qquad (10\text{-}146)$$

Since the masses of the ions are larger than the electron mass by several orders of magnitude, whereas their charges are at most a few times larger than that of the electron, we can retain only the term corresponding to the electrons and write

$$\sigma = -j\frac{N_e Q_e^2}{\omega m_e},\tag{10-147}$$

where N_e is the number of free electrons per cubic meter.

The conductivity σ is therefore imaginary. The electron current *lags* the electric field intensity by $\pi/2$ radians, therefore the electron current can be said to be inductive. Since $\mathbf{E}$ and $\mathbf{J}$ are $\pi/2$ radians out of phase, the scalar product $\mathbf{E}\cdot\mathbf{J}$ is also purely imaginary, and there is no energy loss in the medium. This means that, on the average, the oscillating electrons do not gain energy from the field once it is established. It will be remembered that we assumed at the beginning that the electrons do not lose energy by collision with the gas molecules.

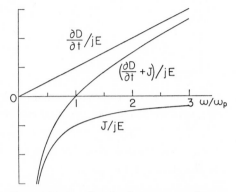

Figure 10-3. *The displacement and convection current densities in an ionized gas as a function of the circular frequency ω. The total current density is inductive below ω_p, zero at ω_p, and is capacitive above ω_p.*

Since the displacement current $\partial D/\partial t = jK_e\epsilon_0 E$ leads the electric field intensity E by $\pi/2$ radians, whereas the electron current *lags* by the same angle, the displacement and electron currents are π radians out phase, and the total current is *less* than if there were no electrons present. For example, if there is an ionized gas between the plates of a capacitor, the total current density is

$$\frac{\partial D}{\partial t} + J = j\omega\epsilon_0 E - j\frac{N_e Q_e^2}{\omega m_e}E,\tag{10-148}$$

$$= j\omega\epsilon_0\left(1 - \frac{N_e Q_e^2}{\omega^2\epsilon_0 m_e}\right)E.\tag{10-149}$$

This is illustrated in Figure 10-3.

We have here a resonance phenomenon which makes the total current zero at a certain critical value of ω. This case is mathematically similar to that in which an alternating voltage is applied to a capacitor and an inductor connected in parallel, as in Figure 10-4. The total current is given by

$$I = \mathcal{V}j\omega C + \frac{\mathcal{V}}{j\omega L},\tag{10-150}$$

$$= j\omega C\left(1 - \frac{1}{\omega^2 LC}\right)\mathcal{V}.\tag{10-151}$$

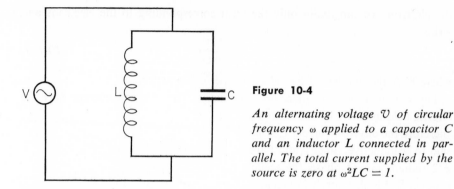

Figure 10-4

An alternating voltage $\mathcal{V}$ of circular frequency ω applied to a capacitor C and an inductor L connected in parallel. The total current supplied by the source is zero at $\omega^2 LC = 1$.

At resonance, both currents remain finite, but they are equal and opposite in sign, with the result that the total current is zero.

10.5.2. The Plasma Angular Frequency ω_p. The ratio of the convection to the displacement current density is

$$\left| \frac{J}{\partial D / \partial t} \right| = \frac{N_e Q_e^2}{\omega^2 \epsilon_0 m_e} = \frac{\omega_p^2}{\omega^2}, \tag{10-152}$$

where

$$\omega_p = \left(\frac{N_e Q_e^2}{\epsilon_0 m_e} \right)^{1/2} \tag{10-153}$$

is called the *plasma angular frequency*. This quantity depends solely on the properties of the gas considered. It corresponds to a frequency

$$f_p = 8.98 N_e^{1/2} \text{ cycles/second.} \tag{10-154}$$

In the plasma of a gas discharge, N_e is typically of the order of 10^{18} electrons/meter³, and f_p is about 10^4 megacycles/second, whereas in the ionosphere N_e is of the order of 10^{11} electrons/meter³ and f_p is about 3 megacycles/second.

Let us investigate further this resonance in ionized gases. The phenomena involved are complex and little understood, but it will nevertheless be instructive to study the plasma frequency ω_p using the following simple model. We consider a neutral ionized gas. The ions being much heavier than the electrons, we shall investigate group motions of the electrons in the *absence* of an electromagnetic wave, assuming that the ions remain essentially fixed in position. We neglect thermal agitation. Under these conditions, the charge density due to the ions is uniform throughout the volume considered, while the electron density N_e can vary from point to point.

Let us assume that the electrons move in the direction of the z-axis distances $\zeta(z_0)$ as in Figure 10-5, $\zeta(z_0)$ being a function only of the original value z_0 of the coordinate z. We make no assumption as to the function $\zeta(z_0)$. Then an electron originally at z_0 moves out to

$$z = z_0 + \zeta(z_0), \tag{10-155}$$

while an electron at $z_0 + dz_0$ moves out to

$$z + dz = z_0 + dz_0 + \zeta(z_0 + dz_0), \tag{10-156}$$

$$= z_0 + dz_0 + \zeta(z_0) + \left(\frac{d\zeta}{dz}\right)_{z_0} dz_0. \tag{10-157}$$

In this process, the charge originally occupying an element of volume of thickness dz_0 and area S comes to occupy a volume

$$\left[dz_0 + \left(\frac{d\zeta}{dz}\right)_{z_0} dz_0\right] S,$$

and the electron density at z is changed from N_e to

$$N_e' = \frac{N_e}{1 + \left(\dfrac{d\zeta}{dz}\right)_z}. \tag{10-158}$$

Assuming now that the displacement ζ is everywhere small and that it varies smoothly with x, we can set

$$\left(\frac{d\zeta}{dz}\right)_{z_0} \approx \left(\frac{d\zeta}{dz}\right) \ll 1, \tag{10-159}$$

and

$$N_e' = N_e\left(1 - \frac{d\zeta}{dz}\right). \tag{10-160}$$

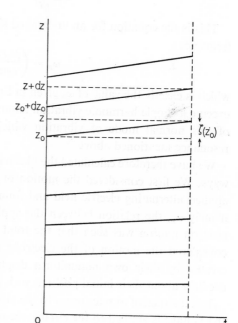

Figure 10-5

The vertical line on the left at $t = 0$ shows schematically the initial uniform distribution of the electrons along the z-axis at positions labeled z_0. The vertical line on the right shows the new distribution for a positive displacement ζ increasing gradually with z_0. The new positions are labeled z. We have assumed for simplicity that ζ increases uniformly with z; however, ζ can be any continuous function of z.

Then the net charge density is

$$\rho = \sum_i N_i Q_i - N_e Q_e \left(1 - \frac{d\zeta}{dz}\right), \tag{10-161}$$

$$= N_e Q_e \frac{d\zeta}{dz}, \tag{10-162}$$

where Q_e is a positive quantity. The first two terms cancel because the net charge density is zero, on the average. The net charge density ρ is positive if $d\zeta/dz$ is positive, because the electrons are then spread out.

From the Maxwell equation 10-4, this net charge density gives rise to an electric field such that

$$\frac{dE}{dz} = \frac{N_e Q_e}{\epsilon_0} \frac{d\zeta}{dz}. \tag{10-163}$$

Integrating and neglecting uniform fields, we find that

$$E_z = \frac{N_e Q_e}{\epsilon_0} \zeta. \tag{10-164}$$

The electric field intensity is thus proportional to ζ, and

$$m_e \frac{d^2 z}{dt^2} = -\frac{N_e Q_e^2}{\epsilon_0} \zeta, \tag{10-165}$$

or, since $z = z_0 + \zeta$, where z_0 is the original position and is a constant, we have

$$m_e \frac{d^2 \zeta}{dt^2} = -\frac{N_e Q_e^2}{\epsilon_0} \zeta. \tag{10-166}$$

This is the equation for an undamped simple harmonic vibration of angular frequency

$$\omega_p = \left(\frac{N_e Q_e^2}{\epsilon_0 m_e}\right)^{1/2}, \tag{10-167}$$

which is exactly the value of ω_p given in Eq. 10-153. Each electron can therefore execute a simple harmonic vibration about its initial position. It is the existence of this normal mode of vibration which gives rise to the phenomenon of resonance mentioned above.

We have therefore calculated the plasma angular frequency ω_p in two different ways. We first considered the motion of the electrons under the action of an applied alternating electric field and found that for one particular value of ω, namely ω_p, the relation between the applied electric field E and the resulting electron motion was such that the total current was equal to zero. We then considered the motion of the electrons under the action of the electric field created by their own nonuniform displacement and found that they could oscillate about their initial position with the angular frequency ω_p.

It is instructive to refer again to the circuit of Figure 10-4. When an alternating voltage is applied to the circuit, the current through the capacitor and that through the inductor both remain finite but become equal and opposite in sign at the resonant frequency. But if the source is removed, and if the circuit is excited in some way, for example, by inducing a sudden voltage in the inductor, then the circuit will oscillate at this same resonant frequency. The resistance in the circuit is assumed to be zero. The resonance phenomenon observed when an alternating electric field is applied to an ionized gas is thus analogous to parallel resonance in an electric circuit.

We can also calculate ω_p in the following manner. If we assume that the electron density can oscillate at some angular frequency ω_p, the resulting electric field intensity E will oscillate at the same frequency. Then we can use Eq. *10-147* for the conductivity σ of the ionized gas. Now Eq. *5-92* for the free charge density ρ is perfectly general and assumes only the conservation of charge and Ohm's law: $\mathbf{J} = \sigma\mathbf{E}$. Substituting the value of σ and setting $K_e = 1$, we find that

$$\rho = \rho_0 \exp\left[j(N_e Q_e^2/\omega_p m_e \epsilon_0)t\right]. \qquad (10\text{-}168)$$

The imaginary exponent shows that ρ oscillates, as expected, at an angular frequency given by the coefficient of jt. This angular frequency must again be ω_p, and

$$\omega_p = \left(\frac{N_e Q_e^2}{m_e \epsilon_0}\right)^{1/2} \qquad (10\text{-}169)$$

as previously.

10.5.3. Wave Propagation at High Frequencies Where $\omega > \omega_p$.

We may use the wave number k for a medium of conductivity σ as given by Eq. *10-55*. We set $K_e = 1$, $K_m = 1$, and substitute the value of σ from Eq. *10-147*. Then

$$k = \pm\frac{\left(1 - \dfrac{N_e Q_e^2}{\omega^2 \epsilon_0 m_e}\right)^{1/2}}{\lambda_0}, \qquad (10\text{-}170)$$

$$= \pm\frac{\left[1 - \left(\dfrac{\omega_p}{\omega}\right)^2\right]^{1/2}}{\lambda_0}, \qquad (10\text{-}171)$$

and

$$\mathbf{E} = E_0 e^{j(\omega t - kz)}\,\mathbf{i}. \qquad (10\text{-}172)$$

It is to be understood that we must use the positive value of k to describe a wave traveling in the positive direction of the z-axis. From the general relationship for E/H, Eq. *10-24*, we have

$$H = \frac{k}{\omega\mu} E \qquad (10\text{-}173)$$

$$= \left(\frac{\epsilon_0}{\mu_0}\right)^{1/2}\left[1 - \left(\frac{\omega_p}{\omega}\right)^2\right]^{1/2} E_0 e^{j(\omega t - kz)}. \qquad (10\text{-}174)$$

Now let us consider the case of high frequencies where $\omega > \omega_p$. Then the wave number k is real and the **E** and **H** vectors are in phase, the ratio E/H being larger than in free space by a factor of $1/[1 - (\omega_p/\omega)^2]$. As $\omega \longrightarrow \omega_p$, $H \longrightarrow 0$ as expected, since the total current density $J + (\partial D/\partial t) \longrightarrow 0$, and the Poynting vector $S \longrightarrow 0$. The index of refraction is given by

$$n = \left[1 - \left(\frac{\omega_p}{\omega}\right)^2\right]^{1/2}, \tag{10-175}$$

$$= \left[1 - 80.5 \frac{N_e}{f^2}\right]^{1/2}, \tag{10-176}$$

and the phase velocity by

$$u = \frac{c}{\left[1 - \left(\frac{\omega_p}{\omega}\right)^2\right]^{1/2}}. \tag{10-177}$$

For high frequencies where $\omega > \omega_p$, the phase velocity u is therefore *greater* than the velocity of light, the wave number k is real, and there is no attenuation.

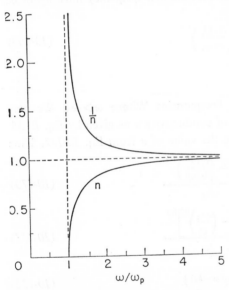

Figure 10-6 shows both n and $1/n$ as functions of ω/ω_p. Since the phase velocity increases with increasing ion density, waves tend to bend away from regions of high ion density. For high frequencies where $\omega^2 \gg \omega^2_p$, the transmission is unaffected by the presence of ionized gas.

The index of refraction and the wave velocity which we have discussed above refer to the *phase velocity*, that is, to the velocity at which a given phase is propagated. This is *not* the velocity at which a *signal* can be transmitted. The reason for this is the following. A signal can be transmitted only if the wave is modulated either in amplitude or in frequency. For example, the source may operate in short bursts of variable length as in telegraphy, or the amplitude may change at an acoustic frequency as in amplitude-modulation radio broadcasting,

Figure 10-6. *The index of refraction n for an ionized gas and its inverse 1/n as functions of the ratio* ω/ω_p.

or the frequency may change as in frequency-modulation broadcasting. Since changes in amplitude necessarily involve frequencies other than the carrier frequency, a signal necessarily involves more than one frequency. In other words, a single frequency corresponds to a pure sine wave extending from $t = -\infty$ to $t = +\infty$ which can transmit no information. Since the phase velocity in an ionized gas is frequency dependent, the various frequency components of a signal are transmitted at different velocities. The result is that a signal travels at a velocity which is different from those of its component waves. It has been shown that a signal can never be transmitted at a velocity exceeding the velocity of light in free space, c.* Moreover, since the component waves travel at different velocities, the shape of the signal, that is, the envelope of the wave, changes with time as the waves progress through the dispersive medium.

10.5.4. Wave Propagation at Low Frequencies Where $\omega < \omega_p$. For $\omega < \omega_p$, the wave number k of Eq. *10-171* is a pure imaginary number. The vectors **E** and **H** are then out of phase by $\pi/2$ radians, and E/H is again larger than in free space. The Poynting vector $\mathbf{S} = (1/2)\,\mathrm{Re}\,(\mathbf{E} \times \mathbf{H}^*)$ is zero, and there is no energy transmission.

The index of refraction and the wave velocity are also imaginary, and

$$\mathbf{E} = \mathbf{E}_0 e^{j\omega t - k'z}, \qquad (10\text{-}178)$$

$$\mathbf{H} = \mathbf{H}_0 e^{j\omega t - k'z}, \qquad (10\text{-}179)$$

where $k' = jk$ is a real number. Thus, there is no wave, the phases of E and of H being independent of z, and the amplitude decreases exponentially with z.

An electromagnetic wave is therefore either transmitted without attenuation or not transmitted at all through an ionized gas, depending on the ratio ω/ω_p. High frequencies are transmitted, whereas low frequencies are not. Our theory is however much simplified. In particular, we have neglected all energy losses, which is justifiable only at low gas pressures.

10.5.5. The Ionosphere. This region of the upper atmosphere ranges in altitude from approximately 50–1000 kilometers, where the ionization is sufficient to interfere with the propagation of electromagnetic waves. The ionization is attributed mostly to the ultraviolet radiation of the sun. On the whole, the ion density first increases with altitude and then decreases, but it shows "ledges" where the ion density varies more slowly with altitude. These ledges are commonly called the D, E, F_1, and F_2 *layers*. These maxima arise from the fact that both the nature of the solar radiation and the composition of the atmosphere change with altitude. Both the heights and the intensities of ionization of these layers change with the hour of the day, the season, the sunspot cycle, and so on. It appears that the conductivity σ is due almost exclusively to the electron density, except possibly near the lower limit of the ionosphere.

* Léon Brillouin, *Wave Propagation and Group Velocity* (Academic, New York, 1960).

The free electron density is typically 10^{11}/meter³, varying by about 10^{10} to 10^{12}/meter³ from the lowest to the highest layer. Over this range of altitudes, the number of molecules per cubic meter varies from about 10^{22} to 10^{15}. The percent ionization therefore increases very rapidly with altitude, but it always remains low. For $N_e = 10^{11}$/meter³, the plasma frequency $f_p \approx 3$ megacycles/second.

Frequencies lower than f_p are not transmitted. At frequencies somewhat higher than f_p, waves are bent back toward the earth, since ion densities generally increase with increasing height and since the phase velocity increases with increasing ion density.

The assumption that there are no collisions between the electrons and the gas atoms or molecules is satisfactory except in the lowest regions of the ionosphere where the pressure is highest, and at frequencies of the order of 1 megacycle/second or higher.

In the presence of the earth's magnetic field the ionized gas becomes doubly refracting, with the result that there are two distinct phase velocities, depending on whether the wave is polarized parallel to the magnetic induction vector or perpendicular to it.

10.6. Summary

In homogeneous, isotropic, linear, and stationary media, a plane electromagnetic wave has the following characteristics:

(1) $\rho = 0$ (Eq. *10-18*);
(2) both **E** and **H** are transverse (Eqs. *10-17* and *10-20*);
(3) **E** and **H** are mutually perpendicular;
(4) $E/H = \omega\mu/k$ (Eq. *10-24*);
(5) **E** and **H** are oriented such that their vector product **E** × **H** points in the direction of propagation.

In nonconductors, the phase velocity is

$$u = \frac{c}{(K_e K_m)^{1/2}}, \tag{10-27}$$

and, in nonmagnetic media ($K_m = 1$), the index of refraction n is related to the dielectric coefficient by the relation

$$n = K_e^{1/2}. \tag{10-29}$$

The vectors **E** and **H** are in phase, and the electric and magnetic energy densities are equal (Eq. *10-38*).

In conducting media we define the Q *of the medium* as

$$Q = \frac{\omega\epsilon}{\sigma}. \tag{10-49}$$

This is the modulus of the ratio of the displacement current density to the conduction current density. The wave number k is complex (Eq. *10-58*), and the **E** vector leads the **H** vector (Eq. *10-67*). The average value of the *Poynting vector* is then given by

$$S_{av.} = \frac{1}{2} \, \mathrm{Re} \, (\mathbf{E} \times \mathbf{H^*}), \qquad (10\text{-}88)$$

which is the product of the average energy density by the phase velocity.

Good conductors are defined as media for which

$$Q \leq \frac{1}{50}. \qquad (10\text{-}93)$$

Then

$$k = \frac{1 - j}{\delta}, \qquad (10\text{-}101)$$

where the *attenuation distance* is given by

$$\delta = \lambda = \left(\frac{2}{\omega\sigma\mu}\right)^{1/2}. \qquad (10\text{-}102)$$

The attenuation is so rapid that the wave is hardly discernible (Figure 10-1). The **E** vector leads the **H** vector by $\pi/4$ radian, and

$$\frac{E}{H} = \left(\frac{\omega\mu}{\sigma}\right)^{1/2} e^{j\pi/4}. \qquad (10\text{-}105)$$

Most of the energy is in the magnetic form.

In a low-pressure ionized gas, the ions move almost exclusively under the action of the electric field, and the *conductivity* σ, defined by

$$\sigma E = J, \qquad (10\text{-}142)$$

is imaginary:

$$\sigma = -j \frac{N_e Q_e^2}{\omega m_e}, \qquad (10\text{-}147)$$

where N_e is the number of electrons per cubic meter, Q_e is the charge of the electron, and m_e its mass. The total current density is *less* than in free space:

$$\frac{\partial D}{\partial t} + J = j\omega\epsilon_0 \left[1 - \left(\frac{\omega_p}{\omega}\right)^2\right] E, \qquad (10\text{-}149)$$

where

$$\omega_p = \left(\frac{N_e Q_e^2}{\epsilon_0 m_e}\right)^{1/2} \qquad (10\text{-}153)$$

is the *plasma angular frequency*.

At high frequencies where $\omega^2 \gg \omega_p^2$, the wave is unaffected by the presence of the ionized gas. As the frequency decreases, the attenuation remains equal to zero, and the phase velocity increases to values greater than c until it becomes equal to infinity at $\omega = \omega_p$. For lower frequencies, the wave number is imaginary, the field is attenuated exponentially with z, and there is no wave.

Problems

10-1. For static fields, Eq. *10-9* gives

$$\nabla^2 \mathbf{D} = \nabla \rho,$$

and thus, from Eq. *10-4*,

$$\nabla \cdot \nabla \mathbf{D} = \nabla (\nabla \cdot \mathbf{D}).$$

Expand in Cartesian coordinates, and show that these two quantities must be equal for static fields.

10-2. The quantity

$$K_e - j \frac{\sigma}{\omega \epsilon_0}$$

is called the complex dielectric coefficient of a medium. Justify the use of this term.

10-3. It was shown in Eq. *5-92* that the charge density ρ in a conductor decreases exponentially with a relaxation time of ϵ/σ:

$$\rho = \rho_0 e^{-\sigma t/\epsilon}.$$

Show that Q must be at most about $1/3$ if ρ/ρ_0 is to be less than 1% within one-fourth of a period.

10-4. Show that, for good conductors,

$$\nabla^2 \mathbf{J} = \sigma \mu \frac{\partial \mathbf{J}}{\partial t},$$

whereas

$$\nabla^2 \mathbf{A} - \epsilon \mu \frac{\partial^2 \mathbf{A}}{\partial t^2} = -\mu \mathbf{J}$$

applies both to good and poor conductors.

10-5. Calculate the attenuation of an electromagnetic wave in sea water and in copper at 20 kilocycles/second and at 20 megacycles/second. State your result in decibels/foot.

10-6. Compare the ratios E/H for an electromagnetic wave in air and in sea water at 20 kilocycles/second.

10-7. Show that the index of refraction n, the attenuation distance δ and the Q of a good conductor are related by the following equations:

$$Q\delta^2 = \frac{2\epsilon}{\mu \sigma^2},$$

$$\frac{Q}{\delta^2} = \frac{K_e K_m}{2\lambda_0^2},$$

$$Qn^2 = \frac{K_e K_m}{2}.$$

Show that the minimum value of n is 5 for "good" conductors.

10-8. Discuss the propagation of a plane electromagnetic wave in a medium where (a) $Q = 1$, (b) $Q^2 \gg 1$.

10-9. Show that $S_{av.}$ is equal to the average energy density multiplied by the phase velocity, whatever the medium.

10-10. It is interesting to draw a parallel between the transfer of heat in a thermally conducting medium and the propagation of an electric or magnetic field in an electrically conducting medium. Letting $\mathbf{I}$ be the heat flux density in watts/meter², we have

$$\mathbf{I} = -K\nabla T,$$

where K is the thermal conductivity in watts/meter-°K and T is the temperature. Then, for conservation of energy,

$$\nabla \cdot \mathbf{I} = -\rho c \frac{\partial T}{\partial t} + Q,$$

where ρ is the density in kilograms/meter³, c is the specific heat in joules/kilogram-°K, and Q is the heat produced within the medium in watts/meter³. Then, setting $Q = 0$, we obtain

$$\nabla^2 T - \frac{\rho c}{K} \frac{\partial T}{\partial t} = 0.$$

This equation is identical in form to that for an electromagnetic wave in a good conductor, $\rho c/K$ corresponding to $\mu\sigma$. Its solution for heat flow in one dimension is entirely similar to Eq. *10-107:*

$$T = T_0 \exp\left[j\left(\omega t - \frac{z}{\delta_t}\right) - \frac{z}{\delta_t}\right],$$

where

$$\delta_t = \sqrt{\frac{2}{\omega} \frac{K}{\rho c}}.$$

Compare the velocities of propagation of T and of H in copper and in iron.

Property	Copper	Iron	Units
σ	5.8×10^7	1.0×10^7	mhos/meter
c	0.092	0.11	calories/gram-°C
ρ	8.9	7.9	grams/centimeter³
K	1.0	0.15	calories/second-centimeter-°C
K_m	1.0	200	

10-11. Using the values of $\mathbf{E}$ and of $\mathbf{H}$ which we have found for plane electromagnetic waves in good conductors, verify that all of Maxwell's equations apply.

10-12. A plane parallel capacitor of capacitance C is immersed in an ionized gas with a plasma angular frequency ω_p. End effects can be neglected. Show that the ionized gas has the same effect as a parallel inductance $L = 1/\omega_p^2 C$.

10-13. A mass m slides on a frictionless horizontal surface under the action of a spring of stiffness (stretching force/elongation) k fixed to a rigid support and of a force $F = F_0 \cos \omega t$ in line with the spring. Show that this mechanical system is mathematically equivalent to a series resonant electric circuit.

Discuss the amplitudes of the displacement and of the velocity as functions of ω.

10-14. A mass m slides on a horizontal frictionless surface under the action of a force $F = F_0 \cos \omega t$ which is applied to it through a spring of stiffness k.

Show that this mechanical system is mathematically equivalent to a parallel resonant circuit. Discuss the amplitudes and the velocities of the two ends of the spring as functions of ω.

10-15. Two different plane electromagnetic waves of equal amplitude propagate in the ionosphere where the electron density is N_e electrons/meter³. One wave has a circular frequency ω_1 and a corresponding wavelength λ_1; the other has a slightly different circular frequency ω_2 and a wavelength λ_2.

At a given time t there exist values of z for which the two waves are in phase and values of z for which they are opposite in phase. What is the distance between the maxima? What is their velocity? This velocity is called the *group velocity* u_g.

Show that, in the limit,

$$u_g = \frac{1}{\dfrac{d}{d\omega}\left(\dfrac{2\pi}{\lambda}\right)}.$$

Show that

$$u_p u_g = c^2,$$

where u_p is the phase velocity given in Eq. *10-177*.

Calculate the phase velocities and the group velocity for $f_1 = 5.3$ megacycles/second, $f_2 = 5.4$ megacycles/second, and $N_e = 5 \times 10^{10}$ electrons/meter³. Calculate the distance and the number of waves between two minima. What happens to the group as N_e increases?

CHAPTER 11

Reflection
and Refraction

In Chapter 10 we considered the propagation of electromagnetic waves in infinite, continuous media. We shall now examine the effect of a discontinuity in the medium of propagation, as shown in Figure 11-1.

We shall investigate again the same three types of media as in Chapter 10: lossless dielectrics, good conductors, and low-pressure ionized gases.

We assume an ideally thin, infinite, plane interface between two homogeneous, isotropic media. Then an incident wave along $\mathbf{n}_i$, as shown in Figure 11-1, gives rise to both a reflected wave along $\mathbf{n}_r$ and a transmitted wave along $\mathbf{n}_t$. We also assume that media 1 and 2 are infinite so that there are no multiple reflections. We shall show that, in general, all three waves are required to satisfy the condition of continuity for the tangential components of $\mathbf{E}$ and of $\mathbf{H}$. For the time being, we shall exclude the subject of total reflection; this will be discussed later in Section 11.4.

This general type of phenomenon is frequently encountered in other fields. For example, a sound wave incident upon a wall results in both a reflected wave which comes back into the room and a transmitted wave which proceeds into the wall. This phenomenon is also well known in electrical transmission lines at points where one type of line is connected to another, for example, at a junction between two different types of coaxial cable. Waves on strings show the same type of behavior (Appendix G). It is *not* suggested, however, that the student attempt to treat acoustical and electrical reflections by the methods used in this chapter.

11.1. The Laws of Reflection and Snell's Law of Refraction

If we assume that the incident electromagnetic wave is planar, then its electric field intensity $\mathbf{E}_i$ is of the form

$$\mathbf{E}_i = \mathbf{E}_{oi} \exp\left[j(\omega t - k_1 \mathbf{n}_i \cdot \mathbf{r})\right] \qquad (11\text{-}1)$$

(see Appendix G). The time $t = 0$ and the origin $\mathbf{r} = 0$ can be chosen arbitrarily. This equation defines a plane wave for all values of t and for all values of $\mathbf{r}$, that is, a wave which extends throughout all time and all space. However, it will be taken to be applicable only in medium 1.

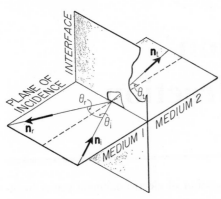

If the incident wave is planar, then both the reflected and the refracted waves from a plane interface must also be planar, since the laws of reflection and of refraction for any given incident ray must be the same at all points on the interface. Then the reflected and the transmitted waves are given by

$$\mathbf{E}_r = \mathbf{E}_{or} \exp\left[j(\omega_r t - k_1 \mathbf{n}_r \cdot \mathbf{r} + A)\right], \qquad (11\text{-}2)$$

$$\mathbf{E}_t = \mathbf{E}_{ot} \exp\left[j(\omega_t t - k_2 \mathbf{n}_t \cdot \mathbf{r} + B)\right], \qquad (11\text{-}3)$$

where the constants A and B allow for possible phase differences with the incident wave at the interface. Note that we have made no assumption whatever as to the amplitudes, phases, frequencies, or directions of the reflected and transmitted waves.

Figure 11-1. *An electromagnetic wave in medium 1 is incident on the interface between media 1 and 2 and gives rise to both a reflected and a transmitted wave. The vectors $\mathbf{n}_i$, $\mathbf{n}_r$, and $\mathbf{n}_t$ are unit vectors normal to the respective wave fronts, and point in the direction of propagation. The angles θ_i, θ_r, and θ_t are, respectively, the angles of incidence, of reflection, and of refraction. (Radio engineers use a different convention and call the complementary angles $(\pi/2) - \theta_i$, $(\pi/2) - \theta_r$, and $(\pi/2) - \theta_t$ the angles of incidence, of reflection, and of refraction, respectively.) Total reflection will be treated separately in Section 11.4.*

We shall be able to determine the characteristics of both the reflected and the transmitted waves from the fact that the tangential component of $\mathbf{E}$ and the tangential component of $\mathbf{H}$ must both be continuous across the interface (Sections 4.1.3 and 7.8). Then the sum of the tangential components of $\mathbf{E}_i$ and $\mathbf{E}_r$ just above the interface must be equal to the tangential component of $\mathbf{E}_t$ just below the interface; a similar situation holds for the magnetic field intensity $\mathbf{H}$. The reflected and the transmitted waves could also be obtained from the continuity of the *normal* components of **D** and of **B** across the interface.

To obtain continuity of the tangential components of **E** and of **H** at the interface, some valid relation must exist between $\mathbf{E}_i$, $\mathbf{E}_r$, and $\mathbf{E}_t$ for all time t and for all vectors $\mathbf{r}_I$ which terminate on the interface, as in Figure 11-2. Such a relation will be possible (a) if all three vectors $\mathbf{E}_i$, $\mathbf{E}_r$, and $\mathbf{E}_t$ are identical functions of the time t and of position $\mathbf{r}_I$ on the interface, and (b) if there exist certain relations between $\mathbf{E}_{oi}$, $\mathbf{E}_{or}$, and $\mathbf{E}_{ot}$.

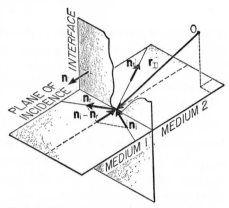

Let us start with the first condition. We must have

$$\omega_i t - k_1 \mathbf{n}_i \cdot \mathbf{r}_I = \omega_r t - k_1 \mathbf{n}_r \cdot \mathbf{r}_I + A$$
$$= \omega_t t - k_2 \mathbf{n}_t \cdot \mathbf{r}_I + B \quad (11\text{-}4)$$

Figure 11-2. *The projection of $\mathbf{r}_I$ on $\mathbf{n}_i - \mathbf{n}_r$ is a constant at any point on the interface, that is, for any value of $\mathbf{r}_I$. The vector $\mathbf{n}$ is normal to the interface.*

for all t and for all $\mathbf{r}_I$. It follows, then, that

$$\omega_i = \omega_r = \omega_t. \qquad (11\text{-}5)$$

All three waves must therefore be of the same frequency. This is intuitively quite obvious, since they are all superpositions of the wave emitted by the source and of those waves emitted by the electrons executing forced vibrations in media 1 and 2. It will be recalled from mechanics that forced vibrations have the same frequency as the applied force.

From Eq. *11-4* we must also have, at any point $\mathbf{r}_I$ on the interface,

$$k_1 \mathbf{n}_i \cdot \mathbf{r}_I = k_1 \mathbf{n}_r \cdot \mathbf{r}_I - A, \qquad (11\text{-}6)$$
$$= k_2 \mathbf{n}_t \cdot \mathbf{r}_I - B. \qquad (11\text{-}7)$$

Then, from the first of these equations,

$$(\mathbf{n}_i - \mathbf{n}_r) \cdot \mathbf{r}_I = -\frac{A}{k_1}, \qquad (11\text{-}8)$$

where the term A/k_1 on the right-hand side is a constant for all $\mathbf{r}_I$. That is, the projection on $(\mathbf{n}_i - \mathbf{n}_r)$ of any vector $\mathbf{r}_I$ terminating on the interface must be a constant. The vector $(\mathbf{n}_i - \mathbf{n}_r)$ is also a constant for any given incident plane wave. Then $\mathbf{n}_i - \mathbf{n}_r$ must be normal to the interface, as in Figure 11-2. The interface itself is defined by

$$\mathbf{n} \cdot \mathbf{r}_I = \text{Constant}, \qquad (11\text{-}9)$$

where **n** is a unit vector normal to the interface.

Since $\mathbf{n}_i - \mathbf{n}_r$ is normal to the interface, the tangential components of these two vectors must be equal and opposite in sign as in Figure 11-2. Then

$$\theta_i = \theta_r, \qquad (11\text{-}10)$$

or *the angle of reflection is equal to the angle of incidence.* We also conclude that *the vectors $\mathbf{n}_i$, $\mathbf{n}_r$, and $\mathbf{n}$ are coplanar,* since $(\mathbf{n}_i - \mathbf{n}_r)$ and $\mathbf{n}$ are parallel. These are the *laws of reflection.* The plane of the above three vectors is called the *plane of incidence;* it is normal to the interface.

Considering now Eq. *11-7,* we have

$$(k_1\mathbf{n}_i - k_2\mathbf{n}_t)\cdot\mathbf{r}_I = -B, \qquad (11\text{-}11)$$

hence the vector $k_1\mathbf{n}_i - k_2\mathbf{n}_t$ must also be normal to the interface, so that $\mathbf{n}_i$, $\mathbf{n}_t$, and $\mathbf{n}$ are coplanar; thus *all four vectors $\mathbf{n}_i$, $\mathbf{n}_r$, $\mathbf{n}_t$, and $\mathbf{n}$ are in the plane of incidence.* Moreover, the tangential components of $k_1\mathbf{n}_i$ and of $k_2\mathbf{n}_t$ must be equal, hence

$$k_1 \sin \theta_i = k_2 \sin \theta_t. \qquad (11\text{-}12)$$

The quantity $k \sin \theta$ is therefore conserved in crossing the interface. We can also write that

$$\frac{\sin \theta_t}{\sin \theta_i} = \frac{k_1}{k_2}, \qquad (11\text{-}13)$$

$$= \frac{n_1}{n_2}, \qquad (11\text{-}14)$$

since the wave number $k = n/\lambda_0$, where n is the index of refraction. This is *Snell's law.* It is important to note that this law, as well as the laws of reflection, are perfectly general. They apply to *any* two media—they even hold true for total reflection, as will be shown later on.

The constants A and B in the above equations are related to the choice of the origin, as can be seen from Eqs. *11-2* and *11-3:* at a given point on the interface and at a given time, the reflected and the transmitted waves have definite phases which are represented by the coefficients of j in the exponents; if the origin is displaced, A and B must be adjusted accordingly. It turns out that if the origin is chosen in the interface, A and B both become equal to zero. This will be shown in Problem 11-1.

If we choose the origin in the interface and place axes as shown in Figure

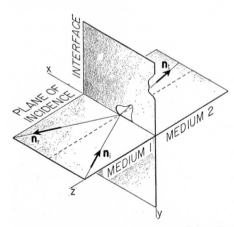

Figure 11-3. *System of axes used for the study of reflection and refraction.*

11-3, then $A = B = 0$, and the expressions for $\mathbf{E}_i$, $\mathbf{E}_r$, and $\mathbf{E}_t$ can be written as follows:

$$\mathbf{E}_i = \mathbf{E}_{oi} \exp\{j[\omega t - k_1(\sin\theta_i\, x - \cos\theta_i\, z)]\}, \qquad (11\text{-}15)$$

$$\mathbf{E}_r = \mathbf{E}_{or} \exp\{j[\omega t - k_1(\sin\theta_i\, x + \cos\theta_i\, z)]\}, \qquad (11\text{-}16)$$

$$\mathbf{E}_t = \mathbf{E}_{ot} \exp\{j[\omega t - k_2(\sin\theta_t\, x - \cos\theta_t\, z)]\}. \qquad (11\text{-}17)$$

11.2. Fresnel's Equations

We shall turn now to the second condition mentioned in the preceding section. We must find the relations between the quantities $\mathbf{E}_{oi}$, $\mathbf{E}_{or}$, $\mathbf{E}_{ot}$ which will ensure continuity of the tangential components of $\mathbf{E}$ and of $\mathbf{H}$ at the interface.

We recall from Section 10.1.1 that the $\mathbf{E}$ and $\mathbf{H}$ vectors in a plane electromagnetic wave are always perpendicular to the direction of propagation and to each other. The $\mathbf{E}$ vector of the incident wave can thus be oriented in any direction perpendicular to the vector $\mathbf{n}_i$.

It will be convenient to divide the discussion into two parts. We shall

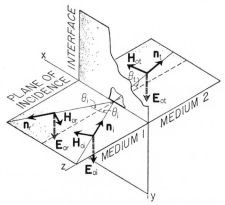

Figure 11-4. *The incident, reflected, and transmitted waves for the case in which the incident wave is polarized with its* $\mathbf{E}$ *vector normal to the plane of incidence. The arrows for* $\mathbf{E}$ *and for* $\mathbf{H}$ *indicate the directions in which the* $\mathbf{E}$ *and* $\mathbf{H}$ *vectors are taken to be positive at the interface.*

first consider the case in which the incident wave is polarized such that its $\mathbf{E}$ vector is normal to the plane of incidence and then consider the case in which its $\mathbf{E}$ vector is parallel to the plane of incidence. Any incident wave can be separated into two such components.

11.2.1. Incident Wave Polarized with Its E Vector Normal to the Plane of Incidence.
The $\mathbf{E}$ and the $\mathbf{H}$ vectors of the incident wave are oriented as in Figure 11-4. If the media are isotropic, as we assumed at the beginning of this chapter, the $\mathbf{E}$ vectors of both the reflected and the transmitted waves will also be perpendicular to the plane of incidence, as in Figure 11-4.

Considering the electric and magnetic field intensities of the incident wave to be known, we now have four unknowns: E_{or}, E_{ot}, H_{or}, and H_{ot}. We also have a total of four equations which are provided (a) by the continuity of the tangential components of both the $\mathbf{E}$ and $\mathbf{H}$ vectors at the interface and (b) by the relations between the $\mathbf{E}$ and $\mathbf{H}$ vectors for plane waves in medium 1 and in medium 2 as given in Eq. *10-24*. It will suffice, for the moment, to calculate only the **E** vectors.

Instead of using the continuity of the tangential components of **E** and **H**, we could also use the continuity of the normal components of **D** and of **B**. This is not desirable, however, because if we did so, and if we wished our results to be applicable to reflection from the surface of a conductor, we would have to take the surface charge density into account. This would introduce another unknown.

The continuity of the tangential component of the electric field intensity at the interface requires that

$$E_{oi} + E_{or} = E_{ot} \tag{11-18}$$

at any given time and at any given point on the interface. Similarly, the continuity of the magnetic field intensity requires that

$$H_{oi} \cos \theta_i - H_{or} \cos \theta_i = H_{ot} \cos \theta_t, \tag{11-19}$$

or, from Eq. *10-24*,

$$\frac{k_1}{\omega \mu_1}(E_{oi} - E_{or}) \cos \theta_i = \frac{k_2}{\omega \mu_2} E_{ot} \cos \theta_t. \tag{11-20}$$

Thus

$$\left(\frac{E_{or}}{E_{oi}}\right)_N = \frac{\frac{n_1}{K_{m1}}\cos \theta_i - \frac{n_2}{K_{m2}}\cos \theta_t}{\frac{n_1}{K_{m1}}\cos \theta_i + \frac{n_2}{K_{m2}}\cos \theta_t}, \tag{11-21}$$

and

$$\left(\frac{E_{ot}}{E_{oi}}\right)_N = \frac{2\frac{n_1}{K_{m1}}\cos \theta_i}{\frac{n_1}{K_{m1}}\cos \theta_i + \frac{n_2}{K_{m2}}\cos \theta_t}, \tag{11-22}$$

where the index N indicates that E_{oi} is normal to the plane of incidence. We have replaced the wave numbers k by the indices of refraction, one being proportional to the other: $k = n/\lambda_0$, where λ_0 is the free space wavelength divided by 2π.

These are two of *Fresnel's equations;* the other pair will be deduced in the next section. Fresnel's equations give the ratios of the amplitudes of the incident, reflected, and transmitted waves. They are completely general and apply to *any* two media. We shall show later on that they are valid even for total reflection and for reflection from the surface of a good conductor.

11.2.2. Fresnel's Equations for the Case Where the Incident Wave Is Polarized with Its E Vector Parallel to the Plane of Incidence. In this case the E vectors of all three waves must be in the plane of incidence as in Figure 11-5. We have chosen the orientations of **E**$_{or}$ and of **E**$_{ot}$ such that Figures 11-4 and

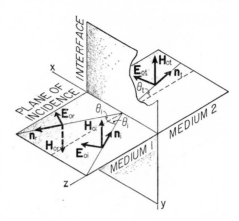

Figure 11-5

*The incident, reflected, and transmitted waves in the case where the incident wave is polarized with its **E** vector parallel to the plane of incidence. The arrows for **E** and for **H** have the same meaning as in Figure 11-4.*

11-5 become identical at normal incidence, except for a rotation of 90 degrees around the normal to the interface.

We now have

$$H_{oi} - H_{or} = H_{ot},\qquad(11\text{-}23)$$

or

$$\frac{k_1}{\omega\mu_1}(E_{oi} - E_{or}) = \frac{k_2}{\omega\mu_2}E_{ot},\qquad(11\text{-}24)$$

and

$$(E_{oi} + E_{or})\cos\theta_i = E_{ot}\cos\theta_t.\qquad(11\text{-}25)$$

Then, solving for E_{or} and E_{ot}, we obtain

$$\left(\frac{E_{or}}{E_{oi}}\right)_P = \frac{-\left(\dfrac{n_2}{K_{m2}}\right)\cos\theta_i + \left(\dfrac{n_1}{K_{m1}}\right)\cos\theta_t}{\left(\dfrac{n_2}{K_{m2}}\right)\cos\theta_i + \left(\dfrac{n_1}{K_{m1}}\right)\cos\theta_t},\qquad(11\text{-}26)$$

$$\left(\frac{E_{ot}}{E_{oi}}\right)_P = \frac{2\left(\dfrac{n_1}{K_{m1}}\right)\cos\theta_i}{\left(\dfrac{n_2}{K_{m2}}\right)\cos\theta_i + \left(\dfrac{n_1}{K_{m1}}\right)\cos\theta_t}.\qquad(11\text{-}27)$$

Equations *11-21, 11-22, 11-26,* and *11-27* are the four *equations of Fresnel.*

At normal incidence $\theta_i = 0$, the plane of incidence becomes undetermined, and both sets of Fresnel's equations give the same result:

$$\frac{E_{or}}{E_{oi}} = \frac{-\dfrac{n_2}{K_{m2}} + \dfrac{n_1}{K_{m1}}}{\dfrac{n_2}{K_{m2}} + \dfrac{n_1}{K_{m1}}},\qquad(11\text{-}28)$$

and

$$\frac{E_{ot}}{E_{oi}} = \frac{2\dfrac{n_1}{K_{m1}}}{\dfrac{n_2}{K_{m2}} + \dfrac{n_1}{K_{m1}}}.\qquad(11\text{-}29)$$

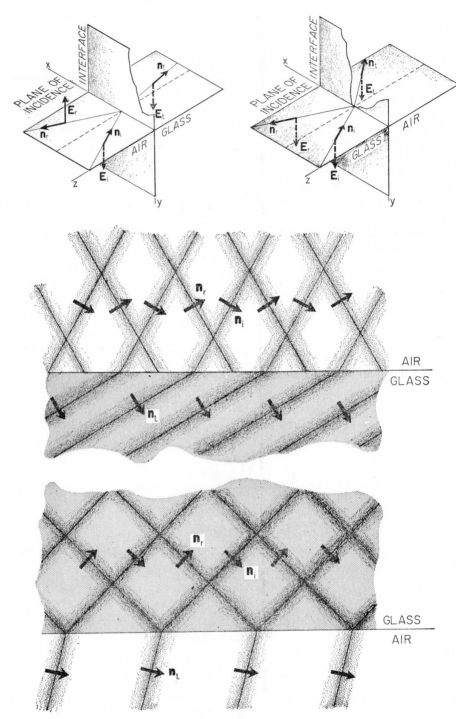

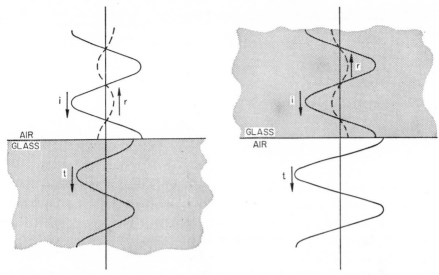

Figure 11-6. *Top, facing page, the relative phases, at the interface, of the electric field intensities in the reflected and transmitted waves for the two cases $n_2 > n_1$ and $n_2 < n_1$ with $\mathbf{E}_{oi}$ normal to the plane of incidence. In the first case the reflected wave is π radians out of phase with the incident wave. The transmitted wave is in phase in both cases. Bottom, "crests" of $\mathbf{E}$ corresponding to the top diagrams at some particular time. They are spaced at one wave length apart and travel in the directions shown. Note the phase shift of π on reflection from a glass surface. Note also the interference pattern resulting from the superposition of the incident and reflected waves. Constructive interference occurs wherever two crests or two troughs meet; and destructive interference occurs where a crest meets a trough. This page, graphs of E_i, E_r, and E_t at normal incidence on an air-glass interface. Where the wave emerges from glass into air, as on the right, E_t is larger than E_i. Conservation of energy still applies, however, as will be shown in Section 11.3.2.*

11.3. Reflection and Refraction at the Interface Between Two Dielectrics

Now that we have established the laws of reflection, Snell's law of refraction, and Fresnel's equations, all of which apply to the interface between any two media, we shall consider the relatively simple case of the interface between two dielectrics. In this case the relative permeabilities K_{mi} and K_{m2} are equal to unity. The indexes of refraction n_1 and n_2 are real numbers equal to or larger than unity, and

$$\frac{\sin \theta_t}{\sin \theta_i} = \frac{n_1}{n_2}, \qquad (11\text{-}30)$$

as in Eq. *11-14*. The larger angle is thus always in the medium with the lower index of refraction.

From Fresnel's equations, we have the equations

$$\left(\frac{E_{or}}{E_{oi}}\right)_N = \frac{\left(\dfrac{n_1}{n_2}\right)\cos\theta_i - \cos\theta_t}{\left(\dfrac{n_1}{n_2}\right)\cos\theta_i + \cos\theta_t} \qquad (11\text{-}31)$$

and

$$\left(\frac{E_{ot}}{E_{oi}}\right)_N = \frac{2\left(\dfrac{n_1}{n_2}\right)\cos\theta_i}{\left(\dfrac{n_1}{n_2}\right)\cos\theta_i + \cos\theta_t} \qquad (11\text{-}32)$$

for a wave polarized with its **E** vector normal to the plane of incidence.

It will be observed that $(E_{ot}/E_{oi})_N$ is always real and positive. This means that at the interface the transmitted wave is always in phase with the incident wave. The ratio $(E_{or}/E_{oi})_N$ can, however, be either positive or negative, depending on the value of n_1/n_2, for if $n_1/n_2 > 1$, then $\theta_t > \theta_i$, and $\cos\theta_i > \cos\theta_t$; whereas if $n_1/n_2 < 1$, then $\theta_t < \theta_i$, and $\cos\theta_i < \cos\theta_t$. The reflected wave is thus either in phase with the incident wave at the interface if $n_1 > n_2$ or is π radians out of phase if $n_1 < n_2$. Figure 11-6 illustrates the E vectors for both types of reflection; Figure 11-7 shows the ratios of Eqs. *11-31* and *11-32* for

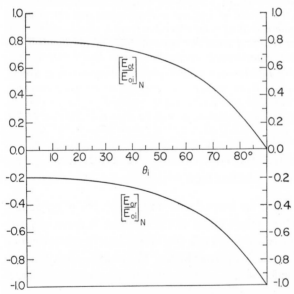

Figure 11-7. *The ratios $(E_{or}/E_{oi})_N$ and $(E_{ot/oi})_N$ as functions of the angle of incidence θ_i for $n_1/n_2 = 1/1.5$. This corresponds to light incident in air on a glass with $n = 1.5$. The wave is polarized with its* **E** *vector* normal *to the plane of incidence.*

$n_1/n_2 = 1/1.5$. This corresponds, for example, to a light wave incident in air on a glass with an index of refraction of 1.5.

At normal incidence, $\theta_i = 0$, and

$$\frac{E_{or}}{E_{oi}} = \frac{\left(\dfrac{n_1}{n_2}\right) - 1}{\left(\dfrac{n_1}{n_2}\right) + 1},$$ (11-33)

$$\frac{E_{ot}}{E_{oi}} = \frac{2\left(\dfrac{n_1}{n_2}\right)}{\left(\dfrac{n_1}{n_2}\right) + 1}.$$ (11-34)

For an incident wave polarized with its **E** vector parallel to the plane of incidence,

$$\left(\frac{E_{or}}{E_{oi}}\right)_P = \frac{-\cos\theta_i + \left(\dfrac{n_1}{n_2}\right)\cos\theta_t}{\cos\theta_i + \left(\dfrac{n_1}{n_2}\right)\cos\theta_t},$$ (11-35)

whereas

$$\left(\frac{E_{ot}}{E_{oi}}\right)_P = \frac{2\left(\dfrac{n_1}{n_2}\right)\cos\theta_i}{\cos\theta_i + \left(\dfrac{n_1}{n_2}\right)\cos\theta_t}.$$ (11-36)

The second ratio is always positive. This indicates that the relative phases of E_{ot} and E_{oi} are as shown in Figure 11-5, which we used in arriving at this result; that is, the tangential components of the incident and transmitted electric field intensities are in phase at the interface.

On the other hand, the ratio for $\mathbf{E}_{or}$ can be either positive or negative, which indicates that $\mathbf{E}_{or}$ can point either as in Figure 11-5 or in the opposite direction. The tangential components of $\mathbf{E}_{oi}$ and of $\mathbf{E}_{or}$ can thus be either in phase or π radians out of phase. The $\mathbf{E}_{or}$ component is in phase with $\mathbf{E}_{oi}$ at the interface if

$$\left(\frac{n_1}{n_2}\right)\cos\theta_t - \cos\theta_i > 0$$ (11-37)

or if

$$\sin\theta_t\cos\theta_t - \cos\theta_i\sin\theta_i > 0,$$ (11-38)

$$\sin 2\theta_t - \sin 2\theta_i > 0,$$ (11-39)

$$\sin(\theta_t - \theta_i)\cos(\theta_t + \theta_i) > 0.$$ (11-40)

This inequality will be satisfied either if

$$\theta_t > \theta_i \quad and \quad \theta_t + \theta_i < \frac{\pi}{2}$$ (11-41)

or if

$$\theta_t < \theta_i \quad and \quad \theta_t + \theta_i > \frac{\pi}{2}.$$ (11-42)

The phase of the reflected wave in this case does *not* therefore depend only on the ratio n_2/n_1; it depends on both θ_i and θ_t. The ratio E_{or}/E_{ot} can be either positive or negative, both for $n_2 > n_1$ and for $n_2 < n_1$. For normal incidence, Eqs. *11-33* and *11-34* apply as expected. Figure 11-8 shows the ratios of Eqs. *11-35* and *11-36* again for $n_1/n_2 = 1/1.5$.

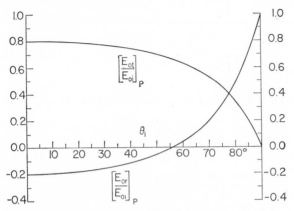

Figure 11-8. *The ratios $(E_{or}/E_{oi})_P$ and $(E_{ot}/{oi})_P$ as functions of the angle of incidence θ_1 for $n_1/n_2 = 1/1.5$. This corresponds to light incident in air on a glass with $n = 1.5$. The wave is polarized with its* **E** *vector parallel to the plane of incidence.*

11.3.1. The Brewster Angle. We have seen in the foregoing that the electric field intensity E_{or} of the reflected wave is either in phase or is π radians out of phase with the incident wave, depending on whether $\sin(\theta_t - \theta_i) \cos(\theta_t + \theta_i)$ is greater or less than zero. It will be gathered from this that there is *no* reflected wave when this expression is equal to zero, that is, when $\theta_i = \theta_t = 0$ or when $\theta_i + \theta_t = \pi/2$. The first condition is incorrect, however; it arises from the fact that we have multiplied the inequality

$$\left(\frac{n_1}{n_2}\right) \cos\theta_t - \cos\theta_i > 0$$

by $\sin\theta_i$, which is equal to zero at $\theta_i = 0$.

Thus, for

$$\theta_i + \theta_t = \frac{\pi}{2}, \tag{11-43}$$

there is a reflected wave only when the incident wave is polarized with its **E** vector normal to the plane of incidence. This is rather remarkable because it involves the passage of a wave through a discontinuity in the medium of propagation *without* the production of a reflected wave. The conditions of continuity at the interface are then satisfied by two waves only—the incident and the transmitted waves—instead of the usual three. This is illustrated in Figure 11-9. The angle of incidence is then called the *Brewster angle*. It is also called

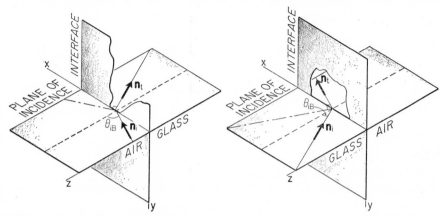

Figure 11-9. *When the incident wave is polarized with its* **E** *vector parallel to the plane of incidence, there is* no *reflected wave at* $\theta_i + \theta_t = \pi/2$. *The angle of incidence* θ_i *is then called the Brewster angle. The position of the missing reflected ray is at 90° to the transmitted ray. For any pair of media, the sum of the two angles* θ_{iB} *is 90°.*

the *polarizing angle*, since an unpolarized wave incident on an interface at this angle is reflected as a polarized wave with its **E** vector normal to the plane of incidence.*

At the Brewster angle,

$$\frac{n_1}{n_2} = \frac{\sin \theta_t}{\sin \theta_{iB}} = \frac{\sin \left(\dfrac{\pi}{2} - \theta_{iB} \right)}{\sin \theta_{iB}}, \tag{11-44}$$

$$= \cot \theta_{iB}. \tag{11-45}$$

For light incident on glass with an index of refraction of 1.6, the Brewster angle is about 58°; for light emerging from this glass the Brewster angle is about 32°. At radio frequencies the index of refraction of water is 9, and the angles are about 84° and 6° respectively; water will therefore *not* reflect a vertically polarized radio wave when the angle of incidence is 84°.

---

* The Brewster angle is often explained *incorrectly* as follows. For this particular angle of incidence, the position of the missing reflected ray is at 90° to the transmitted ray. It is argued that the electrons excited in medium 2 do not radiate in their direction of oscillation (Section 13.2) and hence cannot give rise to a reflected ray in medium 1 in this case. This explanation is incorrect, since the Brewster angle is observed for an incident wave polarized with its **E** vector *normal* to the plane of incidence in nonconducting magnetic materials (Problem 11-10).

11.3.2. The Coefficients of Reflection and of Transmission at an Interface Between Two Dielectrics. It is useful to define coefficients of reflection and of transmission which are related to the flow of energy across the interface. The average energy flux per unit area in the incident wave is given by Poynting's vector, Eq. *10-40.* Setting $K_m = 1$, we find that

$$S_{i \text{ av.}} = \frac{1}{2}\left(\frac{\epsilon_1}{\mu_0}\right)^{1/2} E_{oi}^2 \mathbf{n}_i, \tag{11-46}$$

$$= \frac{1}{2}\left(\frac{\epsilon_1}{\mu_0}\right)^{1/2} E_{or}^2 \mathbf{n}_r, \tag{11-47}$$

$$= \frac{1}{2}\left(\frac{\epsilon_2}{\mu_0}\right)^{1/2} E_{ot}^2 \mathbf{n}_t, \tag{11-48}$$

where $\epsilon = K_e\epsilon_0$, as usual.

The *coefficients of reflection R and of transmission T* are defined as the ratios of the average energy fluxes per unit time and per unit area across the interface:

$$R = \left|\frac{S_{r \text{ av.}} \cdot \mathbf{n}}{S_{i \text{ av.}} \cdot \mathbf{n}}\right| = \frac{E_{or}^2}{E_{oi}^2}, \tag{11-49}$$

where $\mathbf{n}$ is the unit vector normal to the interface;

$$T = \frac{S_{t \text{ av.}} \cdot \mathbf{n}}{S_{i \text{ av.}} \cdot \mathbf{n}} = \left(\frac{K_{e2}}{K_{e1}}\right)^{1/2} \frac{E_{ot}^2 \cos\theta_t}{E_{oi}^2 \cos\theta_i}, \tag{11-50}$$

$$= \frac{n_2 E_{ot}^2 \cos\theta_t}{n_1 E_{oi}^2 \cos\theta_i}. \tag{11-51}$$

Then, from Fresnel's equations for dielectrics,

$$R_N = \left[\frac{\left(\dfrac{n_1}{n_2}\right)\cos\theta_i - \cos\theta_t}{\left(\dfrac{n_1}{n_2}\right)\cos\theta_i + \cos\theta_t}\right]^2, \tag{11-52}$$

$$T_N = \frac{4\left(\dfrac{n_1}{n_2}\right)\cos\theta_i \cos\theta_t}{\left[\left(\dfrac{n_1}{n_2}\right)\cos\theta_i + \cos\theta_t\right]^2}, \tag{11-53}$$

$$R_P = \left[\frac{-\cos\theta_i + \left(\dfrac{n_1}{n_2}\right)\cos\theta_t}{\cos\theta_i + \left(\dfrac{n_1}{n_2}\right)\cos\theta_t}\right]^2, \tag{11\ 54}$$

$$T_P = \frac{4\left(\dfrac{n_1}{n_2}\right)\cos\theta_i \cos\theta_t}{\left[\cos\theta_i + \left(\dfrac{n_1}{n_2}\right)\cos\theta_t\right]^2}. \tag{11-55}$$

In both cases, $R + T = 1$, as expected, since there must be conservation of

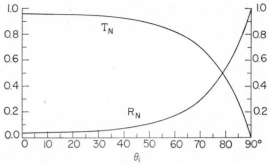

Figure 11-10. *The coefficient of reflection R_N and the coefficient of transmission T_N as functions of the angle of incidence θ_i for $n_1/n_2 = 1/1.5$. The **E** vector of the incident wave is normal to the plane of incidence.*

energy. At the Brewster angle, defined by Eq. *11-45*, $R_P = 0$ and $T_P = 1$, again as expected.

For normal incidence, $\theta_i = 0$, $\theta_t = 0$, and

$$R = \left[\frac{\left(\dfrac{n_1}{n_2}\right) - 1}{\left(\dfrac{n_1}{n_2}\right) + 1} \right]^2, \tag{11-56}$$

$$T = \frac{4\left(\dfrac{n_1}{n_2}\right)}{\left[\left(\dfrac{n_1}{n_2}\right) + 1\right]^2}. \tag{11-57}$$

Figures 11-10 and 11-11 show the coefficients of reflection R and of trans-

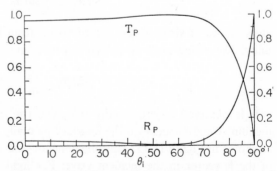

Figure 11-11. *The coefficient of reflection R_P and the coefficient of transmission T_P as functions of the angle incidence θ_i for $n_1/n_2 = 1/1.5$. The **E** vector of the incident wave is parallel to the plane of incidence.*

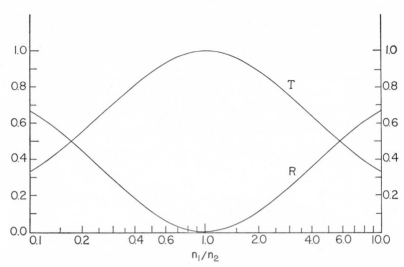

Figure 11-12. *The coefficient of reflection R and the coefficient of transmission T at normal incidence as functions of the ratio n_1/n_2.*

mission T as functions of the angle of incidence θ_i for $n_1/n_2 = 1/1.5$, whereas Figure 11-12 shows R and T as functions of n_1/n_2 at normal incidence.

11.4. Total Reflection at an Interface Between Two Dielectrics

We shall now consider the phenomenon of total reflection, which we have excluded until now. If $n_1 > n_2$, and if θ_i is sufficiently large, Snell's law

$$\sin \theta_t = \frac{n_1}{n_2} \sin \theta_i \qquad (11\text{-}58)$$

gives values of $\sin \theta_t$ which appear to be absurd, since they are greater than unity. *The critical angle of incidence*, where $\sin \theta_t = 1$ and $\theta_t = 90°$, is given by

$$\sin \theta_{ic} = \frac{n_2}{n_1}. \qquad (11\text{-}59)$$

It is observed experimentally that, when $\theta_i \geq \theta_{ic}$, the wave originating in medium 1 and incident on the interface is totally reflected back into medium 1 as shown in Figure 11-13. This phenomenon does *not* depend on the orientation of the **E** vector in the incident wave. For light propagating in glass with an index of refraction of 1.6, the critical angle of incidence is 38.7°. Total reflection is an important limiting factor in the collection of light produced in a dense medium, as will be shown in Problem 11-17.

The critical angle, defined by Eq. *11-59*, is somewhat larger than the Brewster angle (Eq. *11-45*). For example, again in the case of light propagating in a glass with an index of refraction of 1.6, the wave is totally *transmitted* when the angle of incidence is the Brewster angle, 32.0°, and is totally *reflected* at the critical angle of 38.7°. Figure 11-14 shows these two angles as functions of the ratio n_1/n_2. For large values of n_1/n_2, that is, for light incident in a relatively "dense" medium, $\sin \theta_{ic}$ and $\tan \theta_{iB}$ are small, and θ_{ic} is nearly equal to θ_{iB}. For media with more similar indexes of refraction, the Brewster angle approaches 45°, whereas the critical angle approaches 90°.

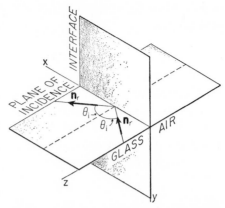

Figure 11-13. *For angles of incidence θ_i equal to or greater than the critical angle θ_{ic}, the wave is totally reflected back into medium 1.*

It is interesting to note that, for a wave polarized with its **E** vector parallel to the plane of incidence, the amplitude of the reflected wave changes very

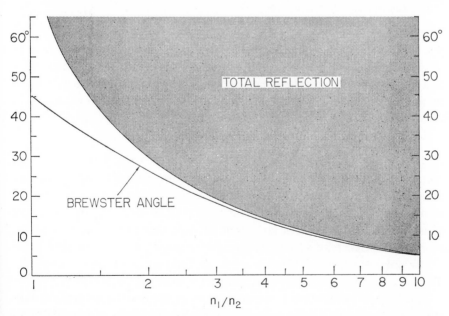

Figure 11-14. *The critical angle and the Brewster angle as functions of the ratio n_1/n_2 of the indexes of refraction on either side of the interface. The wave is incident in medium 1. It is polarized with its **E** vector parallel to the plane of incidence for the Brewster angle curve.*

rapidly when the angle of incidence lies between the Brewster angle and the critical angle.

It turns out that it is impossible to satisfy the requirement of continuity of the tangential components of **E** and of **H**, and of the normal components of **D** and of **B** at the interface, with only the incident and reflected waves in medium 1. We therefore conclude that there must exist some sort of transmitted wave in medium 2.

The transmitted wave must, however, be of a rather special nature, since it is not observable under ordinary conditions. It must of course satisfy the general wave equation for nonconductors (Eq. *10-25*), with the result that

$$\frac{\partial^2 \mathbf{E}_t}{\partial x^2} + \frac{\partial^2 \mathbf{E}_t}{\partial z^2} = \epsilon_2 \mu_0 \frac{\partial^2 \mathbf{E}_t}{\partial t^2}, \tag{11-60}$$

where we have set the derivative with respect to y equal to zero since, by hypothesis, the field does not vary with the y-coordinate (Figure 11-3). We have also set the permeability K_{m2} of medium 2 equal to unity, since we are considering the interface between two dielectrics.

We can use Eq. *11-15* for the incident wave:

$$\mathbf{E}_i = \mathbf{E}_{oi} \exp \{j[\omega t - k_1(\sin \theta_i \, x - \cos \theta_i \, z)]\}. \tag{11-61}$$

For the reflected wave, we can write

$$\mathbf{E}_r = \mathbf{E}_{or} \exp [j(\omega t - k_{1x}x - k_{1z}z)], \tag{11-62}$$

where $\mathbf{E}_{or}$, k_{1x}, and k_{1z} are unknown constants. We have used the same value of ω as for the incident wave, since it can be shown, exactly as in Section 11.1, that all three waves have the same frequency. We have also used only x and z terms in the exponent, since the derivative with respect to y must, again, be zero.

For $\mathbf{E}_t$, we choose a more general expression:

$$\mathbf{E}_t = (E_{otx}\mathbf{i} + E_{oty}\mathbf{j} + E_{otz}\mathbf{k}) \exp [j(\omega t - k_{2x}x - k_{2z}z)], \tag{11-63}$$

where E_{otx}, E_{oty}, E_{otz}, k_{2x}, and k_{2z} are also unknown constants. Again we have the same ω, and we have no y term in the exponent. We let the unknowns be complex in order that the various components of $\mathbf{E}_r$ and of $\mathbf{E}_t$ can be out of phase with each other and in order that the dependence on x and on z can be more general than with a simpler expression such as that for the incident wave.

Our only assumption is that the waves are independent of the y-coordinate. The wave equation *10-60* follows directly from Maxwell's equations.

All of the unknowns are independent both of the coordinates and of time, the only dependence on x, z, and t being represented by the exponential functions.

We represent the **H** vectors by identical expressions, in which the letter E is replaced by the letter H, and for simplicity we choose the origin of coordinates at the interface, as in Figure 11-3. We thus have a large number of unknowns. We shall determine them all, one after the other, using the boundary conditions at the interface, the wave equation, and Maxwell's equations. We shall make no further assumption.

11.4.1. The Wave Numbers k_{1x} and k_{1z} for the Reflected Wave in the Case of Total Reflection. To satisfy the boundary conditions at the interface, we proceed just as we did in Section 11.1. We first require that the exponents be equal at the interface ($z = 0$). Then, from Eqs. *11-61* and *11-62*,

$$k_{1x} = k_1 \sin \theta_i, \tag{11-64}$$

$$= \frac{n_1}{\lambda_0} \sin \theta_i. \tag{11-65}$$

To find k_{1z}, we turn to the wave equation in medium 1. This is similar to Eq. *11-60*, except for the subscripts t and 2, which must be replaced by r and 1. Thus

$$k_{1x}^2 + k_{1z}^2 = \epsilon_1 \mu_0 \omega^2, \tag{11-66}$$

$$= \left(\frac{n_1}{\lambda_0}\right)^2, \tag{11-67}$$

and

$$k_{1z}^2 = \left(\frac{n_1}{\lambda_0}\right)^2 (1 - \sin^2 \theta_i), \tag{11-68}$$

$$k_{1z} = \frac{n_1}{\lambda_0} \cos \theta_i. \tag{11-69}$$

The reflected wave is thus of the form

$$\mathbf{E}_r = \mathbf{E}_{or} \exp \{j[\omega t - k_1(\sin \theta_i \, x + \cos \theta_i \, z)]\}. \tag{11-70}$$

This expression, which is identical to that of Eq. *11-16*, represents a plane wave reflected from the interface at an angle equal to the angle of incidence. The angle of reflection is thus equal to the angle of incidence.

11.4.2. The Wave Numbers k_{2x} and k_{2z} for the Transmitted Wave in the Case of Total Reflection. Equating similarly the exponents for $\mathbf{E}_i$ and for $\mathbf{E}_t$, again at the interface ($z = 0$), we find the wave number k_{2x} of the transmitted wave:

$$k_{2x} = k_1 \sin \theta_i, \tag{11-71}$$

$$= \frac{n_1}{\lambda_0} \sin \theta_i. \tag{11-72}$$

To find the other wave number k_{2z}, we again use the wave equation *11-60* Using the expression for $\mathbf{E}_t$,

$$k_{2x}^2 + k_{2z}^2 = \epsilon_2 \mu_0 \omega^2, \qquad (11\text{-}73)$$

$$k_{2z} = \pm(\epsilon_2 \mu_0 \omega^2 - k_{2x}^2)^{1/2}, \qquad (11\text{-}74)$$

$$= \pm\left(\frac{n_2^2}{\lambda_0^2} - \frac{n_1^2}{\lambda_0^2} \sin^2 \theta_1\right)^{1/2}, \qquad (11\text{-}75)$$

$$= \pm j \frac{n_2}{\lambda_0}\left[\left(\frac{n_1}{n_2}\right)^2 \sin^2 \theta_i - 1\right]^{1/2}. \qquad (11\text{-}76)$$

The exponential function for the transmitted wave is thus

$$\exp\left\{j\left[\omega t - \frac{n_1}{\lambda_0}(\sin \theta_i)x\right] + \frac{n_2}{\lambda_0}\left[\left(\frac{n_1}{n_2}\right)^2 \sin^2 \theta_i - 1\right]^{1/2} z\right\}. \qquad (11\text{-}77)$$

We have replaced the $\pm$ sign before the z term by a $+$ sign since the electric field intensity must not become infinite as $z \longrightarrow -\infty$. Then k_{2z} can be written with a $+$ sign:

$$k_{2z} = +j \frac{n_2}{\lambda_0}\left[\left(\frac{n_1}{n_2}\right)^2 \sin^2 \theta_i - 1\right]^{1/2}. \qquad (11\text{-}78)$$

We still have to determine E_{or}, E_{otx}, E_{oty}, E_{otz}, and the corresponding H components of the transmitted wave, but it is interesting to examine immediately the above exponential function. The transmitted wave is quite remarkable. First of all, it travels unattenuated, parallel to the interface, with a wavelength

$$\lambda_x = \frac{\lambda_0}{n_1 \sin \theta_i}, \qquad (11\text{-}79)$$

$$= \frac{\lambda_1}{\sin \theta_i}, \qquad (11\text{-}80)$$

λ_1 being the wavelength in medium 1 above the interface. The wavelength λ_x is exactly the distance along the x-axis between two neighboring equiphase points in the incident wave. This was to be expected, since the continuity conditions must be satisfied at all points on the interface. On the other hand, this result, namely, that the wave travels unattenuated parallel to the interface, is most surprising if we think of an incident wave of finite cross section. Does the transmitted wave on the other side of the interface extend beyond the illuminated region? Our discussion cannot provide us with an answer, since it is based on the assumption that the incident wave is infinite in extent. Physically, what happens is this: a given incident ray, instead of being reflected abruptly at the interface, penetrates into medium 2, where it is bent back into medium 1. It is this phenomenon which gives rise to the "transmitted" wave.*

The transmitted wave is also damped exponentially in the direction perpendicular to the interface in such a way that its amplitude decreases by a factor of e over a distance

---

* See A. von Hippel, *Dielectrics and Waves* (Wiley, New York), p. 54 for a brief account of work by F. Goos and H. Hanchen on this subject.

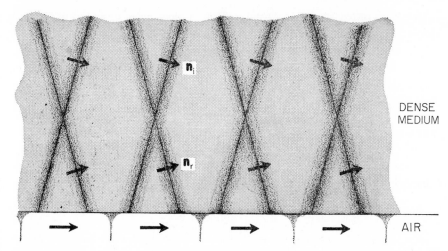

Figure 11-15. *"Crests" of E for the incident, reflected, and transmitted waves are represented here schematically for the case of total reflection. They are spaced one wave length apart. The transmitted wave travels unattenuated below the interface, and its amplitude decreases exponentially with depth in medium 2. The data used for the figure are the following: $n_1 = 3.0$, $n_2 = 1.0$, $\theta_i = 75°$. (See Problem 11-13.)*

$$\delta_z = \frac{\lambda_2}{\left[\left(\frac{n_1}{n_2} \right)^2 \sin^2 \theta_i - 1 \right]^{1/2}}. \qquad (11\text{-}81)$$

This is illustrated qualitatively in Figure 11-15. The ratio δ_z/λ_2 is shown in Figure 11-16 as a function of the angle of incidence θ_i for $n_1/n_2 = 1.5$.

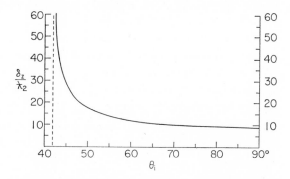

Figure 11-16. *The ratio of δ_z (the depth of penetration) to λ_2 (the wavelength in medium 2 divided by 2π) for the transmitted wave when there is total reflection. The index of refraction of the first medium is 1.50 times that of the second medium.*

The transmitted wave, for total reflection, has been observed both with visible light and with microwaves.*

It is interesting to note that we could have arrived at the exponential function simply by substituting in Eq. *11-17* the expression $(n_1/n_2) \sin \theta_i$ for $\sin \theta_t$ (Snell's law), disregarding the fact that it corresponds to a sine function which is larger than unity (see Problem 11-11).

If θ_t were real, we would expect to have

$$k_{2z} = -\frac{n_2}{\lambda_0} \cos \theta_t. \qquad (11\text{-}82)$$

Comparing with Equation *11-78*, we set†

$$\cos \theta_t = -(1 - \sin^2 \theta_t)^{1/2}, \qquad (11\text{-}83)$$

$$= -\left[1 - \left(\frac{n_1}{n_2}\right)^2 \sin^2 \theta_i\right]^{1/2}, \qquad (11\text{-}84)$$

where we have elected to place the negative sign before the radical to preserve the formalism.

11.4.3. The Electric and Magnetic Fields in the Reflected and Transmitted Waves for the Case of Total Reflection.

We have now determined the two wave numbers k_{2x} and k_{2z} that determine the manner in which the amplitude and phase of the transmitted wave vary with the x- and z-coordinates. It will be recalled from Figure 11-3 that the z-axis is normal to the interface, whereas the x-axis is parallel to the interface and lies in the plane of incidence.

We must still determine the amplitudes of the **E** and **H** vectors for both the reflected and transmitted waves, or, from Eqs. *11-62* and *11-63*, E_{otx}, E_{oty}, E_{otz}, H_{otx}, H_{oty}, H_{otz}, E_{or}, and H_{or}. This is an imposing number of unknowns. We can dismiss H_{or} immediately because the relation between H_{or} and E_{or} is known from our discussion of plane waves in dielectrics (Eq. *10-34*).

To simplify the discussion, we shall proceed as before and discuss separately the cases in which the incident wave is polarized with its **E** vector normal and parallel to the plane of incidence.

* See, for example, J. Strong, *Concepts of Physical Optics* (Freeman, San Francisco), Appendix J by G. F. Hull, p. 516.

† It is probably useful to recall here that, if A is some positive real number, then

$$(-A)^{1/2} = jA^{1/2},$$

and

$$A^{1/2} = -j(-A)^{1/2},$$

but

$$A^{1/2} \neq j(-A)^{1/2}.$$

The explanation of this will be found by representing A, $-A$, and their square roots on the complex plane. If such care is not exercised, it is easy to show that $+1 = -1$:

$$+1 = (+1)^{1/2} = [(-1)(-1)]^{1/2} = j^2 = -1!$$

INCIDENT WAVE POLARIZED WITH ITS **E** VECTOR *normal* TO THE PLANE OF INCIDENCE. We can assume here, as in Section 11.2.1, that the vectors $\mathbf{E}_{or}$ and $\mathbf{E}_{ot}$ for the reflected and transmitted waves are also normal to the plane of incidence. We can therefore represent the incident and reflected waves as in Figure 11-17. Then

$$\mathbf{E}_i = \mathbf{j}E_{oi} \exp\left[j(\omega t - k_1\mathbf{n}_i\cdot\mathbf{r})\right],$$
$$(11\text{-}85)$$

$$\mathbf{E}_r = \mathbf{j}E_{or} \exp\left[j(\omega t - k_1\mathbf{n}_r\cdot\mathbf{r})\right],$$
$$(11\text{-}86)$$

$$\mathbf{E}_t = \mathbf{j}E_{oty} \exp\left[j(\omega t - k_{2x}x - k_{2z}z)\right].$$
$$(11\text{-}87)$$

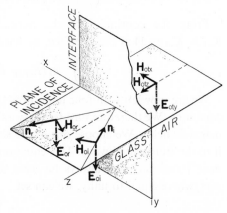

Figure 11-17. *The* **E** *and* **H** *vectors for the incident, reflected, and transmitted waves in the case of total reflection when the incident wave is polarized with its* **E** *vector normal to the plane of incidence. The continuity of the tangential component of* **H** *across the interface makes* $H_{oty} = 0$.

We have written the exponents in the first two cases in a more compact form than previously (Eqs. *11-61* and *11-62*). We have also used k_{2x} and k_{2z} in the last exponent (not their values of Eqs. *11-72* and *11-78*) simply for brevity.

For the incident and reflected waves, H is in the plane of incidence, just as in Figure 11-4, and it has both x- and z-components:

$$\mathbf{H}_i = H_{oi}\,(\cos\theta_i\mathbf{i} + \sin\theta_i\mathbf{k}) \exp\left[j(\omega t - k_1\mathbf{n}_i\cdot\mathbf{r})\right], \qquad (11\text{-}88)$$

and

$$\mathbf{H}_r = H_{or}\,(-\cos\theta_i\mathbf{i} + \sin\theta_i\mathbf{k}) \exp\left[j(\omega t - k_1\mathbf{n}_r\cdot\mathbf{r})\right]. \qquad (11\text{-}89)$$

For the transmitted wave, however, we must use a more general expression, since we know nothing as yet concerning its magnetic field intensity. We therefore set

$$\mathbf{H}_t = (H_{otx}\mathbf{i} + H_{oty}\mathbf{j} + H_{otz}\mathbf{k}) \exp\left[j(\omega t - k_{2x}x - k_{2z}z)\right]. \qquad (11\text{-}90)$$

We now utilize the fact that the tangential component of the electric field intensity must be continuous across the interface. At the origin, which we have chosen at some arbitrary point in the interface, the exponential functions for $\mathbf{E}_i$, $\mathbf{E}_r$, and $\mathbf{E}_t$ all reduce to $e^{j\omega t}$, thus

$$E_{oi} + E_{or} = E_{oty}. \qquad (11\text{-}91)$$

Similarly, the continuity of the tangential component of **H** requires that

$$0 = H_{oty}, \qquad (11\text{-}92)$$

$$(H_{oi} - H_{or})\cos\theta_i = H_{otx}, \qquad (11\text{-}93)$$

or, from Eq. *10-34* which applies to plane waves in dielectrics,

$$\left(\frac{\epsilon_0}{\mu_0}\right)^{1/2} n_1 (E_{oi} - E_{or}) \cos \theta_i = H_{otx}. \tag{11-94}$$

From the continuity of the normal component of **B** (or of **H**, since $K_{m1} = K_{m2} = 1$) at the interface, we have

$$\left(\frac{\epsilon_0}{\mu_0}\right)^{1/2} n_1 (E_{oi} + E_{or}) \sin \theta_i = H_{otz}. \tag{11-95}$$

We are now left with four unknowns (E_{or}, E_{oty}, H_{otx}, and H_{otz}) and only three equations. We therefore turn to Maxwell's equations, which apply to all electromagnetic fields. We choose one of the simpler ones, namely Eq. *8-2*, and apply it to the transmitted wave. This equation states that the divergence of the magnetic induction must always be zero. Since the permeability of medium 2 is everywhere equal to unity, we can set

$$\mathbf{\nabla} \cdot \mathbf{H}_t = 0, \tag{11-96}$$

or

$$k_{2x} H_{otx} + k_{2z} H_{otz} = 0. \tag{11-97}$$

Solving and substituting the values of k_{2x} and of k_{2z}, we find that

$$\left(\frac{E_{or}}{E_{oi}}\right)_N = \frac{\cos \theta_i + j \left[\sin^2 \theta_i - \left(\frac{n_2}{n_1}\right)^2\right]^{1/2}}{\cos \theta_i - j \left[\sin^2 \theta_i - \left(\frac{n_2}{n_1}\right)^2\right]^{1/2}}, \tag{11-98}$$

$$\left(\frac{E_{oty}}{E_{oi}}\right)_N = \frac{2 \cos \theta_i}{\cos \theta_i - j \left[\sin^2 \theta_i - \left(\frac{n_2}{n_1}\right)^2\right]^{1/2}}, \tag{11-99}$$

$$\left(\frac{H_{otx}}{E_{oi}}\right)_N = -\left(\frac{\epsilon_0}{\mu_0}\right)^{1/2} \frac{2 j n_1 \cos \theta_i \left[\sin^2 \theta_i - \left(\frac{n_2}{n_1}\right)^2\right]^{1/2}}{\cos \theta_i - j \left[\sin^2 \theta_i - \left(\frac{n_2}{n_1}\right)^2\right]^{1/2}}, \tag{11-100}$$

and

$$\left(\frac{H_{otz}}{E_{oi}}\right)_N = \left(\frac{\epsilon_0}{\mu_0}\right)^{1/2} \frac{n_1 \sin 2\theta_i}{\cos \theta_i - j \left[\sin^2 \theta_i - \left(\frac{n_2}{n_1}\right)^2\right]^{1/2}}. \tag{11-101}$$

To obtain $\mathbf{E}_r$, the above value for E_{or} must be substituted into Eq. *11-70*. Similarly, to obtain E_{ty}, H_{tx}, and H_{tz}, the above values of E_{oty}, H_{otx}, and H_{otz} must be multiplied by the exponential function *11-77* for the transmitted wave. We have thus found all of the quantities which are required to describe both the reflected and the transmitted waves.

Before discussing the physical meaning of these quantities, let us recapitulate. We have solved this rather complex problem of total reflection by using just a few basic ideas. We first used the wave equation, and then the requirements of continuity at the interface: continuity of the tangential components of **E** and **H** and continuity of the normal component of **B**. Finally, we used one of Maxwell's equations; namely, $\nabla \cdot \mathbf{B} = 0$. It must be realized, however, that both the wave equation and the continuity conditions have themselves been deduced from Maxwell's equations, which represent, therefore, our only basic assumptions.

Let us see how the two first expressions above for E_{or} and E_{ot} compare with Fresnel's equations for dielectrics, Eqs. *11-31* and *11-32*. We have found in Eq. *11-84* that the square root which appears in the Eqs. *11-98* to *11-101* is related to $\cos \theta_t$ as follows:

$$\left[\sin^2 \theta_i - \left(\frac{n_2}{n_1} \right)^2 \right]^{1/2} = \frac{1}{j} \frac{n_2}{n_1} \left[1 - \left(\frac{n_1}{n_2} \right)^2 \sin^2 \theta_i \right]^{1/2}, \qquad (11\text{-}102)$$

$$= j \frac{n_2}{n_1} \cos \theta_t. \qquad (11\text{-}103)$$

Substituting in Eqs. *11-98* and *11-99*, we find that these become Fresnel's equations. *Fresnel's equations are therefore valid in the case of total reflection*, at least in a formal way, if we again disregard the fact that $\sin \theta_t$ is greater than unity, and if $\cos \theta_t$ is defined as in Eqs. *11-83* and *11-84*. We have already found, near the end of Section 11.4.2, that the wave numbers k_{2x} and k_{2z} can be derived directly from Snell's law.

Let us now examine the physical meaning of the expressions which we have found above for E_{or}, E_{oty}, H_{otx}, and H_{otz} in Eqs. *11-98* and *11-101*. We first notice that the amplitude of the reflected wave is equal to that of the incident wave, since

$$\left| \frac{E_{or}}{E_{oi}} \right| = 1. \qquad (11\text{-}104)$$

The coefficient of reflection R is therefore equal to unity. The energy is totally reflected, and, on the average, there is no flux of energy through the interface.

The wave undergoes a phase jump on reflection, since

$$\left(\frac{E_{or}}{E_{oi}} \right)_N = \exp \left\{ 2j \arctan \frac{\left[\sin^2 \theta_i - \left(\frac{n_2}{n_1} \right)^2 \right]^{1/2}}{\cos \theta_i} \right\} = \exp (j\alpha). \qquad (11\text{-}105)$$

The phase jump therefore varies from $0°$ at the critical angle of incidence ($\sin \theta_i = n_2/n_1$) to $180°$ at glancing incidence, through positive angles. This is shown in Figure 11-18.

As regards the transmitted wave, it is obvious that its electric field intensity is not zero, despite the fact that the average flux of energy across the interface

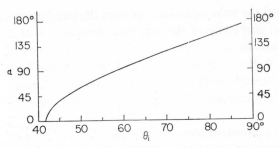

Figure 11-18. *The phase α of the reflected wave with respect to that of the incident wave in the case of total reflection. The incident wave is polarized with its **E** vector normal to the plane of incidence; the ratio n_1/n_2 is set equal to 1.50.*

is zero, as we have just found. This is to be expected, since the incident wave suffers a gradual reflection within medium 2, as explained near the end of Section 11.4.2. Medium 2 can be considered to act like a pure inductance fed by a source of alternating current. The average power input to the inductance is zero, the power flow being alternately one way and then the other, but there is nevertheless a current through the inductance. Figure 11-19 shows how the

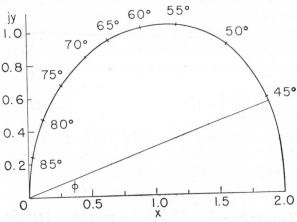

Figure 11-19. *The ratio $(E_{oty}/E_{oi})_N$ of Eq. 11-99 is plotted here in the complex plane for various angles of incidence θ_i larger than the critical angle and for $n_1/n_2 = 1.50$. The amplitude of the transmitted wave is represented by the distance from a point on the curve to the origin, and is greatest at the critical angle. The transmitted wave leads the incident wave by an angle equal to the argument of the complex ratio—for example, the angle ϕ shown.*

electric field intensity of the transmitted wave varies both in amplitude and in phase with the angle of incidence.

The magnetic field intensity of the transmitted wave is given by Eqs. *11-100* and *11-101*. Since both denominators on the right-hand side are identical, whereas one numerator is real and the other imaginary, the two components of the magnetic field intensity are $\pi/2$ radians out of phase, and, at any given point, H has neither a fixed amplitude nor a fixed direction but rotates in the plane of incidence! The transmitted wave in the case of total reflection is thus rather complex.

It is instructive to calculate the Poynting vector for the transmitted wave. From Eq. *10-88*,

$$(\mathbf{S}_{\text{av.}})_N = \frac{1}{2} \, \text{Re} \, (\mathbf{E}_t \times \mathbf{H}_t^*), \tag{11-106}$$

$$= \begin{vmatrix} \mathbf{i} & \mathbf{j} & \mathbf{k} \\ 0 & E_t & 0 \\ H_{tx}^* & 0 & H_{tz}^* \end{vmatrix}, \tag{11-107}$$

$$= \frac{1}{2} \, \text{Re} \, (E_t H_{tz}^*)\mathbf{i} - \frac{1}{2} \, \text{Re} \, (E_t H_{tx}^*)\mathbf{k}, \tag{11-108}$$

where

$$E_t = \frac{2 \cos \theta_i}{\cos \theta_i - j\left[\sin^2 \theta_i - \left(\dfrac{n_2}{n_1}\right)^2 \right]^{1/2}} E_{oi} \tag{11-109}$$

$$\times \exp\left\{ j\left[\omega t - \frac{n_1}{\lambda_0}(\sin \theta_i)x \right] + \left(\frac{n_2}{\lambda_0}\right)^2 (\sin^2 \theta_i - 1)^{1/2}z \right\}.$$

The stars indicate that we must use the complex conjugate.

The quantity H_{tx} is obtained by multiplying the value of H_{otx} of Eq. *11-100* by the exponential function *11-77*, and similarly for H_{otz}. To obtain the complex conjugates of H_{tx} and of H_{tz}, all terms which involve j must change sign. Then the x-component of $\mathbf{S}_{\text{av.}}$ turns out to be

$$\frac{1}{2} \, \text{Re} \, (E_t H_{tz}) = \left(\frac{\epsilon_0}{\mu_0}\right)^{1/2} \frac{n_1 \cos \theta_i \sin 2\theta_i}{1 - \left(\dfrac{n_2}{n_1}\right)^2} E_{ot}^2 \tag{11-110}$$

$$\times \exp\left\{ 2\frac{n_2}{\lambda_0}\left[\left(\frac{n_1}{n_2}\right)^2 \sin^2 \theta_i - 1 \right]^{1/2} z \right\}.$$

There is therefore an energy flow parallel to the interface in the positive direction of the x-axis. At $z = 0$, just below the interface, the exponential function is equal to unity, whereas below this level the flux of energy decreases expo-

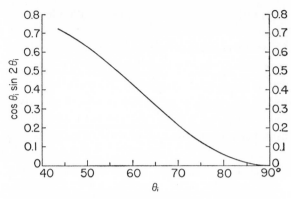

Figure 11-20. *Variation of the flux of energy* $\mathcal{S}_t$*, parallel to and just below the interface, with the angle of incidence in the case of total reflection.*

nentially with z. Figure 11-20 shows the manner in which the flux of energy near the interface varies with the angle of incidence θ_i.

We find similarly that $E_t H_{otx}^*$ is a pure imaginary quantity and that there is no average energy flow normal to the interface. This is consistent with our finding that the coefficient of reflection R is unity.

INCIDENT WAVE POLARIZED WITH ITS **E** VECTOR *parallel* TO THE PLANE OF INCIDENCE. In this case we can also deduce both the reflected and transmitted waves from Snell's law and from Fresnel's equations by choosing the sign for $\cos \theta_t$ as in Eq. *11-84*. The coefficient of reflection R is again equal to unity. The phase jump for reflection differs, however, with the result that total reflection of a wave polarized in some arbitrary direction gives rise to an elliptically polarized wave.

11.5. Reflection and Refraction at the Surface of a Good Conductor

Now that we have discussed at length the phenomena of reflection and refraction at the interface between two dielectrics, let us examine the corresponding phenomena which occur when an electromagnetic wave traveling in a dielectric encounters the plane surface of a good conductor. The results which we shall find below will be used in the next chapter—"Guided Waves."

We have here a case which bears some resemblance to that of total reflection in that the wave numbe of a good conductor is complex, as was shown in Eq. *10-97:*

$$k_2 = \left(\frac{\sigma_2 \mu_2 \omega}{2}\right)^{1/2}(1 - j). \qquad (11\text{-}111)$$

The index of refraction n_2 is therefore also complex, and the direct application of Snell's law, Eq. *11-14*, leads to a very small but complex value for $\sin \theta_t$.

We shall therefore proceed in the same manner as for total reflection and write for the incident, reflected, and transmitted waves,

$$\mathbf{E}_i = \mathbf{E}_{oi} \exp \{j[\omega t - k_1(\sin \theta_i \, x - \cos \theta_i \, z)]\}, \qquad (11\text{-}112)$$

$$\mathbf{E}_r = \mathbf{E}_{or} \ \text{xp} \ \{j[\omega t - k_1(\sin \theta_i \, x + \cos \theta_i \, z)]\}, \qquad (11\text{-}113)$$

and

$$\mathbf{E}_t = (E_{otx}\mathbf{i} + E_{oty}\mathbf{j} + E_{otz}\mathbf{k}) \exp \{j(\omega t - k_{2x}x - k_{2z}z)\}, \qquad (11\text{-}114)$$

respectively, the coordinate axes being chosen as in Figure 11-21. We have not taken the trouble to show that $\mathbf{E}_r$ is of the form shown above; the demonstration is exactly identical to that which led to Eq. *11-70* for the case of total reflection at the interface between two dielectrics. We have set all three circular frequencies equal, as previously.

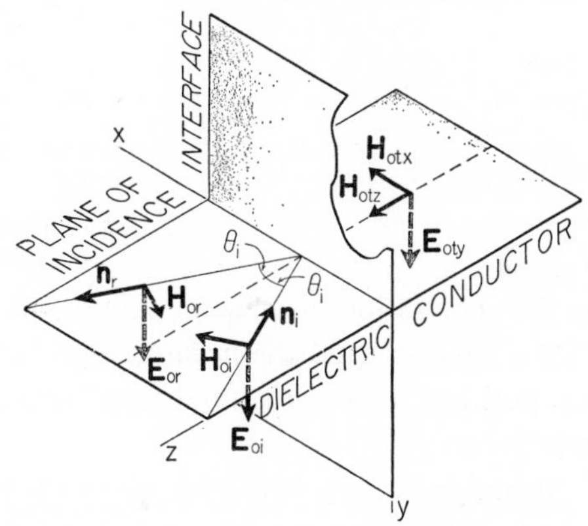

Figure 11-21. *An electromagnetic wave incident on a good conductor, with its* **E** *vector normal to the plane of incidence. The angle of reflection is equal to the angle of incidence. The continuity of the tangential component of* **H** *across the interface makes* $H_{oty} = 0$.

11.5.1. The Wave Numbers k_{2x} and k_{2z} for Refraction into a Good Conductor.
We can again equate the exponential functions for $\mathbf{E}_i$ and $\mathbf{E}_t$ on the interface just as we did in Eq. *11-4*, then

$$k_{2x} = k_1 \sin \theta_i, \qquad (11\text{-}115)$$

$$= \frac{n_1}{\lambda_0} \sin \theta_i, \qquad (11\text{-}116)$$

just as for total reflection.

We can find k_{2z} from the wave equation for good conductors:

$$\frac{\partial^2 E_t}{\partial x^2} + \frac{\partial^2 E_t}{\partial z^2} = j\omega\sigma_2\mu_2 E_t. \qquad (11\text{-}117)$$

This is Eq. *10-95*, except that we have completed the Laplacian on the left-hand side by adding the derivative with respect to x. The derivative with respect to y can be omitted, since the wave is assumed to be independent of the y-coordinate Then

$$-k_{2x}^2 - k_{2z}^2 = j\omega\sigma_2\mu_2, \qquad (11\text{-}118)$$

$$= -k_2^2, \qquad (11\text{-}119)$$

where

$$k_2 = \frac{1-j}{\delta} = \frac{n_2}{\lambda_0} \qquad (11\text{-}120)$$

is the wave number for a plane wave in the conductor, as given in Eq. *10-101*. The quantity n_2 is a complex number, thus we have

$$k_{2z} = \pm k_2 \left(1 - \frac{k_{2x}^2}{k_2^2} \right)^{1/2}, \tag{11-121}$$

$$= \pm k_2 \left[1 - \left(\frac{n_1}{n_2} \right)^2 \sin^2 \theta_i \right]^{1/2}. \tag{11-122}$$

Since the "index of refraction" n_2 of the conductor is much larger than that of the dielectric n_1 (Section 10.4), the second term under the square root can be neglected. We must also use a negative sign before the square root, as will be shown presently. Thus

$$k_{2z} \approx -k_2, \tag{11-123}$$

$$\approx \frac{-1 + j}{\delta}, \tag{11-124}$$

where

$$\delta = \left(\frac{2}{\omega \sigma_2 \mu_2} \right)^{1/2} \tag{11-125}$$

is the penetration distance or skin depth which we found in Eq. *10-102*.

We have selected the negative sign before k_2 to make the imaginary part of k_{2z} positive. This is required to prevent the wave from building up to infinite amplitude as $z \longrightarrow -\infty$.

If both n_1 and n_2 were real, we would have

$$k_{2z} = -k_2 \cos \theta_t. \tag{11-126}$$

Thus we can set

$$\cos \theta_t = + \left[1 - \left(\frac{n_1}{n_2} \right)^2 \sin^2 \theta_i \right]^{1/2}, \tag{11-127}$$

where the second term on the right is complex, on account of n_2, but negligible since $n_2 \gg n_1$. Then $\cos \theta_t$ is real and is equal to unity to a high degree of approximation. It will be observed that we now have a positive sign before the square root, whereas we had a negative sign in the corresponding equation for the case of total reflection at the interface between two dielectrics. Using Snell's law in the above equation,

$$\cos \theta_t = +(1 - \sin^2 \theta_t)^{1/2}. \tag{11-128}$$

The exponential function for E_t is thus

$$\exp \left\{ j \left[\omega t - \frac{n_1}{\lambda_0} (\sin \theta_i) x + \frac{z}{\delta} \right] + \frac{z}{\delta} \right\}. \tag{11-129}$$

Let us consider the second and third terms in the exponent. The term $\frac{n_1}{\lambda_0} (\sin \theta_i) x$ gives the rate at which the phase changes with distance along the surface of the conductor and is exactly the same as in the case of total reflection (*11-77*). The third term gives similarly the rate at which the phase changes in the direction normal to the surface of the conductor. Now, from Eq. *11-120*,

$$\frac{n_2}{\lambda_0} = \frac{1-j}{\delta}, \tag{11-130}$$

where n_2 is large compared to unity. Thus

$$\lambda_0 \gg \delta. \tag{11-131}$$

This was to be expected, since the skin depth δ is equal to λ in the conductor and is much smaller than λ_0. The coefficient of x is therefore much smaller than that of z,

$$k_{2x} \ll k_{2z}, \tag{11-132}$$

and *the wave penetrates into the conductor essentially along the normal to the surface, whatever the angle of incidence.* We discovered this above when we found $\cos \theta_t$ to be approximately unity.

We can therefore neglect the second term in the exponent of expression *11-129*. We are then left with the exponential function for a plane wave traveling in the negative direction of the z-axis, as can be seen by comparing with Eq. *10-107*. The coordinate z is negative here, and, according to the last term in the exponent, the wave is attenuated by a factor e in penetrating a distance δ into the conductor. *The concept of skin depth therefore applies to an electromagnetic wave incident at any angle on a good conductor.* Whatever the angle of incidence θ_i, the transmitted wave can be considered to be a plane wave propagating along the normal to the surface, with the enormous damping which is characteristic of electromagnetic waves in good conductors. At high frequencies the skin depth is small (see Table 10-1), and conductors can be hollow instead of solid if this is convenient. Nonconductors can also be covered with metal a few skin depths thick to simulate solid conductors.

11.5.2. The Electric and Magnetic Fields in the Reflected and Transmitted Waves for the Case of Reflection at the Surface of a Good Conductor. Incident Wave Polarized with Its E Vector Normal to the Plane of Incidence.

To calculate E_{or}, E_{otx}, E_{oty}, E_{otz}, H_{otx}, H_{oty}, and H_{otz}, we consider again successively the two cases in which the incident wave is polarized with its $\mathbf{E}$ vector normal, and then parallel, to the plane of incidence. In the first case, the $\mathbf{E}$ vectors are all normal to the plane of incidence, as in Figure 11-21. Then Eqs. *11-91* to *11-97* are applicable, except that we now wish to take into account the relative permeability K_{m2} of the conductor. Thus

$$E_{oi} + E_{or} = E_{oty}, \tag{11-133}$$

$$0 = H_{oty}, \tag{11-134}$$

$$\left(\frac{\epsilon_0}{\mu_0}\right)^{1/2} n_1(E_{oi} - E_{or}) \cos \theta_i = H_{otz}, \tag{11-135}$$

$$\left(\frac{\epsilon_0}{\mu_0}\right)^{1/2} n_1(E_{oi} + E_{or}) \sin \theta_i = K_{m2} H_{otz},\qquad (11\text{-}136)$$

and

$$k_{2x} H_{otx} + k_{2z} H_{otz} = 0.\qquad (11\text{-}137)$$

From the last equation,

$$H_{otx} \gg H_{otz},\qquad (11\text{-}138)$$

since k_{2x} is much smaller k_{2z} (Eq. *11-132*). The wave in the conductor therefore has its **E** vector parallel to the y-axis and its **H** vector parallel to the x-axis. It propagates in the negative direction of the z-axis.

From the above,

$$\left(\frac{E_{or}}{E_{oi}}\right)_N = \frac{n_1 K_{m2} \cos \theta_i - \dfrac{\lambda_0}{\delta}(1-j)}{n_1 K_{m2} \cos \theta_i + \dfrac{\lambda_0}{\delta}(1-j)}.\qquad (11\text{-}139)$$

We would again have obtained the same result by the direct application of Fresnel's equation (*11-21*) with $\cos \theta_t$ as in Eq. *11-127*.

We have shown above in Eq. *11-131* that $\lambda_0 \gg \delta$. Then

$$\frac{E_{or}}{E_{oi}} \approx -1,\qquad (11\text{-}140)$$

at least if K_{m2} is much smaller than λ_0/δ. The coefficient of reflection R is thus approximately equal to unity, and **E** is reflected π radians out of phase as in

Figure 11-22

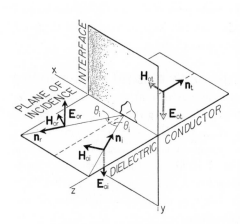

*The incident, reflected, and transmitted waves at the interface between a dielectric and a good conductor. The incident wave is in the dielectric and is polarized with its **E** vector normal to the plane of incidence. The **H** vector of the transmitted wave is parallel to the interface, as shown, but it lags the **E** vector by $\pi/4$ radians, from Eq. 10-105. The coefficient of reflection R is approximately equal to unity; the electric fields of the incident and reflected waves nearly cancel on the surface and a weak, highly attenuated wave penetrates perpendicularly into the conductor.*

Figure 11-22. This is not surprising, since the electric field in the conductor must be expected to be quite small.

It is interesting to note that there is some loss of intensity on reflection from a good conductor, since E_{or} is somewhat smaller than E_{oi}. In total reflection, on the other hand, there is no loss of intensity and the coefficient of reflection is exactly equal to unity from Eq. *11-104.*

Also, from Eq. *11-133,*

$$\left(\frac{E_{oty}}{E_{oi}}\right)_N = \frac{2n_1 K_{m2} \cos \theta_i}{n_1 K_{m2} \cos \theta_i + \frac{\lambda_0}{\delta}(1 - j)} \ll 1. \qquad (11\text{-}141)$$

The transmitted wave is therefore both relatively weak and, as we have seen, highly attenuated. Solving for H_{otx} shows that E and H are related as in Eq. *10-105,* which applies to plane waves in good conductors.

Reflection from the surface of a dielectric with $n_2 \gg 1$ would also lead to Eq. *11-140* (see Eq. *11-21*) and to a weak transmitted wave.

11.5.3. The Electric and Magnetic Fields in the Reflected and Transmitted Waves for the Case of Reflection at the Surface of a Good Conductor. Incident Wave Polarized with Its E Vector Parallel to the Plane of Incidence.

It is found similarly that

$$\left[\frac{E_{or}}{E_{oi}}\right]_P \approx -1. \qquad (11\text{-}142)$$

The three waves are as shown in Figure 11-23. The negative sign in the above equation means that the **E** vector of the reflected wave is in the direction oppo-

Figure 11-23

*Reflection and refraction at the interface between a dielectric and a good conductor. The incident wave is in the dielectric and is polarized with its **E** vector parallel to the plane of incidence. The **E** vector of the transmitted wave is as shown, but it leads the **H** vector by $\pi/4$ radians. Just as in Figure 11-22, the coefficient of reflection R is approximately unity; the tangential components of the **E** vectors of the incident and reflected waves nearly cancel on the interface; and a weak attenuated wave penetrates perpendicularly into the conductor.*

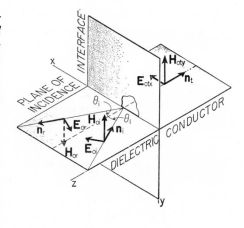

site to that shown in Figure 11-21, which was used for the calculations. The tangential components of $\mathbf{E}_{oi}$ and of $\mathbf{E}_{or}$ nearly cancel at the surface of the conductor, as expected.

The transmitted wave is again a weak, highly attenuated plane wave which penetrates perpendicularly into the conductor.

One interesting application of the above discussion is the problem of communication with submarines at sea. For shore-to-ship communication with the submarine antenna submerged, the efficiency is extremely low, first because most of the incident energy is reflected upwards at the surface of the sea, and second because the weak transmitted wave is highly attenuated. It was shown in Problem 10-5 that the attenuation is about 17 decibels/foot at a frequency of 20 megacycles per second and 1.7 decibels/foot at 20 kilocycles per second. Very low frequencies (VLF) are used at high power. The response of a submerged receiving antenna will be calculated in Problem 13-20. Communication in the direction ship-to-shore is presently impossible at these low frequencies, since the power required at the transmitter is too large, and since it is not possible to use a sufficiently large antenna on the submarine. Two-way communication is achieved at frequencies of a few megacycles per second with the submarine antenna projecting from the water.

11.5.4. Reflection and Refraction at the Surface of a Good Conductor at Normal Incidence. At normal incidence, $\theta_i = 0$, and, from Eq. *11-139*,

$$\frac{E_{or}}{E_{oi}} = \frac{K_{m2} - \dfrac{\lambda_0}{n_1\delta}(1-j)}{K_{m2} + \dfrac{\lambda_0}{n_1\delta}(1-j)}. \tag{11-143}$$

We again have $E_{or} \approx -E_{oi}$ for a good conductor, that is, for $\lambda_0 \gg \delta$

The electric field intensity $\mathbf{E}$ of the reflected wave is opposite that of the incident wave, or approximately so. This makes for a weak electric field intensity in the conductor, since the tangential component of $\mathbf{E}$ is the same on either side of the interface.

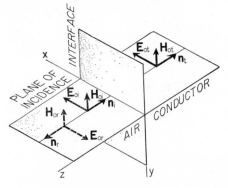

Figure 11-24

Reflection at normal incidence from the surface of a good conductor. The electric fields of the incident and reflected waves cancel at the interface, or nearly so. The magnetic field intensities add, however, with the result that the amplitude of the $\mathbf{H}_{ot}$ vector at the interface is $2H_{oi}$.

The incident and reflected waves are shown in Figure 11-24. Since the direction of the reflected wave is opposite to that of the incident wave, and since the vector product $\mathbf{E} \times \mathbf{H}$ must always give the direction of propagation, the magnetic field intensity of the reflected wave must be *in* phase with that of the incident wave, as shown in the figure.

It is interesting to consider the standing wave pattern which is produced by the reflection of an electromagnetic wave from a good conductor at normal incidence. At the reflecting surface the electric field intensities nearly cancel, and we have a *node* of **E**; the magnetic field intensities add, and we have a *loop* of **H**. This is shown in Figure 11-25. The nodes of **E** and of **H** are thus not coincident but are spaced a quarter wavelength apart.

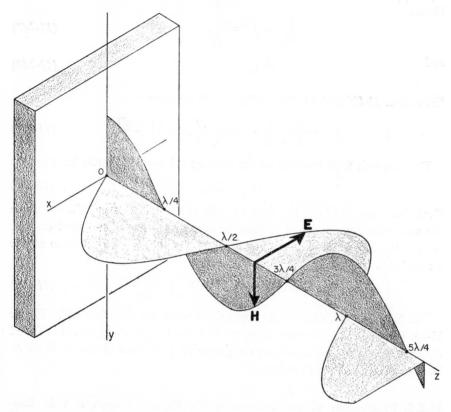

Figure 11-25. *The standing-wave pattern resulting from the reflection of an electromagnetic wave at the surface of a good conductor. The curves show the standing waves of* **E** *and of* **H** *at some particular time. The nodes of* **E** *and of* **H** *are not coincident but are spaced λ/4 apart as shown. It is shown in Problem 11-18 that* **H** *leads* **E** *by π/2, thus the maximum values of* **E** *and of* **H** *do not occur at the same time.*

A little thought will show that a similar situation exists for reflection from any surface. Either the **E** or the **H** vector must change direction on reflection, in order that the Poynting vector **E** × **H** can change direction.

At normal incidence it is a simple matter to calculate E_{ot} and H_{ot} for the transmitted wave. We can find the value of E_{ot} from Eq. *11-143*. Since

$$E_{ot} = E_{oi} + E_{or}, \qquad (11\text{-}144)$$

$$\frac{E_{ot}}{E_{oi}} = 1 + \frac{E_{or}}{E_{oi}}, \qquad (11\text{-}145)$$

$$= \frac{2K_{m2}}{K_{m2} + \dfrac{\lambda_0}{n_1 \delta}(1 - j)}. \qquad (11\text{-}146)$$

Hence

$$\frac{E_{ot}}{E_{oi}} \approx \frac{2K_{m2}n_1\delta}{\lambda_0(1 - j)}, \qquad (11\text{-}147)$$

and

$$\ll 1. \qquad (11\text{-}148)$$

From Eqs. *11-129* and *11-132*, setting $\theta_i = 0$, we have

$$E_t \approx \frac{2K_{m2}n_1\delta}{\lambda_0(1 - j)} E_{oi} \exp\left[j\left(\omega t + \frac{z}{\delta}\right) + \frac{z}{\delta}\right]. \qquad (11\text{-}149)$$

The magnetic field intensity of the transmitted wave $\mathbf{H}_{ot}$ must be given by

$$\mathbf{H}_{ot} \approx 2\mathbf{H}_{oi}, \qquad (11\text{-}150)$$

since the value of $\mathbf{H}$ on the dielectric side of the interface is $2\mathbf{H}_{oi}$ and since the tangential component of $\mathbf{H}$ must be continuous across the interface. The vectors $\mathbf{H}_{ot}$ and $\mathbf{H}_{oi}$ are, from Figure 11-24, in the negative direction of the y-axis. Thus

$$\mathbf{H}_t \approx 2\mathbf{H}_{oi} \exp\left[j\left(\omega t + \frac{z}{\delta}\right) + \frac{z}{\delta}\right]. \qquad (11\text{-}151)$$

The $\mathbf{E}$ and $\mathbf{H}$ vectors for the transmitted wave are therefore as in Figure 11-24. If we calculate the ratio E/H, we find that it agrees with the ratio found for plane waves in good conductors as given in Eq. *10-105* and that the $\mathbf{E}$ vector leads the $\mathbf{H}$ vector by $\pi/4$ radians.

11.5.5. Penetration of an Electromagnetic Wave Through a Thin Conducting Sheet.

As an illustration, let us consider the penetration of an electromagnetic wave through a thin sheet of a nonmagnetic good conductor of conductivity σ at normal incidence. We shall assume that the sheet is in air, as in Figure 11-26.

Let us use the index t for the wave transmitted through the first interface, the index tr for the wave reflected back at the second interface, and the index tt for the wave which emerges on the other side of the sheet, as in Figure 11-26. We shall neglect multiple reflections for the moment; this approximation is satisfactory if the attenuation inside the conductor is large.

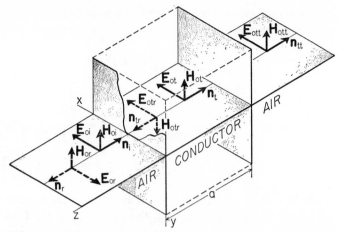

Figure 11-26. *An electromagnetic wave incident normally on a conducting sheet of thickness a. The indexes i, r, t, tr, and tt refer, respectively, to the incident wave, to the wave reflected at the first interface, to the wave transmitted at the first interface, and so on. Multiple reflections inside the sheet are neglected.*

From Eq. *11-149*, setting $n_1 = 1$, $K_{m2} = 1$, we have

$$E_t \approx \frac{2\delta}{\lambda_0(1 - j)} E_{oi} \exp\left[j\left(\omega t + \frac{z}{\delta}\right) + \frac{z}{\delta}\right], \qquad (11\text{-}152)$$

and, from Eqs. *10-101* and *10-104*,

$$H_t = 2\left(\frac{\epsilon_0}{\mu_0}\right)^{1/2} E_{oi} \exp\left[j\left(\omega t + \frac{z}{\delta}\right) + \frac{z}{\delta}\right]. \qquad (11\text{-}153)$$

For the second interface, we again have three waves. The t wave, with E_t and H_t as above; the tr wave, with

$$E_{tr} = E_{otr} \exp\left[j\left(\omega t - \frac{z}{\delta}\right) - \frac{z}{\delta}\right], \qquad (11\text{-}154)$$

$$H_{tr} = \left(\frac{\sigma}{2\mu_0\omega}\right)^{1/2}(1 - j)E_{otr} \exp\left[j\left(\omega t - \frac{z}{\delta}\right) - \frac{z}{\delta}\right]; \qquad (11\text{-}155)$$

and the tt wave, with

$$E_{tt} = E_{ott} \exp\left[j\left(\omega t + \frac{z}{\lambda_0}\right)\right], \qquad (11\text{-}156)$$

$$H_{tt} = \left(\frac{\epsilon_0}{\mu_0}\right)^{1/2} E_{ott} \exp\left[j\left(\omega t + \frac{z}{\lambda_0}\right)\right]. \qquad (11\text{-}157)$$

The continuity equations require that

$$E_t + E_{tr} = E_{tt}, \qquad (11\text{-}158)$$

$$H_t - H_{tr} = H_{tt} \qquad (11\text{-}159)$$

at $z = -a$. Solving these equations, keeping in mind that $(\sigma/\epsilon_0\omega)^{1/2} \gg 1$ for a good conductor, we find that

$$\frac{E_{otr}}{E_{ot}} \approx \exp\left[-\frac{2a}{\delta}(1+j)\right], \qquad (11\text{-}160)$$

$$\frac{E_{ott}}{E_{ot}} \approx 2 \exp\left[j\frac{a}{\lambda_0} - \frac{a}{\delta}(1+j)\right], \qquad (11\text{-}161)$$

$$E_{tr} \approx E_{ot} \exp\left[j\left(\omega t - \frac{z+2a}{\delta}\right) - \frac{z+2a}{\delta}\right], \qquad (11\text{-}162)$$

$$E_{tt} \approx 2E_{ot} \exp\left[j\left(\omega t + \frac{z+a}{\lambda_0} - \frac{a}{\delta}\right) - \frac{a}{\delta}\right]. \qquad (11\text{-}163)$$

It will be noticed that at $z = -a$ the **E** vector of the *tr* wave has approximately the same phase and amplitude as the *t* wave, while the **E** vector of the *tt* wave is also in phase but has twice the amplitude, approximately.

To investigate the transmission of energy, we calculate the average values of the Poynting vectors. In the incident wave,

$$\mathcal{S}_{i\,\text{av.}} = \frac{1}{2} \operatorname{Re}(E_i \times H_i^*), \qquad (11\text{-}164)$$

$$= \frac{1}{2}\left(\frac{\epsilon_0}{\mu_0}\right)^{1/2} E_{oi}^2, \qquad (11\text{-}165)$$

whereas in the *t* wave,

$$\mathcal{S}_{t\,\text{av.}} = \frac{1}{2} \operatorname{Re}(E_t \times H_t^*), \qquad (11\text{-}166)$$

$$= 2^{3/2}\left(\frac{\omega\epsilon_0}{\sigma}\right)^{1/2} e^{2z/\delta}\mathcal{S}_{i\,\text{av.}}. \qquad (11\text{-}167)$$

Just below the first interface, at $z = 0$, $\mathcal{S}_{t\,\text{av.}} \ll \mathcal{S}_{i\,\text{av.}}$, since $(\omega\epsilon_0/\sigma)^{1/2} \approx Q \lesssim (1/50)$. The energy flux is thus reduced by a large factor upon crossing the first interface. Then, upon penetrating through the sheet, the Poynting vector is further reduced by a factor of $e^{-2a/\delta}$. Once the wave has traversed the conducting sheet, just after the interface, we have, from Eqs. *11-152* and *11-161*,

$$\mathcal{S}_{tt\,\text{av.}} = \frac{1}{2}\left(\frac{\epsilon_0}{\mu_0}\right)^{1/2} |E_{ott}|^2, \qquad (11\text{-}168)$$

$$= 16\frac{\omega\epsilon_0}{\sigma} e^{-2a/\delta}\mathcal{S}_{i\,\text{av.}}, \qquad (11\text{-}169)$$

or

$$\mathcal{S}_{tt\,\text{av.}} = \left[2^{3/2}\left(\frac{\omega\epsilon_0}{\sigma}\right)^{1/2}\right]\left[e^{-2a/\delta}\right]\left[2^{5/2}\left(\frac{\omega\epsilon_0}{\sigma}\right)^{1/2}\right]\mathcal{S}_{i\,\text{av.}}, \qquad (11\text{-}170)$$

where the quantities in enclosures show respectively the loss in energy flux which occurs at the first interface, in traversing the sheet of thickness a, and at the second interface.

As an example, for a sheet of copper 0.001 inch thick at 1.0 megacycle/second, with $\sigma = 5.80 \times 10^7$ mhos/meter and $\delta = 6.6 \times 10^{-5}$ meter (Table 10-1), we have

$$\mathcal{S}_{tt\,\text{av.}} = (2.8 \times 10^{-6})(0.46)(5.5 \times 10^{-6})\mathcal{S}_{i\,\text{av.}}, \quad (11\text{-}171)$$

$$= 7.1 \times 10^{-12}\mathcal{S}_{i\,\text{av.}}. \quad (11\text{-}172)$$

It will be observed that the enormous attenuation arises mostly from reflection at the faces of the conducting sheet, whereas the attenuation within the sheet is relatively unimportant for the thickness we have chosen.

Let us now take into consideration multiple reflections within the copper sheet. We have seen above that reflection is nearly perfect at the second interface. This reflected wave proceeds to the left through the conductor and is similarly reflected to the right at the first interface, and so on. If we neglect multiple reflections, we have Eq. *11-163* for E_{tt}. To take into account the contribution from the wave which is reflected back at the second and then at the first interface, we must add the term

$$2E_{ot} \exp\left[j\left(\omega t + \frac{z+a}{\lambda_0} - \frac{a}{\delta} \right) - \frac{a}{\delta} - \frac{2a}{\delta}(1+j) \right].$$

For the wave which is reflected twice, we add the term

$$2E_{ot} \exp\left[j\left(\omega t + \frac{z+a}{\lambda_0} - \frac{a}{\delta} \right) - \frac{a}{\delta} - \frac{4a}{\delta}(1+j) \right],$$

and so forth. Then the value of the electric field intensity of the wave transmitted through the conducting sheet, taking into account multiple reflections, is

$$E'_{tt} \approx 2E_{ot} \exp\left[j\left(\omega t + \frac{z+a}{\lambda_0} - \frac{a}{\delta} \right) - \frac{a}{\delta} \right]$$

$$\times \left\{ 1 + \exp\left[-\frac{2a}{\delta}(1+j) \right] + \exp\left[-\frac{4a}{\delta}(1+j) \right] + \cdots \right\},$$

where the quantity between braces is of the form

$$1 + x^2 + x^4 + \cdots = \frac{1}{1-x^2}. \quad (11\text{-}173)$$

Then

$$E'_{tt} = \frac{E_{ot} \exp\left[j\left(\omega t + \frac{z+a}{\lambda_0} \right) \right]}{\sinh\left[\frac{a}{\delta}(1+j) \right]}, \quad (11\text{-}174)$$

$$\frac{E'_{ott}}{E_{ot}} = \frac{\exp\left[j(a/\lambda_0) \right]}{\sinh\left[\frac{a}{\delta}(1+j) \right]}, \quad (11\text{-}175)$$

and

$$\mathcal{S}'_{tt\,\text{av.}} = \frac{1}{2}\left(\frac{\epsilon_0}{\mu_0} \right)^{1/2} |E'_{ott}|^2, \quad (11\text{-}176)$$

$$\mathcal{S}'_{tt \text{ av.}} = \frac{\frac{1}{2}\left(\frac{\epsilon_0}{\mu_0}\right)^{1/2}|E_{ot}|^2}{\sinh^2\frac{a}{\delta}\cos^2\frac{a}{\delta} + \cosh^2\frac{a}{\delta}\sin^2\frac{a}{\delta}}, \tag{11-177}$$

$$= \frac{4\frac{\omega\epsilon_0}{\sigma}}{\sinh^2\frac{a}{\delta}\cos^2\frac{a}{\delta} + \cosh^2\frac{a}{\delta}\sin^2\frac{a}{\delta}}\mathcal{S}_{i \text{ av.}}, \tag{11-178}$$

$$= 12.9 \times 10^{-12}\mathcal{S}_{i \text{ av.}}. \tag{11-179}$$

The transmitted energy is thus roughly 50% larger than when multiple reflections are neglected. This is of course true only for the particular conducting sheet considered; with a much thicker sheet multiple reflections would have a negligible effect on $\mathcal{S}_{tt \text{ av.}}$.

11.6. Radiation Pressure

We have now discussed at some length the reflection and the refraction of an electromagnetic wave at the interface between two dielectrics, and then at the interface between a dielectric and a good conductor. We also wish to investigate the same phenomena for the case of a dielectric and an ionized gas. Before going on with this, however, we shall study another phenomenon which is related to reflection from conductors, namely, radiation pressure.

Let us consider an electromagnetic wave incident on a good conductor. We limit ourselves to normal incidence. As we have seen above, the electric field intensity transmitted into the metal is small compared to that of the incident wave, but it is not zero. The **E** and **H** vectors of the transmitted wave inside the conductor are also orthogonal, just as in the incident wave.

The electric field intensity $\mathbf{E}_{ot}$ in the conductor gives rise to a current density $\sigma\mathbf{E}_{ot}$, where σ is the conductivity of the medium. This current, which is oriented like $\mathbf{E}_{ot}$, is perpendicular to the magnetic field of the wave. It turns out, as we shall see below, that under these conditions the electrons carrying the current are pushed by the Lorentz force $\mathbf{B} \times Q\mathbf{u}$ in the direction of propagation of the wave.

We must stop here for a moment to consider the meaning of the conductivity of a conductor. It is observed experimentally that the conduction current density is proportional to the electric field intensity. This is Ohm's law. Physically, this means that conduction electrons acquire an average drift velocity which is proportional to, and in phase with, the force acting on them, that is, to **E**, the drift velocity being limited by collisions with the atoms of the conductor. The conduction electrons are therefore not quite free. The situation would be very different if the electrons were entirely free to move through the metal: the conductivity would then be imaginary, as in the low density gases which we studied in Section 10.5.

We have seen above that the electrons are pushed by the wave in its direction of propagation. The electrons in turn push on the conductor in the process of colliding with the atoms in their path, giving rise to radiation pressure.

To summarize, radiation pressure comes from the fact that the **E** and **H** vectors in a plane electromagnetic wave are orthogonal, phased, and oriented in such a way that the interaction between the conduction current and the magnetic induction produces a force in the direction of propagation.

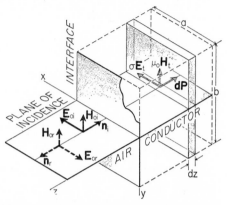

11.6.1. Normal Incidence on a Good Conductor.
Let us study radiation pressure quantitatively for the case of a wave incident normally on a good conductor. We consider a thin slice of the conductor, parallel to the interface, of thickness dz as in Figure 11-27, and ab meters^2 in area. It carries a current $\sigma E ab\, dz$,

Figure 11-27. *The conduction current σE_t and the magnetic induction $\mu_0 H$ which give rise to radiation pressure in an element of volume of a reflector. The sides of the element of volume are parallel to the **E** and **H** vectors. The element has a thickness dz and is ab square meters in area.*

and is submitted to a Lorentz force $\sigma E \mu_0 H ab\, dz$ in the negative direction of the z-axis. It must be noted here that the permeability K_{m2} of the conductor does *not* enter into the calculation. It has been shown that the Lorentz force exerted on an electron within a magnetic material is proportional to $\mu_0 H$ and *not* to $\mu_0 K_{m2}H$, for *slow* electrons like the ones we are considering.[*]

Then the pressure dP exerted by the wave on the sheet of thickness dz is

$$dP = \sigma E_t \mu_0 H_t\, ab\, dz. \qquad (11\text{-}180)$$

With E_t and H_t chosen to be positive in the direction shown in Figure 11-27, a positive result will show that the wave pushes on the conductor.

From Eqs. *11-149* and *11-151*,

$$E_t = \frac{2K_{m2}n_1\delta}{\lambda_0(1-j)} E_{oi} \exp\left[j\left(\omega t + \frac{z}{\delta}\right) + \frac{z}{\delta}\right], \qquad (11\text{-}181)$$

[*] G. H. Wannier, *Phys. Rev.* **72**, 304 (1947).

and, from Eqs. *11-149* and *11-151*,

$$H_t = 2H_{oi} \exp\left[j\left(\omega t + \frac{z}{\delta}\right) + \frac{z}{\delta}\right]. \qquad (11\text{-}182)$$

We cannot use the exponential functions, however, since we must evaluate their *product* (see Appendix F). We must therefore rewrite them in the form

$$E_t = \frac{2K_{m2}n_1\delta}{2^{1/2}\lambda_0} E_{oi}e^{z/\delta} \cos\left(\omega t + \frac{z}{\delta} + \frac{\pi}{4}\right), \qquad (11\text{-}183)$$

$$H_t = 2H_{oi}e^{z/\delta} \cos\left(\omega t + \frac{z}{\delta}\right). \qquad (11\text{-}184)$$

Then

$$dP = \sigma\mu_0\delta E_t H_t \frac{dz}{\delta}, \qquad (11\text{-}185)$$

$$= 4(2^{1/2})n_1 \frac{E_{oi}H_{oi}}{c} e^{2z/\delta} \cos\left(\omega t + \frac{z}{\delta}\right) \cos\left(\omega t + \frac{z}{\delta} + \frac{\pi}{4}\right) \frac{dz}{\delta}. \qquad (11\text{-}186)$$

This is the *instantaneous* value of the pressure on the elementary sheet of thickness dz at z. To find the *average* pressure we must replace the two cosine terms by their average value over one period $T = 2\pi/\omega$:

$$\frac{1}{T} \int_0^T \cos\left(\omega t + \frac{z}{\delta}\right) \cos\left(\omega t + \frac{z}{\delta} + \frac{\pi}{4}\right) dt = \frac{1}{T} \int_0^T \cos \omega t' \cos\left(\omega t' + \frac{\pi}{4}\right) dt', \qquad (11\text{-}187)$$

where we have set

$$\omega t' = \omega t + \frac{z}{\delta}, \qquad (11\text{-}188)$$

or

$$t' = t + \frac{z}{\delta\omega}. \qquad (11\text{-}189)$$

Integrating, we find that this average value is independent of z and equals $1/2^{3/2}$. Then

$$dP_{\text{av.}} = 2n_1 \frac{E_{oi}H_{oi}}{c} e^{2z/\delta} \frac{dz}{\delta}. \qquad (11\text{-}190)$$

The average pressure is thus in the same direction at all depths within the conductor.

Finally, integrating over all z within the conductor from $-\infty$ to 0,

$$P_{\text{av.}} = 2n_1 \frac{E_{oi}H_{oi}}{c} \int_{-\infty}^0 e^{2z/\delta} \frac{dz}{\delta}, \qquad (11\text{-}191)$$

$$= n_1 \frac{E_{oi}H_{oi}}{c}. \qquad (11\text{-}192)$$

This is a positive quantity despite the square root; the calculation has involved several square roots, but they were all positive. As we saw at the beginning of this calculation, the fact that $P_{av.}$ is positive means that it is in the direction of propagation of the incident wave. The quantity $P_{av.}$ is the average force on a unit area of the conductor due to the incident radiation, or the *radiation pressure*.

We can also write that

$$P_{av.} = \frac{E_{oi}H_{oi}}{u}, \tag{11-193}$$

$$= 2\frac{S_{av.}}{u}, \tag{11-194}$$

where u is the velocity and $S_{av.}$ is the average of the absolute value of the Poynting vector for the *incident* wave (Eq. *10-39*).

We can ascribe this pressure to a change in momentum of $2S_{av.}/u$ per unit time and per unit area in the incident wave, the factor 2 being required because the wave is reflected with a momentum equal to its initial momentum but of opposite sign.

An electromagnetic wave can therefore be considered to involve a flux of momentum which is equal to $S_{av.}/u$, or to its energy density, according to Eq. *10-42;* that is,

(Flux of momentum) = (Momentum density) × (Wave velocity),   *(11-195)*

= (Energy density).   *(11-196)*

These results agree with those of atomic physics, where we consider an electromagnetic wave to involve photons of energy $\hbar\omega$ ($\hbar = 1.05 \times 10^{-34}$ joule-second is Planck's constant divided by 2π) and of momentum $\hbar/\lambda$ traveling with a velocity u:

$$\frac{\hbar}{\lambda}u = \hbar\omega. \tag{11-197}$$

The radiation pressure of an electromagnetic wave has been observed experimentally and has been found to agree with theory. This can be taken as confirmation that the effective magnetic induction acting on a *slow* electron inside a magnetic material is $\mu_0 H$, and not $K_m\mu_0 H$.

Radiation pressure is very small indeed for the usual radiation intensities. For example, the Poynting vector for sunlight is approximately 1.4 kilowatts/meter² at the surface of the earth, giving a radiation pressure of about 10^{-5} newton/meter² or 10^{-7} gram/centimeter² on a metallic reflector. The radiation pressure P varies as the inverse square of the distance from the source, as does the Poynting vector S. To find P at the surface of the sun we must multiply the above figures by

$$\left(\frac{\text{mean distance of earth to sun}}{\text{radius of sun}}\right)^2 = \left(\frac{1.5 \times 10^{11}}{7 \times 10^8}\right)^2, \tag{11-198}$$

$$= 4 \times 10^4, \tag{11-199}$$

which still gives only 4×10^{-3} gram/centimeter^2, or 4×10^{-6} atmosphere. Radiation pressure is unimportant even in the interior of the sun, but it possibly plays an important role in the more luminous stars. As is well known, comet tails point predominantly away from the sun. This phenomenon is explained, at least in part, by radiation pressure.

Much higher power densities and pressures are available in waveguides, where $\mathcal{S}_{av}$. can reach values of the order of 10^9 watts/meter^2 with velocities of the order of the velocity of light c. Then the radiation pressure is 0.1 gram/centimeter^2, assuming that the waves propagating within waveguides are plane. This is not correct, as we shall see, but the error is unimportant here, since we are concerned only with orders of magnitude.

11.7. Reflection of an Electromagnetic Wave by an Ionized Gas

Let us now examine the behavior of an electromagnetic wave which encounters an ionized gas. We assume, as in Section 10-5, that the electrons have an infinite mean free path and thus do not collide with the atoms of the gas. Under these conditions, the phase velocity is *greater* in the ionized gas than in free space, the index of refraction being given by

$$n = \frac{c}{u} = \left[1 - \left(\frac{\omega_p}{\omega} \right)^2 \right]^{1/2}, \tag{11-200}$$

$$= \left[1 - 80 \, \frac{N_e}{f^2} \right]^{2}, \tag{11-201}$$

from Eqs. *10-175* and *10-176*. Here c is the velocity of light, u is the phase velocity of the wave, ω_p is the plasma angular frequency, N_e is the number of free electrons per cubic meter, and f is the frequency of the wave.

If an ionized gas could be produced with a definite boundary and with a uniform value of N_e throughout its volume, reflection and refraction at its surface would be simple to describe: the ionized gas would simply act as a dielectric with an index of refraction less than unity, and the laws of reflection, Snell's law and Fresnel's equations would apply.

The situation is much more complex than this in the ionosphere. We shall not attempt here a rigorous discussion of wave propagation in such inhomogeneous media. This would involve the solution of a nonlinear wave equation (Eq. *10-10*), where the conductivity σ (Eq. *10-147*) is a function of the coordinates.

When an electromagnetic wave is incident on an ionized region at oblique incidence, it is reflected in much the same way that a light wave is reflected in a mirage. Let us examine this phenomenon. It is of great practical importance because the propagation of radio waves over large distances beyond the horizon depends on this reflection.

   We shall neglect the curvature of the earth's surface, as well as the earth's magnetic field. We shall also assume that the index of refraction n varies slowly with the altitude z, but not with the other two coordinates x and y. To be more specific, we shall assume that n varies by a negligible amount in a distance Δz of one wavelength. If N_e gradually increases with z, a given ray gradually bends down as in Figure 11-28 to an angle θ, at a point where the index of refraction is n.

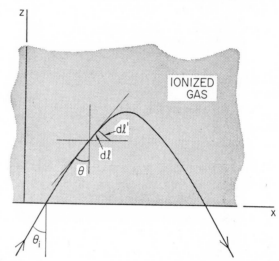

Figure 11-28

An electromagnetic wave incident on an ionized region at an angle θ_i is deflected at an angle θ after penetrating to a distance z.

   We can calculate θ in the following way. When refraction occurs at an interface between any two media of indices n_1 and n_2, Snell's law (Eq. *11-14*) shows that the quantity $n \sin \theta$ is conserved in going from one side of the interface to the other. If the index of refraction varies continuously, the medium can be imagined to be stratified in infinitely thin layers and $n \sin \theta$ is similarly conserved all along the ray. The index of refraction n at the point where the angle between the ray and the normal is θ is therefore again given by Snell's law:

$$n \sin \theta = n_1 \sin \theta_i, \qquad (11\text{-}202)$$

where $n_1 \sin \theta_i$ is a constant for the ray considered. In the case of reflection in the ionosphere, we can set $n_1 = 1$, and then

$$n \sin \theta = \sin \theta_i. \qquad (11\text{-}203)$$

   It is interesting to differentiate this equation with respect to the distance l measured along a ray. We find that

$$\frac{d\theta}{dl} = -\frac{1}{n}\frac{dn}{dl} \tan \theta. \qquad (11\text{-}204)$$

If the ray penetrates into an ionized region where the ion density *increases* with z, the index of refraction n *decreases* with l and the derivative dn/dl is negative, so that the angle θ *increases* with the distance as in Figure 11-28. After some distance, if n becomes sufficiently large, θ becomes equal to 90°. At that point the tangent of θ becomes infinite but dn/dl becomes zero, the ray being horizontal. After this, θ becomes negative, whereas the derivative dn/dl becomes positive, and θ keeps increasing until the ray escapes from the ionized region at an angle equal to the angle of incidence θ_i.

At the highest altitude attained,

$$\sin \theta = 1, \qquad (11\text{-}205)$$

and

$$n_{90°} = \sin \theta_i. \qquad (11\text{-}206)$$

This is the index of refraction required for reflection when the angle of incidence is θ_i.

From the above value of n,

$$\sec \theta_i = \frac{\omega}{\omega_p}, \qquad (11\text{-}207)$$

where ω is the angular frequency of the wave and ω_p is the plasma frequency at the level where reflection occurs, that is, where $\theta = 90°$. At normal incidence, $\theta_i = 0$, $\sec \theta_i = 1$, and reflection occurs at a height such that $\omega_p = \omega$, that is, at the point where $n = 0$ and the phase velocity becomes infinite. At oblique incidence, however, $\sec \theta_i > 1$, and reflection occurs where $\omega_p < \omega$, that is, at a *lower* altitude, if we assume that the electron density N_e, and hence ω_p, increase with height.

We have found above the value of $d\theta/dl$. This is the reciprocal of the radius of curvature R, thus

$$\frac{1}{R} = -\frac{1}{n}\frac{dn}{dl}\tan \theta. \qquad (11\text{-}208)$$

A positive value of R corresponds to a positive value of $d\theta/dl$ and to a trajectory which is concave downwards in this case. We also have

$$\frac{1}{R} = -\frac{1}{n}\frac{dn}{dl'}, \qquad (11\text{-}209)$$

where l' is perpendicular to the direction of propagation, as in Figure 11-28. The ray therefore bends most sharply where the index of refraction n varies most rapidly in the direction perpendicular to the ray.*

---

* For a more detailed discussion of the reflection of radio waves in the ionosphere, the student is referred to engineering texts such as F. E. Terman, *Electronic and Radio Engineering*, Chapter 22 (McGraw-Hill, New York, 1955) and to S. K. Mitra, *The Upper Atmosphere*, Chapter 6 (The Asiatic Society, Calcutta, 1952).

11.8. Summary

For a plane electromagnetic wave incident on the interface between two different media, we define the *plane of incidence* as containing the normal **n** to the interface and the normal $\mathbf{n}_i$ to a wave front of the incident wave.

From the requirement of continuity for the tangential components of **E** and of **H** across the interface, we find the laws of reflection, Snell's law, and Fresnel's equations.

The *laws of reflection* are (a) the angle of reflection is equal to the angle of incidence and (b) the normal to a wavefront of the reflected wave is in the plane of incidence.

Snell's law gives θ_t if n_1, n_2, and θ_i are known:

$$\frac{\sin \theta_t}{\sin \theta_i} = \frac{n_1}{n_2}, \tag{11-14}$$

where θ_i and θ_t are the angles of incidence and of refraction respectively and where n_1 is the index of refraction of the first medium and n_2 is that of the second medium.

Fresnel's equations give the amplitudes and phases of the reflected and transmitted waves with respect to the incident wave. The indexes N and P in Eqs. *11-21* to *11-27* indicate that the **E** vector of the incident wave is either *normal* or *parallel* to the plane of incidence.

$$\left(\frac{E_{or}}{E_{oi}}\right)_N = \frac{\dfrac{n_1}{K_{m1}} \cos \theta_i - \dfrac{n_2}{K_{m2}} \cos \theta_t}{\dfrac{n_1}{K_{m1}} \cos \theta_i + \dfrac{n_2}{K_{m2}} \cos \theta_t}, \tag{11-21}$$

$$\left(\frac{E_{ot}}{E_{oi}}\right)_N = \frac{2\,\dfrac{n_1}{K_{m1}} \cos \theta_i}{\dfrac{n_1}{K_{m1}} \cos \theta_i + \dfrac{n_2}{K_{m2}} \cos \theta_t}, \tag{11-22}$$

$$\left(\frac{E_{or}}{E_{oi}}\right)_P = \frac{-\left(\dfrac{n_2}{K_{m2}}\right) \cos \theta_i + \left(\dfrac{n_1}{K_{m1}}\right) \cos \theta_t}{\left(\dfrac{n_2}{K_{m2}}\right) \cos \theta_i + \left(\dfrac{n_1}{K_{m1}}\right) \cos \theta_t}, \tag{11-26}$$

$$\left(\frac{E_{ot}}{E_{oi}}\right)_P = \frac{2\left(\dfrac{n_1}{K_{m1}}\right) \cos \theta_i}{\left(\dfrac{n_2}{K_{m2}}\right) \cos \theta_i + \left(\dfrac{n_1}{K_{m1}}\right) \cos \theta_t}. \tag{11-27}$$

At the *Brewster angle* for dielectrics there is *no* reflected wave if the incident wave is polarized with its vector **E** in the plane of incidence:

$$\frac{n_1}{n_2} = \cot \theta_{iB}. \tag{11-45}$$

The coefficient of reflection R gives the fraction of the incident power which is reflected. Similarly, the *coefficient of transmission T* is the fraction of the incident power which is transmitted. Thus $R + T = 1$. At normal incidence

$$R = \left[\frac{\left(\dfrac{n_1}{n_2}\right) - 1}{\left(\dfrac{n_1}{n_2}\right) + 1} \right]^2, \tag{11-56}$$

$$T = \frac{4\left(\dfrac{n_1}{n_2}\right)}{\left[\left(\dfrac{n_1}{n_2}\right) + 1\right]^2}. \tag{11-57}$$

Total reflection occurs when Snell's law gives $\sin \theta_t \geq 1$. Then $R = 1$. The transmitted wave travels along the interface, and is attenuated exponentially in the direction perpendicular to the interface. The average energy flow across the interface is zero, but the instantaneous flow is alternately one way and then the other. Snell's law and Fresnel's equations give the correct results when applied to total reflection if we set

$$\cos \theta_t = -(1 - \sin^2 \theta_t)^{1/2}. \tag{11-83}$$

Good conductors have a coefficient of reflection R close to unity. The transmitted wave penetrates nearly perpendicularly into the conductor, whatever the angle of incidence, n_2 being much larger than n_1. It is attenuated by a factor e in one skin depth

$$\delta = \left(\frac{2}{\omega \sigma_2 \mu_2}\right)^{1/2}. \tag{11-125}$$

The Fresnel equations again apply if we set

$$\cos \theta_t = +[1 - \sin^2 \theta_t]^{1/2}. \tag{11-128}$$

At normal incidence, *standing waves* are formed in front of a good conductor, the reflecting surface giving a node of $\mathbf{E}$ and a loop of $\mathbf{H}$. Nodes of $\mathbf{E}$ and of $\mathbf{H}$ are spaced $\lambda/4$ apart.

Radiation pressure is due to the Lorentz force on the electrons oscillating under the influence of the $\mathbf{E}$ and $\mathbf{H}$ vectors of the incident wave. It is shown that

$$P = 2\frac{\mathcal{S}_{\text{av}}}{u}. \tag{11-194}$$

where P is the radiation pressure in newtons/meter^2, $\mathcal{S}_{\text{av.}}$ is the magnitude of the Poynting vector in watts/meter^2, and u is the phase velocity of the wave in meters/second. This leads to the concepts of flux of momentum and of momentum density for an electromagnetic wave. The forces due to radiation pressure are small and are usually negligible from a mechanical point of view.

An *ionized gas* will reflect an electromagnetic wave just as light waves are reflected in a mirage, the velocity in the gas being greater than in free space. Assuming that the ionization density does not vary parallel to the interface, we find that Snell's law applies:

$$n \sin \theta = n_1 \sin \theta_i, \qquad (11\text{-}202)$$

where θ_i is the angle of incidence, n_1 is the index of refraction of medium 1, and θ gives the orientation of the ray at the point where the index of refraction is n. In the ionosphere, $n_1 = 1$, and reflection occurs when

$$n_{90°} = \sin \theta_i. \qquad (11\text{-}206)$$

The height at which reflection occurs increases as the angle of incidence θ_i decreases, and, at normal incidence, reflection occurs at the altitude where ω is equal to the plasma frequency ω_p. At this point the phase velocity is infinite.

Problems

11-1. Show that the constants A and B of Eqs. *11-2* and *11-3* are zero if the origin is chosen to be in the interface.

11-2. In the general case of a plane wave in a nonconductor, we have

$$\mathbf{E} = (E_{ox}\mathbf{i} + E_{oy}\mathbf{j} + E_{oz}\mathbf{k}) \exp [j(\omega t - k_x x - k_y y - k_z z)],$$

where the coefficients E_{ox}, E_{oy}, E_{oz}, k_x, k_y, k_z are constants which can be complex. The vector $\mathbf{H}$ is given by a similar expression with the same values of k_x, k_y, k_z.
Show that

$$k_x^2 + k_y^2 + k_z^2 = k^2,$$

where k is the wave number corresponding to the medium and the frequency under consideration.
Show that $\mathbf{E}$, $\mathbf{B}$, and $\mathbf{k}$ are mutually orthogonal.

11-3. A 60-watt light bulb is situated in air at 1 meter from a water surface. Calculate the rms values of E and H for the incident, reflected, and refracted rays at the surface of the water directly under the bulb. Assume that all the power is dissipated as electromagnetic radiation. The index of refraction of water is 1.33.
Calculate the coefficients of reflection and of transmission.

11-4. Deduce the Fresnel equations for the $\mathbf{H}$ vectors for the case in which the $\mathbf{E}$ vector of the incident wave is normal to the plane of incidence.

11-5. A plane wave is reflected at the interface between two dielectrics whose indexes of refraction are slightly different. The wave is incident in medium 1, and $n_1/n_2 = 1 + a$. Show that the coefficients of reflection for waves polarized with their $\mathbf{E}$ vectors in the plane of incidence, and normal to this plane, are both given approximately by

$$R = \frac{1 - A}{1 + A},$$

where

$$A^2 = 1 - 2a \tan^2 \theta_i,$$

θ_i being the angle of incidence.

11-6. Show that the coefficient of reflection R and the coefficient of transmission T are equal at normal incidence if the ratio of the indices of refraction is 5.83. Assume that both media are dielectrics.

11-7. How could one eliminate the reflected wave in the case of normal incidence on a dielectric? Take multiple reflections into account.

11-8. Light is transmitted at normal incidence from a medium with index of refraction n to another of index $n + a$. Express the coefficient of transmission T as a power series in a/n, and show that the first two terms give an accuracy of 1% for $(a/n) \leqq 1/3$, approximately.

What is the value of T for light emerging from ordinary glass ($n = 1.52$) into air?

Do reflection-reducing coatings on lenses improve the transmission significantly? Why are they used?

11-9. Show that a wave incident on a plate of dielectric at the Brewster angle goes through the plate without producing any reflected ray.

11-10. In the case of a wave incident in air on a medium with $K_m \neq 1$, show that $(E_{or}/E_{oi})_P$ is zero for $\tan^2 \theta_i = K_e(K_e - K_m)/(K_eK_m - 1)$, and hence that the Brewster angle exists only if $K_e > K_m$. Show that $(E_{oi}/E_{or})_N$ can also be zero.

11-11. Construct $\sin (a + jb)$ and $\cos (a + jb)$, where a and b are both real, in the complex plane. Over what ranges of values can these two functions vary?

11-12. For a plane sinusoidal wave, all of the rectangular components of the field vectors $\mathbf{E}$, $\mathbf{D}$, $\mathbf{B}$, and $\mathbf{H}$ are of the form

$$W = W_0 \exp [j(\omega t - \mathbf{k} \cdot \mathbf{r})],$$

where W_0 can be complex. In the general case, $\mathbf{k}$ is also complex and can be set equal to $a\mathbf{n}_1 - jb\mathbf{n}_2$.

Show that surfaces of constant phase are normal to $\mathbf{n}_1$ and that surfaces of constant amplitude are normal to $\mathbf{n}_2$.

Show also that a is related to the wavelength and b to the attenuation.

Show that, in all the operations involving ∇, this operator can be replaced by $-j\mathbf{k}$. Rewrite Maxwell's equations utilizing this fact.

Show that $\mathbf{E}$ is normal to the wave number $\mathbf{k}$ and that $\mathbf{H}$ is necessarily normal to $\mathbf{E}$, assuming zero space charge density and uniform K_e and K_m throughout the medium.

11-13. An electromagnetic wave polarized with its $\mathbf{E}$ vector normal to the plane of incidence is totally reflected at the interface between air and a dielectric whose index of refraction is 3.0. The angle of incidence is 75°.

Calculate δ_z/λ_2 and δ_z/λ_1.

Calculate the phases of the reflected and transmitted waves with respect to the incident wave at any point on the interface.

Draw wave fronts for all three waves in the neighborhood of the interface, showing the phase shifts found above. Draw parallel lines spaced 2π apart to represent the wave fronts.

Check the continuity of E across the interface.

Compare your results with Figure 11-15.

11-14. In the case of total reflection of a wave polarized with its $\mathbf{E}$ vector normal to the plane of incidence, we have found in Eqs. *11-100* and *11-101* that the x- and z-components of the $\mathbf{H}$ vector are out of phase by $\pi/2$ radians. In what direction does the **H** vector rotate with respect to the direction of propagation of the transmitted wave: does it rotate like the wheels of a moving vehicle or in the opposite direction?

11-15. A wave polarized with its **E** vector parallel to the plane of incidence is totally reflected at the interface between two dielectrics. Show that both the reflected and transmitted waves can be deduced from Snell's law and Fresnel's equations if $\cos \theta_t$ is written as in Eq. *11-84*.

Show that the coefficient of reflection R is equal to unity.

Show that

$$\left(\frac{E_{or}}{E_{oi}}\right)_P = -\exp\left\{2j \arctan \frac{\left[\left(\frac{n_1}{n_2}\right)^2 \sin^2 \theta_i - 1\right]^{1/2}}{\frac{n_2}{n_1} \cos \theta_i}\right\}$$

11-16. A wave travels in a medium with index of refraction n_1 and is totally reflected at an interface with a medium n_2. The incident wave is polarized such that its **E** vector has components parallel and normal to the plane of incidence. Show that the reflected wave is elliptically polarized and that its component which has its **E** vector parallel to the plane of incidence leads the other component by an angle of

$$\frac{\cos \theta_i \left[\sin^2 \theta_i - \left(\frac{n_2}{n_1}\right)^2\right]^{1/2}}{\sin^2 \theta_i}.$$

11-17. A scintillator is a substance which emits light when traversed by an ionizing particle, such as an electron. This light is then detected by a photomultiplier, which produces electric pulses that actuate counters and other electronic equipment. The scintillator has an index of refraction n_1 and is fixed to the face of the photomultiplier with a cement of index n_2. Light is emitted in all directions in the scintillator, a fraction F being transmitted out of the scintillator in the direction of the photomultiplier.

Calculate this fraction F as a function of $\frac{n_1}{n_2}$, assuming that all the light is transmitted for angles of incidence smaller than the critical angle and that the scintillator is not surrounded by a reflecting substance.

How would the efficiency of light collection be affected by a plane reflector parallel to the photomultiplier face?

Draw a graph of F for values of n_2/n_1 ranging from 0.1 to 1.0.

Evaluate roughly the error involved in assuming that the coefficient of transmission is equal to unity for all angles smaller than the critical angle.

11-18. Show that the standing wave pattern resulting from the reflection of an electromagnetic wave at the surface of a good conductor as shown in Figure 11-25 is correct at $\omega t = (2n + 1)\pi$.

11-19. A wave is incident on a plate of dielectric backed by a perfect conductor. Under what conditions will there be no multiple reflections?

11-20. Show that the ratio of the amplitudes of the reflected and incident waves for reflection at the surface of a good conductor in air is given by

$$\frac{E_{or}}{E_{oi}} = 1 - \frac{\delta}{\lambda_0} \cos \theta_i$$

if the conductor is nonmagnetic.

11-21. Calculate $(E_{or}/E_{oi})_P$ for the reflection of an electromagnetic wave from the surface of a good conductor when the incident wave is polarized with its **E** vector parallel to the plane of incidence.

Show that the reflected wave leads the incident wave by an angle ϕ_p such that

$$\phi_p = \text{arc tan } \frac{2\alpha \cos \theta_i}{\alpha^2 - 2 \cos^2 \theta_i},$$

where

$$\alpha = \frac{n_1}{\lambda_0} K_{m2}\delta \ll 1.$$

11-22. Compare the forces due to the gravitational attraction and to the radiation pressure of the sun on a spherical particle of radius r and of specific gravity 5. The sun has a mass of 2.0×10^{30} kilograms, and it radiates 3.8×10^{26} watts in the form of electromagnetic radiation. The gravitational constant is 6.7×10^{-11} newton-meter^2/kilogram^2. In computing the radiation pressure, assume a flat area of πr^2 normal to the incident rays, and assume that the particle is conducting. For what radius are the two forces equal?

11-23. A radio wave is incident at an angle θ_i on the ionosphere. Assuming that the index of refraction n decreases linearly with altitude, calculate the radius of curvature R of a ray as a function of n.

Sketch the trajectory of rays incident at three different angles of incidence.

Show that a ray would describe a circular arc of radius R if the index of refraction were given by

$$n = \frac{R \sin \theta_i}{z + R \sin \theta_i}.$$

Draw a sketch of the ray showing θ_i and the center of curvature. Show that $n = \sin \theta_i$ at the top of the trajectory.

CHAPTER 12

Guided Waves

In Chapters 9 and 10 we studied the propagation of plane waves in an infinite, unbounded region, first in a vacuum, and then in various media. Then in Chapter 11 we studied reflection and refraction of plane waves at the boundary between two different media. We now wish to study the manner in which waves can be guided in prescribed directions by conducting *wave guides*. Various types of such wave guides are illustrated in Figures 12-1, 12-2, and 12-3.

We shall first investigate the propagation of waves in the positive direction of the z-axis, but without making any assumption as to their dependence on the x- and y-coordinates. This discussion will therefore be more general than that of Chapters 9 and 10. The plane wave will follow as a particular case. Finally, we shall study two relatively simple types of guided waves.

12.1. The General Case of a Wave Propagating in the Positive Direction Along the z-Axis

If we assume that the medium of propagation is linear and homogeneous, then

$$\mathbf{D} = K_e\epsilon_0\mathbf{E} = \epsilon\mathbf{E}, \qquad (12\text{-}1)$$

and

$$\mathbf{H} = \frac{\mathbf{B}}{K_m\mu_0} = \frac{\mathbf{B}}{\mu}, \qquad (12\text{-}2)$$

where ϵ and μ are constant.

We set the conductivity σ of the medium of propagation to be equal to zero; since electromagnetic waves are highly attenuated in conductors, they cannot be used as the medium of propagation. This does *not* exclude metallic wave guides, for even in these the conductivity is zero in the medium of propagation: the wave is propagated *outside* the conductors whose presence determines certain boundary conditions. We also set the charge density $\rho = 0$ in the medium of propagation.

409

We finally assume that propagation occurs in a straight line, namely, in the positive direction along the z-axis. Then, in the general case, the wave has both transverse and longitudinal components, and, for a sinusoidal wave,

$$\mathbf{E} = (E_{ox}\mathbf{i} + E_{oy}\mathbf{j} + E_{oz}\mathbf{k}) \exp[j(\omega t - k_g z)] = \mathbf{E}_0 \exp[j(\omega t - k_g z)] \quad (12\text{-}3)$$

$$\mathbf{H} = (H_{ox}\mathbf{i} + H_{oy}\mathbf{j} + H_{oz}\mathbf{k}) \exp[j(\omega t - k_g z)] = \mathbf{H}_0 \exp[j(\omega t - k_g z)] \quad (12\text{-}4)$$

where the coefficients E_{ox}, E_{oy}, E_{oz}, H_{ox}, $\cdots$ are as yet unspecified functions of x and of y only. All of the dependence on t and on z appears in the exponential function, which is characteristic of a wave propagating in the positive direction of the z-axis.

The wave number

$$k_g = \frac{1}{\lambda_g} \quad (12\text{-}5)$$

is that for the guided wave; it is *not* necessarily equal to

$$k = \frac{1}{\lambda} = \frac{\omega}{u} = \omega(\epsilon\mu)^{1/2} = \omega(K_e\epsilon_0 K_m\mu_0)^{1/2}, \quad (12\text{-}6)$$

which is the wave number for a *plane* wave in the medium under consideration (Section 10.2) and which depends exclusively on the circular frequency ω, the dielectric coefficient K_e, and the relative permeability K_m of the medium of propagation. Since this medium is either dry air or some appropriate dielectric, K_m can be set equal to unity. The wave number k_g is in general complex:

$$k_g = k_{gr} - jk_{gi}. \quad (12\text{-}7)$$

If the imaginary part is not zero, the wave is attenuated, as can be seen from Eqs. *12-3* and *12-4*.

It is interesting to compare our present procedure with that of the preceding chapter. In discussing reflection and refraction, we used exponential functions to describe the dependence of the reflected and transmitted waves on all three coordinates, as, for example, in Eq. *11-63*. Here we have used an exponential function only for the z-coordinate, whereas the dependence on x and on y is left unspecified; our treatment is therefore more general than was required in Chapter 11.

Let us write out Maxwell's equations for this field. Since $\mathbf{\nabla \cdot D} = 0$, and since $\epsilon = $ constant, it follows that $\mathbf{\nabla \cdot E} = 0$. Then

$$\frac{\partial E_{ox}}{\partial x} + \frac{\partial E_{oy}}{\partial y} = jk_g E_{oz}. \quad (12\text{-}8)$$

Similarly, since $\mathbf{\nabla \cdot B} = 0$ and, since $\mu = $ constant, $\mathbf{\nabla \cdot H} = 0$, and

$$\frac{\partial H_{ox}}{\partial x} + \frac{\partial H_{oy}}{\partial y} = jk_g H_{oz}. \quad (12\text{-}9)$$

From $\nabla \times \mathbf{E} = -\partial \mathbf{B}/\partial t$,

$$\frac{\partial E_{oz}}{\partial y} + jk_g E_{oy} = -j\omega\mu H_{ox}, \qquad (12\text{-}10)$$

$$jk_g E_{ox} + \frac{\partial E_{oz}}{\partial x} = j\omega\mu H_{oy}, \qquad (12\text{-}11)$$

$$\frac{\partial E_{oy}}{\partial x} - \frac{\partial E_{ox}}{\partial y} = -j\omega\mu H_{oz}, \qquad (12\text{-}12)$$

and, from $\nabla \times \mathbf{H} = \partial \mathbf{D}/\partial t$,

$$\frac{\partial H_{oz}}{\partial y} + jk_g H_{oy} = j\omega\epsilon E_{ox}, \qquad (12\text{-}13)$$

$$jk_g H_{ox} + \frac{\partial H_{oz}}{\partial x} = -j\omega\epsilon E_{oy}, \qquad (12\text{-}14)$$

$$\frac{\partial H_{oy}}{\partial x} - \frac{\partial H_{ox}}{\partial y} = j\omega\epsilon E_{oz}. \qquad (12\text{-}15)$$

We can now deduce the important result that all four transverse components E_{ox}, E_{oy}, H_{ox}, and H_{oy} can be calculated from the two longitudinal components E_{oz} and H_{oz}. From Eqs. *12-11* and *12-13*,

$$E_{ox} = \frac{-j\omega\mu}{\dfrac{1}{\lambda^2} - \dfrac{1}{\lambda_g^2}} \left(\frac{k_g}{\omega\mu} \frac{\partial E_{oz}}{\partial x} + \frac{\partial H_{oz}}{\partial y} \right) \qquad (\lambda_g \neq \lambda). \qquad (12\text{-}16)$$

We have made the additional assumption that the wave length λ for a plane wave is different from the wavelength of the guided wave, or that $\lambda \neq \lambda_g$. The case in which $\lambda = \lambda_g$ will be discussed separately below.

Similarly,

$$E_{oy} = \frac{j\omega\mu}{\dfrac{1}{\lambda^2} - \dfrac{1}{\lambda_g^2}} \left(-\frac{k_g}{\omega\mu} \frac{\partial E_{oz}}{\partial y} + \frac{\partial H_{oz}}{\partial x} \right) \qquad (\lambda_g \neq \lambda), \qquad (12\text{-}17)$$

$$H_{oz} = \frac{j\omega\epsilon}{\dfrac{1}{\lambda^2} - \dfrac{1}{\lambda_g^2}} \left(\frac{\partial E_{oz}}{\partial y} - \frac{k_g}{\omega\epsilon} \frac{\partial H_{oz}}{\partial x} \right) \qquad (\lambda_g \neq \lambda), \qquad (12\text{-}18)$$

$$H_{oy} = \frac{-j\omega\epsilon}{\dfrac{1}{\lambda^2} - \dfrac{1}{\lambda_g^2}} \left(\frac{\partial E_{oz}}{\partial x} + \frac{k_g}{\omega\epsilon} \frac{\partial H_{oz}}{\partial y} \right) \qquad (\lambda_g \neq \lambda), \qquad (12\text{-}19)$$

It is obvious, by inspection of the above equations, that the wave is completely determined once E_{oz} and H_{oz} are known.

The wave equation *10-25*

$$\nabla^2 \mathbf{E} = \epsilon\mu \frac{\partial^2 \mathbf{E}}{\partial t^2} = -k^2 \mathbf{E} \qquad (12\text{-}20)$$

supplies a differential equation for E_{oz}:

$$\frac{\partial^2 E_{oz}}{\partial x^2} + \frac{\partial^2 E_{oz}}{\partial y^2} - k_g^2 E_{oz} = -k^2 E_{oz}, \qquad (12\text{-}21)$$

or

$$\frac{\partial^2 E_{oz}}{\partial x^2} + \frac{\partial^2 E_{oz}}{\partial y^2} = -\left(\frac{1}{\lambda^2} - \frac{1}{\lambda_g^2}\right) E_{oz}. \qquad (12\text{-}22)$$

An identical equation applies to H_{oz}:

$$\frac{\partial^2 H_{oz}}{\partial x^2} + \frac{\partial^2 H_{oz}}{\partial y^2} = -\left(\frac{1}{\lambda^2} - \frac{1}{\lambda_g^2}\right) H_{oz}. \qquad (12\text{-}23)$$

The problem is therefore to solve these two partial differential equations for E_{oz} and H_{oz}.

The radian length of the guided wave λ_g is as yet unspecified; this is a constant which must be selected properly in order that E_{oz} and H_{oz} can satisfy the above differential equations, as well as the boundary conditions defined by the structure guiding the wave. It turns out, as we shall see in Section 12.3.1, that only certain discrete values of $\lambda_g = 1/k_g$ are appropriate. These values are called the *characteristic* or *eigen values* of the equation, and they depend (a) on the frequency, (b) on the electrical characteristics (K_e, K_m) of the medium of propagation, and (c) on the geometry and on the electrical properties (σ, K_e, and K_m) of the guiding structure.

The general procedure for calculating the field vectors **E** and **H** is therefore the following. We first solve the above wave equations for E_{oz} and for H_{oz}, using the boundary conditions for the wave guide under consideration. This gives not only E_{oz} and H_{oz}, but also λ_g. The transverse components of **E** and of **H** are then deduced from Eqs. *12-16* to *12-19*. It is of course also possible to use Maxwell's equations directly, in conjunction with the boundary conditions.

12.1.1. TE and TM Waves. It is convenient to consider separately two different types of wave: *Transverse Electric*, or TE waves, for which the longitudinal component of the electric field intensity $E_{oz} = 0$, and *Transverse Magnetic*, or TM waves, for which $H_{oz} = 0$. It will be observed from the above equations for E_{ox}, E_{oy}, H_{ox}, and H_{oy} that, as long as $\lambda_g \neq \lambda$, any wave propagating in the positive direction of the z-axis can be considered to be the superposition of these two types of waves. We shall study one particular type of TE wave later on in this chapter.

Let us write out the transverse components of **E** and of **H** in vector form:

$$\mathbf{E}_{ot} = E_{ox}\mathbf{i} + E_{oy}\mathbf{j}, \qquad (12\text{-}24)$$

$$\mathbf{H}_{ot} = H_{ox}\mathbf{i} + H_{oy}\mathbf{j}. \qquad (12\text{-}25)$$

We can gain information on the relative orientations of these two vectors from their scalar product. We find that

$$\mathbf{E}_{ot}\cdot\mathbf{H}_{ot} = E_{ox}H_{ox} + E_{oy}H_{oy} = 0 \qquad (12\text{-}26)$$

for both TE and TM waves. *The transverse components of* **E** *and of* **H** *are thus everywhere mutually perpendicular.* This applies to *any* TE or TM wave propagating in a straight line. Our demonstration is valid only for $\lambda_g \neq \lambda$, but the result is correct for any value of λ_g, as we shall see in Section 12.1.3.

We also have, for TE waves ($E_{oz} = 0$),

$$\left|\frac{E_{ot}}{H_{ot}}\right| = \left(\frac{E_{ox}^2 + E_{oy}^2}{H_{ox}^2 + H_{oy}^2}\right)^{1/2}, \qquad (12\text{-}27)$$

$$= \frac{\omega\mu}{k_g} = \left(\frac{\mu}{\epsilon}\right)^{1/2}\frac{\lambda_g}{\lambda}, \qquad (12\text{-}28)$$

$$= 377\frac{\lambda_g}{\lambda_0} \quad \text{(ohms)} \qquad (K_e = 1, K_m = 1), \qquad (12\text{-}29)$$

and, for TM waves ($H_{oz} = 0$),

$$\left|\frac{E_{ot}}{H_{ot}}\right| = \frac{k}{\omega\epsilon} = \left(\frac{\mu}{\epsilon}\right)^{1/2}\frac{\lambda}{\lambda_g}, \qquad (12\text{-}30)$$

$$= 377\frac{\lambda_0}{\lambda_g} \quad \text{(ohms)} \qquad (K_e = 1, K_m = 1). \qquad (12\text{-}31)$$

The ratio $|E_{ot}/H_{ot}|$ is called the *wave impedance.* Our demonstration is again valid only for $\lambda_g \neq \lambda$, but the result is really correct for any value of λ_g, as will also be shown in Section 12.1.3.

12.1.2. Boundary Conditions for Metallic Wave Guides.

The solution of the differential equations *12-22* and *12-23* for E_{oz} and for H_{oz} requires some knowledge of the boundary conditions. For TM waves and metallic wave guides, the boundary conditions are simple: the tangential component of **E** must vanish at the surfaces of an infinitely conducting guide. Then, at the surface of the guide, **E** must be normal, and E_{oz} must be equal to zero. Real conduc-

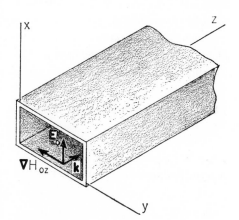

Figure 12-1. *Portion of a rectangular wave guide. The electromagnetic wave propagates inside the tube. If the guide is perfectly conducting, the electric field intensity* **E** *is zero in the conductor, and* **E** *is either normal or zero at the surface. For a TE wave, it is shown that* ∇H_{oz} *is tangent to the wall.*

tors, of course, do not have infinite conductivity and we shall deal with this matter in Section 12.3.4.

For TE waves and metallic wave guides, the boundary conditions are not quite as simple, since E_{oz} is then zero everywhere. We again assume a perfectly conducting guide, and $\mathbf{E}$ is therefore normal to its surface. Substituting the values of E_{ox} and E_{oy} in the expression for $\mathbf{E}_{ot}$, which is equal to $\mathbf{E}_0$ in this case, since $\mathbf{E}_0$ is transverse by definition, we find that

$$\mathbf{E}_0 = \frac{j\omega\mu}{\dfrac{1}{\lambda^2} - \dfrac{1}{\lambda_g^2}} \left(-\frac{\partial H_{oz}}{\partial y}\mathbf{i} + \frac{\partial H_{oz}}{\partial x}\mathbf{j} \right), \tag{12-32}$$

$$= \frac{j\omega\mu}{\dfrac{1}{\lambda^2} - \dfrac{1}{\lambda_g^2}} \mathbf{k} \times \nabla H_{oz}. \tag{12-33}$$

The three vectors $\mathbf{E}_0$, $\mathbf{k}$, and ∇H_{oz} are shown in Figure 12-1: it will be seen that ∇H_{oz} is necessarily tangent to the conducting wall. Thus the rate of change of H_{oz} in the direction normal to the surface is zero. This is the required boundary condition for the H_{oz} component in a perfectly conducting wave guide.

There is also another boundary condition, which applies to any perfectly conducting wave guide, and which is interesting from a qualitative point of view. Since the current density in the guide is tangent to its surface, we may use the results of Problem 8-9. Then the magnetic field intensity $\mathbf{H}$ close to the guide must be (a) tangent to the surface, (b) perpendicular to the current density, and (c) equal in magnitude to the surface current density expressed in amperes per meter. For example, in the case of TM waves, $\mathbf{H}$ is everywhere transverse, and the currents in the guide must be therefore longitudinal.

12.1.3. TEM Waves. Let us consider the case in which $\lambda_g = \lambda$. Since the factor

$$\frac{1}{\lambda^2} - \frac{1}{\lambda_g^2} \tag{12-34}$$

is zero, the parentheses on the right in Eqs. *12-16* to *12-19* must also be zero:

$$\frac{k}{\omega\mu}\frac{\partial E_{oz}}{\partial x} + \frac{\partial H_{oz}}{\partial y} = 0, \tag{12-35}$$

$$\frac{k}{\omega\mu}\frac{\partial E_{oz}}{\partial y} - \frac{\partial H_{oz}}{\partial x} = 0, \tag{12-36}$$

$$\frac{\partial E_{oz}}{\partial y} - \frac{k}{\omega\epsilon}\frac{\partial H_{oz}}{\partial x} = 0, \tag{12-37}$$

$$\frac{\partial E_{oz}}{\partial x} + \frac{k}{\omega\epsilon}\frac{\partial H_{oz}}{\partial y} = 0. \tag{12-38}$$

The last two equations are equivalent to the first two, since, by hypothesis, $\lambda_g = \lambda$ and $k_g/\omega\mu = \omega\epsilon/k_g = (\mu/\epsilon)^{1/2}$ in this case.

Let us consider the field for which

$$E_{oz} = 0$$

and

$$H_{oz} = 0. \qquad (12\text{-}39)$$

This corresponds to a TEM, or *Transverse Electric and Magnetic* wave, in which both **E** and **H** are transverse.

TEM waves have several interesting characteristics. To begin with, $\lambda_g = \lambda$, hence the velocity $u = \omega\lambda$ is the same as that of a plane wave in the medium of propagation. This velocity is given by $1/(\epsilon\mu)^{1/2}$, from Eq. *10-27*, and is independent of the frequency. That is, for a given medium of propagation, all TEM waves propagate at the same velocity $1/(\epsilon\mu)^{1/2}$, whatever the geometry of the wave guide, and whatever the frequency.

Another characteristic of TEM waves is that, since **H** is transverse, the guide currents must be longitudinal (Section 12.1.2). This also applies to TM waves.

TEM waves also have the following remarkable property. We have seen in Eq. *6-16* that the electric field intensity **E** is given by

$$\mathbf{E} = -\frac{\partial \mathbf{A}}{\partial t} - \nabla V, \qquad (12\text{-}40)$$

where the first term arises from changes in the magnetic field, and the second from accumulations of charge. Since the currents are all longitudinal, then **A** must also be longitudinal, as well as $\partial\mathbf{A}/\partial t$. Then $\mathbf{A} = A\mathbf{k}$, and

$$\mathbf{E} = -\frac{\partial V}{\partial x}\mathbf{i} - \frac{\partial V}{\partial y}\mathbf{j} - \left(\frac{\partial V}{\partial z} + \frac{\partial A}{\partial t}\right)\mathbf{k}. \qquad (12\text{-}41)$$

But **E** is transverse, thus the longitudinal component of ∇V must cancel that of $\partial\mathbf{A}/\partial t$ exactly at all points, and

$$\frac{\partial V}{\partial z} = -\frac{\partial A}{\partial t}. \qquad (12\text{-}42)$$

Because of this fact, the electric field intensity is given by

$$\mathbf{E} = -\frac{\partial V}{\partial x}\mathbf{i} - \frac{\partial V}{\partial y}\mathbf{j}. \qquad (12\text{-}43)$$

Since we are dealing with a wave, the potential V must be of the form

$$V = V_0 \exp\left[j\left(\omega t - \frac{z}{\lambda}\right)\right], \qquad (12\text{-}44)$$

where V_0 is some function of x and of y only, and thus

$$\mathbf{E} = -\left(\frac{\partial V_0}{\partial x}\mathbf{i} + \frac{\partial V_0}{\partial y}\mathbf{j}\right)\exp\left[j\left(\omega t - \frac{z}{\lambda}\right)\right], \qquad (12\text{-}45)$$

or

$$E_{ox} = -\frac{\partial V_0}{\partial x}, \qquad E_{oy} = -\frac{\partial V_0}{\partial y}, \qquad E_{oz} = 0. \qquad (12\text{-}46)$$

Therefore, if we write

$$\mathbf{E} = \mathbf{E}_0 \exp\left[j\left(\omega t - \frac{z}{\lambda}\right)\right], \qquad (12\text{-}47)$$

then

$$\mathbf{E}_0 = -\frac{\partial V_0}{\partial x}\,\mathbf{i} - \frac{\partial V_0}{\partial y}\,\mathbf{j}. \qquad (12\text{-}48)$$

This quantity $\mathbf{E}_0$ gives the electric field intensity $\mathbf{E}$ in a plane perpendicular to the direction of propagation (that is, in a plane parallel to the xy-plane) for corre-

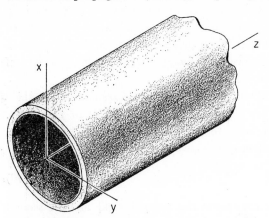

sponding values of z and t, which make the phase angle $\omega t - (z/\lambda) = 0$. This field is derivable from the potential V_0 in exactly the same manner as an electrostatic field.

If the wave guide is a hollow, perfectly conducting tube as in Figure 12-2, the tangential component of $\mathbf{E}$ at its surface is zero, V_0 is a constant all around the tube, and the only possible solution is $V_0 = $ constant inside. This property of the Laplacian was demonstrated in Problem 4-14. Now,

Figure 12-2. *A hollow, perfectly conducting tube. It is* not *possible to propagate a TEM wave inside such a guide.*

if $V_0 = $ constant throughout the inside of the guide, $\mathbf{E}_0$ is zero, $\mathbf{E} = 0$, and, since $\nabla \times \mathbf{E} = -\partial\mathbf{B}/\partial t$, there is no $\mathbf{H}$ wave either. Therefore, a *transverse electric and magnetic, or TEM wave, cannot be transmitted inside a hollow conducting tube.*

In a coaxial line, as in Figure 12-4, the inner conductor need not be at the

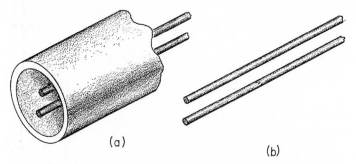

(a)   (b)

Figure 12-3. (*a*) *Shielded-pair line. The signal is applied between the two wires; the outer cylindrical shield is grounded.* (*b*) *Parallel-wire line.*

same potential as the outer one, and $\mathbf{E}$ need not be zero. A field is therefore possible, and a TEM wave *can* be transmitted. Other lines with more than one conductor, such as the shielded pair or the parallel-wire lines illustrated in Figure 12-3, can also transmit TEM waves.

Let us rewrite Eqs. *12-8* to *12-15* for $E_{oz} = 0$, $H_{oz} = 0$. These eight equations are simply Maxwell's equations, as applied to a wave propagating in the positive direction along the z-axis. We now have only six distinct equations:

$$\frac{\partial E_{ox}}{\partial x} + \frac{\partial E_{oy}}{\partial y} = 0, \tag{12-49}$$

$$\frac{\partial H_{ox}}{\partial x} + \frac{\partial H_{oy}}{\partial y} = 0, \tag{12-50}$$

$$E_{oy} = -\left(\frac{\mu}{\epsilon}\right)^{1/2} H_{ox}, \tag{12-51}$$

$$E_{ox} = \left(\frac{\mu}{\epsilon}\right)^{1/2} H_{oy}, \tag{12-52}$$

$$\frac{\partial E_{oy}}{\partial x} - \frac{\partial E_{ox}}{\partial y} = 0, \tag{12-53}$$

$$\frac{\partial H_{oy}}{\partial x} - \frac{\partial H_{ox}}{\partial y} = 0. \tag{12-54}$$

In the case of a plane wave propagating along the z-axis, as in Chapter 9, the field vectors depend solely on z and on t, and the derivatives with respect to x and to y are zero. Then Eqs. *12-49*, *12-50*, *12-53* and *12-54* become identities, and Eqs. *12-51* and *12-52* are simply Eq. *10-34*. Such a plane wave is the simplest form of TEM wave.

From the third and fourth of the above equations, $\mathbf{E}$ *and* $\mathbf{H}$ *are mutually perpendicular*, just as for the transverse components of TE and TM waves, and the wave impedance is now given by

$$\left|\frac{E_{ot}}{H_{ot}}\right| = \left(\frac{E_{ox}^2 + E_{oy}^2}{H_{ox}^2 + H_{oy}^2}\right)^{1/2} = \left(\frac{\mu}{\epsilon}\right)^{1/2}, \tag{12-55}$$

$$= 377 \text{ ohms} \qquad (K_e = 1, K_m = 1). \tag{12-56}$$

In addition, the electric and magnetic energy densities are equal:

$$\frac{1}{2} \epsilon E^2 = \frac{1}{2} \mu H^2, \tag{12-57}$$

hence the total energy density is ϵE^2, or μH^2.

From Eqs. *12-51* and *12-52*, the Poynting vector is given by

$$\mathbf{S}_{\text{av.}} = \frac{1}{2} \text{Re} (\mathbf{E} \times \mathbf{H}^*) = \frac{1}{2} \left(\frac{\epsilon}{\mu}\right)^{1/2} (E_{ox}^2 + E_{oy}^2)\mathbf{k}, \tag{12-58}$$

$$S_{av.} = \left(\frac{\epsilon}{\mu}\right)^{1/2} E_{rms}^2 \mathbf{k}, \qquad (12\text{-}59)$$

$$= u\epsilon E_{rms}^2 \mathbf{k}, \qquad (12\text{-}60)$$

$$= u\mu H_{rms}^2 \mathbf{k}. \qquad (12\text{-}61)$$

The Poynting vector is thus directed in the positive direction of the z-axis, which is the direction of propagation of the wave, and its modulus is equal to the phase velocity $u = 1/(\epsilon\mu)^{1/2}$ multiplied by the energy density, just as for a plane wave (Section 10.2).

12.2. Coaxial Line

In the coaxial line illustrated in Figure 12-4 the electromagnetic wave propagates in the annular region between two coaxial cylindrical conductors, and there is zero field outside. This type of wave guide is found in almost all types of electronic equipment for use both at low and at high frequencies. The medium of propagation is a low-loss dielectric.

We shall make several simplifying assumptions, namely, that (a) the guide is straight, and its cross section is constant throughout its length; (b) the electrical conductivity of the walls is infinite; (c) the time dependence of the wave is described by a cosine function; and (d) the wave travels in the positive direction of the z-axis, and there is no reflected wave in the opposite direction. The last two assumptions do not limit the generality of our calculation, since, according to the principle of superposition, the net field of a number of waves is simply given by the vector sum of their fields.

We have seen above that a TEM wave can be transmitted down such a guide; this is the mode which we shall study in this section. TE and TM modes are also possible, but they are much more complex and are not used in practice.

Thus we can set

$$E_{oz} = 0, \qquad H_{oz} = 0, \qquad (12\text{-}62)$$

and, from Eq. *12-45*,

$$E = -\left(\frac{\partial V_0}{\partial x}\mathbf{i} + \frac{\partial V_0}{\partial y}\mathbf{j}\right)\exp\left[j\left(\omega t - \frac{z}{\lambda}\right)\right]. \qquad (12\text{-}63)$$

The dependence of $\mathbf{E}$ on the coordinates x and y is the same as for a two-dimensional electrostatic field. For a given position z along the guide, and for a given time t, $\mathbf{E}$ is therefore radial and varies as $1/\rho$, where ρ is the radial distance from the axis to the point considered. Then V_0 is of the form C/ρ, where C is a constant, and

$$E = \frac{C}{\rho}\mathbf{i}\exp\left[j\left(\omega t - \frac{z}{\lambda}\right)\right] \qquad (12\text{-}64)$$

in cylindrical coordinates $\mathbf{i}$ being the unit vector in the radial direction.

Since we have a TEM wave, the radian length λ_g of the guided wave is the same as that for an infinite plane wave, that is, λ or $1/[\omega(\epsilon\mu)^{1/2}]$, and the velocity of propagation $\omega\lambda = 1/(\epsilon\mu)^{1/2}$ is the same for all frequencies.* The quantity C/ρ_1 is the maximum electric field intensity on the line.

The line voltage $\mathcal{V}$ of the inner conductor with respect to the outer conductor is given by

$$\mathcal{V} = \int_1^2 E\, d\rho, \tag{12-65}$$

$$= C \ln \frac{\rho_2}{\rho_1} \exp\left[j\left(\omega t - \frac{z}{\lambda}\right) \right]. \tag{12-66}$$

From the previous section, the magnetic field intensity $\mathbf{H}$ is orthogonal to $\mathbf{E}$, and

$$\mathbf{H} = \left(\frac{\epsilon}{\mu}\right)^{1/2} \frac{C}{\rho} j \exp\left[j\left(\omega t - \frac{z}{\lambda}\right) \right]. \tag{12-67}$$

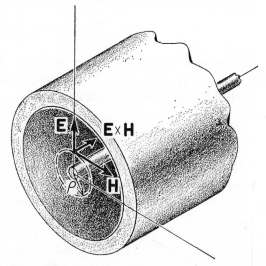

Figure 12-4. *The* $\mathbf{E}$ *and* $\mathbf{H}$ *vectors inside a coaxial line. They are both transverse,* $\mathbf{E}$ *being radial and* $\mathbf{H}$ *azimuthal. The vector product* $\mathbf{E} \times \mathbf{H}$ *always points in the direction of propagation.*

The vectors $\mathbf{E}$ and $\mathbf{H}$ are oriented such that the Poynting vector $\mathbf{E} \times \mathbf{H}$ points in the direction of propagation, as in Figure 12-4.

The line current I flowing along the surface of the inner conductor can be calculated from the circuital law of Eq. *7-84:*

$$I = \oint H_{\rho_1}\, d\varphi, \tag{12-68}$$

$$= 2\pi\rho_1 \left(\frac{\epsilon}{\mu}\right)^{1/2} \frac{C}{\rho_1} \exp\left[j\left(\omega t - \frac{z}{\lambda}\right) \right] = \frac{C}{60} \exp\left[j\left(\omega t - \frac{z}{\lambda}\right) \right]. \tag{12-69}$$

An equal current flows in the opposite direction along the inner surface of the outer conductor.

The transmitted power can be calculated by integrating the Poynting vector over the annular area between the two conductors:

$$W_T = \int_{\rho_2}^{\rho_1} S_{\text{av}}.2\pi\rho\, d\rho, \tag{12-70}$$

---

* This assumes that the line has infinite conductivity. In practice, the velocity of propagation does depend somewhat on the frequency.

where

$$\mathbf{S}_{\text{av.}} = \frac{1}{2} \operatorname{Re}(\mathbf{E} \times \mathbf{H}^*) = \left(\frac{\epsilon}{\mu}\right)^{1/2} \frac{C^2}{2\rho^2} \mathbf{k}. \qquad (12\text{-}71)$$

Thus

$$W_T = \frac{C^2}{120} \ln \frac{\rho_2}{\rho_1} \quad \text{(watts)}. \qquad (12\text{-}72)$$

The average transmitted power can also be calculated from $I_{\text{rms}} \mathcal{V}_{\text{rms}} = (1/2) I_{\text{max}} \mathcal{V}_{\text{max}}$, which leads to the same result. We have already found this result in Problem 9-6 for direct currents.

12.3. Hollow Rectangular Wave Guide

Hollow wave guides are extensively used for transmitting high intensity micro-waves. These wave guides are simply metallic tubes inside which electromagnetic

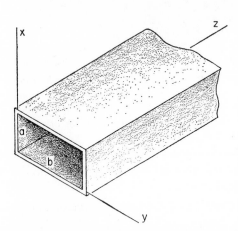

waves can propagate through reflection from the inner surfaces, in much the same way that sound waves can propagate through a tube. We shall consider hollow wave guides of rectangular cross section because their guided waves are relatively simple and because, of all possible hollow wave guides, they are the most widely used. The only other type which is used to any extent is the circular wave guide.

We make the same simplifying assumptions as for the coaxial line of the previous section. We also assume that the dielectric is air in order that

Figure 12-5. *A hollow, rectangular wave guide. The wave propagates in the positive direction along the z-axis.*

$$\lambda = \lambda_0 = \frac{1}{\omega(\epsilon_0 \mu_0)^{1/2}}. \qquad (12\text{-}73)$$

We have shown in Section 12.1.3 that TEM waves cannot propagate inside a hollow tube. Thus, only TE or TM waves are possible, and the radian length λ_g of the guided wave is different from λ: $\lambda_g \neq \lambda$.

We select axes as in Figure 12-5, with the wave propagating in the positive direction along the z-axis, and we write $\mathbf{E}$ and $\mathbf{H}$ as in Eqs. *12-3* and *12-4*.

12.3.1. Hollow Rectangular Wave Guide. The *TE* Wave ($E_{oz} = 0$). We shall consider the Transverse Electric wave. This wave is simply a plane electro-

magnetic wave whose **E** and **H** vectors are oriented as in Figure 12-6 and which is reflected back and forth on the walls parallel to the *xz*-plane. We shall use this fact to simplify the analysis somewhat, but we could also find the TE wave by choosing the proper boundary conditions and solving for H_{oz}, without referring to the reflection. This is suggested in Problem 12-7.

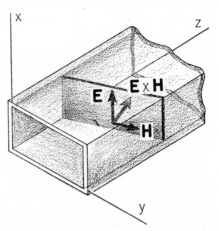

Our problem is to determine six quantities: E_{ox}, E_{oy}, H_{ox}, H_{oy}, H_{oz}, and $\lambda_g = 1/k_g$. From Figure 12-6 we can see immediately that

$$E_{oy} = 0,$$
$$H_{ox} = 0. \qquad (12\text{-}74)$$

To determine the remaining four quantities we shall proceed as indicated at the end of Section 12.1: we shall solve the wave equation for H_{oz} for the proper boundary conditions. This will give both H_{oz} and λ_g. The values of E_{ox} and of H_{oy} will then follow from Eqs. *12-16* and *12-19*.

Figure 12-6. *Typical plane wavefront with the **E**, **H**, and **E** × **H** vectors inside a rectangular wave guide. The reflection occurs on the faces parallel to the xz-plane. The **E** vector is always transverse, that is, perpendicular to the direction of propagation Oz, and the wave is TE.*

We have found in Eq. *12-23* that H_{oz} obeys the wave equation

$$\frac{\partial^2 H_{oz}}{\partial x^2} + \frac{\partial^2 H_{oz}}{\partial y^2} = \left(\frac{1}{\lambda_g^2} - \frac{1}{\lambda_0^2}\right) H_{oz}. \qquad (12\text{-}75)$$

In the simple TE wave illustrated in Figure 12-6, the wave is independent of the *x*-coordinate, and

$$\frac{\partial^2 H_{oz}}{\partial y^2} = \left(\frac{1}{\lambda_g^2} - \frac{1}{\lambda_0^2}\right) H_{oz}. \qquad (12\text{-}76)$$

Solving this equation, we find that

$$H_{oz} = F \sin Cy + G \cos Cy, \qquad (12\text{-}77)$$

where

$$-C^2 = \frac{1}{\lambda_g^2} - \frac{1}{\lambda_0^2}. \qquad (12\text{-}78)$$

We now apply the boundary condition discussed in Section 12.1.2:

$$\frac{\partial H_{oz}}{\partial x} = 0 \qquad (x = 0 \text{ and } x = a), \qquad (12\text{-}79)$$

$$\frac{\partial H_{oz}}{\partial y} = 0 \qquad (y = 0 \text{ and } y = b). \qquad (12\text{-}80)$$

The first condition is already satisfied, since H_{oz} is not a function of x. As regards the second condition,

$$\frac{\partial H_{oz}}{\partial y} = C(F \cos Cy - G \sin Cy). \qquad (12\text{-}81)$$

Then, to satisfy the boundary condition at $y = 0$, we must have $F = 0$. The condition $C = 0$ must be rejected because it implies that $\lambda_g = \lambda_0$, which is not compatible with a TE wave. At $y = b$, we must have

$$\sin Cb = 0 \qquad (12\text{-}82)$$

and

$$C = \frac{n\pi}{b}, \qquad (12\text{-}83)$$

where n is an integer which cannot be zero, for then C would also be zero. Then

$$H_{oz} = G \cos \frac{n\pi}{b} y. \qquad (12\text{-}84)$$

Let us find λ_g. This is easy now that we know H_{oz}. We can either substitute H_{oz} into the wave equation or use Eqs. 12-78 and 12-83 to obtain

$$-\frac{n^2\pi^2}{b^2} = \frac{1}{\lambda_g^2} - \frac{1}{\lambda_0^2} \qquad (n = 1, 2, 3, \cdots). \qquad (12\text{-}85)$$

It will be noticed that λ_g can have only certain discrete characteristic values corresponding to $n = 1, 2, 3, \cdots$.

Since the left-hand side of Eq. 12-85 is negative, $\lambda_g > \lambda_0$. This means that the wave length in the guide is *longer* than that of a plane wave of the same frequency propagating in free space. Then the wave velocity u is *larger* than c. We shall return to this later.

Now that we have found H_{oz} and λ_g, we can calculate the two remaining unknowns E_{ox} and H_{oy} from Eqs. 12-16 and 12-19 with $\lambda = \lambda_0$, since the medium of propagation has $K_e = 1$, $K_m = 1$, by hypothesis:

$$E_{ox} = \frac{j\omega\mu_0 bG}{n\pi} \sin \frac{n\pi}{b} y, \qquad (12\text{-}86)$$

$$H_{oy} = \frac{jbG}{n\pi\lambda_g} \sin \frac{n\pi}{b} y, \qquad (12\text{-}87)$$

or, setting

$$E_{oox} = \frac{j\omega\mu_0 bG}{n\pi}, \qquad (12\text{-}88)$$

then

$$E_x = E_{oox} \sin \left(\frac{n\pi}{b} y\right) \exp \left[j\left(\omega t - \frac{z}{\lambda_g}\right)\right], \qquad (12\text{-}89)$$

$$H_y = \frac{E_{ooz}}{\omega\mu_0\lambda_g} \sin\left(\frac{n\pi}{b}y\right)\exp\left[j\left(\omega t - \frac{z}{\lambda_g}\right)\right], \qquad (12\text{-}90)$$

$$H_z = \frac{E_{ooz}n\pi}{j\omega\mu_0 b} \cos\left(\frac{n\pi}{b}y\right)\exp\left[j\left(\omega t - \frac{z}{\lambda_g}\right)\right], \qquad (12\text{-}91)$$

where the permissible values for λ_g are given by Eq. *12-85*. The coefficient E_{ooz} is the maximum value of E inside the guide. We have already found that $E_{oy} = 0$, $H_{oz} = 0$ (Eq. *12-74*).

Let us consider the value of E_z. It can be understood qualitatively as follows. In any plane wave front such as that shown in Figure 12-6, the vector **E** is independent of the x-coordinate. Since the wave along the z-axis results from the superposition of such plane waves by multiple reflections, its **E** vector must also be independent of the x-coordinate. The same cannot be said about the y dependence, however. If we consider a single elementary plane wave progressing at an angle along the guide, the amplitude and the phase of **E** are constant over a wave front such as that shown in the figure. The amplitude of **E** for a single elementary plane wave is also independent of y, but the *phase* is not. The superposition of such waves by multiple reflections gives an interference pattern such that the resulting amplitude varies with the y-coordinate.

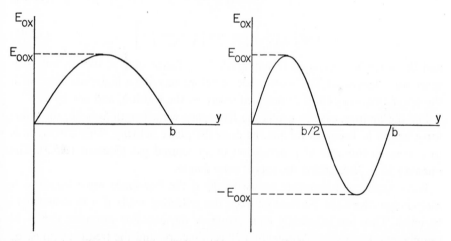

Figure 12-7. *The amplitude of* **E** *for a TE wave in a hollow rectangular waveguide. On the left the value of n of Eq. 12-86 is 1; on the right it is 2.*

Let us now consider the meaning of the quantity n. For $n = 1$, E_{ox} varies from 0 at $y = 0$ to a maximum of E_{oox} at $y = b/2$ and to zero again at $y = b$ as in Figure 12-7a. For $n = 2$, E_{ox} is zero in the middle of the guide at $y = b/2$, and is of opposite sign on either side, as in Figure 12-7b. The different values of n thus correspond to different *modes of propagation* inside the guide.

Now let us return to Eq. *12-85* for λ_g. It can be rewritten as

$$\frac{\lambda_g}{\lambda_0} = \frac{1}{\left[1 - \left(\frac{n\lambda_0}{2b}\right)^2\right]^{1/2}} \tag{12-92}$$

or

$$\frac{\lambda_g}{\lambda_0} = \frac{1}{\left[1 - \left(\frac{\lambda_0}{2b}\right)^2\right]^{1/2}} \tag{12-93}$$

for $n = 1$. This equation shows that λ_g is real if $\lambda_0 < 2b$. If λ_g is real, the exponential functions of Eqs. *12-89* to *12-91* describe an *un*attenuated wave. Therefore, if the above inequality is satisfied, that is, if the frequency is high enough, and if the walls are perfectly conducting, a wave can propagate inside the hollow wave guide without attenuation.

If the above inequality is not satisfied, that is, if the frequency is too low, the guide wavelength λ_g becomes imaginary, and the exponential functions show that the field is attenuated exponentially with z. Then the phase does not vary with z, and there is no wave. The attenuation is rapid. For example, if the frequency is too low by a factor of 2, $\lambda_0 = 4b$. Then, from Eq. *12-93*,

$$\frac{1}{\lambda_g} = j\frac{3^{1/2}}{\lambda_0}, \tag{12-94}$$

$$\exp\left[j\left(\frac{z}{\lambda_g}\right)\right] = \exp\left[\left(\frac{2\pi 3^{1/2}}{\lambda_0}\right)z\right], \tag{12-95}$$

and the wave is attenuated in amplitude by a factor of 2×10^{-5} in one free-space wave length λ_0! The wave guide therefore acts like a high-pass filter, with the lower frequency limit determined solely by the width b, and not by a.

For the limiting case in which the free-space wave length λ_0 is $2b$, the guide wave length λ_g becomes infinite, as does the phase velocity. This corresponds to $\omega = \omega_p$ in the case of propagation in an ionized gas (Section 10.5.3). The quantity $\lambda_c = 2b$ is called the *cut-off wave length*.

Wave guides can therefore be used only if the free-space wave length λ_0 is *shorter* than twice the distance between the reflecting walls if n is assumed to be unity. They are inherently *high*-frequency devices. For example, if $b = 10$ centimeters, λ_0 must be shorter than 20 centimeters, and the frequency must be higher than $3 \times 10^8/0.2$, or 1500 megacycles/second.

The guide wave length λ_g is longer than the free space wave length λ_0, and the phase velocity is *larger* than c, just as for propagation in an ionized gas.

Let us now rewrite the components of the **E** and **H** vectors for the usual field with $n = 1$:

$$E_x = E_{ooz}\sin\left(\frac{\pi y}{b}\right)\exp\left[j\left(\omega t - \frac{z}{\lambda_g}\right)\right], \tag{12-96}$$

$$E_y = 0, \tag{12-97}$$

$$E_z = 0, \tag{12-98}$$

$$H_x = 0, \tag{12-99}$$

$$H_y = \frac{E_{oox}}{\omega\mu_0\lambda_g} \sin\left(\frac{\pi y}{b}\right) \exp\left[j\left(\omega t - \frac{z}{\lambda_g}\right)\right], \tag{12-100}$$

$$H_z = \frac{\pi E_{oox}}{\omega\mu_0 b} \cos\left(\frac{\pi y}{b}\right) \exp\left[j\left(\omega t - \frac{z}{\lambda_g} - \frac{\pi}{2}\right)\right], \tag{12-101}$$

$$= \frac{\pi E_{oox}}{\omega\mu_0 b} \cos\left(\frac{\pi y}{b}\right) \exp\left\{j\left[\omega t - \frac{1}{\lambda_g}\left(z + \frac{\lambda_g}{4}\right)\right]\right\}, \tag{12-102}$$

where the guide wave length is given by

$$\lambda_g = \frac{\lambda_0}{\left[1 - \left(\frac{\lambda_0}{2b}\right)^2\right]^{1/2}} > \lambda_0, \tag{12-103}$$

and the phase velocity by

$$u_p = \frac{c}{\left[1 - \left(\frac{\lambda_0}{2b}\right)^2\right]^{1/2}} > c. \tag{12-104}$$

It will be observed that E_x and H_y are in phase but that H_z has the same phase at $\left(z + \frac{\lambda_g}{4}\right)$ as have the two other vectors at z. Figure 12-8 shows the electric and

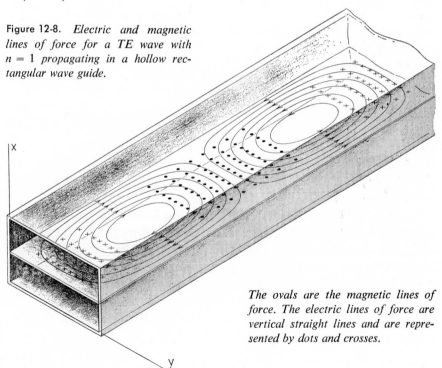

Figure 12-8. *Electric and magnetic lines of force for a TE wave with $n = 1$ propagating in a hollow rectangular wave guide.*

The ovals are the magnetic lines of force. The electric lines of force are vertical straight lines and are represented by dots and crosses.

magnetic lines of force for a TE wave with $n = 1$ propagating in a hollow rectangular wave guide.

12.3.2. Hollow Rectangular Wave Guide. Internal Reflections. Let us return to Figure 12-6, which shows a typical wave front for a wave zigzagging down the guide. It will be instructive to investigate the field by considering the interference resulting from the multiple reflections.

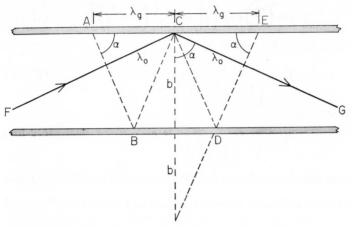

Figure 12-9. *A plane electromagnetic wave propagating in a rectangular hollow wave guide along a zigzag path. The lines AB and CD are parallel to wave fronts for the wave propagating to the right and upward. Similarly, BC and DE are parallel to wave fronts traveling to the right and downward. The angle α is the angle of incidence; the broken line FCG represents a ray reflected at C.*

Figure 12-9 shows the multiple reflections in more detail. Let us assume that along the fixed line AB the electric field intensity of the wave which is directed upward and to the right is $E_0 \exp(j\omega t)$. The line AB is thus parallel to the wave fronts for this wave. The lines BC and DE are similarly parallel to wave fronts for the wave propagating to the right and downward.

These two waves must interfere at B to give zero field intensity at the perfectly conducting wall, since their electric field intensities **E** are perpendicular to the paper and are parallel to the wall. Then the electric field intensity along BC must be $E_0 \exp[j(\omega t + \pi)] = -E_0 \exp(j\omega t)$. At the point C, interference must again give zero net field, such that, along CD, $E = E_0 \exp[j(\omega t + 2\pi)] = E_0 \exp(j\omega t)$.

Thus, AB and CD are one free-space wave length λ_0 apart, and, from the geometrical construction shown,

$$\cos \alpha = \frac{\lambda_0}{2b}. \qquad (12\text{-}105)$$

We could also have chosen the lines AB and CD to be *n* wave lengths apart. Then we would have had

$$\cos \alpha = \frac{n\lambda_0}{2b}. \qquad (12\text{-}106)$$

The angle α can thus have only certain discrete values which permit destructive interference to occur at the walls of the guide.

We have therefore found a geometrical interpretation for the ratio $\lambda_0/(2b/n)$. From Eq. *12-92*,

$$\frac{\lambda_g}{\lambda_0} = \frac{1}{\sin \alpha}, \qquad (12\text{-}107)$$

where the guide wave length λ_g is equal to AC, CE, or BD. At the critical wave length $\lambda_0 = 2b/n$, $\cos \alpha = 1$, $\alpha = 0$, and the wave fronts are parallel to the axis of the guide. For $\lambda_0 \ll 2b/n$, $\cos \alpha \longrightarrow 0$, and $\alpha \longrightarrow \pi/2$. The TE wave then approaches a TEM mode as a limit.

The phase velocity is given by

$$u_p = \frac{\lambda_g}{\lambda_0} c = \frac{c}{\sin \alpha} > c. \qquad (12\text{-}108)$$

This is the velocity at which the phase propagates along the guide. It is larger than c because the individual plane wave fronts are inclined at an angle with respect to the axis of the guide. This can be seen from Figure 12-9 as follows. Consider AB to be a wave front propagating parallel to itself and to the right at a velocity c. Then the point A moves along the z-axis at a velocity which is larger than c.

We can also consider the velocity at which a given signal progresses along the length of the guide. The z component of the velocity of an individual wave front is only $c \sin \alpha$ and is *smaller* than c. Thus, if we call this velocity u_s, then

$$u_s = c \sin \alpha, \qquad (12\text{-}109)$$

$$= c \left[1 - \left(\frac{n\lambda_0}{2b}\right)^2 \right]^{1/2} < c, \qquad (12\text{-}110)$$

and

$$u_s u_p = c^2. \qquad (12\text{-}111)$$

12.3.3. Hollow Rectangular Wave Guide. Energy Transmission. Let us consider the energy transmitted by a TE wave in a low-loss rectangular wave guide. We shall assume the usual case, in which $n = 1$. The field is then completely described by Eqs. *12-89* to *12-91*, with $n = 1$, or by Eqs. *12-96* to *12-102*. The first set is slightly more convenient for our purpose.

From Eq. *10-88*, the average value of the Poynting vector is given by

$$\mathbf{S}_{\text{av.}} = \frac{1}{2} \operatorname{Re} (\mathbf{E} \times \mathbf{H}^*), \qquad (12\text{-}112)$$

where $\mathbf{H^*}$ is the complex conjugate of $\mathbf{H}$. In the present case,

$$\mathbf{S}_{\text{av.}} = \frac{1}{2} \operatorname{Re} \begin{vmatrix} \mathbf{i} & \mathbf{j} & \mathbf{k} \\ E_x & 0 & 0 \\ 0 & H_y^* & H_z^* \end{vmatrix}, \qquad (12\text{-}113)$$

$$= \frac{1}{2} \operatorname{Re} \left(-E_x H_z^* \mathbf{j} + E_x H_y^* \mathbf{k} \right). \qquad (12\text{-}114)$$

Substituting the values of E_x, H_y, H_z, we find that the first term in the parentheses is imaginary, whereas the second term is real.

The energy therefore flows only in the direction of the z-axis, and

$$\mathbf{S}_{\text{av.}} = \frac{E_{oox}^2}{2\omega\mu_0\lambda_g} \sin^2\left(\frac{\pi}{b}y\right) \mathbf{k}. \qquad (12\text{-}115)$$

This is the energy flux in watts per square meter in the direction of the z-axis within the guide. The value of $\mathbf{S}_{\text{av.}}$ is independent of x, as expected, since the amplitude and phase of the wave are independent of the x coordinate. It is zero at the walls $y = 0$ and $y = b$, where $\mathbf{E}$ is zero, and it is maximum at $y = b/2$, again as expected.

The total transmitted power is thus given by

$$W_T = \int_{y=0}^{y=b} \frac{E_{oox}^2}{2\omega\mu_0\lambda_g} \sin^2\left(\frac{\pi}{b}y\right) a \, dy, \qquad (12\text{-}116)$$

$$= \frac{E_{oox}^2 ab}{4\omega\mu_0\lambda_g}, \qquad (12\text{-}117)$$

$$= \frac{E_{oox}^2 ab}{4c\mu_0} \left[1 - \left(\frac{\lambda_0}{2b}\right)^2 \right]^{1/2} \quad \text{(watts)}, \qquad (12\text{-}118)$$

where E_{oox} is the maximum value of E in the guide in volts/meter, a and b are the dimensions of the cross section of the guide in meters, as in Figure 12-5, and λ_g is the guide wave length in meters, as in Eq. *12-103*.

Let us compare this transmitted power with the average electromagnetic energy per unit length within the guide. The instantaneous electric energy density is $(1/2)\epsilon_0 E^2$, and its average value is $(1/4)\epsilon_0 E_0^2$. The average electric energy per unit length is thus

$$\int_0^b \frac{1}{4} \epsilon_0 E_{oox}^2 \sin^2\left(\frac{\pi}{b}y\right) a \, dy = \frac{\epsilon_0}{8} ab E_{oox}^2. \qquad (12\text{-}119)$$

To find the average magnetic energy content per unit length, we proceed similarly for both the y- and z-components of $\mathbf{H}$ and add the results, since

$$H^2 = H_y^2 + H_z^2. \qquad (12\text{-}120)$$

Again the result is $(\epsilon_0/8)ab E_{oox}^2$, and the average electric and magnetic energies per unit length are equal. This is reasonable, since the plane electromagnetic waves which produce the field configuration by reflection at the side walls involve equal electric and magnetic energy densities. It is not at all obvious, however, because the interference effects tend to confuse the picture.

The total electromagnetic energy content per unit length in the guide is therefore $\epsilon_0 ab E_{oox}^2/4$. Upon dividing the total transmitted power by this quantity, we find

$$E_{oox}^2 \frac{ab}{4\omega\mu_0\lambda_g} \frac{4}{E_{oox}^2\epsilon_0 ab} = c\frac{\lambda_0}{\lambda_g}, \qquad (12\text{-}121)$$

$$= c\left[1 - \left(\frac{\lambda_0}{2b}\right)^2\right]^{1/2}, \qquad (12\text{-}122)$$

$$= u_s. \qquad (12\text{-}123)$$

The transmitted power is thus equal to the product of the energy per unit length times the signal velocity, as could have been expected intuitively.

12.3.4. Attenuation in Hollow Rectangular Wave Guides. We have assumed until now that the walls were perfectly conducting; let us now consider real wave guides of finite conductivity.

In the process of guiding electromagnetic waves, conductors waste part of the wave energy in the form of Joule losses. This is because the guided waves always induce electric currents in the conductors. However, a rigorous calculation of the field for a guide of finite conductivity is difficult and, fortunately, unnecessary.

The procedure used for calculating the Joule losses is the following. We have performed a calculation on the assumption that the guide is perfectly conducting. This has led to a field in which there is a tangential magnetic field intensity H at the surface of the guide. Since the tangential H must be continuous across any interface, we have a known H inside the conductor. Then, using Maxwell's equations, we can find the corresponding tangential electric field intensity E, which is not zero unless the guide material is a perfect conductor. This small tangential E is then considered to be a perturbation of the ideal field obtained with perfect conductors. The method is entirely satisfactory because this E is so small that it hardly disturbs the wave. We thus have a tangential E, a tangential H, and a Poynting vector which is normal to the conducting surface and directed into the metal.

That both **E** and **H** vectors must exist inside the conducting walls can also be shown as follows. To begin with, we must have a tangential H just inside the wall. On the other hand, at some distance within the wall, there must be zero field, since the attenuation distance δ (Section 10.4) is quite short at frequencies which are high enough to propagate in wave guides. For example, if $b = 7.5$ centimeters, the frequency can be, say, 3000 megacycles/second, and δ is then only 1.2 microns in copper (Table 10-1). The tangential component of H thus decreases rapidly with depth inside the conducting wall. Then $\nabla \times H$ is not zero, and there is a current density J parallel to the surface and normal to H, since $\nabla \times H = J$. We must therefore have both a tangential E to produce the tangential current density J, and a tangential H.

From the Poynting vector directed into the guide wall we can calculate the power W_L which is removed from the wave per meter of length; we then wish to calculate the attenuation constant k_{gi} of Eq. 12-7. This constant must be such that, when both the E and H of the transmitted wave are multiplied by $e^{-k_{gi}z}$, both the Poynting vector for the transmitted wave and the transmitted power W_T must decrease by a factor of

$$\exp(-2k_{gi}\Delta z) \approx 1 - 2k_{gi}\Delta z \qquad (12\text{-}124)$$

in a distance Δz. The approximation is excellent for ordinary types of wave guides. Then

$$W_L \Delta z = (2k_{gi}\Delta z)W_t, \qquad (12\text{-}125)$$

or

$$k_{gi} = \frac{W_L}{2W_T}. \qquad (12\text{-}126)$$

The real part k_{gr} of k_g (Eq. 12-7) can be taken to be the k_g obtained on the assumption of perfectly conducting walls.

It might be expected at first sight that the attenuation could be calculated from the reflection losses. It will be recalled from Section 11.5.2 that an electromagnetic wave reflected from a good conductor is slightly weaker than the incident wave. This method of calculation is incorrect because, as we shall see, there are also energy losses in the guide faces parallel to the yz-plane. It will be shown in Problem 12-9 that the two calculations agree when the guide height a approaches infinity, for then the losses in the faces parallel to the yz-plane become negligible compared to the reflection losses.

Let us examine the process whereby energy is removed from the wave. The tangential H produces an electromagnetic wave which penetrates perpendicularly into the wall. Inside the conducting wall,

$$\frac{E}{H} = \left(\frac{\mu_0 \omega}{\sigma}\right)^{1/2} e^{j\pi/4}, \qquad (12\text{-}127)$$

as in Eq. 10-105. We can also arrive at this equation by first assuming that H propagates into the wall as a damped wave and then using the two Maxwell equations $\nabla \times H = \partial D/\partial t$ and $\nabla \times E = -\partial B/\partial t$.

We assume again that the dielectric inside the guide is dry air, and is therefore lossless. We also assume that $n = 1$ in order that the field be described, as a first approximation, by Eqs. 12-96 to 12-102.

Along the face which lies in the *xz*-plane,

$$H_z = \frac{\pi E_{ooz}}{\omega \mu_0 b} \exp\left[j\left(\omega t - \frac{z}{\lambda_g} - \frac{\pi}{2} \right) \right] \qquad (y = 0). \qquad (12\text{-}128)$$

Then E_x is *not* equal to zero for $y = 0$, as in Eq. *12-96*, but is instead given by the above two equations:

$$E_x = \left(\frac{\mu_0 \omega}{\sigma} \right)^{1/2} \frac{\pi E_{ooz}}{\omega \mu_0 b} \exp\left[j\left(\omega t - \frac{z}{\lambda_g} - \frac{\pi}{4} \right) \right] \qquad (y = 0). \quad (12\text{-}129)$$

When σ approaches infinity, E_x approaches zero. The Poynting vector $\mathbf{S}_{av.} = (1/2)\,\mathrm{Re}\,(\mathbf{E} \times \mathbf{H}^*)$ directed into the guide wall is equal to

$$\left(\frac{\pi E_{ooz}}{b} \right)^2 \frac{1}{\sigma^{1/2}(2\omega\mu_0)^{3/2}} \qquad (y = 0).$$

This is the energy flowing into the wall ($y = 0$) per square meter and per second. It is interesting to note that this energy flux is the same at all points on the face $y = 0$. The power lost to the wall per meter of length is a times the above expression and, for the two faces parallel to the *xz*-plane,

$$W_{xz} = \left(\frac{\pi E_{ooz}}{b} \right)^2 \frac{2a}{\sigma^{1/2}(2\omega\mu_0)^{3/2}}. \qquad (12\text{-}130)$$

This is the power lost by reflection.

For the face at $x = 0$, $\mathbf{H}$ has *y*- and *z*-components as in Eqs. *12-100* and *12-101*. For the *y*-component,

$$H_y = \frac{E_{ooz}}{\omega \mu_0 \lambda_g} \sin\left(\frac{\pi y}{b} \right) \exp\left[j\left(\omega t - \frac{z}{\lambda_g} \right) \right], \qquad (12\text{-}131)$$

and then E_z is not zero, but rather

$$E_z = \left(\frac{\mu_0 \omega}{\sigma} \right)^{1/2} \frac{E_{ooz}}{\omega \mu_0 \lambda_g} \sin\left(\frac{\pi y}{b} \right) \exp\left[j\left(\omega t - \frac{z}{\lambda_g} + \frac{\pi}{4} \right) \right]. \quad (12\text{-}132)$$

The modulus of the corresponding Poynting vector directed into the wall is now

$$\left(\frac{E_{ooz}}{\lambda_g} \right)^2 \frac{1}{\sigma^{1/2}(2\omega\mu_0)^{3/2}} \sin^2 \frac{\pi y}{b}.$$

Similarly, the modulus of the Poynting vector corresponding to H_z is

$$\left(\frac{\pi E_{ooz}}{b} \right)^2 \frac{1}{\sigma^{1/2}(2\omega\mu_0)^{3/2}} \cos^2 \frac{\pi y}{b}.$$

Integrating the sum of these two quantities from $y = 0$ to $y = b$ and multiplying by 2, we obtain the power lost per meter in the two walls parallel to the *yz*-plane:

$$W_{yz} = \frac{(\pi E_{ooz})^2}{b\sigma^{1/2}(2\omega\mu_0)^{3/2}}\left[1 + \left(\frac{2b}{\lambda_g} \right)^2 \right] \qquad (12\text{-}133)$$

or, using Eq. *12-103*, we obtain

$$W_{yz} = \frac{(\pi E_{ooz})^2}{b\sigma^{1/2}(2\omega\mu_0)^{3/2}}\left(\frac{2b}{\lambda_0} \right)^2. \qquad (12\text{-}134)$$

The total power loss per meter is then

$$W_L = W_{xz} + W_{yz}, \tag{12-135}$$

$$= \frac{\pi^2 E_{oox}^2}{b\sigma^{1/2}(2\omega\mu_0)^{3/2}} \left[\frac{2a}{b} + \left(\frac{2b}{\lambda_0} \right)^2 \right]. \tag{12-136}$$

To find the attenuation constant k_{gi} for the wave, we now use Eqs. *12-126* and *12-118:*

$$k_{gi} = \frac{W_L}{2W_T}, \tag{12-137}$$

$$= \frac{1}{a(120\sigma\lambda_0)^{1/2}} \frac{\left[1 + \frac{2a}{b} \left(\frac{\lambda_0}{2b} \right)^2 \right]}{\left[1 - \left(\frac{\lambda_0}{2b} \right)^2 \right]^{1/2}}. \tag{12-138}$$

For an infinite guide height a, only the second term remains in the numerator, and

$$k_{gi} = \frac{1}{b(30\sigma\lambda_0)^{1/2}} \frac{\left(\frac{\lambda_0}{2b} \right)^2}{\left[1 - \left(\frac{\lambda_0}{2b} \right)^2 \right]^{1/2}} \qquad (a \longrightarrow \infty). \tag{12-139}$$

This term comes from W_{zz}, and the losses then occur only on the guide faces parallel to the *xz*-plane. It is shown in Problem 12-9 that this value of k_{gi} can be accounted for entirely by the reflection losses.

In practice, the ratio $2a/b$ is of the order of unity, except for the smallest wave guides, where it can be as high as 1.4, whereas $(\lambda_0/2b)^2$ is of the order of one-half. The losses on the faces parallel to *xz*-plane are thuse of the same order of magnitude as those on the other pair of faces, but smaller by a factor of about 2.

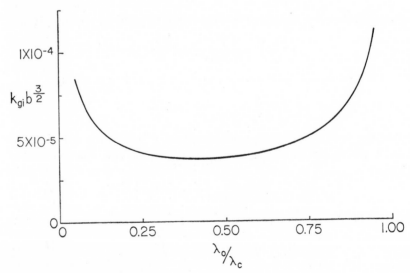

Figure 12-10. *Dependence of $k_{gi}b^{3/2}$ on λ_0/λ_c for $a/b = 0.5$.*

Figure 12-10 shows the dependence of $k_{gi}b^{3/2}$ on the ratio $\lambda_0/\lambda_c = \lambda_0/2b$ for the usual case, in which $2a/b$ is unity. According to this curve, the optimum value of $\lambda_0/2b$ is about 0.4. Actual values of $\lambda_0/2b$ are somewhat larger so as to achieve strong attenuation for the $n = 2$ mode.

The attenuation is of the order of a few decibels per 100 feet at frequencies of a few kilomegacycles/second, increasing as $f^{3/2}$ when the ratios a/b and $\lambda_0/2b$ are kept constant (Problem 12-8).

Table 12-1 shows the characteristics of some commonly used hollow rectangular wave guides.

TABLE 12-1.   Characteristics of Common Types of Rectangular Wave Guides
(TE Mode with $n = 1$)

Outside Dimensions and Wall Thickness (inches)	Cut-off Wave Length (centimeters)	Wave Length Range (centimeters)	Attenuation Within Wave Length Range (decibels/100 feet)
3.000 × 1.500 × 0.080	14.2	7.60–11.5	0.752–1.10
2.000 × 1.000 × 0.064	9.50	5.13–7.60	1.44–2.08
1.500 × 0.750 × 0.064	6.98	3.66–5.13	2.30–2.87
1.000 × 0.500 × 0.050	4.57	2.44–3.66	4.48–6.45
0.702 × 0.391 × 0.040	3.16	1.67–2.44	8.31–9.51
0.500 × 0.250 × 0.040	2.13	1.13–1.67	14.8–20.7
0.360 × 0.220 × 0.040	1.42	0.75–1.13	15.0–21.9*

* Silvered; the other types are brass.

12.4. Summary

For *any* wave with $\lambda \neq \lambda_g$, propagating in the positive direction along the z-axis, we must have

$$E_{ox} = \frac{-j\omega\mu}{\frac{1}{\lambda^2} - \frac{1}{\lambda_g^2}}\left(\frac{k_g}{\omega\mu}\frac{\partial E_{oz}}{\partial x} + \frac{\partial H_{oz}}{\partial y}\right) \qquad (\lambda_g \neq \lambda), \qquad (12\text{-}16)$$

$$E_{oy} = \frac{j\omega\mu}{\frac{1}{\lambda^2} - \frac{1}{\lambda_g^2}}\left(-\frac{k_g}{\omega\mu}\frac{\partial E_{oz}}{\partial y} + \frac{\partial H_{oz}}{\partial x}\right) \qquad (\lambda_g \neq \lambda), \qquad (12\text{-}17)$$

$$H_{ox} = \frac{j\omega\epsilon}{\frac{1}{\lambda^2} - \frac{1}{\lambda_g^2}}\left(\frac{\partial E_{oz}}{\partial y} - \frac{k_g}{\omega\epsilon}\frac{\partial H_{oz}}{\partial x}\right) \qquad (\lambda_g \neq \lambda), \qquad (12\text{-}18)$$

$$H_{oy} = \frac{-j\omega\epsilon}{\frac{1}{\lambda^2} - \frac{1}{\lambda_g^2}}\left(\frac{\partial E_{oz}}{\partial x} + \frac{k_g}{\omega\epsilon}\frac{\partial H_{oz}}{\partial y}\right) \qquad (\lambda_g \neq \lambda), \qquad (12\text{-}19)$$

where the wave number $k_g = 1/\lambda_g$ is real if there is no attenuation, and complex if there is. The vectors $\mathbf{E}$ and $\mathbf{H}$ can therefore be calculated once E_{oz} and H_{oz} are known.

If $E_{oz} = 0$ we have a TE wave, and if $H_{oz} = 0$ we have a TM wave. If both E_{oz} and H_{oz} are zero, then we have a TEM wave, in which case the wave length λ_g of the guided wave is equal to the wave length λ of a plane wave in the medium of propagation.

For TE and TM waves, we determine E_{oz} or H_{oz} from the wave equation for E_{oz}

$$\frac{\partial^2 E_{oz}}{\partial x^2} + \frac{\partial^2 E_{oz}}{\partial y^2} = -\left(\frac{1}{\lambda^2} - \frac{1}{\lambda_g^2}\right) E_{oz} \tag{12-22}$$

or from the corresponding equation for H_{oz}. For perfectly conducting wave guides (a) E_{oz} must equal zero at the surface, or $\mathbf{E}$ must be normal, and (b) ∇H_{oz} must be tangential, or the rate of change of H_{oz} in the direction normal to the surface must be zero. The currents in the guide are everywhere perpendicular to the tangential H at the point considered. Thus, in TM and TEM waves, the currents can only be longitudinal.

In TEM waves,

$$\frac{\partial V}{\partial z} = -\frac{\partial A}{\partial t}, \tag{12-42}$$

and

$$\mathbf{E} = -\left(\frac{\partial V_0}{\partial x}\mathbf{i} + \frac{\partial V_0}{\partial y}\mathbf{j}\right) \exp\left[j\left(\omega t - \frac{z}{\lambda}\right)\right], \tag{12-45}$$

$$= \mathbf{E}_0 \exp\left[j\left(\omega t - \frac{z}{\lambda}\right)\right]. \tag{12-47}$$

The field $\mathbf{E}_0$ can be derived from the potential V_0 in exactly the same manner as can an electrostatic field. Then, inside a hollow perfectly conducting tube, $\mathbf{E}_0$ must be zero, with the result that TEM waves are impossible.

The transverse components of $\mathbf{E}$ and $\mathbf{H}$ are mutually perpendicular, whether we have TE, TM, or TEM waves. The wave impedance is given by

$$\left|\frac{E_{ot}}{H_{ot}}\right| = \left(\frac{\mu}{\epsilon}\right)^{1/2} \frac{\lambda_g}{\lambda} \qquad \text{(for TE waves)}, \tag{12-28}$$

$$= \left(\frac{\mu}{\epsilon}\right)^{1/2} \frac{\lambda}{\lambda_g} \qquad \text{(for TM waves)}, \tag{12-30}$$

$$= \left(\frac{\mu}{\epsilon}\right)^{1/2} \qquad \text{(for TEM waves)}. \tag{12-55}$$

In a coaxial line,

$$\mathbf{E} = \frac{C}{\rho}\mathbf{i} \exp\left[j\left(\omega t - \frac{z}{\lambda}\right)\right], \tag{12-64}$$

$$\mathbf{H} = \left(\frac{\epsilon_0}{\mu_0}\right)^{1/2} \frac{C}{\rho}\mathbf{j} \exp\left[j\left(\omega t - \frac{z}{\lambda}\right)\right], \tag{12-67}$$

and the transmitted power is given by

$$W_T = \frac{C^2}{120} \ln \frac{\rho_2}{\rho_1} \quad \text{(watts)}. \qquad (12\text{-}72)$$

The case of the TE wave in a rectangular wave guide is used to illustrate the general method for determining $\mathbf{E}$ and $\mathbf{H}$ for a guided wave. To simplify the calculation somewhat, we assume a plane wave zigzagging down the guide, as in Figure 12-6. We then determine H_{oz} from the wave equation and from the required boundary condition. The other components follow immediately. The six components are shown in Eqs. *12-96* to *12-102* for $n = 1$. This parameter n corresponds to the number of "half cycles of $\mathbf{E}$" in the guide as in Figure 12-7.

Rectangular wave guides are *high*-frequency devices, the cut-off wave length λ_c being equal to twice the distance between the reflecting sides. The phase velocity u_p is larger than c, whereas the signal velocity u_s is smaller, and $u_p u_s = c^2$.

The transmitted power is given by

$$W_T = \frac{E_{ooz}^2 ab}{4c\mu_0} \left[1 - \left(\frac{\lambda_0}{2b}\right)^2 \right]^{1/2} \quad \text{(watts)}, \qquad (12\text{-}118)$$

where E_{ooz} is the maximum value of E in the guide.

It is possible to take into account the finite conductivity of the guide by deducing the tangential E in the guide from the value of the tangential H calculated on the assumption of infinite conductivity as above. This leads to a Poynting vector which points into the guide material and which corresponds to the Joule losses. The result is that the complex part of the wave number is given by

$$k_{gi} = \frac{1}{a(120\sigma\lambda_0)^{1/2}} \frac{\left[1 + \frac{2a}{b}\left(\frac{\lambda_0}{2b}\right)^2\right]}{\left[1 - \left(\frac{\lambda_0}{2b}\right)^2\right]^{1/2}}. \qquad (12\text{-}138)$$

It corresponds to losses in all four faces.

Problems

12-1. Show that the current in a coaxial line is given by the product (surface charge density) $\times$ (velocity of propagation).

12-2. Show that the z-component of the Poynting vector $\mathbf{S}_{av}$. for unattenuated TE and TM waves is given, respectively, by

$$\frac{k\omega\mu}{2\left[\frac{1}{\lambda^2} - \frac{1}{\lambda_g^2}\right]^2} \left[\left(\frac{\partial H_{0z}}{\partial x}\right)^2 + \left(\frac{\partial H_{oz}}{\partial y}\right)^2\right]$$

and

$$\frac{k\omega\epsilon}{2\left[\frac{1}{\lambda^2} - \frac{1}{\lambda_g^2}\right]^2} \left[\left(\frac{\partial E_{oz}}{\partial x}\right)^2 + \left(\frac{\partial E_{oz}}{\partial y}\right)^2\right].$$

12-3. A plane electromagnetic wave is incident at an angle θ_i on a perfectly reflecting plane surface, and **E** is normal to the plane of incidence. Draw solid lines for the "crests" of E for the incident wave, and draw broken lines for the "troughs." Draw similar lines for the reflected wave. Now crosshatch the regions where E is positive. Where is E equal to zero? How does the pattern change with time?

Can you relate this to a rectangular wave guide?

12-4. How would the pattern of Figure 12-8 be affected if the wave guide were filled with a dielectric of dielectric coefficient 2.0? How would the cut-off wave length be affected?

12-5. Are the potentials V and **A** zero outside a rectangular wave guide?

12-6. A rectangular wave guide of outside dimensions 3.000×1.500 inches and wall thickness 0.080 inch carries a TE wave with $n = 1$ and with **E** parallel to the short side. What is the maximum voltage across the guide when it carries 1.00 megawatt of power at a frequency of 3.00 kilomegacycles/second? The maximum permissible gradient is about 3×10^4 volts/centimeter at sea level.

12-7. Using only Maxwell's equations and the boundary conditions, deduce Eqs. *12-86* to *12-91* for the electromagnetic field inside a rectangular wave guide without assuming reflections as in Figure 12-6.

12-8. Show that the attenuation constant k_{gi} for a TE ($n = 1$) wave in a rectangular wave guide, as given in Eq. *12-138*, varies as $f^{3/2}$ when the ratios a/b and $\lambda_0/2b$ are kept constant.

12-9. Show that an electromagnetic wave is reduced in amplitude by a factor of approximately

$$1 - \left(\frac{2\omega\epsilon_0}{\sigma}\right)^{1/2} \cos\theta_i$$

upon reflection from a good conductor of conductivity σ, the angle of incidence being θ_i. The dielectric is assumed to have an index of refraction of unity.

Show that this loss leads to an attenuation constant k_{gi}, as in Eq. *12-139*, for a TE wave in a rectangular wave guide.

12-10. What is the current density in the face $y = 0$ of the wave guide illustrated in Figure 12-5 when it carries a TE ($n = 1$) wave.

Show that the power loss in the wall is the same as if the current were distributed uniformly in a thickness δ near the surface, δ being the attenuation distance (Section 10.4).

Show that this result always applies to a plane conducting surface and that it applies in particular to the face $x = 0$.

The quantity $1/\sigma\delta$ is called the *surface resistivity* and is expressed in ohms/square. A square sheet of given surface resistivity and of any size has a resistance of $1/\sigma\delta$ ohms between two parallel edges.

12-11. Use the above result to show that the attenuation constant k_{gi} for a coaxial line is given by

$$\left(\frac{\omega\epsilon_0}{2\sigma}\right)^{1/2} \frac{\dfrac{1}{\rho_1} + \dfrac{1}{\rho_2}}{\ln\dfrac{\rho_2}{\rho_1}}.$$

The outer radius of the *inner* conductor is ρ_1, and the inner radius of the *outer* conductor is ρ_2. The dielectric is air. Assume that the conductors are much thicker than the attenuation distance δ and that the wave which penetrates into the conductor is planar.

Show that, for a given value of ρ_2, k_{gi} is a minimum for $\rho_2/\rho_1 = 3.6$.

Calculate the attenuation in decibels per 100 feet for a copper line with $\rho_2 = 7/16$ inch and with the optimum value of ρ_2/ρ_1 at 3.0 kilomegacycles per second.

Would the attenuation be lower with a rectangular brass wave guide?

CHAPTER 13

Radiation of Electromagnetic Waves

We have now studied the propagation of electromagnetic waves in considerable detail. In Chapters 9 to 12 we have studied successively their propagation in free space, in various media, across an interface, and then along various guiding structures. The present chapter will now be devoted to the processes whereby these waves are produced. It may not seem logical to proceed in this order, but the reason is one of convenience and will become apparent after a while: the phenomenon of radiation is rather complex, and its discussion was best delayed until now.

Most of this chapter will be based on the scalar potential V and on the vector potential **A** which we first encountered in Chapters 2 and 5, respectively. It will first be necessary to study them further. We shall then calculate the fields of oscillating electric and magnetic dipoles and quadrupoles and the field of a half-wave antenna. We shall also deduce a reciprocity theorem which is equally valid for antennas and for electric circuits.

13.1. The Electromagnetic Potentials V and **A**

We first used the potential

$$V = \frac{1}{4\pi\epsilon} \int_\infty \frac{\rho \, d\tau}{r} \qquad (13\text{-}1)$$

in Section 2.3 for electrostatic fields. The quantity ρ is the electric charge density at a point (x', y', z'), and r is the distance from this point to the point (x, y, z)

where V is calculated. The integral is evaluated over all space. The vector potential

$$\mathbf{A} = \frac{\mu}{4\pi} \int_{\infty} \frac{\mathbf{J} \, d\tau}{r} \tag{13-2}$$

was later introduced in Section 5.5. In this equation, $\mathbf{J}$ is the current density at the source point (x', y', z'); the integral is again evaluated over all space.

These two quantities are both simpler to calculate than the field vectors $\mathbf{E}$ and $\mathbf{B}$ which can be deduced from them by simple differentiation:

$$\mathbf{E} = -\frac{\partial \mathbf{A}}{\partial t} - \nabla V, \tag{13-3}$$

$$\mathbf{B} = \nabla \times \mathbf{A}. \tag{13-4}$$

These are Eqs. *6-16* and *5-56*, respectively. The latter follows directly from one of Maxwell's equations, namely $\nabla \cdot \mathbf{B} = 0$. In the former, $-\nabla V$ gives the part of the electric field intensity which comes from the accumulations of electric charge, whereas $-\partial \mathbf{A}/\partial t$ gives the part which comes from changing magnetic fields, and hence from changing electric currents. This remarkable equation was deduced in Section 6.1.4 from another of Maxwell's equations, $\nabla \times \mathbf{E} = -\partial \mathbf{B}/\partial t$. At the time we were interested only in the electric fields arising from changing electric currents, hence we neglected the $-\nabla V$ term. At the present stage, however, we wish to be completely general, and so we shall use both terms.

For linear and isotropic media, $\mathbf{D} = \epsilon \mathbf{E}$, $\mathbf{H} = \mathbf{B}/\mu$, and all four field vectors $\mathbf{E}$, $\mathbf{D}$, $\mathbf{B}$, and $\mathbf{H}$ can be completely determined from only four quantities: V and the three components of $\mathbf{A}$.

The potentials V and $\mathbf{A}$ are thus quite well known to us, and they have proved highly useful. We shall now find that they play a fundamental role in electromagnetic theory. We shall call them the *electromagnetic potentials*, V being the *scalar potential*, and $\mathbf{A}$ the *vector potential*.

13.1.1. The Lorentz Condition. Although Eqs. *13-1* and *13-2* determine V and $\mathbf{A}$ uniquely, they cannot be considered to be entirely proper definitions of the electromagnetic potentials, since they each involve one arbitrary assumption.

Let us return to Chapter 2 and examine the reasoning which led us to Eq. *2-16*, which is the same as Eq. *13-1* except that ϵ_0 has been replaced by ϵ to take into account the dielectric coefficient K_e of the medium. We deduced from Coulomb's law that the curl of $\mathbf{E}$ in an electrostatic field is always zero. We then concluded that, for an electrostatic field, $\mathbf{E}$ must be of the form $-\nabla V$, since $\nabla \times \nabla V \equiv 0$. This, however, determines V only within a constant, thus the point in space where V is taken to be zero can be chosen arbitrarily. If we choose V to be zero at infinity for a finite charge distribution, we find the integral of

Eq. *13-1.* We could add to this integral any function whose gradient is zero, that is, any scalar quantity which is independent of position, without affecting **E**. Equation *13-1* therefore involves implicitly the assumption that this additive function is zero.

Later on, in Chapter 5, we deduced the magnetic induction

$$\mathbf{B} = \frac{\mu_0}{4\pi} \int_\tau \frac{\mathbf{J} \times \mathbf{r}_1}{r^2}\, d\tau \tag{13-5}$$

from the magnetic force law, and we discovered that **B** could be written as the curl of a vector **A**, as in Eq. *13-2.* Here again we could add to the integral for **A** any function whose curl is zero without affecting **B**.

Both **E** and **B** are measurable. They can be measured, for example, by observing the deflection of a beam of electrons. At any given point in space, **E** and **B** therefore have definite values, whereas V and **A** do not. The electric field intensity **E** and the magnetic induction **B** are thus physically significant quantities, whereas V and **A** must be considered as useful mathematical auxiliaries which can be modified at will, as long as **E** and **B** are not affected.

It will be observed that **E** depends on *both* electromagnetic potentials V and **A**. As noted above, this follows from the fact that an electric field can be produced either by an accumulation of charge or by a varying current. It is therefore to be expected that terms cannot be added to V and to **A** indiscriminately without affecting **E**.

Let us consider two pairs of electromagnetic potentials: V and **A**, as defined uniquely by Eqs. *13-1* and *13-2*, and V' and **A'**, which give the same **E** and **B**:

$$\mathbf{E} = -\frac{\partial \mathbf{A}}{\partial t} - \nabla V = -\frac{\partial \mathbf{A'}}{\partial t} - \nabla V', \tag{13-6}$$

$$\mathbf{B} = \nabla \times \mathbf{A} = \nabla \times \mathbf{A'}. \tag{13-7}$$

From the second pair,

$$\mathbf{A'} = \mathbf{A} + \nabla\theta, \tag{13-8}$$

where θ is *any* scalar function of the coordinates and of the time, since $\nabla \times \nabla\theta$ is identically equal to zero. Then, from the first pair,

$$\frac{\partial \mathbf{A}}{\partial t} + \nabla V = \frac{\partial}{\partial t}(\mathbf{A} + \nabla\theta) + \nabla V', \tag{13-9}$$

$$\nabla\left(V' - V + \frac{\partial\theta}{\partial t}\right) = 0, \tag{13-10}$$

or

$$V' = V - \frac{\partial\theta}{\partial t}. \tag{13-11}$$

We could also add on the right any quantity which is independent of the coordinates.

Thus, if **A** is *increased* by $\nabla\theta$, V must correspondingly be *decreased* by $\partial\theta/\partial t$ so as to leave the field vectors **E** and **B** undisturbed. An electromagnetic field is therefore unaffected by such a transformation. This is called *gauge invariance*, and the operation is called a *gauge transformation*.

The Lorentz condition of Eq. *5-107*, generalized to apply to any medium by the substitution of $\epsilon\mu$ for $K_e\epsilon_0\mu_0$, is

$$\nabla\cdot\mathbf{A} + \epsilon\mu\,\frac{\partial V}{\partial t} = 0. \tag{13-12}$$

It imposes a limitation on the choice of θ. If we substitute into it $V' + (\partial\theta/\partial t)$ for V and $\mathbf{A}' - \nabla\theta$ for **A**, we find that θ must satisfy the equation

$$\nabla^2\theta - \epsilon\mu\,\frac{\partial^2\theta}{\partial t^2} = -\left(\nabla\cdot\mathbf{A}' + \epsilon\mu\,\frac{\partial V'}{\partial t}\right). \tag{13-13}$$

The term on the left is not zero, in general, since θ is *any* function of the coordinates and of the time. If the Lorentz condition is to apply also to V' and $\mathbf{A}'$, then we must have

$$\nabla^2\theta - \epsilon\mu\,\frac{\partial^2\theta}{\partial t^2} = 0. \tag{13-14}$$

This is the restriction imposed on θ. It does *not* determine θ uniquely, however. For example, we can still add a constant K to V, or a constant $K'\mathbf{i}$ to **A**, without affecting either **E** or **B** or the Lorentz condition.

We shall assume henceforth that V and **A** are defined as in Eqs. *13-1* and *13-2* and that the Lorentz condition applies. This is satisfactory for finite charge and current distributions.

13.1.2. The Wave Equations for V and A.
We have already used two of Maxwell's equations above to express **E** and **B** in terms of V and **A**. We shall now use a third one, namely,

$$\nabla\times\mathbf{H} - \frac{\partial\mathbf{D}}{\partial t} = \mathbf{J}, \tag{13-15}$$

and shall express it in terms of V and **A**:

$$\nabla\times\nabla\times\mathbf{A} + \epsilon\mu\left(\frac{\partial^2\mathbf{A}}{\partial t^2} + \nabla\,\frac{\partial V}{\partial t}\right) = \mu\mathbf{J}, \tag{13-16}$$

or, from Equation *1-30*,

$$\nabla\times\nabla\times\mathbf{A} = \nabla(\nabla\cdot\mathbf{A}) - \nabla^2\mathbf{A}, \tag{13-17}$$

we have

$$\nabla^2\mathbf{A} - \epsilon\mu\,\frac{\partial^2\mathbf{A}}{\partial t^2} = -\mu\mathbf{J} + \nabla\left(\nabla\cdot\mathbf{A} + \epsilon\mu\,\frac{\partial V}{\partial t}\right), \tag{13-18}$$

$$= -\mu\mathbf{J}, \tag{13-19}$$

since the second term on the right is zero because of the Lorentz condition. This result was found earlier, in Problem 10-4. Note that this equation is *not* valid in other than Cartesian coordinates.

When the current density $\mathbf{J}$ is constant, the vector potential $\mathbf{A}$ is also constant, and

$$\nabla^2\mathbf{A} = -\mu\mathbf{J}, \tag{13-20}$$

which is similar to Eq. *5-129*, except that here we have taken into account the relative permeability of the medium.

Let us now use the last of Maxwell's equations, $\nabla\cdot\mathbf{D} = \rho$, and substitute into it the value of $\mathbf{E}$ in terms of V and $\mathbf{A}$:

$$\nabla\cdot\epsilon\left(-\frac{\partial\mathbf{A}}{\partial t} - \nabla V\right) = \rho, \tag{13-21}$$

$$\nabla^2 V = -\frac{\rho}{\epsilon} - \nabla\cdot\frac{\partial\mathbf{A}}{\partial t}. \tag{13-22}$$

Adding on both sides the term $\epsilon\mu(\partial^2 V/\partial t^2)$, we obtain

$$\nabla^2 V - \epsilon\mu\frac{\partial^2 V}{\partial t^2} = -\frac{\rho}{\epsilon} - \frac{\partial}{\partial t}\left(\nabla\cdot\mathbf{A} + \epsilon\mu\frac{\partial V}{\partial t}\right), \tag{13-23}$$

$$= -\frac{\rho}{\epsilon}. \tag{13-24}$$

This equation is valid in any coordinate system, since we have not had to expand the curl of the curl of a vector this time. We have assumed, as usual, that the medium is homogeneous and isotropic.

For an electrostatic field the scalar potential V is independent of time, and

$$\nabla^2 V = -\frac{\rho}{\epsilon}, \tag{13-25}$$

which is Eq. *2-28* applied to a dielectric.

Equations *13-24* and *13-19* are the *wave equations for V and for A*. They are nonhomogeneous because of the presence of the right-hand terms involving the quantities ρ and $\mathbf{J}$ which give rise to the field.

Let us see if they are compatible with the equation for the conservation of charge:

$$\nabla\cdot\mathbf{J} = -\frac{\partial\rho}{\partial t}. \tag{13-26}$$

Taking the divergence of the first equation and the time derivative of the second and substituting in the above, we find that

$$\nabla\cdot\left(\nabla^2\mathbf{A} - \epsilon\mu\frac{\partial^2\mathbf{A}}{\partial t^2}\right) = -\epsilon\mu\frac{\partial}{\partial t}\left(\nabla^2 V - \epsilon\mu\frac{\partial^2 V}{\partial t^2}\right). \tag{13-27}$$

Now $\nabla\cdot\nabla^2\mathbf{A} = \nabla^2(\nabla\cdot\mathbf{A})$, as can be easily verified in Cartesian coordinates. Rearranging,

$$\nabla^2\left(\nabla\cdot\mathbf{A} + \epsilon\mu\,\frac{\partial V}{\partial t}\right) - \epsilon\mu\,\frac{\partial^2}{\partial t^2}\left(\nabla\cdot\mathbf{A} + \epsilon\mu\,\frac{\partial V}{\partial t}\right) = 0. \qquad (13\text{-}28)$$

This is correct because the terms between parentheses are zero, according to the Lorentz condition. The wave equations for V and for **A** are therefore compatible with the conservation of charge. This was to be expected since our deduction of the Lorentz condition itself involved the conservation of charge.

In regions of space where there is zero net charge density and zero current density **J**,

$$\nabla^2 V - \epsilon\mu\,\frac{\partial^2 V}{\partial t^2} = 0, \qquad (13\text{-}29)$$

$$\nabla^2\mathbf{A} - \epsilon\mu\,\frac{\partial^2\mathbf{A}}{\partial t^2} = 0, \qquad (13\text{-}30)$$

and the electromagnetic potentials V and **A** propagate, as do the field vectors **E, D, B,** and **H**, with the same phase velocity

$$1/(\epsilon\mu)^{1/2} = c/(K_e K_m)^{1/2}.$$

13.1.3. Retarded Potentials. Let us now solve the nonhomogeneous partial differential equation *13-24* for the scalar potential V. Our solution will be partly intuitive. We shall assume at first that the charge is limited to the immediate neighborhood of the origin within a radius r_0; later we shall generalize to a finite charge distribution. We shall also assume that the charge Q is a sinusoidal function of the time:

$$Q = Q_0 e^{i\omega t}. \qquad (13\text{-}31)$$

This temporary violation of the law of conservation of charge will disappear when we consider the finite distribution.

In the immediate neighborhood of the origin, where the electric charge density ρ is not zero, Eq. *13-24* applies; at all other points $\rho = 0$, and Eq. *13-29* must be used.

Now we expect V to be a function of r and of t only, except possibly close to the origin, where the dipole, quadrupole, . . . terms of the charge distribution can take on some importance. It will be recalled from Section 2.11 that the potential due to a charge distribution reduces to the monopole term for far away points if the total charge in the distribution is not zero. Then, for $r \gg r_0$, the Laplacian of V can be expressed in spherical polar coordinates, and the derivatives with respect to θ and to φ can be neglected, thus

$$\frac{1}{r^2}\frac{\partial}{\partial r}\left(r^2\frac{\partial V}{\partial r}\right) - \epsilon\mu\,\frac{\partial^2 V}{\partial t^2} = 0. \qquad (13\text{-}32)$$

We expect that the radial dependence of V will be of the form $1/r$, since it must agree with the electrostatic potential for the limiting case where $\omega \longrightarrow 0$.

We therefore set

$$V = \frac{V'}{r},$$ (13-33)

and then

$$\frac{\partial^2 V'}{\partial r^2} - \epsilon\mu \frac{\partial^2 V'}{\partial t^2} = 0.$$ (13-34)

This equation is identical in form to Eq. G-28. Its solution, in exponential form, is as follows:

$$V' = V_1' \exp\left\{ j\omega\left(t - \frac{r}{u}\right)\right\} + V_2' \exp\left\{ j\omega\left(t + \frac{r}{u}\right)\right\},$$ (13-35)

where

$$u = \frac{1}{(\epsilon\mu)^{1/2}} = \frac{c}{(K_e K_m)^{1/2}}.$$ (13-36)

The V_1' term corresponds to a wave radiating outwards from the origin with a velocity u, whereas the V_2' term corresponds to a similar wave moving inwards. Let us first consider only the outgoing wave. Then

$$V = \frac{V_1'}{r} \exp\left\{ j\omega\left(t - \frac{r}{u}\right)\right\}.$$ (13-37)

We now have to determine V_1'. This can be done by considering a point close to the origin, but still far enough away such that $r \gg r_0$. This is possible because the radius r_0 is infinitesimal. For

$$\frac{\omega}{u} r = \frac{r}{\lambda} \ll 1,$$ (13-38)

the phase of the wave is simply ωt, and

$$V = \frac{V_1'}{r} e^{j\omega t} = \frac{V_1'}{r} \frac{Q}{Q_0} \qquad (r_0 \ll r \ll \lambda).$$ (13-39)

In this region, V is proportional to Q and inversely proportional to r, just like an electrostatic potential. Therefore

$$V = \frac{Q_0 e^{j\omega t}}{4\pi\epsilon r} \qquad (r_0 \ll r \ll \lambda),$$ (13-40)

and

$$V_1' = \frac{Q_0}{4\pi\epsilon}.$$ (13-41)

Thus, for any value of $r \gg r_0$, where r_0 approaches zero,

$$V = \frac{Q_0 \exp\left\{ j\omega\left(t - \frac{r}{u}\right)\right\}}{4\pi\epsilon r} = \frac{Q_0 \exp\left\{ i\left(\omega t - \frac{r}{\lambda}\right)\right\}}{4\pi\epsilon r}.$$ (13-42)

The scalar potential V due to the point charge $Q_0 e^{j\omega t}$ is identical to the electrostatic potential, except that we must substitute $t - (r/u)$ for t in the exponential. The potential is therefore *retarded* by the time required for a wave of velocity $u = \lambda\omega$ to travel the distance between the charge Q and the point under consideration; that is, the potential V corresponds to the state of the charge Q at a previous time $t - (r/u)$. A well-known illustration of this is the fact that we see the distant stars, not as they are now, but as they were millions of years ago. We can now neglect the V_2' term in Eq. *13-35*, for it would make the effect appear before the cause.

If the charge is not limited to a small region close to the origin but is instead distributed throughout a finite volume τ with a density ρ, then the potential at $P(x, y, z)$ is simply the sum of the potentials due to the elements of charge $\rho\,dx'\,dy'\,dz'$ situated at (x', y', z'):

$$V = \int_\tau \frac{\rho \exp\left\{j\omega\left(t - \frac{r}{u}\right)\right\}}{4\pi\epsilon r}\,d\tau, \tag{13-43}$$

where r is now given by

$$r = [(x - x')^2 + (y - y')^2 + (z - z')^2]^{1/2}. \tag{13-44}$$

The charge densities ρ may be complex to allow for phase differences between the various parts of the volume τ. There need not be violation of the conservation of charge in this general case, because charge can flow from one element of volume to another.

Our demonstration is not general, however, in that it assumes that ρ varies everywhere at some definite frequency $f = \omega/2\pi$. More general arguments show that

$$V = \frac{1}{4\pi\epsilon} \int_\infty \frac{[\rho]}{r}\,d\tau \tag{13-45}$$

where $[\rho]$ is the *retarded* value of the charge density ρ. This is the value of ρ at the previous time $t - (r/u)$, the velocity u being the velocity of light in the medium and r being defined as above. In a vacuum, $u = c$. *Square brackets will be used exclusively to identify retarded values from now on.*

The equation (*13-19*) for the vector potential **A** yields similarly

$$A_x = \frac{\mu}{4\pi} \int_\infty \frac{[J_x]}{r}\,d\tau, \tag{13-46}$$

and corresponding expressions for A_y and A_z, or

$$\mathbf{A} = \frac{\mu}{4\pi} \int_\infty \frac{[\mathbf{J}]}{r}\,d\tau, \tag{13-47}$$

where $[\mathbf{J}]$ is the current density at (x', y', z') at a previous time $t - (r/u)$.

The equations we have found above for V and **A** take into account the fact that changes in ρ or **J** at the source affect the potentials V and **A** only after a delay of r/u seconds. They are therefore more general than Equations *13-1* and *13-2*.

13.2. Electric Dipole Radiation

Let us now consider the processes whereby an electromagnetic wave is radiated into space. We shall start with the electric dipole, which is the simplest

type of source. After having mastered the electric dipole, we shall be able to study the radiation field of the half-wave antenna—the type commonly used for transmitting radio waves. We shall then go on to magnetic dipole radiation, which is closely related to electric dipole radiation. It will be relatively easy to deduce the radiation fields of simple electric and magnetic quadrupoles.

Figure 13-1. *An electric dipole. The total charge is zero. The vector* s *is oriented from* −Q *to* +Q *as shown.*

It will be recalled from Section 2.8 that an electric dipole is formed of a pair of charges of equal magnitude and of opposite signs, as shown in Figure 13-1. Its dipole moment is $\mathbf{p} = Q\mathbf{s}$.

One can imagine an electric dipole whose moment is a sinusoidal function of the time, with

$$Q = Q_0 e^{j\omega t}. \tag{13-48}$$

Then

$$\mathbf{p} = Q_0 e^{j\omega t}\mathbf{s} = \mathbf{p}_0 e^{j\omega t}, \tag{13-49}$$

where

$$\mathbf{p}_0 = Q_0\mathbf{s}. \tag{13-50}$$

Such an oscillating electric dipole could be made up of a pair of conductors of finite capacitance, such as spheres or plates, joined by a thin wire of negligible capacitance. The charges would then be situated mostly on the electrodes, but could still flow from one to the other.

Figure 13-2 shows the charges $-Q$ and $+Q$ as a function of the time for such an oscillating electric dipole. The upward current I flowing through the connecting wire is

$$I = \frac{dQ}{dt} = j\omega Q_0 e^{j\omega t}, \tag{13-51}$$

$$= I_0 e^{j\omega t}, \tag{13-52}$$

and

$$I_0 = j\omega Q_0, \tag{13-53}$$

$$I\mathbf{s} = j\omega\mathbf{p}. \tag{13-54}$$

Note that

$$I_0\mathbf{s} = j\omega\mathbf{p}_0. \tag{13-55}$$

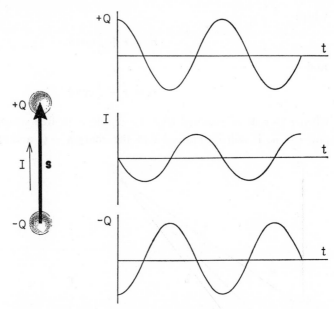

Figure 13-2. *The charges* $-Q$ *and* $+Q$ *and the current* I *as functions of time in the oscillating dipole.*

We shall use this simple model, but electric dipole radiation is also produced by any charge distribution whose dipole moment

$$\mathbf{p} = \int \rho \mathbf{r} \, d\tau \qquad (13\text{-}56)$$

is a sinusoidal function of the time. For example, charge oscillations can be imagined to occur on the surface of a conducting sphere in such a way that the electrons are driven alternately from one pole to the other. Figure 13-3 shows schematically an electric dipole antenna fed by an oscillator.

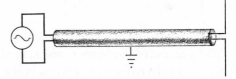

Figure 13-3. *Electric dipole antenna fed by an oscillator.*

We shall calculate successively the electromagnetic potentials V and $\mathbf{A}$, then the field vectors $\mathbf{E}$ and $\mathbf{H}$, and, finally, the Poynting vector $\mathbf{S}_{av.}$ and the radiated power W for electric dipole radiation.

13.2.1. The Scalar Potential V. The retarded scalar potential V for the oscillating dipole as illustrated in Figure 13-4 is

$$V = \frac{Q_0 \exp\left\{ j\omega \left(t - \dfrac{r_b}{c} \right) \right\}}{4\pi\epsilon_0 r_b} - \frac{Q_0 \exp\left\{ j\omega \left(t - \dfrac{r_a}{c} \right) \right\}}{4\pi\epsilon_0 r_a}, \qquad (13\text{-}57)$$

where

$$r_a = r + \frac{s}{2} \cos \theta \tag{13-58}$$

and

$$r_b = r - \frac{s}{2} \cos \theta \tag{13-59}$$

when $r \gg s$. It is assumed that the dipole is in free space, such that $K_e = 1$ and $\epsilon = \epsilon_0$. It will be noticed that the charges $-Q$ and $+Q$ give scalar po-

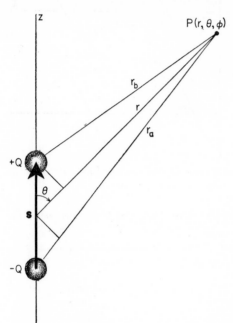

Figure 13-4

An oscillating electric dipole situated at the origin gives rise to a scalar potential V at the point $P(r, \theta, \phi)$.

tentials which differ not only in amplitude but also in phase. The amplitudes differ because of the terms r_a and r_b in the denominators, and the phases differ because of the r_a/c and r_b/c terms in the exponentials. Now

$$\omega \left(t - \frac{r_b}{c} \right) = \omega \left(t - \frac{r}{c} + \frac{s \cos \theta}{2c} \right), \tag{13-60}$$

$$= \omega \left(t - \frac{r}{c} \right) + \frac{s}{2\lambda} \cos \theta, \tag{13-61}$$

and

$$V = \frac{Q_0 \exp \left\{ j\omega \left(t - \frac{r}{c} \right) \right\}}{4\pi \epsilon_0 r} \left(\frac{\exp \left\{ j \left(\frac{s}{2\lambda} \right) \cos \theta \right\}}{1 - \frac{s}{2r} \cos \theta} - \frac{\exp \left\{ -j \left(\frac{s}{2\lambda} \right) \cos \theta \right\}}{1 + \frac{s}{2r} \cos \theta} \right). \tag{13-62}$$

Expanding both the exponential functions and the denominators of the two terms within the braces as power series, and neglecting terms of the third order and higher in s/r and s/λ, we obtain

$$V = \frac{p_0 \exp\left\{j\omega\left(t - \frac{r}{c}\right)\right\}}{4\pi\epsilon_0 r\lambda}\left(\frac{\lambda}{r} + j\right)\cos\theta, \qquad (13\text{-}63)$$

where we have substituted p_0 for $Q_0 s$. The only approximation is that we have assumed the length of the dipole s to be small compared to both r and λ: $s \ll r$

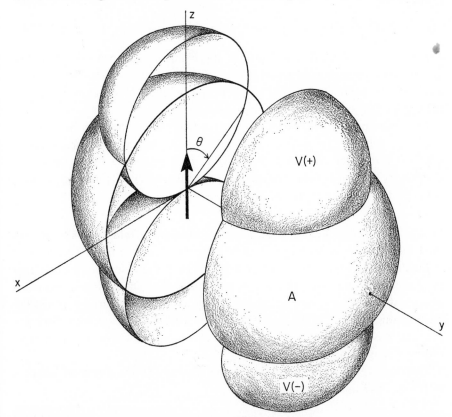

Figure 13-5. *The scalar potential V and the magnitude of the vector potential **A** are shown here as functions of θ and ϕ about an oscillating electric dipole oriented as shown. The radial distance from the center of the dipole to the spheres marked V is proportional to the value of V in this particular direction. The scalar potential V is maximum at the poles; it vanishes at the equator, where the individual potentials of the charge $-Q$ and $+Q$ of the dipole cancel. It is positive in the northern hemisphere, where the field of $+Q$ is predominant, and is negative in the southern hemisphere. The magnitude of the vector potential **A** is similarly represented by the sphere marked **A**. The vector potential is independent, both in magnitude and in direction, of the coordinates θ and ϕ.*

and $s \ll \lambda$. We have made *no* assumption as to the relative orders of magnitude of r and of λ.

It is important to check this result with the electrostatic potential for the static dipole (Eq. *2-70*). For zero frequency, $\omega = 0$, $\lambda = \infty$, and the two expressions agree as expected.

For a non-zero frequency, the exponential term appears to show that the scalar potential V propagates as a wave with a velocity c. This is not quite correct, however, because of the complex factor $(\lambda/r) + j$. Rewriting Eq. *13-63*, we have

$$V = \frac{p_0}{4\pi\epsilon_0 r \lambda} \left(\frac{\lambda^2}{r^2} + 1\right)^{1/2} \exp\left\{ j\omega \left(t - \frac{r}{c} + \frac{1}{\omega} \arctan \frac{r}{\lambda}\right)\right\} \cos\theta. \quad (13\text{-}64)$$

For $r \gg \lambda$, $\arctan (r/\lambda) \approx \pi/2$ and is approximately independent of r. The phase velocity is then c. However, closer in to the dipole, where r is not much larger than λ, $\arctan (r/\lambda)$ is not constant, and the effect of this term is to give a velocity of propagation which is larger than c.

The scalar potential V varies as $\cos\theta$ and is zero in the equatorial plane, where the fields of the two charges cancel exactly, just as in electrostatics. It varies as $1/r^2$ in the static case, but only as $1/r$ when $r \gg \lambda$. Also, for $r \gg \lambda$, V varies as $1/\lambda$ and is thus proportional to the frequency. Figure 13-5 shows a radial plot of V as a function of θ and φ.

13.2.2. The Vector Potential A and the Magnetic Field Intensity H.

We shall calculate the vector potential **A** at the point $P(r, \theta, \varphi)$ from the current I in the dipole, and then the **H** vector from the curl of **A**. We assume again that the dipole is in free space, that $s \ll r$, and that $s \ll \lambda$. The last condition eliminates standing-wave effects in the connecting wire, and the current is then the same throughout the length s of the dipole. We have already used these approximations in calculating V. We again make no assumption as to the relative orders of magnitude of r and λ.

The vector potential **A** is related to the current I in the dipole of length **s** as in Eq. *13-47* and Figure 13-6:

$$\mathbf{A} = \frac{\mu_0}{4\pi r} I_0 \exp\left\{ j\omega\left(t - \frac{r}{c}\right)\right\} \mathbf{s}. \quad (13\text{-}65)$$

It is independent of both θ and φ and depends only on the distance r to the dipole. This is illustrated in Figure 13-5. It is also everywhere parallel to **s**, and is thus parallel to the polar axis. Expressing **s** in polar coordinates, we have

$$\mathbf{A} = \frac{\mu_0}{4\pi r} I_0 s \exp\left\{ j\omega\left(t - \frac{r}{c}\right)\right\}(\cos\theta\, \mathbf{i} - \sin\theta\, \mathbf{j}), \quad (13\text{-}66)$$

$$= \frac{j\omega\mu_0 p_0}{4\pi r} \exp\left\{ j\omega\left(t - \frac{r}{c}\right)\right\}(\cos\theta\, \mathbf{i} - \sin\theta\, \mathbf{j}), \quad (13\text{-}67)$$

where the polar unit vectors **i, j, k** are as in Figure 1-16. The vector potential **A** propagates as a wave with velocity c, even for $r \gg \lambda$.

We should really have integrated $d\mathbf{A}$ over the length s of the dipole. However, it will be shown in Problem 13-3 that the integration leads to the above result when $s \ll \lambda$. The situation here is different from what it was for V, which is the *difference* between the scalar potentials of the two charges $-Q$ and $+Q$. Since the two scalar potentials are very nearly equal in magnitude, their difference must be evaluated with care. For **A**, however, the $d\mathbf{A}$'s all add up, and the phase angle $\omega\{(t - (r/c)\} = \omega t - r/\lambda$ changes but slightly from one element to the next, since $s \ll \lambda$.

Turning now to **H**, we have

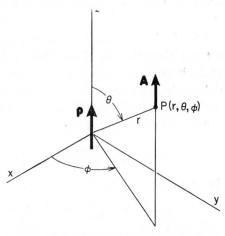

Figure 13-6. *An oscillating electric dipole of moment* **p** *situated at the origin gives rise to a vector potential* **A** *parallel to* **p** *at the point* $P(r, \theta, \phi)$.

$$\mathbf{H} = \frac{1}{\mu_0} \nabla \times \mathbf{A}, \qquad (13\text{-}68)$$

$$\mathbf{H} = \frac{1}{\mu_0 r} \left\{ \frac{\partial}{\partial r}(rA_\theta) - \frac{\partial A_r}{\partial \theta} \right\} \mathbf{k}. \qquad (13\text{-}69)$$

The two other components of the curl are zero in this case, because **A** has no φ component, and because it is not a function of φ. Thus

$$\mathbf{H} = \frac{I_0 s}{4\pi r \lambda} \exp\left\{ j\omega \left(t - \frac{r}{c} \right) \right\} \left(\frac{\lambda}{r} + j \right) \sin \theta \, \mathbf{k}. \qquad (13\text{-}70)$$

As usual, we compare this new result with a previously acquired one, namely, the Biot-Savart law for steady currents, as stated in Eq. 5-9. According to this equation, the magnetic field intensity due to an element of current Is at the position of the dipole is given by

$$\mathbf{H} = \frac{I\mathbf{s} \times \mathbf{r_1}}{4\pi r^2} = \frac{Is \sin \theta}{4\pi r^2} \mathbf{k} \qquad (\omega = 0). \qquad (13\text{-}71)$$

Thus at zero frequency $\omega = 0$, $\lambda = \infty$, and the two results agree. For a non-zero frequency, **H** propagates with a velocity c when $r \gg \lambda$. Closer in, the velocity is larger than c, as it is for V.

For a constant current, it will be observed that only the first term remains and that it varies as $1/r^2$. This term comes from $\partial A_r/\partial \theta$; that is, it is proportional to the rate of change of the radial component of **A** with θ.

The second term in Eq. *13-70*, however, decreases only as $1/r$, and it leads the first by $\pi/2$ radians. It becomes prominent at large distances from the dipole where $r \gg \lambda$. This is the *radiation term*. It comes from the $\partial(rA_\theta)/\partial r$ derivative, which is zero for a constant current. It is proportional to the rate of change of the exponential function in **A** with the distance r.

Since both terms involve $\sin\theta$, they are maximum in the equatorial plane and are zero along the axis of the dipole. It is interesting to note how the amplitude of the **H** vector changes from a $1/r^2$ dependence for a constant current to a $1/r$ dependence for a varying current. We have already observed a similar behavior for V. The magnitude of **H** as a function of θ and φ is plotted in Figure 13-8.

Since $I_0s = j\omega p_0$ (Eq. *13-55*),

$$\mathbf{H} = \frac{cp_0}{4\pi r\lambda^2} \exp\left\{ j\omega\left(t - \frac{r}{c}\right)\right\}\left(j\frac{\lambda}{r} - 1\right)\sin\theta \,\mathbf{k}. \qquad (13\text{-}72)$$

For $r \gg \lambda$,

$$\mathbf{H} = -\frac{cp_0}{4\pi r\lambda^2} \exp\left\{ j\omega\left(t - \frac{r}{c}\right)\right\}\sin\theta \,\mathbf{k}. \qquad (r \gg \lambda) \qquad (13\text{-}73)$$

13.2.3. The Electric Field Intensity E.

To obtain **E**, we require the time derivative of **A**,

$$-\frac{\partial \mathbf{A}}{\partial t} = \frac{p_0}{4\pi\epsilon_0 r\lambda^2}\exp\left\{ j\omega\left(t - \frac{r}{c}\right)\right\}(\cos\theta\,\mathbf{i} - \sin\theta\,\mathbf{j}), \qquad (13\text{-}74)$$

and the gradient of the scalar potential of Eq. *13-63*,

$$-\nabla V = -\left(\frac{\partial V}{\partial r}\mathbf{i} + \frac{1}{r}\frac{\partial V}{\partial\theta}\mathbf{j} + \frac{1}{r\sin\theta}\frac{\partial V}{\partial\varphi}\mathbf{k}\right), \qquad (13\text{-}75)$$

$$= \frac{-p_0}{4\pi\epsilon_0 r\lambda^2}\exp\left\{ j\omega\left(t - \frac{r}{c}\right)\right\}$$

$$\times \left\{\left(-2\frac{\lambda^2}{r^2} - 2j\frac{\lambda}{r} + 1\right)\cos\theta\,\mathbf{i} - \left(\frac{\lambda^2}{r^2} + j\frac{\lambda}{r}\right)\sin\theta\,\mathbf{j}\right\}. \qquad (13\text{-}76)$$

Then

$$\mathbf{E} = -\frac{\partial \mathbf{A}}{\partial t} - \nabla V, \qquad (13\text{-}77)$$

$$= -\frac{p_0}{4\pi\epsilon_0 r\lambda^2}\exp\left\{ j\omega\left(t - \frac{r}{c}\right)\right\} \qquad (13\text{-}78)$$

$$\times \left(\left\{(-1) + \left(-2\frac{\lambda^2}{r^2} - 2j\frac{\lambda}{r} + 1\right)\right\}\cos\theta\,\mathbf{i} + \left\{(+1) + \left(-\frac{\lambda^2}{r^2} - j\frac{\lambda}{r}\right)\right\}\sin\theta\,\mathbf{j}\right).$$

$$\left(\text{from } \frac{\partial \mathbf{A}}{\partial t}\right) \quad \left(\text{from } \frac{\partial V}{\partial r}\right) \qquad \left(\text{from } \frac{\partial \mathbf{A}}{\partial t}\right)\left(\text{from } \frac{1}{r}\frac{\partial V}{\partial\theta}\right)$$

We have shown the origins of the various terms. At distances where $r \gg \lambda$, the terms in λ/r and λ^2/r^2 become negligible, and the only remaining term comes from the time derivative of **A**, and hence from the time derivative of the current. In the coefficient of $\cos \theta$ the first and last terms are the largest, but they cancel. One of these comes from the current in the dipole; the other comes from the charges $-Q$ and $+Q$. Finally,

$$\mathbf{E} = \frac{p_0}{4\pi\epsilon_0 r\lambda^2} \exp\left\{ j\omega \left(t - \frac{r}{c} \right) \right\} \left\{ 2 \left(\frac{\lambda^2}{r^2} + j\frac{\lambda}{r} \right) \cos\theta \, \mathbf{i} + \left(\frac{\lambda^2}{r^2} + j\frac{\lambda}{r} - 1 \right) \sin\theta \, \mathbf{j} \right\}.$$

$$(13\text{-}79)$$

Contrary to the **H** vector, which is entirely along **k** and is thus perpendicular to the direction of propagation, or transverse, **E** has a longitudinal component along the radial direction, at least close to the dipole, where $r \gg \lambda$.

We can compare **E** with the electric field intensity of a static electric dipole, as given in Eqs. *2-73* and *2-74*. The product $\omega\lambda$ remains equal to c as $\omega \longrightarrow 0$ and $\lambda \longrightarrow \infty$, thus

$$\mathbf{E} = \frac{p_0}{4\pi\epsilon_0 r^3} (2\cos\theta \, \mathbf{i} + \sin\theta \, \mathbf{j}) \qquad (\omega = 0) \qquad (13\text{-}80)$$

as required. These are the *static terms*.

The electric field intensity **E** propagates through space with a velocity c for $r \gg \lambda$, as do V, **A**, and **H**.

Close to the dipole, where r is not much larger than λ, the electric field intensity involves *five* different terms. Two of these vary as $1/r^3$; two others lead them by $\pi/2$ radians and vary as $1/r^2$; and, finally, a fifth term varies as $1/r$ and leads the first pair by π radians.

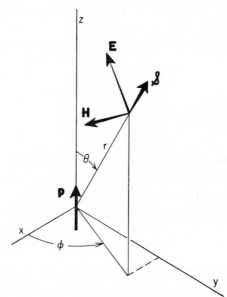

Figure 13-7

*The **E**, **H**, and **S** vectors for an oscillating dipole are oriented as shown at $r \gg \lambda$ when the phase angle $\omega[t - (r/c)] = 0$.*

Far from the source, where $r \gg \lambda$, we are left only with the *radiation term*

$$\mathbf{E} = -\frac{p_0}{4\pi\epsilon_0 r \lambda^2} \exp\left\{ j\omega\left(t - \frac{r}{c}\right)\right\} \sin\theta\, \mathbf{j} \qquad (r \gg \lambda), \qquad (13\text{-}81)$$

which comes only from $\partial\mathbf{A}/\partial t$. The modulus of $\mathbf{E}$ is plotted as a function of θ and φ in Figure 13-8.

In this case, $\mathbf{E}$ changes from a $1/r^3$ dependence for a static field to a $1/r$ dependence for a varying field. We shall see later on that a $1/r$ dependence is required of both $\mathbf{E}$ and $\mathbf{H}$ for an oscillating dipole to ensure conservation of energy.

If we consider both $\mathbf{E}$ and $\mathbf{H}$ far from the source, where $r \gg \lambda$, we notice that $\mathbf{E}$ lies in a plane passing through the polar axis, whereas $\mathbf{H}$ is azimuthal. The Poynting vector $\mathbf{E} \times \mathbf{H}$ is radial, as in Figure 13-7. We shall consider the Poynting vector in the next section. The ratio

$$\frac{E}{H} = \mu_0 c = \left(\frac{\mu_0}{\epsilon_0}\right)^{1/2} = 377 \text{ ohms}, \qquad (13\text{-}82)$$

just as for a plane wave in free space, as we found in Eq. *9-28*. The electric and magnetic energy densities $\epsilon_0 E^2/2$ and $\mu_0 H^2/2$ are equal.

We have therefore discovered that the *E and H vectors at points remote from the oscillating dipole are related to each other exactly as in a plane electromagnetic wave.*

13.2.4. The Poynting Vector and the Radiated Power. It is interesting to calculate the power radiated by an oscillating electric dipole. This can be found by integrating the Poynting vector $\mathbf{S}_{av.}$ over a spherical surface centered on the dipole. Let us first calculate $\mathbf{S}_{av.}$:

$$\mathbf{S}_{av.} = \frac{1}{2} \operatorname{Re}(\mathbf{E} \times \mathbf{H}^*), \qquad (13\text{-}83)$$

$$= \frac{1}{2} \operatorname{Re}\{(E_r\mathbf{i} + E_\theta\mathbf{j}) \times H_\varphi^*\mathbf{k}\}. \qquad (13\text{-}84)$$

Recalling that

$$\mathbf{i} \times \mathbf{k} = -\mathbf{j}, \qquad \mathbf{j} \times \mathbf{k} = \mathbf{i} \qquad (13\text{-}85)$$

in any orthogonal system of coordinates, we write

$$\mathbf{S}_{av.} = \frac{1}{2} \operatorname{Re}(-E_r H_\varphi^*\mathbf{j} + E_\theta H_\varphi^*\mathbf{i}), \qquad (13\text{-}86)$$

the components of $\mathbf{E}$ and of $\mathbf{H}$ being given by Eqs. *13-79* and *13-72*. Thus

$$\mathbf{S}_{av.} = \frac{cp_0^2 \sin^2\theta}{32\pi^2\epsilon_0 r^2 \lambda^4}\, \mathbf{i}. \qquad (13\text{-}87)$$

If we wish to express the Poynting vector in terms of the current I_0, it is *not* proper to substitute $I_0 s/j\omega$ for p_0 in this equation, for this would give the wrong sign. Both **E** and **H** must be expressed instead in terms of I_0 by using Eq. *13-55*, and **S**$_{av.}$ must be calculated anew. Then

$$\mathbf{S}_{av.} = \frac{\mu_0 c I_0^2 s^2}{32\pi^2 r^2 \lambda^2} \sin^2 \theta \; \mathbf{i}. \tag{13-88}$$

One striking feature about the Poynting vector is that it involves only the radiation terms, despite the fact that our calculation is valid even near the dipole, where r is not much larger than λ. In fact, it could have been calculated correctly by disregarding the terms which are unimportant far away from the dipole. The energy flow is everywhere purely radial, at least as long as the dipole length s is small compared to both r and λ.

The Poynting vector varies as $1/r^2$. This is required for conservation of energy, since, under steady state conditions, the energy flow through any given solid angle must be the same for all r. This $1/r^2$ dependence results from the fact that the radiation terms for **E** and for **H** both vary as $1/r$.

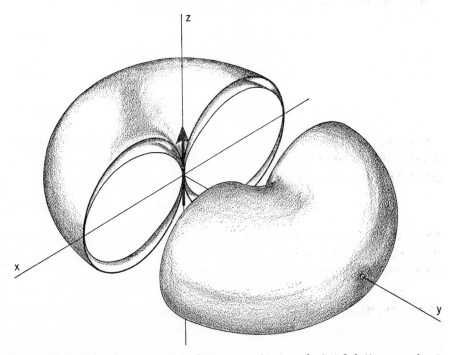

Figure 13-8. *Polar diagrams of sin θ (outer surface) and of sin^2 θ (inner surface) showing, respectively, the angular distributions of E or H, and of $\mathcal{S}_{av.}$ for an oscillating electric dipole situated at the origin. The radial distance from the dipole to one of the surfaces is proportional to the magnitude of these quantities in the corresponding direction. Most of the energy is radiated near the equatorial plane; none is radiated along the axis.*

Since the energy flow varies as $\sin^2 \theta$, it is zero along the axis of the dipole and is maximum in the equatorial plane, as shown in Figure 13-8. *An electric dipole does not radiate energy along its axis.*

The total radiated power W is obtained by integrating $\mathbf{S}_{\text{av.}}$ over the surface of a sphere of radius r:

$$W = \frac{c p_0^2}{32 \pi^2 \epsilon_0 \lambda^4} \int_0^{2\pi} \int_0^{\pi} \frac{\sin^2 \theta}{r^2} r^2 \sin \theta \, d\theta \, d\varphi, \qquad (13\text{-}89)$$

$$= \frac{c}{12 \pi \epsilon_0} \frac{p_0^2}{\lambda^4}, \qquad (13\text{-}90)$$

$$= 9.00 \times 10^{17} \frac{p_0^2}{\lambda^4} \qquad \text{(watts)}. \qquad (13\text{-}91)$$

The radiated energy varies as the *square* of the dipole moment $p_0 = Q_0 s$, and inversely as the *fourth* power of the wave length, or directly as the *fourth* power of the frequency.

When the Poynting vector is expressed in terms of I_0,

$$W = \frac{\mu_0 c}{12 \pi} \left(\frac{s}{\lambda} \right)^2 I_0^2, \qquad (13\text{-}92)$$

$$= 10.0 \left(\frac{s}{\lambda} \right)^2 I_0^2 \qquad \text{(watts)}, \qquad (13\text{-}93)$$

$$= 20.0 \left(\frac{s}{\lambda} \right)^2 I_{\text{rms}}^2 \qquad \text{(watts)}. \qquad (13\text{-}94)$$

It will be observed that the energy radiated by the electric dipole is proportional to the square of the current flowing through it. The coefficient of I_{rms}^2 is called the *radiation resistance:*

$$R_{rad} = 20.0 \left(\frac{s}{\lambda} \right)^2 \qquad \text{(ohms)}. \qquad (13\text{-}95)$$

This is the resistance which would dissipate in the form of heat the same power that the dipole radiates in the form of an electromagnetic wave, if it carried the same current. It will be recalled that we have assumed $s \ll \lambda$.

13.2.5. The Electric and Magnetic Lines of Force. We have already found the electric field intensity $\mathbf{E}$ in Eq. *13-79*. To find the electric lines of force, we can set

$$\frac{E_r}{dr} = \frac{E_\theta}{r \, d\theta}, \qquad (13\text{-}96)$$

since an element of a line of force, having components dr and $r \, d\theta$, is parallel to the local electric field intensity, whose components are E_r and E_θ. We have used this same method to determine the lines of force of the static electric dipole in

Section 2.8. In the present case, the calculation is considerably simplified by using the vector

$$\mathbf{C} = \frac{p_0}{4\pi\epsilon_0 r\lambda}\, \exp\left\{ j\omega\left(t - \frac{r}{c}\right)\right\}\left(\frac{\lambda}{r} + j\right)\sin\theta\,\mathbf{k}. \qquad (13\text{-}97)$$

This vector is chosen such that

$$\mathbf{E} = \boldsymbol{\nabla} \times \mathbf{C}. \qquad (13\text{-}98)$$

Then

$$E_r = \frac{1}{r\sin\theta}\frac{\partial}{\partial\theta}\,(C\sin\theta), \qquad (13\text{-}99)$$

and

$$E_\theta = -\frac{1}{r}\frac{\partial(rC)}{\partial r}. \qquad (13\text{-}100)$$

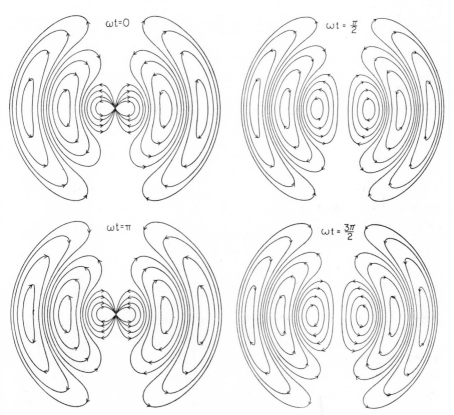

Figure 13-9. *The electric lines of force of an oscillating dipole for $\omega t = 0$, $\pi/2$, π, and $3\pi/2$. The dipole is situated in the center and is oriented in the vertical direction. The decrease in wave length with distance is quite obvious in these figures. The magnetic lines of force are circles perpendicular to the paper and centered on the axis of the dipole.*

The differential equation for the lines of force is therefore

$$\frac{1}{\sin\theta}\frac{\partial}{\partial\theta}(C\sin\theta)\,d\theta = -\frac{1}{r}\frac{\partial}{\partial r}(rC)\,dr, \tag{13-101}$$

or

$$\frac{\partial}{\partial\theta}(Cr\sin\theta)\,d\theta + \frac{\partial}{\partial r}(Cr\sin\theta)\,dr = 0, \tag{13-102}$$

and the total differential of the quantity $Cr\sin\theta$ is zero. Then we can set

$$Cr\sin\theta = \text{constant},$$

or, substituting the value of C and omitting the constant terms, we can write

$$\frac{\sin^2\theta}{\lambda}\left(\frac{\lambda}{r}+j\right)\exp\left\{j\omega\left(t-\frac{r}{c}\right)\right\} = \text{constant}, \tag{13-103}$$

$$\sin^2\theta\left(\frac{\lambda^2}{r^2}+1\right)^{1/2}\cos\left(\omega t - \frac{r}{\lambda} + \arctan\frac{r}{\lambda}\right) = K\lambda, \tag{13-104}$$

where K is a real parameter which varies from one line of force to the next. The calculation is exact as long as $r \gg s$. The first two factors determine the shape of the line of force as a function of r and θ, whereas the cosine term gives the radial motion. The electric lines of force are shown in Figure 13-9.

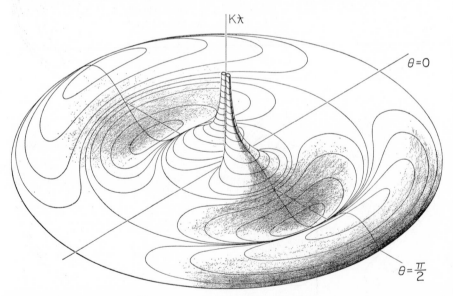

Figure 13-10. *The parameter $K\lambda$ of Eq. 13-104 is plotted here as a function of the coordinates r and θ. The surface shown is that corresponding to $t = 0$; with increasing time t, the central peaks oscillate together from $-\infty$ to $+\infty$, and the ripples move out radially. The loops are electric lines of force corresponding to constant values of $K\lambda$.*

For $r \gg \lambda$,

$$\sin^2 \theta \cos \left(\omega t - \frac{r}{\lambda} + \frac{\pi}{2} \right) = K\lambda, \qquad (13\text{-}105)$$

and the lines of force travel outward at a velocity $\omega\lambda = c$. Closer in, however, the arc tan term varies with r, with the result that the velocity of the lines of force increases above c.

The magnetic lines of force are much simpler: they are circles perpendicular to, and centered on, the axis of the dipole. This can be seen from Eq. *13-72*, which shows that **H** is everywhere azimuthal.

13.2.6. The $K\lambda$ Surface. It is instructive to represent the above equation in the form of a three-dimensional surface, as in Figure 13-10. This shows $K\lambda$ as a function of r and θ, as in Eq. *13-104*, for $t = 0$. The loops drawn on the surface correspond to constant values of $K\lambda$ and are therefore lines of force. They are in fact the same lines of force as those shown in Figure 13-9, $\omega t = 0$.

As time goes on, the angle $\{\omega t - (r/\lambda) + \text{arc tan}\,(r/\lambda)\}$ increases, and the result is that the ripples move out, somewhat like a damped wave, carrying the lines of force with them. Let us examine what happens to the lines of force.

Figure 13-11 shows the intersection of the $K\lambda$ surface, again for $t = 0$, with

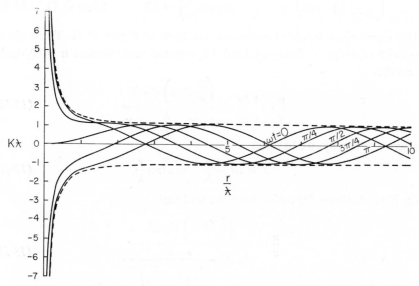

Figure 13-11. *This figure illustrates how the intersection of the $K\lambda$ surface (Figure 13-10) with $\theta = \pi/2$ changes with time. The curves are all situated within the envelope shown, thus the amplitude is infinite at $r = 0$ and approaches unity for $r \gg \lambda$.*

the plane $\theta = \pi/2$. This curve is situated inside its envelope, defined by the curves

$$K\lambda = \pm\left\{\left(\frac{\lambda}{r}\right)^2 + 1\right\}^{1/2} \qquad (\sin^2\theta = 1), \qquad (13\text{-}106)$$

which are shown by broken lines. These curves approach infinity as $r/\lambda \longrightarrow 0$ and approach unity when $(r/\lambda)^2 \gg 1$. All values of $K\lambda$ are possible, from $-\infty$ to $+\infty$. The figure also shows a succession of curves for successive values of t.

As the ripples move out, their height decreases rapidly at first, and soon approaches unity. It is clear that lines of force with $K\lambda < 1$ can travel out to infinity. They give the *radiation field*. It is also clear that if $K\lambda > 1$, they cannot go far. Let us consider the case in which $K\lambda$ is slightly larger than unity. The loop formed by the corresponding line of force shrinks until it reaches the top of the ripple and then disappears. This explains the relatively rapid decrease in the field intensity in the region where r is of the order of λ or less.

Closer to the dipole, which is situated at the origin, some lines of force such as that for which $K\lambda = 5$ do not even get into a ripple. These lines of force simply pulsate in and out without ever escaping into space. This is the *static field*.

Let us analyze the motion of the lines of force quantitatively. We can set $\sin^2\theta = 1$ and consider their motion only in the $\theta = \pi/2$ plane. Then

$$\left(\frac{\lambda^2}{r^2} + 1\right)^{1/2} \cos\left(\omega t - \frac{r}{\lambda} + \arctan\frac{r}{\lambda}\right) = K\lambda \qquad (\sin\theta = 1). \quad (13\text{-}107)$$

This represents a family of curves such as those of Figure 13-11. To obtain the velocity of a line of force, we keep $K\lambda$ constant and calculate $u = \partial r/\partial t$. We find that

$$\frac{u}{c} = \frac{1}{c}\frac{\partial r}{\partial t} = \frac{\left(\dfrac{\lambda^2}{r^2} + 1\right)\sin X}{\sin X - \dfrac{\lambda^3}{r^3}\cos X}, \qquad (13\text{-}108)$$

where, for brevity, we have set

$$X = \omega t - \frac{r}{\lambda} + \arctan\frac{r}{\lambda}, \qquad (13\text{-}109)$$

or, if we eliminate the cosine term, we find that

$$\frac{u}{c} = \frac{\left(\dfrac{\lambda^2}{r^2} + 1\right)\sin X}{\sin X - \dfrac{K\lambda}{\dfrac{r^2}{\lambda^2}\left(1 + \dfrac{r^2}{\lambda^2}\right)^{1/2}}}. \qquad (13\text{-}110)$$

The velocity u of the line of force becomes zero for $\sin X = 0$, or $\cos X = 1$. This corresponds to a point where the ripple touches the envelope. The curve then "rolls" on the envelope and the line of force momentarily has zero velocity.

The velocity u also approaches plus or minus infinity near

$$\tan X = \frac{\lambda^3}{r^3} \qquad\qquad (13\text{-}111)$$

or

$$\sin X = \frac{K\lambda}{\dfrac{r^2}{\lambda^2}\left(1 + \dfrac{r^2}{\lambda^2}\right)^{1/2}}. \qquad\qquad (13\text{-}112)$$

Now this is precisely the condition which defines the top of a crest, or the bottom of a trough. The infinite velocity simply results from the fact that, as the ripple decreases in amplitude with increasing r, the line of force closes in with infinite velocity just before disappearing. This is interesting in that it tells us where the lines of force disappear.

Note that the top of a crest does *not* occur at $\cos X = 1$, or $\sin X = 0$, where the curve touches its envelope, but somewhat closer to the dipole at a value of X defined by the Eq. *13-112*, since the cosine term in Eq. *13-107* is multiplied by another term which decreases with increasing r, namely $\{(\lambda/r)^2 + 1\}^{1/2}$. For large values of r/λ, $K\lambda$ is about unity, and the top of a crest, or the bottom of a trough, occurs at $X \approx 0$. For small values of r/λ, and for large values of $K\lambda$, these occur at $|\sin X| > 0$.

For $r \gg \lambda$, $K\lambda$ is about unity or less, and $u \longrightarrow c$. The lines of force then travel outward at the velocity of light, as expected.

For $K\lambda \gg 1$ and $r \gg \lambda$,

$$\frac{u}{c} = -\frac{\left(\dfrac{r^2}{\lambda^2} + 1\right)^{3/2}}{K\lambda}\sin X, \qquad\qquad (13\text{-}113)$$

and these lines pulsate in and out without ever escaping.

It is important to note that the $K\lambda$ surface and Figure 13-9 do *not* give the modulus of $\mathbf{E}$, but only its direction. For example, in drawing a figure such as 13-9, one naturally selects equal intervals of $K\lambda$; this leads to a constant density of lines of force for $r \gg \lambda$, which *appears* to indicate that the amplitude of $\mathbf{E}$ does not decrease with r. In fact, $\mathbf{E}$ decreases as $1/r$ for $r \gg \lambda$, from Eq. *13-81*. There is, of course, no such thing as a distinct line of force; the $K\lambda$ surface provides only the direction of $\mathbf{E}$ as a function of the position r, θ, and of the time t.

13.3. Radiation from a Half-wave Antenna

The half-wave antenna illustrated in Figure 13-12 is commonly used for radiating electromagnetic waves into space. It is simply a straight conductor whose length is half a free-space wave length. When a current $I_0 \cos \omega t$ is established at the center by means of a suitable electronic circuit, a standing wave

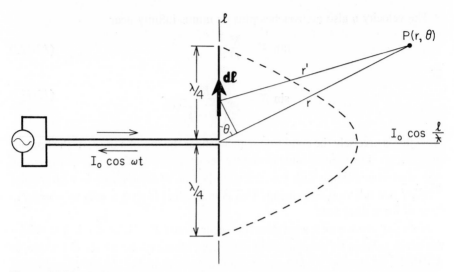

Figure 13-12. *Half-wave antenna. The current distribution shown as a broken line is $I_0 \cos (l/\lambda) \cos \omega t$. This is the standing wave pattern at some particular time when $\cos \omega t = 1$.*

is formed along the conductor such that the current I at any position l is given by

$$I = I_0 \cos \frac{l}{\lambda} \cos \omega t. \qquad (13\text{-}114)$$

Each element $I\,dl$ of the antenna then radiates an electromagnetic wave similar to that of an electric dipole, and the field at any given point in space is obtained by integrating over the length of the antenna. In many cases the half-wave antenna is a one-quarter wave length mast set vertically on the ground, which then acts as a mirror. The mast and its image in the ground together form a half-wave antenna. Radio broadcast antennas are often of this type. To achieve good conductivity, the ground in the neighborhood of the antenna can be covered with a conducting screen.

This description of the half-wave antenna is really contradictory, because the standing wave along the wire can be truly sinusoidal only if there is no energy loss, and hence no radiated wave. It turns out, however, that a rigorous calculation, although too involved to discuss here, leads to nearly the same result as the approximate one. The current distribution is not quite sinusoidal, but the distortion has little effect on the field. It will therefore be sufficient for our purposes to assume a pure sinusoidal current distribution.

The standing wave can be expressed in exponential form as follows:

$$I = \mathrm{Re}\,\frac{I_0}{2}\left(\exp\left\{j\left(\omega t - \frac{l}{\lambda}\right)\right\} + \exp\left\{i\left(\omega t + \frac{l}{\lambda}\right)\right\}\right), \qquad (13\text{-}115)$$

where "Re" means, as usual, "Real part of." The right-hand side shows that the standing wave is the sum of two traveling waves, one in the positive direction, and one in the negative direction, with amplitudes $I_0/2$.

Then, from Eq. *13-49*, using the usual complex notation, we can express the electric dipole moment p of the element dl as

$$j\omega p = \frac{I_0}{2}\left(\exp\left\{j\left(\omega t - \frac{l}{\lambda}\right)\right\} + \exp\left\{j\left(\omega t + \frac{l}{\lambda}\right)\right\}\right)dl, \qquad (13\text{-}116)$$

$$= j\omega p_0 e^{j\omega t}. \qquad (13\text{-}117)$$

13.3.1. The Electric Field Intensity E.
In calculating the electric field intensity at the point (r, θ, φ), we shall assume that the distance r to the point of observation is much greater than λ. Then the electric field intensity $d\mathbf{E}$ from the element dl is given by Eq. *13-81*, in which we must substitute the value of p_0 obtained from the above equations. Thus

$$d\mathbf{E} = -\frac{I_0}{j8\pi c\epsilon_0\lambda r'}\left(\exp\left\{j\left(\omega t - \frac{l}{\lambda} - \frac{r'}{\lambda}\right)\right\} + \exp\left\{j\left(\omega t + \frac{l}{\lambda} - \frac{r'}{\lambda}\right)\right\}\right)\sin\theta\, dl\,\mathbf{j},$$

$$(13\text{-}118)$$

where r' is the distance between the element dl and the point (r, θ, φ), as in Figure 13-12,

$$r' = r - l\cos\theta, \qquad (13\text{-}119)$$

and

$$\mathbf{E} = -\frac{I_0\exp\left\{j\omega\left(t - \frac{r}{c}\right)\right\}}{j8\pi c\epsilon_0\lambda r}$$

$$\times \sin\theta\int_{-\lambda/4}^{+\lambda/4}\left(\exp\left\{j\frac{l}{\lambda}(\cos\theta - 1)\right\} + \exp\left\{j\frac{l}{\lambda}(\cos\theta + 1)\right\}\right)dl\,\mathbf{j}. \quad (13\text{-}120)$$

We have removed the $1/r'$ from under the integral sign and set it equal to $1/r$, since it is assumed that $r \gg \lambda$: with this condition, the $d\mathbf{E}$'s can all be taken to be parallel for a given point of observation and can be assumed to have the same amplitude but different phases, and the integration can be limited to the phases. Integrating, we obtain

$$\mathbf{E} = -\frac{I_0\exp\left\{j\omega\left(t - \frac{r}{c}\right)\right\}}{j8\pi c\epsilon_0\lambda r}$$

$$\times \sin\theta\left(\frac{\lambda\exp\left\{j\frac{l}{\lambda}(\cos\theta - 1)\right\}}{j(\cos\theta - 1)} + \frac{\lambda\exp\left\{j\frac{l}{\lambda}(\cos\theta + 1)\right\}}{j(\cos\theta + 1)}\right)\Bigg|_{-\lambda/4}^{+\lambda/4}\mathbf{j}. \quad (13\text{-}121)$$

It is not permissible to expand the exponential functions between the main parentheses in series form, since l is not small with respect to λ in this case. We have

$$E = \frac{jI_0 \exp\left\{ j\omega\left(t - \frac{r}{c}\right)\right\}}{4\pi c\epsilon_0 r} \sin\theta \left(\frac{\sin\left\{\frac{\pi}{2}(\cos\theta - 1)\right\}}{\cos\theta - 1} + \frac{\sin\left\{\frac{\pi}{2}(\cos\theta + 1)\right\}}{\cos\theta + 1}\right) \mathbf{j}.$$

$$(13\text{-}122)$$

The expression between the braces can be simplified by setting

$$\sin\left\{\frac{\pi}{2}(\cos\theta - 1)\right\} = -\cos\left(\frac{\pi}{2}\cos\theta\right) \tag{13-123}$$

and

$$\sin\left\{\frac{\pi}{2}(\cos\theta + 1)\right\} = +\cos\left(\frac{\pi}{2}\cos\theta\right) \tag{13-124}$$

and adding the two terms. Then

$$\mathbf{E} = \frac{j\mu_0 c}{2\pi r} I_0 \exp\left\{ j\omega\left(t - \frac{r}{c}\right)\right\} \frac{\cos\left(\frac{\pi}{2}\cos\theta\right)}{\sin\theta}\mathbf{j}, \tag{13-125}$$

$$\mathbf{E} = 60.0\, j\frac{I_0 \exp\left\{ j\omega\left(t - \frac{r}{c}\right)\right\} \cos\left(\frac{\pi}{2}\cos\theta\right)}{r} \frac{}{\sin\theta}\mathbf{j} \quad \text{(volts/meter)} \qquad (r \gg \lambda).$$

$$(13\text{-}126)$$

At $\theta = 0$, the above equation is indeterminate because the trigonometric term becomes $0/0$. The student is presumably familiar with l'Hospital's rule, according to which the limiting value of such a ratio is equal to the ratio of the derivatives of the two functions at the limit. In the present case,

$$\lim_{\theta\to 0} \frac{\cos\left(\frac{\pi}{2}\cos\theta\right)}{\sin\theta} = \left\{ \frac{\frac{d}{d\theta}\cos\left(\frac{\pi}{2}\cos\theta\right)}{\frac{d}{d\theta}\sin\theta}\right\}_{\theta=0} \tag{13-127}$$

$$= \left\{ \frac{\sin\left(\frac{\pi}{2}\cos\theta\right)\frac{\pi}{2}\sin\theta}{\cos\theta}\right\}_{\theta=0} \tag{13-128}$$

$$= 0. \tag{13-129}$$

It is interesting to note that the electric field intensity for a half-wave antenna is independent of the frequency for a given current I_0: the $\mathbf{E}$ for an elementary dipole is proportional to $1/\lambda$ for a given current amplitude, and the integration over the length of the antenna has introduced a factor of λ.

Figure 13-13 shows the radiation pattern for a half-wave antenna. It is quite similar to that for the dipole, except that a somewhat larger part of the field is radiated in the region of the equator. The reason for this similarity is that the phase difference between $d\mathbf{E}$'s from the elements of current along the antenna is small, except when the point of observation is near the polar axis, where the electric field intensity is zero in any case.

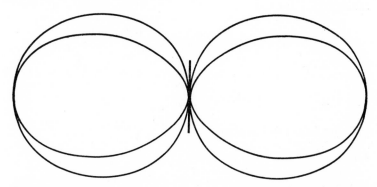

Figure 13-13. *Polar diagrams of* $\cos\{(\pi/2)\ \cos\ \theta\}/\sin\ \theta$ *and of* $\cos^2\{(\pi/2)\ \cos\ \theta\}/\sin^1\ \theta$ *showing, respectively, the angular distributions of E or H and of* $\mathbf{S}_{av.}$ *for the half-wave antenna at* $r \gg \lambda$. *The angular distributions are quite similar to those for the dipole, except that the half-wave antenna radiates a larger fraction of its power in the region of the equatorial plane.*

13.3.2. The Magnetic Field Intensity H. It is now a simple matter to find the **H** vector. For the electric dipole, we found that **H** is azimuthal, as in Figure 13-7, and that

$$\frac{E}{H} = \left(\frac{\mu_0}{\epsilon_0}\right)^{1/2} = 377 \text{ ohms},\qquad(13\text{-}130)$$

as in Eq. *13-82*. For the half-wave antenna, **H** is again azimuthal, and the above equation also applies, thus

$$\mathbf{H} = \frac{j}{2\pi r}\,I_0\,\exp\left\{j\omega\left(t - \frac{r}{c}\right)\right\}\frac{\cos\left(\dfrac{\pi}{2}\cos\theta\right)}{\sin\theta}\,\mathbf{k}.\qquad(13\text{-}131)$$

13.3.3. The Poynting Vector and the Radiated Power. The Poynting vector $\mathbf{S}_{av.}$ gives the average flux of radiated energy:

$$\mathbf{S}_{av.} = \frac{1}{2}\,\text{Re}\,(\mathbf{E} \times \mathbf{H}^*),\qquad(13\text{-}132)$$

$$= \frac{\mu_0 c\,I_0^2}{8\pi^2\,r^2}\frac{\cos^2\left(\dfrac{\pi}{2}\cos\theta\right)}{\sin^2\theta}\,\mathbf{i},\qquad(13\text{-}133)$$

$$= 9.55\,\frac{I_{\text{rms}}^2}{r^2}\frac{\cos^2\left(\dfrac{\pi}{2}\cos\theta\right)}{\sin^2\theta}\,\mathbf{i}\qquad(\text{watts/meter}^2).\qquad(13\text{-}134)$$

It points radially outward and varies as $1/r^2$, which ensures conservation of energy. The Poynting vector is shown as a function of θ in Figure 13-13.

The radiated power is again obtained by integrating $S_{av.}$ over a sphere of radius r:

$$W = 9.55\, I_{rms}^2 \int_0^{2\pi} \int_0^{\pi} \frac{\cos^2\left(\dfrac{\pi}{2}\cos\theta\right)}{r^2 \sin^2\theta}\, r^2 \sin\theta\, d\theta\, d\varphi, \qquad (13\text{-}135)$$

$$= 60.0\, I_{rms}^2 \int_0^{\pi} \frac{\cos^2\left(\dfrac{\pi}{2}\cos\theta\right)}{\sin\theta}\, d\theta. \qquad (13\text{-}136)$$

To perform this integration, we set

$$\frac{\pi}{2}\cos\theta = \frac{\alpha}{2} - \frac{\pi}{2} \qquad (13\text{-}137)$$

and

$$W = 60.0\pi I_{rms}^2 \int_0^{2\pi} \frac{1 - \cos\alpha}{\alpha(4\pi - 2\alpha)}\, d\alpha. \qquad (13\text{-}138)$$

Then if we write

$$\frac{1}{\alpha(4\pi - 2\alpha)} = \frac{1}{4\pi}\left(\frac{1}{\alpha} + \frac{1}{2\pi - \alpha}\right), \qquad (13\text{-}139)$$

the radiated power becomes

$$W = 15.0\, I_{rms}^2 \left(\int_0^{2\pi} \frac{1 - \cos\alpha}{\alpha}\, d\alpha + \int_0^{2\pi} \frac{1 - \cos\alpha}{2\pi - \alpha}\, d\alpha\right). \qquad (13\text{-}140)$$

Now the two integrals between the braces are equal, as can be seen from the curves for $1 - \cos\alpha$, for α, and for $2\pi - \alpha$ shown in Figure 13-14. Since the curve for $1 - \cos\alpha$ is symmetrical about $\alpha = \pi$, the area under the curve

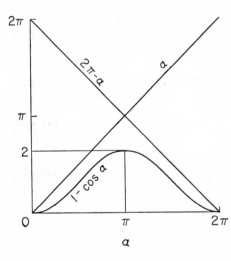

Figure 13-14

The three functions $1 - \cos\alpha$, α, and $2\pi - \alpha$ as functions of α for $\alpha = 0$ to 2π. By symmetry, the curves for $(1 - \cos\alpha)/\alpha$ and for $(1 - \cos\alpha)/(2\pi - \alpha)$ are symmetrical about $\alpha = \pi$, thus the areas under them must be equal for the interval shown.

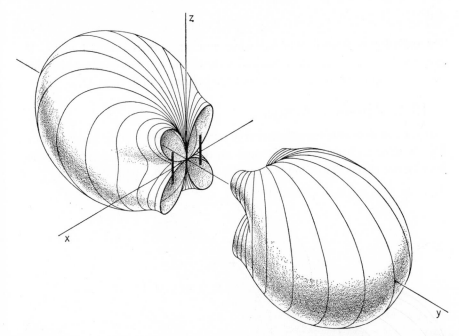

Figure 13-15. *A simple antenna array, represented by the two vertical bars, and its radiation pattern for r ≫ λ. The two half-wave antennas are spaced λ/2 apart and are excited in phase. The surface shows the magnitude of* **E** *plotted radially as a function of θ and φ. The curves shown are situated on the surface for constant values of θ chosen at 10° intervals. The surface is cut into two parts for clarity. Along the y-axis the two waves add, and the resulting electric field intensity is twice that produced by a single antenna. The same applies to all of the yz-plane, at least for r ≫ λ. Along the x-axis, however, the two waves arrive in opposite phases and cancel. For other directions along the xz-plane the waves do not cancel completely, since the difference in path is smaller than λ/2. There is zero field along the z-axis for each of the antennas, and hence for the array.*

$(1 - \cos \alpha)/\alpha$ must be equal to that under $(1 - \cos \alpha)/(2\pi - \alpha)$ between the limits 0 and 2π. Thus,

$$W = 30.0 \, I_{\text{rms}}^2 \int_0^{2\pi} \frac{1 - \cos \alpha}{\alpha} \, d\alpha. \qquad (13\text{-}141)$$

This integration cannot be performed analytically; it can, however, be performed numerically by calculating $(1 - \cos \alpha)/\alpha$ for a series of values of α, multiplying by the appropriate $d\alpha$, and summing the results. From tables that are available,* we find that the integral equals 2.44, such that

$$W = 73.1 \, I_{\text{rms}}^2, \qquad (13\text{-}142)$$

* See, for example, Jahnke and Emde, *Tables of Functions* (Dover, New York, 1945), pp. 3 and 6.

and

$$R_{\text{rad}} = 73.1 \text{ ohms.} \qquad (13\text{-}143)$$

The radiation resistance of a half-wave antenna is therefore 73.1 ohms. This assumes that the current distribution on the antenna is sinusoidal, which, however, is not quite correct, as we saw at the beginning of Section 13.3.

13.4. Antenna Arrays

It is often desirable to radiate energy predominantly in some given direction. This is done with arrays of antennas arranged so as to produce appropriate interference effects. Two simple examples are shown in Figures 13-15 and 13-16.

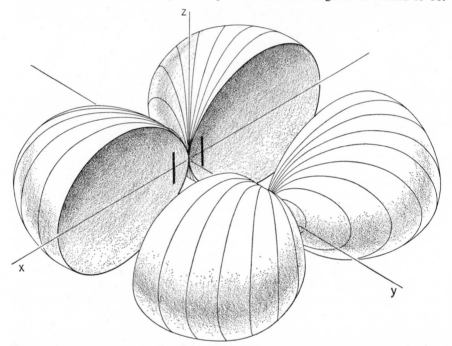

Figure 13-16. *The two half-wave antennas shown as vertical bars are spaced $\lambda/2$ apart, but the one at $x = -D/2$ leads the other by π radians. See legend of Figure 13-15 for an explanation of the surface shown. The two waves now cancel everywhere on the yz-plane. All along the x-axis, the two waves arrive in phase to give twice the field of a single antenna. There is again no radiation in the direction of the z-axis.*

It is clear that by phasing and by spacing antennas properly a great variety of radiation patterns can be achieved.*

Let us calculate the radiation pattern of Figure 13-15. We choose coordinates as in Figure 13-17 and assume that $r \gg \lambda$. Then the electric field intensities of

---

* See, for example, F. E. Terman, *Electronic and Radio Engineering* (McGraw-Hill, New York, 1955).

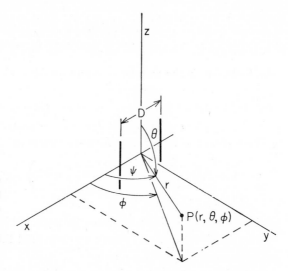

Figure 13-17

Pair of parallel half-wave antennas D meters apart. The point P is at distances $r - (D/2) \cos \psi$ and $r + (D/2) \cos \psi$ from the centers of the antennas.

both antennas are given by Eq. *13-126*, and, if the antennas are excited in phase, the total field is given by

$$E = 60.0j \frac{I_0 \exp\left\{ j\omega\left(t - \dfrac{r}{c}\right)\right\} \cos\left(\dfrac{\pi}{2}\cos\theta\right)}{r \qquad\qquad \sin\theta}$$

$$\times \left(\exp\left\{-j\left(\frac{D\cos\psi}{2\lambda}\right)\right\} + \exp\left\{j\left(\frac{D\cos\psi}{2\lambda}\right)\right\}\right) \mathbf{j}, \qquad (13\text{-}144)$$

where the quantity on the second line accounts for the fact that the two waves arrive out of phase, one having traveled a distance $r + (D/2) \cos \psi$, and the other a distance $r - (D/2) \cos \psi$. Thus,

$$E = 120.0j \frac{I_0 \exp\left\{ j\omega\left(t - \dfrac{r}{c}\right)\right\} \cos\left(\dfrac{\pi}{2}\cos\theta\right)}{r \qquad\qquad \sin\theta} \cos\left(\frac{D}{2\lambda}\cos\psi\right) \mathbf{j}. \quad (13\text{-}145)$$

We can replace the angle ψ by θ and φ, since

$$r \cos \psi = r \sin\theta \cos\varphi, \qquad (13\text{-}146)$$

then

$$E = 120.0j \frac{I_0 \exp\left\{ j\omega\left(t - \dfrac{r}{c}\right)\right\} \cos\left(\dfrac{\pi}{2}\cos\theta\right)}{r \qquad\qquad \sin\theta} \cos\left(\frac{D}{2\lambda}\sin\theta\cos\varphi\right) \mathbf{j}. \quad (13\text{-}147)$$

When the antennas are one-half a wave length apart, $D/(2\lambda) = \pi/2$. Then, in the xz-plane, where $\theta = \pi/2$, E varies as

$$\cos\left(\frac{\pi}{2}\cos\varphi\right).$$

At $\varphi = 0$ or π, this function is zero; at $\varphi = \pi/2$, it is maximum. There is constructive interference along the y-axis and destructive interference along the x-axis, as must be expected. In the xz-plane, $\varphi = 0$, and E varies as

$$\frac{\cos\left(\dfrac{\pi}{2}\cos\theta\right)}{\sin\theta}\cos\left(\dfrac{\pi}{2}\sin\theta\right).$$

The first term is the angular distribution for a single half-wave antenna; it is zero at $\theta = 0$ and is maximum at $\theta = \pi/2$. The second term comes from the interference between the two antennas; it is maximum at $\theta = 0$ and is zero at $\theta = \pi/2$. The product of the two is zero both at $\theta = 0$ and $\theta = \pi/2$. Finally, in the yz-plane, $\varphi = \pi/2$, and $\mathbf{E}$ varies simply as

$$\frac{\cos\left(\dfrac{\pi}{2}\cos\theta\right)}{\sin\theta},$$

as does the $\mathbf{E}$ of a single half-wave antenna. This is to be expected, since the two waves arrive there in phase, and the total field is exactly twice that of a single antenna, at least for $r \gg \lambda$.

If the antenna centered at $x = -D/2$ has a phase lead of π, then the total electric field intensity $\mathbf{E}$ is given by

$$\mathbf{E} = j60.0\,\frac{I_0\exp\left\{j\omega\left(t-\dfrac{r}{c}\right)\right\}}{r}\frac{\cos\left(\dfrac{\pi}{2}\cos\theta\right)}{\sin\theta} \tag{13-148}$$

$$\left(\exp\left\{-j\left(\frac{D\cos\psi}{2\lambda}\right)\right\}+\exp\left\{j\left(\frac{D\cos\psi}{2\lambda}+\pi\right)\right\}\right)\mathbf{j},$$

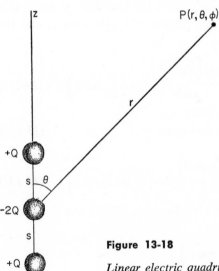

Figure 13-18

Linear electric quadrupole formed of two dipoles of opposite polarity one above the other. The dipole centered at $-s/2$ has a moment of $-Qs$; the dipole centered at $+s/2$ has a moment of $+Qs$. The charges are assumed to pulsate with $Q = Q_oe^{j\omega t}$.

which is the same as Eq. *13-144* except for the addition of $j\pi$ in the last exponent. Recalling that $e^{j\pi} = -1$, we may now write that

$$\mathbf{E} = 120.0 \frac{I_0 \exp\left\{j\omega\left(t - \dfrac{r}{c}\right)\right\}}{r} \frac{\cos\left(\dfrac{\pi}{2}\cos\theta\right)}{\sin\theta} \sin\left(\frac{D}{2\lambda}\sin\theta\cos\varphi\right)\mathbf{j}. \quad (13\text{-}149)$$

The radiation pattern is shown in Figure 13-16.

13.5. Electric Quadrupole Radiation

We now go on to the more elaborate type of radiation produced by a linear electric quadrupole whose moment is a sinusoidal function of time.

The linear electric quadrupole was studied in Section 2.9. It is composed of two dipoles of opposite polarity arranged in line to give three charges $+Q$, $-2Q$, and $+Q$ as in Figure 13-18. The dipole moment of such a charge distribution is zero, but the quadrupole moment is not:

$$p_{zz} = \sum Qz^2 = 2Qs^2. \quad (13\text{-}150)$$

If

$$Q = Q_0 e^{j\omega t}, \quad (13\text{-}151)$$

then

$$p_{zz} = 2Q_0 s^2 e^{j\omega t}, \quad (13\text{-}152)$$

and

$$p_{zz0} = 2Q_0 s^2. \quad (13\text{-}153)$$

There is no dipole radiation, since the dipole moment $p = \sum Qz$ is always equal to zero. Nevertheless, there must be some sort of radiation from the moving charges. This is what we shall investigate.

We shall use the above model to calculate the radiation field of a linear quadrupole, although *any charge distribution will produce exactly the same field if it oscillates in such a fashion that*

$$p_{zz} = \int \rho z^2 \, d\tau \quad (13\text{-}154)$$

is a sinusoidal function of time. This type of radiation would arise, for example, if currents were excited at the surface of a sphere in such a way as to drive the electrons alternately to both poles and then to the equator.

We could proceed exactly as for electric dipole radiation and calculate successively V, $\mathbf{A}$, $\mathbf{E}$, and $\mathbf{H}$. This will be done in Problem 13-15. It is easier, however, to add the fields of the two component dipoles as follows. For simplicity, we shall consider only the radiation field and set $r \gg \lambda$.

We now have two dipoles, one with moment

$$-p_0 e^{j\omega t}$$

centered at $-s/2$, and another with moment

$$+p_0 e^{j\omega t}$$

centered at $+s/2$, as in Figure 13-18. The electric field intensities of the two dipoles at the point (r, θ) add vectorially, according to the principle of superposition (Section 8.1). From Eq. *13-81*, the electric field intensity in the radiation field of an electric dipole situated at the origin is

$$\mathbf{E} = -\frac{p_0}{4\pi\epsilon_0 r\lambda^2} \exp\left\{j\omega\left(t - \frac{r}{c}\right)\right\} \sin\theta\,\mathbf{j} \qquad (r \gg \lambda). \qquad (13\text{-}155)$$

Since the two dipoles forming the quadrupole are centered some distance away from the origin, their electric field intensities at the point (r, θ, φ) will differ slightly in direction, in amplitude, and in phase. We may easily neglect the dif-

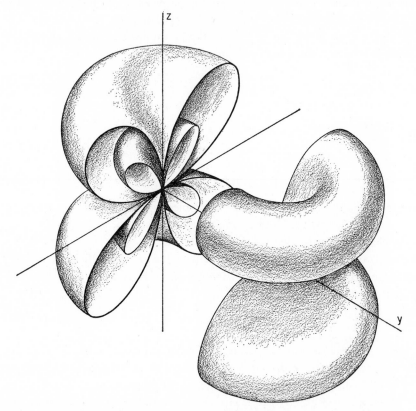

Figure 13-19. *Radiation pattern for a vertical oscillating electric quadrupole at the origin. The amplitude of* **E** *or of* **H** *in any given direction is proportional to the distance between the origin and the outer surface in that direction. The inner surface is a similar plot of the modulus of* $\mathbf{S}_{av}$*. There is no field along the axis or along the equator of the quadrupole. The maximum field intensity occurs along the surface of a cone at 45° to the axis.*

ference in direction and in amplitude for $r \gg s$, but not the difference in phase.
Thus

$$\mathbf{E} = -\frac{p_0}{4\pi\epsilon_0 r \lambda^2} \exp\left\{ j\omega\left(t - \frac{r}{c}\right)\right\}$$

$$\times \sin\theta \left(\exp\left\{ j\left(\frac{s}{2\lambda}\cos\theta\right)\right\} - \exp\left\{ -j\left(\frac{s}{2\lambda}\cos\theta\right)\right\}\right)\mathbf{j}. \qquad (13\text{-}156)$$

The exponential functions between the outer parentheses can be expanded as
power series in s/λ for $s \ll \lambda$, and their sum then reduces to $(js/\lambda)\cos\theta$. Thus that

$$\mathbf{E} = -\frac{jp_{zz0}}{4\pi\epsilon_0 r \lambda^3} \exp\left\{ j\omega\left(t - \frac{r}{c}\right)\right\} \sin\theta\cos\theta\,\mathbf{j} \qquad (r \gg \lambda \gg s). \quad (13\text{-}157)$$

There can be no radiation along the axis $\theta = 0$ or π, where neither of the dipoles
forming the quadrupole radiate energy; there is also zero radiation along the
equator $\theta = \pi/2$, where the two dipoles give equal and opposite fields.

The magnetic field intensity $\mathbf{H}$ is found in the same manner from Eq. *13-73*,
and

$$\mathbf{H} = \left(\frac{\epsilon_0}{\mu_0}\right)^{1/2} E\mathbf{k}. \qquad (13\text{-}158)$$

The $\mathbf{E}$ and $\mathbf{H}$ vectors for electric quadrupole radiation are therefore oriented
in the same manner as those for electric dipole radiation. This was to be expected, since we have simply superposed the fields of two electric dipoles. The
amplitudes of both $\mathbf{E}$ and $\mathbf{H}$ decrease as $1/r$, that is, at the *same* rate as for dipole
radiation. This makes the Poynting vector $\mathbf{S}_{av.} = 1/2\,\mathrm{Re}\,(\mathbf{E} \times \mathbf{H}^*)$ decrease
again as $1/r^2$, which is necessary for conservation of energy.

There are two differences between electric dipole and electric quadrupole
radiation: the former field increases with the square of the frequency, whereas
the latter increases as the cube of the frequency; the dipole field is zero along
the polar axis, whereas the quadrupole field is zero both at the poles and at the
equator. Figure 13-19 shows the radiation pattern for an oscillating electric
quadrupole at the origin.

13.6. Magnetic Dipole Radiation

The static magnetic dipole was studied in Section 5.13, where a current loop
of area S and current I was defined to have a magnetic moment

$$\mathbf{m} = I\mathbf{S}. \qquad (13\text{-}159)$$

The vector S is perpendicular to the small area limited by the loop, and its
direction is related to the current by the right-hand screw rule.

Let us consider a magnetic dipole carrying an alternating current

$$I = I_0 e^{j\omega t}. \qquad (13\text{-}160)$$

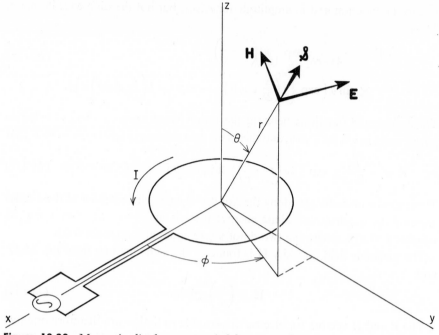

Figure 13-20. *Magnetic dipole antenna fed by an oscillator.*

We shall consider the current to flow through a circular wire as in Figure 13-20, *but magnetic dipole radiation can also be produced in the more general case by motion within a charge distribution such that the magnetic dipole moment*

$$\mathbf{m} = \frac{1}{2} \int_\tau (\mathbf{r} \times \mathbf{J}) \, d\tau \qquad (13\text{-}161)$$

is a sinusoidal function of the time. The above general definition of the magnetic dipole moment was stated in Eq. *5-196.* The conducting sphere can again be used to illustrate the oscillating magnetic dipole. In this case charge would flow parallel to the equator, alternately in one direction and then in the other.

We shall first calculate V and $\mathbf{A}$, and then $\mathbf{E}$ and $\mathbf{H}$. We assume that the loop is small with respect to λ; if it were not, there would be wave effects along its circumference, and the current would not be the same all around it. We also assume that the impedance of the loop is small in order that all points of the loop will be at some constant potential V, which can be taken to be zero.

13.6.1. The Electromagnetic Potentials. From Eq. *13-47,* the retarded vector potential is

$$\mathbf{A} = \frac{\mu_0}{4\pi} \int_0^{2\pi} \frac{I_0 \exp\left\{ j\omega\left(t - \frac{r'}{c} \right) \right\}}{r'} \, a \, d\varphi \, \mathbf{k}, \qquad (13\text{-}162)$$

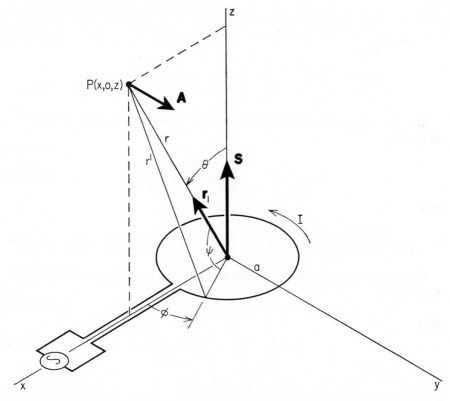

Figure 13-21. *Magnetic dipole formed of a loop of area* **S** *carrying a current I. When the current is constant, the vector potential* **A** *is azimuthal and is oriented as shown. For an alternating current,* **A** *is again azimuthal, but it is retarded and its amplitude and phase depend on interference effects between* **dA***'s from the various parts of the loop.*

where we have set r' to be the distance between the element $\mathbf{dl} = a\,d\varphi\,\mathbf{k}$ and the point of observation P, as in Figure 13-21. We shall call r the distance between the point of observation and the center of the loop. We have chosen a simple circular loop for the moment, but later on we shall be able to calculate the field of any plane loop which is small compared to λ.

The above integral is the sum of the contributions to **A** of all the elements $I\,\mathbf{dl}$ around the loop. Each of these contributions is retarded by a time r'/c and has an amplitude which varies inversely as its distance r' from the point of observation.

By symmetry, **A** must be azimuthal, as shown in the figure. If the x-axis is chosen such that the point of observation is in the xz-plane, then the only component of **dl** which need be considered is its projection on the y-axis. Hence

$$\mathbf{A} = \frac{\mu_0}{4\pi} \int_0^{2\pi} \frac{I_0 \exp\left\{ j\omega \left(t - \frac{r'}{c} \right) \right\}}{r'} \, a \cos \varphi \, d\varphi \, \mathbf{k}, \qquad (13\text{-}163)$$

$$= \frac{\mu_0 a I_0 \exp\left\{ j\omega \left(t - \frac{r}{c} \right) \right\}}{4\pi} \int_0^{2\pi} \frac{\exp\left\{ j\omega \left(\frac{r - r'}{\lambda} \right) \right\}}{r'} \cos \varphi \, d\varphi \, \mathbf{k}. \qquad (13\text{-}164)$$

We may now make a few approximations. If the loop is small with respect to λ, then

$$r - r' \ll \lambda, \qquad (13\text{-}165)$$

$$\exp\left\{ j \left(\frac{r - r'}{\lambda} \right) \right\} \approx 1 + j \frac{r - r'}{\lambda}, \qquad (13\text{-}166)$$

and

$$\mathbf{A} = \frac{\mu_0 a I_0 \exp\left\{ j\omega \left(t - \frac{r}{c} \right) \right\}}{4\pi r} \int_0^{2\pi} \left\{ \frac{r}{r'} + j \frac{r}{\lambda} \left(\frac{r}{r'} - 1 \right) \right\} \cos \varphi \, d\varphi \, \mathbf{k}. \qquad (13\text{-}167)$$

We require the value of r/r' in terms of the angle φ. It is clear from Figure 13-21 that

$$r'^2 = r^2 + a^2 - 2ar \cos \psi, \qquad (13\text{-}168)$$

thus

$$\frac{r}{r'} = \left(1 - \frac{a^2}{r'^2} + \frac{2ar}{r'^2} \cos \psi \right)^{1/2}, \qquad (13\text{-}169)$$

$$\approx 1 - \frac{a^2}{2r^2} + \frac{a}{r} \cos \psi, \qquad (13\text{-}170)$$

where we have assumed that $a \ll r$. Since the ratio r/r' is close to unity, we have substituted r for r' in the two correction terms on the right-hand side.

To find a relation between the angles ψ and φ, we use the scalar product of $\mathbf{r}$ and $\mathbf{a}$. In Cartesian coordinates,

$$\mathbf{r} \cdot \mathbf{a} = (x\mathbf{i} + z\mathbf{k}) \cdot (a \cos \varphi \, \mathbf{i} + a \sin \varphi \, \mathbf{j}), \qquad (13\text{-}171)$$

$$= ax \cos \varphi, \qquad (13\text{-}172)$$

from the definition of the scalar product. Also, since ψ is the angle between $\mathbf{r}$ and $\mathbf{a}$,

$$\mathbf{r} \cdot \mathbf{a} = ar \cos \psi. \qquad (13\text{-}173)$$

Then

$$\cos \psi = \frac{x}{r} \cos \varphi, \qquad (13\text{-}174)$$

and

$$\frac{r}{r'} \approx 1 - \frac{a^2}{2r^2} + \frac{ax}{r^2} \cos \varphi. \qquad (13\text{-}175)$$

Substituting in the above integral and integrating around the loop from $\varphi = 0$ to $\varphi = 2\pi$, we obtain

$$A = \frac{\mu_0}{4\pi} \frac{I_0 \exp\left\{j\omega\left(t - \frac{r}{c}\right)\right\} \pi a^2}{r\lambda} \left(\frac{\lambda}{r} + j\right) \sin\theta\, \mathbf{k}, \qquad (13\text{-}176)$$

where we have substituted $r\sin\theta$ for x. This is the vector potential for a small circular current loop of area πa^2 situated at the origin. The loop, whose plane is perpendicular to the polar axis, carries an alternating current of amplitude I_0 and circular frequency ω.

For zero frequency, $\omega = 0$, $\lambda = \infty$, and

$$A = \frac{\mu_0}{4\pi} \frac{\mathbf{m} \times \mathbf{r}_1}{r^2}, \qquad (13\text{-}177)$$

which is the result found in Problem 5-25.

We have assumed a circular loop so as to make the integral for $\mathbf{A}$ tractable. If the loop is plane but not circular, it can be considered to be formed of closely packed circles of various sizes, and the vector potential is then given by the same expression as above, except that πa^2 must be replaced by the area S of the loop. Then, in general,

$$A = \frac{\mu_0}{4\pi} \frac{m_0 \exp\left\{j\omega\left(t - \frac{r}{c}\right)\right\}}{r\lambda} \left(\frac{\lambda}{r} + j\right) \sin\theta\, \mathbf{k}, \qquad (13\text{-}178)$$

$$= \frac{\mu_0}{4\pi} \frac{\mathbf{m}_0 \times \mathbf{r}_1}{r\lambda} \left(\frac{\lambda}{r} + j\right) \exp\left\{j\omega\left(t - \frac{r}{c}\right)\right\}, \qquad (13\text{-}179)$$

where

$$\mathbf{m}_0 = I_0 S. \qquad (13\text{-}180)$$

13.6.2. The E and H Vectors.

We can now find $\mathbf{E}$ and $\mathbf{H}$ for a magnetic dipole with a little more effort:

$$\mathbf{H} = \frac{1}{\mu_0} \nabla \times \mathbf{A}, \qquad (13\text{-}181)$$

$$= \frac{m_0}{4\pi r\lambda^2} \exp\left\{j\omega\left(t - \frac{r}{c}\right)\right\}\left\{2\left(\frac{\lambda^2}{r^2} + j\frac{\lambda}{r}\right)\cos\theta\, \mathbf{i} + \left(\frac{\lambda^2}{r^2} + j\frac{\lambda}{r} - 1\right)\sin\theta\, \mathbf{j}\right\}, \qquad (13\text{-}182)$$

$$= \frac{-m_0}{4\pi r\lambda^2} \exp\left\{j\omega\left(t - \frac{r}{c}\right)\right\}\sin\theta\, \mathbf{j} \qquad (r \gg \lambda); \qquad (13\text{-}183)$$

$$\mathbf{E} = -\frac{\partial \mathbf{A}}{\partial t} - \nabla V, \qquad (13\text{-}184)$$

$$= -\left(\frac{\mu_0}{\epsilon_0}\right)^{1/2} \frac{m_0}{4\pi r\lambda^2} \exp\left\{j\omega\left(t - \frac{r}{c}\right)\right\}\left(j\frac{\lambda}{r} - 1\right)\sin\theta\, \mathbf{k}, \qquad (13\text{-}185)$$

$$= \left(\frac{\mu_0}{\epsilon_0}\right)^{1/2} \frac{m_0}{4\pi r\lambda^2} \exp\left\{j\omega\left(t - \frac{r}{c}\right)\right\}\sin\theta\, \mathbf{k} \qquad (r \gg \lambda). \qquad (13\text{-}186)$$

The scalar potential V is zero in this case, as we assumed at the beginning, and the electric field intensity arises solely from the changing magnetic field. The vector $\mathbf{H}$ lies in a plane passing through the z-axis, whereas $\mathbf{E}$ is azimuthal, as in Figure 13-20.

For zero frequency, $\omega = 0$, $\lambda = \infty$, thus

$$\mathbf{H} = \frac{m_0}{4\pi r^3}(2\cos\theta\,\mathbf{i} + \sin\theta\,\mathbf{j}) \qquad (\omega = 0), \qquad (13\text{-}187)$$

and

$$\mathbf{E} = 0. \qquad (\omega = 0). \qquad (13\text{-}188)$$

This is the field of a static magnetic dipole at a distance r that is large compared to the radius of the loop. The value for $\mathbf{H}$ agrees with that found in Eqs. 5-181, 5-183, and 5-184.

It is interesting to compare magnetic and electric dipole radiation. The $\mathbf{E}$ and $\mathbf{H}$ vectors for the latter are given by Eqs. 13-81 and 13-73 for $r \gg \lambda$. It will be observed that the two fields are quite similar, except that the expressions for $\mathbf{E}$ and for $\mathbf{H}$ are interchanged. Also, the sign of $\mathbf{E}$ for the magnetic dipole is opposite that of $\mathbf{H}$ for the electric dipole. Such a change in sign is required to keep the Poynting vector directed outwards. The similarity between the fields of the electric and of the magnetic dipole is a good illustration of the symmetry between $\mathbf{E}$ and $\mathbf{H}$ which was discussed in Section 8.3. It will be found that these two fields satisfy the symmetry conditions and that the constant of proportionality α is here equal to m_0/p_0 when the magnetic dipole field is chosen as the primed field.

The lines of force are similar to those of electric dipole radiation, except that, again, $\mathbf{E}$ and $\mathbf{H}$ must be interchanged.

13.6.3. The Poynting Vector and the Radiated Power. The Poynting vector and the radiated power for the magnetic dipole are calculated as in Section 13.2.4:

$$\mathbf{S}_{\text{av.}} = \frac{c\,\mu_0\,m_0^2\,\sin^2\theta}{32\pi^2 r^2\lambda^4}\,\mathbf{i}, \qquad (13\text{-}189)$$

$$= 1.11\,\frac{m_0^2\,\sin^2\theta}{r^2\lambda^4}\,\mathbf{i}; \qquad (13\text{-}190)$$

$$W = \frac{c\,\mu_0\,m_0^2}{12\pi\lambda^4}, \qquad (13\text{-}191)$$

$$= 10.0\,\frac{m_0^2}{\lambda^4} \qquad \text{(watts)}. \qquad (13\text{-}192)$$

To find the radiation resistance of a circular loop of radius a, we set

$$m_0 = \pi a^2 I_0 \qquad (13\text{-}193)$$

for the amplitude of the dipole moment, and then

$$W = 10.0\pi^2 \left(\frac{a}{\lambda}\right)^4 I_0^2. \qquad (13\text{-}194)$$

The radiation resistance is the coefficient of $I_0/2$:

$$R_{\text{rad}} = 197 \left(\frac{a}{\lambda}\right)^4 \qquad (a \ll \lambda). \qquad (13\text{-}195)$$

The radiation resistance of the magnetic dipole is proportional to the *fourth* power of the frequency, whereas that of the electric dipole was found to be proportional only to the *second* power of the frequency in Eq. *13-95*.

13.7. Magnetic Quadrupole Radiation

In the previous section we studied an oscillating magnetic dipole consisting of a circular loop centered on the origin and carrying an alternating current. We can now form an oscillating magnetic quadrupole with two such loops parallel to each other on either side of the origin and oscillating in opposition. We shall consider the simplest case, in which the distance between the loops is equal to the radius a of the loops, as in Figure 13-22, and we shall restrict our

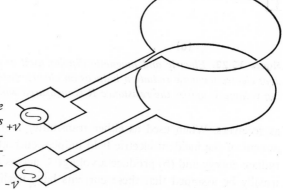

Figure 13-22

Simple magnetic quadrupole comprising two parallel loops of radius a *separated by a distance* a *and excited in opposite phases, as indicated schematically by* $+\mathcal{V}$ *and* $-\mathcal{V}$.

discussion to the radiation field where $r \gg \lambda$. The lower dipole is centered at $z = -a/2$ and has a moment $-m_0 e^{i\omega t}$, whereas the upper dipole is centered at $z = +a/2$ and has a moment $+m_0 e^{i\omega t}$. This arrangement is purposely made similar to that of the linear electric quadrupole studied in Section 13.5.

As for the electric quadrupole, we may add the fields of the two magnetic dipoles, neglecting the differences in amplitude and in direction, but taking into account the difference in retardation. This is done by multiplying the dipole field by the factor $(ja/\lambda) \cos \theta$, as in Section 13.5 on the electric quadrupole. Thus,

$$\mathbf{E} = j \left(\frac{\mu_0}{\epsilon_0}\right)^{1/2} \frac{m_0 a}{4\pi r \lambda^3} \exp\left\{j\omega\left(t - \frac{r}{c}\right)\right\} \sin\theta \cos\theta \, \mathbf{k} \qquad (r \gg \lambda), \quad (13\text{-}196)$$

and

$$\mathbf{H} = -j \frac{m_0 a}{4\pi r \lambda^3} \exp\left\{j\omega\left(t - \frac{r}{c}\right)\right\} \sin\theta \cos\theta \, \mathbf{j}. \qquad (r \gg \lambda). \quad (13\text{-}197)$$

13.8. The Electric and Magnetic Dipoles as Receiving Antennas

The electric and magnetic dipole antennas can be used not only as transmitters of electromagnetic radiation but also as receivers. Figure 13-23 shows them used

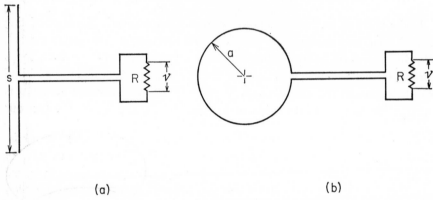

(a)   (b)

Figure 13-23. *Electric and magnetic dipoles used as receiving antennas. The incident electromagnetic radiation induces an electric field in the wires, and the resulting voltage $\mathcal{V}$ across the resistance R is measured with a suitable electronic circuit.*

as receivers. When used as either transmitter or receiver the tangential component of the incident electric field induces currents in the wires which (a) re-radiate energy and (b) produce a voltage $\mathcal{V}$ across the load resistance R. It can usually be assumed that these currents have negligible effect on those of the transmitting antenna. The voltage across R can be measured with some appropriate electronic circuit.

For the electric dipole, it can be shown that

$$\mathcal{V} = E_t s, \qquad (13\text{-}198)$$

where E_t is the component of the incident electric field intensity which is tangent to the antenna and s is the length of the antenna. This assumes that $(s/2)^2 \ll \lambda^2$ and that $R \longrightarrow \infty$. A proper demonstration of the above equation is quite elaborate and will not be gone into here.*

* R. W. P. King, *Handbuch der Physik* (Springer-Verlag, Göttingen, 1958), Vol. XVI, p. 267.

For the magnetic dipole, the induced electromotance is relatively easy to calculate:

$$\oint_C \mathbf{E} \cdot \mathbf{dl} = -\oint_C \left(\frac{\partial \mathbf{A}}{\partial t} + \nabla V \right) \cdot \mathbf{dl}, \tag{13-199}$$

$$= -\int_S \left(\nabla \times \frac{\partial \mathbf{A}}{\partial t} + \nabla \times \nabla V \right) \cdot \mathbf{da}, \tag{13-200}$$

where S is any surface bounded by the circuit. The second term on the right vanishes, since the curl of a gradient is identically zero. Also, the order of the operations in the first term can be interchanged to give

$$\oint_C \mathbf{E} \cdot \mathbf{dl} = -\frac{\partial}{\partial t} \int_S \nabla \times \mathbf{A} \cdot \mathbf{da} = -\frac{\partial}{\partial t} \int_S \mathbf{B} \cdot \mathbf{da}. \tag{13-201}$$

The induced electromotance in the loop is therefore equal to the rate of change of the flux linking the loop. It is maximum when the normal to the loop is parallel to the local $\mathbf{B}$.

The voltage υ when $R \longrightarrow \infty$ would be expected to equal the induced electromotance

$$\upsilon = -\frac{\partial}{\partial t} \int_S \mathbf{B} \cdot \mathbf{da} \tag{13-202}$$

except for the fact that the circuit may also be excited in the electric dipole mode. For example, with a symmetrical loop such as that shown in Figure 13-23b, if the $\mathbf{E}$ vector is parallel to the wires leading to R, charge oscillates from one end of the circuit to the other, and V is not affected by the electric dipole oscillation, thus the above relation is correct. On the other hand, if the $\mathbf{E}$ vector is in the plane of the loop but is perpendicular to the pair of wires, an extra voltage appears on R which comes from the dipole excitation and adds to the above induced electromotance.

13.9. The Reciprocity Theorem

According to the reciprocity theorem, the *current* produced in a detector divided by the *voltage* applied at the source remains constant when source and detector are interchanged, as long as the frequency and all the impedances are left unchanged. This theorem is widely used for investigating both electric circuits and antennas. We shall prove it in the general case by using Maxwell's equations.

It was shown in Section 8.4 that, for *any* two fields $\mathbf{E}_a$, $\mathbf{H}_a$ and $\mathbf{E}_b$, $\mathbf{H}_b$ of the same frequency,

$$\nabla \cdot (\mathbf{E}_a \times \mathbf{H}_b) = \nabla \cdot (\mathbf{E}_b \times \mathbf{H}_a) \tag{13-203}$$

at every point except within the sources. This is Lorentz's lemma.

In the more general case, where an electric field is applied at the point by means of some external source of energy, the situation is more complex, but also more interesting.

A pair of loop antennas, one of which is used as transmitter and the other as receiver, will serve to illustrate the discussion without restricting its generality.

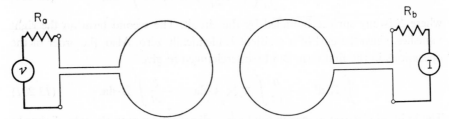

Figure 13-24. *Pair of loop antennas. The one on the left is fed by an oscillator supplying a voltage $\mathcal{V}$; the other is connected to a load resistance R_b and to a zero impedance ammeter. The current I could also be measured with a high-impedance voltmeter across R_b. When a current I is drawn from a source such as an oscillator, the voltage drops at the output by an amount $\Delta\mathcal{V}$. The ratio $\Delta\mathcal{V}/I$ is called the output impedance of the source. It is shown here as the resistance R_a.*

These are illustrated in Figure 13-24. There is no restriction as to the media, except that they are assumed to be isotropic.

Let us consider the field $\mathbf{E}_a$, $\mathbf{H}_a$, which is obtained when the antennas are used as in Figure 13-24, and the totally different field $\mathbf{E}_b$, $\mathbf{H}_b$, which is obtained when the source is inserted in b and the current detector is in a. *Both the frequency and the impedances are assumed to be the same in the two cases.*

Then, at any point in space including the loops, and even including the source in loop a, we first have the mathematical identity

$$\boldsymbol{\nabla}\cdot(\mathbf{E}_a \times \mathbf{H}_b - \mathbf{E}_b \times \mathbf{H}_a) = \mathbf{H}_b\cdot\boldsymbol{\nabla} \times \mathbf{E}_a - \mathbf{E}_a\cdot\boldsymbol{\nabla} \times \mathbf{H}_b \\ - \mathbf{H}_a\cdot\boldsymbol{\nabla} \times \mathbf{E}_b + \mathbf{E}_b\cdot\boldsymbol{\nabla} \times \mathbf{H}_a, \qquad (13\text{-}204)$$

and then, using Maxwell's equations,

$$\boldsymbol{\nabla}\cdot(\mathbf{E}_a \times \mathbf{H}_b - \mathbf{E}_b \times \mathbf{H}_a) = -\mathbf{H}_b \cdot \frac{\partial\mathbf{B}_a}{\partial t} - \mathbf{E}_a \cdot \left(\mathbf{J}_b + \frac{\partial\mathbf{D}_b}{\partial t}\right) \\ + \mathbf{H}_a \cdot \frac{\partial\mathbf{B}_b}{\partial t} + \mathbf{E}_b \cdot \left(\mathbf{J}_a + \frac{\partial\mathbf{D}_a}{\partial t}\right), \qquad (13\text{-}205)$$

or, replacing the operator $\partial/\partial t$ by $j\omega$, we obtain

$$\boldsymbol{\nabla}\cdot(\mathbf{E}_a \times \mathbf{H}_b - \mathbf{E}_b \times \mathbf{H}_a) = \mathbf{E}_b\cdot\mathbf{J}_a - \mathbf{E}_a\cdot\mathbf{J}_b. \qquad (13\text{-}205)$$

For points outside the source, the current density $\mathbf{J}$ is simply given by the product of the conductivity by the electric field intensity $\sigma\mathbf{E}$, if we assume that

Ohm's law applies. However, within the source, there is a further electric field intensity $\mathbf{E}_s$ (Eq. *8-6*), and, in general,

$$\mathbf{J}_a = \sigma(\mathbf{E}_a + \mathbf{E}_{sa}), \qquad (13\text{-}207)$$

$$\mathbf{J}_b = \sigma(\mathbf{E}_b + \mathbf{E}_{sb}). \qquad (13\text{-}208)$$

The quantities $\mathbf{E}_{sa}$ and $\mathbf{E}_{sb}$ are the applied electric field intensities within the source when it is in loop a and when it is in loop b, respectively. The current density at any point in space is given by $\mathbf{J}_a$ when the source is in a, and similarly for $\mathbf{J}_b$. Eliminating $\mathbf{E}_a$ and $\mathbf{E}_b$ on the right-hand side of Eq. *13-206*, we find that

$$\nabla \cdot (\mathbf{E}_a \times \mathbf{H}_b - \mathbf{E}_b \times \mathbf{H}_a) = \mathbf{E}_{sa} \cdot \mathbf{J}_b - \mathbf{E}_{sb} \cdot \mathbf{J}_a. \qquad (13\text{-}209)$$

In general, the right-hand side is *not* equal to zero. This relation applies to *any* pair of electromagnetic fields at *any* point in space, even inside the sources.

Let us integrate over all space:

$$\int_\infty \nabla \cdot (\mathbf{E}_a \times \mathbf{H}_b - \mathbf{E}_b \times \mathbf{H}_a)\, d\tau = \int_\infty (\mathbf{E}_{sa} \cdot \mathbf{J}_b - \mathbf{E}_{sb} \cdot \mathbf{J}_a)\, d\tau, \qquad (13\text{-}210)$$

or, from the divergence theorem,

$$\int_\infty (\mathbf{E}_a \times \mathbf{H}_b - \mathbf{E}_b \times \mathbf{H}_a) \cdot d\mathbf{a} = \int_\infty (\mathbf{E}_{sa} \cdot \mathbf{J}_b - \mathbf{E}_{sb} \cdot \mathbf{J}_a)\, d\tau. \qquad (13\text{-}211)$$

If we now assume that the sources are limited to a finite volume, the surface of integration on the left-hand side is infinitely remote from them, and we have a plane wave with the field vectors $\mathbf{E}$ and $\mathbf{H}$ orthogonal and transverse:

$$\mathbf{E} \times \mathbf{H} = EH\,\mathbf{r}_1, \qquad (13\text{-}212)$$

where $\mathbf{r}_1$ is the unit radial vector. This is shown in Figure 13-25. Then

$$\mathbf{H}_a = \left(\frac{\epsilon_0}{\mu_0}\right)^{1/2} \mathbf{r}_1 \times \mathbf{E}_a, \qquad (13\text{-}213)$$

Figure 13-25. *The field vectors* $\mathbf{E}$ *and* $\mathbf{H}$ *at a point infinitely remote from a source of radiation are orthogonal and transverse, as in a plane wave.*

and similarly for $\mathbf{H}_b$ and $\mathbf{E}_b$. Thus

$$\mathbf{E}_a \times \mathbf{H}_b - \mathbf{E}_b \times \mathbf{H}_a = \left(\frac{\epsilon_0}{\mu_0}\right)^{1/2} \{\mathbf{E}_a \times (\mathbf{r}_1 \times \mathbf{E}_b) - \mathbf{E}_b \times (\mathbf{r}_1 \times \mathbf{E}_a)\} = 0 \qquad (13\text{-}214)$$

at points infinitely remote from the sources. We can show the quantity within braces to be equal to zero merely by expanding it, recalling that $\mathbf{r}_1$ is perpendicular to both $\mathbf{E}_a$ and $\mathbf{E}_b$. Therefore, the integral on the right-hand side of Eq. *13-211* must also be zero:

$$\int_\infty (\mathbf{E}_{sa} \cdot \mathbf{J}_b - \mathbf{E}_{sb} \cdot \mathbf{J}_a)\, d\tau = 0. \qquad (13\text{-}215)$$

The integration is extended to all space, but it can of course be limited to the sources, since $\mathbf{E}_{sa}$ and $\mathbf{E}_{sb}$ are zero everywhere else. Thus

$$\int_a \mathbf{E}_{sa} \cdot \mathbf{J}_b \, d\tau = \int_b \mathbf{E}_{sb} \cdot \mathbf{J}_a \, d\tau, \tag{13-216}$$

where the integrals are evaluated over the regions where $\mathbf{E}_{sa}$ and $\mathbf{E}_{sb}$ are non-zero.

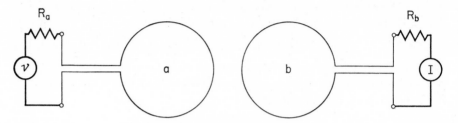

Field vectors E_a, H_a

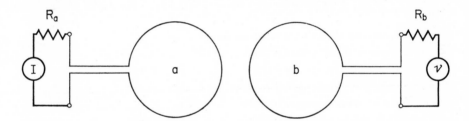

Field vectors E_b, H_b

Figure 13-26. *Pair of loop antennas with the source in* a *(top), and then in* b *(bottom). The frequency and the impedances are the same in both cases.*

The meaning of this equation can be illustrated by referring again to our pair of loop antennas. These are shown in Figure 13-26 for the field a which obtains when the source is in a and for the field b with the source in b.

For these antennas

$$\int_a \mathbf{E}_{sa} \cdot \mathbf{J}_b \, d\tau = \int_a \mathbf{E}_{sa} \cdot \mathbf{dl} \, J_b \, da, \tag{13-217}$$

$$= \mathcal{U}_{sa} I_{b \text{ in } a} \tag{13-218}$$

where $\mathcal{U}_{sa}$ is the voltage supplied by the source in a, and $I_{b \text{ in } a}$ is the current in the *same* loop a *when* b *is energized.* The other integral of Eq. *13-216* can be expressed similarly, and

$$\mathcal{U}_{sa} I_{b \text{ in } a} = \mathcal{U}_{sb} I_{a \text{ in } b}, \tag{13-219}$$

or

$$\frac{I_{a\text{ in }b}}{\mathcal{V}_{sa}} = \frac{I_{b\text{ in }a}}{\mathcal{V}_{sb}}. \tag{13-220}$$

Physically, this means that the current induced in b when a is energized, divided by the applied voltage on a, is the same as the current induced in a when b is energized, divided by the applied voltage on b. Or, stated in another way, the ratio of the induced current in the receiving antenna to the applied voltage on the transmitting antenna remains the same when the roles of the antennas are reversed, *as long as the frequency and the impedances remain unchanged. This is the reciprocity theorem.* We have illustrated it by referring to a pair of magnetic dipoles, but it is equally valid for any pair of antennas.

It must be kept in mind that this theorem is concerned solely with the ratio $I/\mathcal{V}$; it says nothing about the power expended by the source. This usually changes when the source is moved from one position to the other.

One important consequence of the reciprocity theorem is that the radiation pattern of an antenna must have exactly the same shape as the corresponding plot of the response of the antenna as a function of angle when it is used as a receiver. This fact is commonly used for the determination of radiation patterns.

Our demonstration of the theorem has been kept perfectly general, except that the media have been assumed to be isotropic and to obey Ohm's law $\mathbf{J} = \sigma\mathbf{E}$. It therefore applies to ordinary electric circuits.

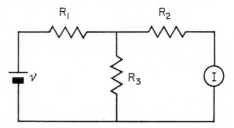

Figure 13-27. *Simple electric circuit comprising a source of voltage $\mathcal{V}$ and an ammeter I. The reciprocity theorem applies, thus the ratio $I/\mathcal{V}$ remains constant when source and ammeter are interchanged, provided the frequency and the impedances remain unchanged.*

This well-known fact proves to be of great practical value. It is a simple matter to check the reciprocity theorem for the circuit of Figure 13-27.

13.10. Summary

This chapter has dealt with various sources of electromagnetic waves. It is based entirely on the *electromagnetic potentials* V and $\mathbf{A}$, which are related to the field vectors $\mathbf{E}$ and $\mathbf{B}$ through the equations

$$\mathbf{E} = -\nabla V - \frac{\partial \mathbf{A}}{\partial t} \tag{13-3}$$

and

$$\mathbf{B} = \nabla \times \mathbf{A}. \tag{13-4}$$

Both **E** and **B** are physically significant quantities in that they are measurable, whereas V and **A** are useful mathematical auxiliaries. The vector potential **A** can be increased by any term of the form $\nabla\theta$ without affecting **B**, and then V can be increased by $-\partial\theta/\partial t$ without affecting **E**. The *Lorentz condition* of Eq. 5-107,

$$\nabla\cdot\mathbf{A} + \epsilon\mu\frac{\partial V}{\partial t} = 0, \qquad (13\text{-}12)$$

imposes a limitation on the choice of θ.

For finite charge and current distributions and for steady state conditions one can set

$$V = \frac{1}{4\pi\epsilon}\int_\infty \frac{\rho\,d\tau}{r} \qquad (13\text{-}1)$$

and

$$\mathbf{A} = \frac{\mu}{4\pi}\int_\infty \frac{\mathbf{J}\,d\tau}{r}, \qquad (13\text{-}2)$$

and the Lorentz condition is then satisfied.

The electromagnetic potentials satisfy the following nonhomogeneous *wave equations:*

$$\nabla^2 V - \epsilon\mu\frac{\partial^2 V}{\partial t^2} = -\frac{\rho}{\epsilon}, \qquad (13\text{-}24)$$

$$\nabla^2\mathbf{A} - \epsilon\mu\frac{\partial^2\mathbf{A}}{\partial t^2} = -\mu\mathbf{J}, \qquad (13\text{-}19)$$

where ρ and **J** are the local charge and current density, respectively. For time-dependent charges and currents,

$$V = \frac{1}{4\pi\epsilon}\int_\infty \frac{[\rho]}{r}\,d\tau, \qquad (13\text{-}45)$$

and

$$\mathbf{A} = \frac{\mu}{4\pi}\int_\infty \frac{[\mathbf{J}]}{r}\,d\tau. \qquad (13\text{-}47)$$

The *brackets* indicate that one must use the values of ρ and of **J** at a previous time $t - (r/u)$, the time r/u being that taken for an electromagnetic wave to travel the distance r between the element of volume where ρ or **J** are evaluated to the point of observation. These are the *retarded potentials.*

Electric dipole radiation is produced by a charge distribution whose dipole moment p is a function of time. For example,

$$p = p_0 e^{j\omega t}. \qquad (13\text{-}49)$$

To obtain the field vectors **E** and **H**, one first calculates the retarded potentials V and **A**. One finds that, in free space,

$$\mathbf{E} = -\frac{p_0}{4\pi\epsilon_0 r \lambda^2} \exp\left\{j\omega\left(t - \frac{r}{c}\right)\right\} \sin\theta\, \mathbf{j} \qquad (r \gg \lambda), \qquad (13\text{-}81)$$

and

$$\mathbf{H} = -\frac{c p_0}{4\pi r \lambda^2} \exp\left\{i\omega\left(t - \frac{r}{c}\right)\right\} \sin\theta\, \mathbf{k}. \qquad (13\text{-}73)$$

A transverse spherical wave therefore radiates away from the dipole, and E/H is the same as for a plane wave in free space. Closer in, the wave is more complex: there is a total of 7 different terms, and $\mathbf{E}$ has a radial component. The Poynting vector is everywhere radial, and

$$\mathbf{S}_{\text{av.}} = \frac{c p_0^2 \sin^2\theta}{32\pi^2\epsilon_0 r^2 \lambda^4}\, \mathbf{i}. \qquad (13\text{-}87)$$

There is *no* energy radiated along the axis of the dipole.

The *half-wave antenna* is a conductor $\lambda/2$ long on which a standing wave of electric current is established. Its field is calculated by adding the radiation fields of the individual dipoles formed by the elements $\mathbf{dl}$ along its length. The field of the half-wave antenna is qualitatively quite similar to that of a dipole, and, for $r \gg \lambda$,

$$\mathbf{E} = \frac{j\mu_0 c}{2\pi r} I_0 \exp\left\{i\omega\left(t - \frac{r}{c}\right)\right\} \frac{\cos\left(\frac{\pi}{2}\cos\theta\right)}{\sin\theta}\, \mathbf{j}, \qquad (13\text{-}125)$$

and

$$\mathbf{H} = \frac{j}{2\pi r} I_0 \exp\left\{j\omega\left(t - \frac{r}{c}\right)\right\} \frac{\cos\left(\frac{\pi}{2}\cos\theta\right)}{\sin\theta}\, \mathbf{k}. \qquad (13\text{-}131)$$

The radiated power is

$$W = 73.1\, I_{\text{rms}}^2, \qquad (13\text{-}142)$$

where I_{rms} is the rms current at the center of the antenna at the point where it is fed by a source of power. The coefficient 73.1 is the *radiation resistance* of the antenna.

Antenna arrays are sets of antennas properly spaced and phased so as to obtain, by interference, appropriate radiation patterns.

Electric quadrupole radiation is produced by a charge distribution whose quadrupole moment is a function of time. The simplest quadrupole source is the linear quadrupole. It is a simple matter to deduce its field from that of the electric dipole:

$$\mathbf{E} = -\frac{j p_{zz0}}{4\pi\epsilon_0 r \lambda^3} \exp\left\{j\omega\left(t - \frac{r}{c}\right)\right\} \sin\theta \cos\theta\, \mathbf{j} \qquad (r \gg \lambda \gg s). \quad (13\text{-}157)$$

The vectors $\mathbf{H}$ and $\mathbf{E}$ are related as in the electric dipole.

Magnetic dipole radiation is produced when the magnetic dipole moment of a current distribution is a function of time. If we assume a circular current loop of negligible impedance, then $V = 0$. From the retarded vector potential $\mathbf{A}$, we then find values of $\mathbf{E}$ and $\mathbf{H}$ which are related to those of electric dipole radiation according to the symmetry conditions of Section 8.3.

Magnetic quadrupole radiation is similarly related to electric quadrupole radiation.

Both electric and magnetic dipoles can be used as *receiving antennas*, the source of power being then replaced by a suitable detector. For a short electric dipole, the voltage which appears on a high resistance at the position of the detector is equal to the tangential electric field strength multiplied by the length of the dipole. In the case of the magnetic dipole, this voltage is the electromotance induced by the changing magnetic flux linking the dipole.

The *reciprocity theorem* states that the current in a detector divided by the voltage applied at the source remains constant when source and detector are interchanged, as long as the frequency and the impedances are left unchanged. This applies to any electromagnetic field and, in particular, to electric circuits and to antennas.

Problems

13-1. Show that the scalar potential V can be set equal to zero everywhere without affecting the field vectors $\mathbf{E}$ and $\mathbf{H}$, but only in regions where the charge density ρ is equal to zero.

13-2. The Hertz vector $\mathbf{\Pi}$ is defined by the equations

$$\mathbf{A} = \epsilon\mu \frac{\partial \mathbf{\Pi}}{\partial t}, \qquad V = -\mathbf{\nabla} \cdot \mathbf{\Pi}.$$

Show that the Lorentz condition is satisfied and that

$$\mathbf{E} = -\epsilon\mu \frac{\partial^2 \mathbf{\Pi}}{\partial t^2} + \mathbf{\nabla}(\mathbf{\nabla} \cdot \mathbf{\Pi}),$$

$$\mathbf{H} = \epsilon\mathbf{\nabla} \times \frac{\partial \mathbf{\Pi}}{\partial t}.$$

Find $\mathbf{\Pi}$ for the field of a point charge and for that of an oscillating electric dipole.

13-3. Calculate the vector potential $\mathbf{A}$ at a distance r on the axis of an electric dipole of length s. Show that the result is the same as it would be if the current were localized at the center of the dipole.

13-4. Show that the Lorentz condition applies to the electromagnetic potentials V and $\mathbf{A}$ for an oscillating electric dipole.

13-5. Calculate the ratio of electric to magnetic energy densities in the field of an electric dipole (a) for $r \ll \lambda$, (b) for $r = \lambda$, (c) for $r \gg \lambda$.

13-6. Show that the phase velocity of the **H** vector for an electric dipole is given by

$$u = \left(1 + \frac{1}{r'^2}\right) c,$$

where $r' = r/\lambda$. Draw a qualitative graph of u as a function of r'.

13-7. Show that the phase velocities of the r and θ components of **E** for an oscillating electric dipole are given by

$$u_r = \left(1 + \frac{1}{r'^2}\right) c$$

and

$$u_\theta = \left\{\frac{r'^4 - r'^2 + 1}{r'^4 - 2r'^2 + 2}\right\} c.$$

Draw qualitative graphs of u_r and of u_θ as functions of r'.

13-8. What fraction of the total power radiated by an electric dipole is radiated between ± 45 degrees of the equatorial plane?

13-9. Show that, for the electric dipole,

$$E_{\text{rms}} = 6.71 W^{1/2}(\sin \theta)/r,$$

and, for the half-wave antenna,

$$E_{\text{rms}} = 7.01 W^{1/2} \cos\left(\frac{\pi}{2}\cos\theta\right) \Big/ r \sin\theta,$$

where W is the radiated power and $r \gg \lambda$.

13-10. Calculate the electric field intensity in millivolts per meter at a distance of 1 mile in the equatorial plane of a half-wave antenna radiating 1 kilowatt of power. The radian length $\lambda \ll 1$ mile.

13-11. We have shown that the radiation resistance of a half-wave antenna is 73.1 ohms. Show that the radiation resistance of a quarter-wave antenna perpendicular to a conducting plane is one-half of this, or 36.6 ohms.

13-12. Identical parallel half-wave antennas are arranged in line with a uniform spacing D and are excited in phase. Show that the angular dependence of the electric field intensity **E** in the plane perpendicular to the antennas is given by

$$\frac{\sin\{(ND/2\lambda)\cos\varphi\}}{\sin\{(D/2\lambda)\cos\varphi\}},$$

where N is the number of antennas and φ is the angle between the direction of observation and the plane containing the antennas. Hint: Perform the summation graphically in the complex plane.

13-13. Determine the angular positions of the maxima and minima of E for the radiation pattern found above. Differentiation of the above formula will yield only the maxima.

Show that, for a given spacing D, the main lobe at $\varphi = \pi/2$ becomes narrower as the number of antennas N is increased.

Show graphically, by considering the summation in the complex plane, that the main lobe is sharp and that the side lobes are small when N is large and $D < \lambda$.

13-14. Plot the radiation pattern for an array composed of 4 parallel half-wave antennas spaced $\lambda/2$ apart.

13-15. Calculate the electromagnetic potentials V and $\mathbf{A}$ and the field vectors $\mathbf{E}$ and $\mathbf{H}$ for the oscillating linear electric quadrupole directly, without using the field of the oscillating electric dipole.

13-16. Show that the Lorentz condition applies to the radiation field of a linear electric quadrupole for $r \gg \lambda$.

13-17. Calculate the Poynting vector for the radiation field of an oscillating linear electric quadrupole, and show that the total radiated power is given by

$$W = 1.8 \times 10^{17} \frac{Q_0^2 s^4}{\lambda^6} \quad \text{(watts)}.$$

13-18. Could you distinguish between electric dipole and magnetic dipole radiation if you were given a small movable loop antenna and an appropriate detector?

13-19. Show that the electric dipole and magnetic dipole fields satisfy the symmetry conditions of Section 8.3 and that the constant of proportionality α is here equal to m_0/p_0 when the magnetic dipole field is chosen as the primed field.

13-20. Compare the responses of the electric and of the magnetic dipole antennas when used as receivers (a) in air and (b) in sea water. In (b) assume a frequency of 20 kilocycles/second. Assume that the loop antenna has a single turn, that its diameter is equal to the length l of the electric dipole, and that $l \ll \lambda$.

13-21. The gain G of an antenna is defined as the ratio of the Poynting vector at the maximum of the radiation pattern to the average value of the Poynting vector:

$$G = \frac{\mathbb{S}_{max}}{\dfrac{1}{4\pi} \displaystyle\int_0^{2\pi} \int_0^{\pi} \mathbb{S} \sin \theta \, d\theta \, d\varphi}.$$

It is a measure of the directivity of the antenna.

Show that the gain of an electric or magnetic dipole is 1.5 and that the gain of a half-wave antenna is 1.64.

13-22. Calculate the ratio $I/\mathbb{U}$ for the circuit of Figure 13-27, and show that the reciprocity theorem applies.

Calculate the power expended by the source when the circuit is as shown and when $\mathbb{U}$ and I are interchanged.

CHAPTER 14

Electromagnetic Field of a Moving Charge

This final chapter is devoted to the electromagnetic field of a small moving charge. It is based entirely on the electromagnetic potentials V and $\mathbf{A}$, as was Chapter 13. We shall discuss several simple cases in considerable detail so as to illustrate the meaning of the retarded electromagnetic potentials and of the field vectors $\mathbf{E}$ and $\mathbf{H}$. It will not be possible for us to arrive at expressions for these quantities which apply to the most general case where the velocity and the acceleration vectors can have any value, but we shall state the general results as given by the theory of relativity, and then illustrate them in various ways.

The electromagnetic radiation studied in Chapter 13 is produced by oscillating currents, and hence by moving charges, thus the results obtained in these two last chapters can be related. We shall see, indeed, that the basic characteristics of dipole radiation can be deduced equally well with the methods of the present chapter.

14.1. The Electromagnetic Potentials V and $\mathbf{A}$ for a Line Charge Moving with a Constant Velocity Along its Length

Let us consider the electromagnetic field produced by a moving charge. We shall first calculate the scalar potential V and the vector potential $\mathbf{A}$ for a line charge moving with a constant velocity $\mathbf{u}$ along its length, as in Figure 14-1. It would seem more appropriate at this stage to consider the field of a moving *point* charge. If we did so immediately, we would arrive at the wrong result, as will become clear later on. The field of a small charge distribution will follow as a limiting case of that of a line charge.

14.1.1. Point of Observation P on the Trajectory.

We first assume that the point of observation is on the trajectory, at the origin. Then the distance from an element of charge to P is simply its z-coordinate. We calculate V from Eq. 13-45, where the integration is to be extended over the elements of charge $\nu\, dz$ in their retarded positions:

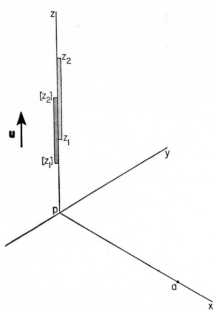

$$V = \frac{1}{4\pi\epsilon_0} \int_{[z_1]}^{[z_2]} \frac{\nu\, dz}{z}, \qquad (14\text{-}1)$$

$$= \frac{\nu}{4\pi\epsilon_0} \ln \frac{[z_2]}{[z_1]}. \qquad (14\text{-}2)$$

The distance $z_1 - [z_1]$ is the distance traveled by the lower end in the time taken by light to travel through the distance $[z_1]$:

$$z_1 - [z_1] = u\frac{[z_1]}{c}, \qquad (14\text{-}3)$$

or

$$[z_1] = \frac{z_1}{1 + \dfrac{u}{c}}, \qquad (14\text{-}4)$$

and, similarly,

$$[z_2] = \frac{z_2}{1 + \dfrac{u}{c}}. \qquad (14\text{-}5)$$

Thus

$$V = \frac{\nu}{4\pi\epsilon_0} \ln \frac{z_2}{z_1}. \qquad (14\text{-}6)$$

Figure 14-1. *Line charge of density ν coulombs/meter moving in the positive direction along the z-axis with a velocity* **u.** *The point of observation P is taken to be at the origin. The shaded area extending from z_1 to z_2 shows the position of the charge at the time t, whereas that extending from $[z_1]$ to $[z_2]$ shows the charge as it appears from P. It is shown that $[z_2] - [z_1]$ is shorter than $z_2 - z_1$.*

The scalar potential V is therefore independent of the velocity u, and we would have obtained exactly the same result if we had taken the charge to be stationary. We shall see later on that V is independent of u only in this very special case where the charge moves along the line joining it to the point of observation.

It is obvious from Eqs. 14-4 and 14-5 that the extremities z_1 and z_2 are retarded by different amounts, hence $[z_2] - [z_1]$ differs from $z_2 - z_1$. Thus

$$Q_{\text{retarded}} = \int_{[z_1]}^{[z_2]} \nu\, dz, \qquad (14\text{-}7)$$

$$Q_{\text{retarded}} = \nu([z_2] - [z_1]), \tag{14-8}$$

$$= \nu \frac{(z_2 - z_1)}{1 + \dfrac{u}{c}}, \tag{14-9}$$

$$= \frac{Q}{1 + \dfrac{u}{c}}. \tag{14-10}$$

The retarded Q is thus smaller than Q by the factor $1/\{1 + (u/c)\}$. The reason for this paradoxical result is that the contributions to V from the various elements of charge must be evaluated at a different time $t - ([z]/c)$.

Let us now calculate V when the length of the charge $z_2 - z_1 = s$ approaches zero. Then

$$V = \frac{\nu}{4\pi\epsilon_0} \ln\left(\frac{z_1 + s}{z_1}\right), \tag{14-11}$$

$$= \frac{\nu}{4\pi\epsilon_0} \ln\left(1 + \frac{s}{z}\right), \tag{14-12}$$

$$= \frac{\nu s}{4\pi\epsilon_0 z}, \tag{14-13}$$

$$= \frac{Q}{4\pi\epsilon_0 z}. \tag{14-14}$$

This potential is again independent of the velocity u despite the fact that, from Eq. *13-45*, one could have expected to find the retarded value of z, that is, $[z]$, instead of z in the denominator. The explanation is that not only must the *position* of the charge be retarded, but its *magnitude* must also be changed, and the two effects cancel in this particular case. The retarded position $[z]$ is less than z by a factor of $1/\{1 + (u/c)\}$, as in Eq. *14-4*, and the effective charge is also less than Q by the same factor.

The calculation for the vector potential **A** is quite similar:

$$\mathbf{A} = \frac{\mu_0}{4\pi} \int_{[z_1]}^{[z_2]} \frac{\nu \mathbf{u}\, dz}{z}, \tag{14-15}$$

$$= \frac{\mu_0 \nu \mathbf{u}}{4\pi} \ln \frac{z_2}{z_1}. \tag{14-16}$$

When the length s of the line charge approaches zero,

$$\mathbf{A} = \frac{\mu_0 Q u}{4\pi z} \mathbf{k}. \tag{14-17}$$

The result is again precisely the same as if we had neglected retardation effects. The reason for this is the same as that given for V.

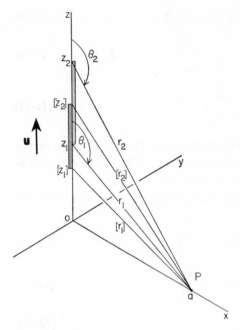

Figure 14-2

Line charge of charge density v cou-lombs/meter moving in the positive direction along the z-axis with a ve-locity **u**. *The point of observation P is at a distance a along the x-axis. As in the previous figure, the charge ex-tends from z_1 to z_2 at time t, and the retarded positions of z_1 and z_2 are shown as $[z_1]$ and $[z_2]$.*

14.1.2. Point of Observation at a Distance a from the Trajectory. The point of observation is now at a distance a from the trajectory, as in Figure 14-2. Then

$$V = \frac{v}{4\pi\epsilon_0} \int_{[z_1]}^{[z_2]} \frac{dz}{(a^2 + z^2)^{1/2}}, \tag{14-18}$$

$$= \frac{v}{4\pi\epsilon_0} \ln\left(\frac{[z_2] + [r_2]}{[z_1] + [r_1]}\right). \tag{14-19}$$

We can check whether or not this result agrees with that of Eq. *14-6* by letting a approach zero. Then $[r_2] \longrightarrow [z_2]$, $[r_1] \longrightarrow [z_1]$, and the two equations agree. We can calculate the vector potential similarly.

14.2. The Lienard-Wiechert Potentials for a Small Moving Charge

When the length $z_2 - z_1 = s$ of the charge distribution approaches zero, we set

$$[s] = [z_2] - [z_1]. \tag{14-20}$$

Then

$$[r_2] = ([r_1]^2 + [s]^2 - 2[r_1][s] \cos [\theta_1])^{1/2}, \tag{14-21}$$

$$\approx [r_1]\left(1 - \frac{[s]}{[r_1]} \cos [\theta_1]\right) = [r_1] - [s] \cos [\theta_1] \tag{14-22}$$

for $[s] \ll [r_1]$. We have put the angle θ_1 between brackets because it corresponds to the retarded position. Substituting in the above equation for V, we obtain

$$V = \frac{\nu}{4\pi\epsilon_0} \ln\left(1 + \frac{[s](1 - \cos[\theta])}{[r] + [z]}\right), \tag{14-23}$$

$$= \frac{\nu}{4\pi\epsilon_0} \frac{[s](1 - \cos[\theta])}{[r] + [z]} \qquad ([s] \longrightarrow 0). \tag{14-24}$$

We have omitted the index 1, since the length of the distribution approaches zero. Now

$$\frac{[z]}{[r]} = -\cos[\theta], \tag{14-25}$$

and thus

$$V = \frac{\nu[s]}{4\pi\epsilon_0[r]}, \tag{14-26}$$

where the distance $[r]$ is the retarded distance between the charge and the point of observation P.

Let us calculate $[s]$:

$$[s] = [z_2] - [z_1] = z_2 - z_1 + (z_1 - [z_1]) - (z_2 - [z_2]), \tag{14-27}$$

as in Figure 14-2. Now $z_1 - [z_1]$ is the distance traveled by the charge in the time that light takes to travel the distance $[r_1]$ from the point $(O, O, [z_1])$ to the point of observation $P(a, O, O)$:

$$z_1 - [z_1] = u\frac{[r_1]}{c}, \tag{14-28}$$

and similarly,

$$z_2 - [z_2] = u\frac{[r_2]}{c}. \tag{14-29}$$

Thus, for $s \longrightarrow 0$, Eq. *14-7* becomes

$$[s] = s + \frac{u}{c}([r_1] - [r_2]), \tag{14-30}$$

$$= s + \frac{u}{c}[s]\cos[\theta], \tag{14-31}$$

$$= \frac{s}{1 - \frac{u}{c}\cos[\theta]}. \tag{14-32}$$

The retarded length $[s]$ is thus *smaller* than s when the charge moves *away* from P as in the figure, since $\cos[\theta]$ is negative. Thus, finally, from Eq. *14-26*,

$$V = \frac{\nu s}{4\pi\epsilon_0[r]\left(1 - \frac{u}{c}\cos[\theta]\right)} \tag{14-33}$$

or, if we choose [**r**] to be the vector pointing *from* the charge in its retarded position *to* the point of observation, as in Figure 14-3, then

$$V = \frac{1}{4\pi\epsilon_0} \frac{Q}{[r] - \frac{[\mathbf{r}]\cdot[\mathbf{u}]}{c}}. \tag{14-34}$$

This is the *Lienard-Wiechert scalar potential.* We have shown the velocity **u** as retarded because this expression applies also to the more general case where the velocity **u** is not constant. When the point of observation is on the trajectory, as in Section 14.1.1, $[\mathbf{r}]\cdot\mathbf{u}/c = -[r]u/c$, and V agrees with Eq. *14-14* as required. We shall use this potential below to calculate the field of a small moving charge. The quantity Q is the charge moving with the velocity [**u**] at the retarded position, and c is the velocity of light. It is assumed that the phenomenon occurs in a vacuum.

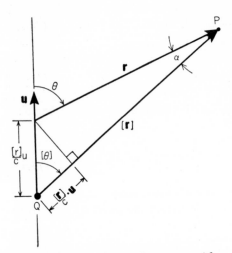

Figure 14-3. *A charge Q moves with a velocity* [**u**] *at its retarded position defined by* [**r**]. *The point of observation P is fixed. The Lienard-Wiechert potentials of Eqs.* 14-34 *and* 14-41 *give the electromagnetic potentials V and* **A** *at P.*

Let us return to the case in which the velocity **u** is constant. It is interesting to express V as a function of the values of r and of θ at the time t. Figure 14-3 shows the positions **r** and [**r**] of Q at times t at $t - [r]/c$. We have

$$[r] - \frac{[\mathbf{r}]\cdot\mathbf{u}}{c} = r\cos\alpha, \tag{14-35}$$

$$= r(1 - \sin^2\alpha)^{1/2}. \tag{14-36}$$

Now

$$\frac{\sin\alpha}{\dfrac{[r]u}{c}} = \frac{\sin\theta}{[r]}, \tag{14-37}$$

hence

$$[r] - \frac{[\mathbf{r}]\cdot\mathbf{u}}{c} = r\left(1 - \frac{u^2}{c^2}\sin^2\theta\right)^{1/2}. \tag{14-38}$$

and

$$V = \frac{Q}{4\pi\epsilon_0 r \left(1 - \dfrac{u^2}{c^2}\sin^2\theta\right)^{1/2}}. \tag{14-39}$$

The effects of retardation appear in the square root term in the denominator. They are maximum when $\theta = \pi/2$, that is, when the velocity $\mathbf{u}$ is perpendicular to the unretarded $\mathbf{r}$. When $\mathbf{u}$ is along the line of observation, $\theta = 0$, and the velocity can be disregarded, as we found previously. It is important to remember that the velocity $\mathbf{u}$ of the charge Q is always smaller than the velocity of light c, and usually much smaller. Furthermore, the correction term involves the *square* of the ratio u/c, thus retardation introduces only a second-order effect.

The calculation for $\mathbf{A}$ is again entirely similar:

$$\mathbf{A} = \frac{\mu_0\, \nu\, \mathbf{u}}{4\pi} \int_{[z_1]}^{[z_2]} \frac{dz}{(a^2 + z^2)^{1/2}}, \tag{14-40}$$

$$= \frac{\mu_0}{4\pi} \frac{Q[\mathbf{u}]}{[r] - \dfrac{[\mathbf{r}]\cdot[\mathbf{u}]}{c}}. \tag{14-41}$$

This is the *Lienard-Wiechert vector potential*. It applies even when the velocity $\mathbf{u}$ is not constant. When $\mathbf{u}$ is constant,

$$\mathbf{A} = \frac{\mu_0}{4\pi} \frac{Q\,\mathbf{u}}{r\left(1 - \dfrac{u^2}{c^2}\sin^2\theta\right)^{1/2}} \qquad (\mathbf{u} = \text{constant}). \tag{14-42}$$

14.3. The Field Vectors **E** and **H** for a Small Moving Charge

Now that we have found the electromagnetic potentials V and $\mathbf{A}$ for a small moving charge, we expect to deduce the field vectors $\mathbf{E}$ and $\mathbf{H}$ from

$$\mathbf{E} = -\frac{\partial \mathbf{A}}{\partial t} - \nabla V \tag{14-43}$$

and

$$\mathbf{H} = \frac{1}{\mu_0} \nabla \times \mathbf{A}. \tag{14-44}$$

Unfortunately, the calculation is much more complex than would appear at first sight, and it is *not* correct to operate on V and $\mathbf{A}$ in the usual way. Let us first consider the term ∇V. It involves partial derivatives with respect to the coordinates, corresponding to rates of change of V with *position* at some *fixed time t*. If the potential at the point of observation P and at some time t is related to a charge Q at $-[\mathbf{r}]$, then the potential at a neighboring point at the *same* time t is due to the charge Q at some *other* position $-[\mathbf{r} + d\mathbf{r}]$. This will be clear from the examples given below. The evaluation of ∇V must therefore be made with care, and the same applies to $\nabla \times \mathbf{A}$.

In evaluating $\partial \mathbf{A}/\partial t$, similar considerations apply: the time derivative must be calculated at a *fixed point* of observation. However, during a time dt the charge Q moves over a distance $\mathbf{u}\, dt$ and the time derivative must therefore take this into account.

14.3.1. The E Vector for a Charge Moving with a Constant Velocity u. Point of Observation on the Trajectory.

Let us return again to the relatively simple case of a small charge Q moving with a constant velocity $\mathbf{u}$ along the z-axis, with the point of observation at the origin. We require ∇V and $\partial \mathbf{A}/\partial t$. We assume that the position of the charge $z' = 0$ at $t = 0$, in order that $z' = ut$.

To calculate ∇V, we first note that, by symmetry, it must be along the z-axis. We therefore calculate V at the origin at some time t, and then at some neighboring point $(0, 0, \Delta z)$ at the *same* time t. The difference between these two values of V divided by Δz at the limit $\Delta z \longrightarrow 0$ will then give ∇V.

We have found in Eq. *14-14* that

$$V_{0,\,t} = \frac{Q}{4\pi\epsilon_0 z'}. \tag{14-45}$$

This is the potential at the origin at the time

$$t = \frac{z'}{u}. \tag{14-46}$$

At the neighboring point $(0, 0, \Delta z)$ at the same time t,

$$V_{\Delta z,\,t} = \frac{Q}{4\pi\epsilon_0(z' - \Delta z)}. \tag{14-47}$$

The charge is again at $z' = ut$, since the time t is the same, but the distance from the charge to the point of observation is now $z' - \Delta z$. Then, at the origin,

$$\frac{\Delta V}{\Delta z} = \frac{Q}{4\pi\epsilon_0}\left(\frac{1}{z' - \Delta z} - \frac{1}{z'}\right)\frac{1}{\Delta z}, \tag{14-48}$$

$$= \frac{Q}{4\pi\epsilon_0}\frac{1}{z'(z' - \Delta z)}, \tag{14-49}$$

and, at the limit $\Delta z \longrightarrow 0$,

$$\nabla V = \frac{Q}{4\pi\epsilon_0 z'^2}\mathbf{k}. \tag{14-50}$$

In this particular case, ∇V is calculated in exactly the same way as if the charge were fixed in space.

It is more instructive, although more complicated, to calculate ∇V as follows. We again calculate V at the origin and at a neighboring point, but now we use the retarded position $[z']$, that is, the position of the charge at a time $t - ([z']/c)$. At the origin,

$$V_{0,\,t} = \frac{[Q]}{4\pi\epsilon_0[z']}, \tag{14-51}$$

where we have written

$$[Q] = \frac{Q}{1 + \dfrac{u}{c}} \tag{14-52}$$

and

$$[z'] = \frac{z'}{1 + \dfrac{u}{c}}. \tag{14-53}$$

The time t is again the time taken for the charge to travel a distance z':

$$t = \frac{z'}{u}. \tag{14-54}$$

At the neighboring point $(0, 0, \Delta z)$,

$$V_{\Delta z,\,t} = \frac{[Q]}{4\pi\epsilon_0([z''] - \Delta z)}, \tag{14-55}$$

where $[Q]$ is the same as in Eq. *14-52*, and where $[z''] - \Delta z$ is the distance between the new point of observation $(0, 0, \Delta z)$ and the new retarded position $[z'']$ of the charge Q. At the time t the charge is at the position ut, whatever be the point of observation, and $z' = z''$. The quantity $[z'']$ is unknown for the moment, but

$$t = \frac{[z'']}{u} + \frac{[z''] - \Delta z}{c}. \tag{14-56}$$

The first term is the time taken by the charge to reach the position $[z'']$; the second term is the time taken by the signal to travel back to the position $(0, 0, \Delta z)$. Equating the two values of t expressed in terms of z' and of $[z'']$, we find that

$$z' = [z'']\left(1 + \frac{u}{c}\right) - \frac{u}{c}\Delta z. \tag{14-57}$$

It will be noted that $[z''] > [z']$. This is correct, as will be discovered with a little thought. Rearranging Eq. *14-57*, we obtain

$$[z''] - \Delta z = \frac{z' - \Delta z}{1 + \dfrac{u}{c}}, \tag{14-58}$$

and

$$\frac{\Delta V}{\Delta z} = \frac{[Q]}{4\pi\epsilon_0 \Delta z} \left(\frac{1 + \dfrac{u}{c}}{z' - \Delta z} - \frac{1 + \dfrac{u}{c}}{z'} \right), \tag{14-59}$$

$$= \frac{[Q]}{4\pi\epsilon_0 \Delta z} \left\{ \frac{\Delta z \left(1 + \dfrac{u}{c}\right)}{z'(z' - \Delta z)} \right\}, \tag{14-60}$$

$$\nabla V = \frac{Q}{4\pi\epsilon_0 z'^2} \mathbf{k}, \tag{14-61}$$

as in Eq. *14-50*.

It will be instructive to calculate ∇V in still another way. We have

$$V_z = \frac{Q}{4\pi\epsilon_0(z' - z)}, \tag{14-62}$$

where $(z' - z)$ is the distance from the charge Q to a point of observation P situated at z. Then

$$\frac{\partial V_z}{\partial z} = -\frac{Q}{4\pi\epsilon_0(z' - z)^2} \frac{\partial}{\partial z}(z' - z), \tag{14-63}$$

where the derivative $\partial(z' - z)/\partial z$ must be evaluated at a fixed time t, that is, for a fixed position z' of the charge Q. Then

$$\frac{\partial(z' - z)}{\partial z} = -1, \tag{14-64}$$

and

$$\nabla V = -\frac{\partial V}{\partial z}\mathbf{k} = \frac{Q}{4\pi\epsilon_0 z'^2}\mathbf{k} \tag{14-65}$$

at the origin, where $z = 0$.

As a fourth and last method of calculating ∇V, let us differentiate V_z expressed in terms of the retarded distance $[z' - z]$, where $z' = ut$ is the position of the charge, and z is the fixed point of observation. Then

$$V_z = \frac{[Q]}{4\pi\epsilon_0[z' - z]}, \tag{14-66}$$

where

$$[Q] = \frac{Q}{1 + \dfrac{u}{c}}, \tag{14-67}$$

$$[z' - z] = [z'] - z = \frac{z' - z}{1 + \dfrac{u}{c}}, \tag{14-68}$$

and

$$t = \frac{z'}{u} = \frac{[z']}{u} + \frac{[z'] - z}{c}. \tag{14-69}$$

Then

$$\frac{\partial V_z}{\partial z} = -\frac{[Q]}{4\pi\epsilon_0[z'-z]^2} \frac{\partial([z']-z)}{\partial z}. \tag{14-70}$$

In this case the last derivative is *not* equal to -1, since $[z']$ is a function of z when the time is kept constant, as can be seen from the above value of t. Setting $dt = 0$, we have

$$0 = d[z']\left(\frac{1}{u}+\frac{1}{c}\right) - \frac{dz}{c} \tag{14-71}$$

and

$$\frac{\partial[z']}{\partial z} = \frac{1}{1+\dfrac{c}{u}}. \tag{14-72}$$

Then

$$\frac{\partial([z']-z)}{\partial z} = \frac{1}{1+\dfrac{c}{u}} - 1, \tag{14-73}$$

$$= -\frac{1}{1+\dfrac{u}{c}}, \tag{14-74}$$

and

$$\nabla V = -\frac{\partial V}{\partial z}\mathbf{k} = \frac{Q}{4\pi\epsilon_0 z'^2}\mathbf{k} \tag{14-75}$$

at the origin.

Now that we have calculated ∇V, let us find $\partial\mathbf{A}/\partial t$. This time we must be careful to keep the point of observation fixed at the origin in the process of evaluating the time derivative. We found in Eq. *14-17* that

$$\mathbf{A}_t = \frac{\mu_0 Q u}{4\pi z'}\mathbf{k} \tag{14-76}$$

for the present case. The time t is z'/u. At the time $t + \Delta t$,

$$\mathbf{A}_{t+\Delta t} = \frac{\mu_0}{4\pi}\frac{Q u}{z'''}\mathbf{k}, \tag{14-77}$$

where $z''' - z$ is the distance traveled by the charge in the time Δt, with the result that

$$z''' = z' + u\,\Delta t. \tag{14-78}$$

Then

$$\frac{\Delta\mathbf{A}}{\Delta t} = \frac{1}{\Delta t}\frac{\mu_0 Q u}{4\pi}\left(\frac{1}{z'+u\,\Delta t}-\frac{1}{z'}\right)\mathbf{k}, \tag{14-79}$$

$$= -\frac{1}{\Delta t}\frac{\mu_0 Q u}{4\pi}\left\{\frac{u\,\Delta t}{z'(z'+u\,\Delta t)}\right\}\mathbf{k}, \tag{14-80}$$

and, at the limit $\Delta t \longrightarrow 0$,

$$\frac{\partial \mathbf{A}}{\partial t} = -\frac{\mu_0 Q u^2}{4\pi z'^2} \mathbf{k}, \tag{14-81}$$

$$= -\frac{Q}{4\pi \epsilon_0 z'^2} \frac{u^2}{c^2} \mathbf{k}. \tag{14-82}$$

We can now calculate the electric field intensity $\mathbf{E}$ at the origin for the case illustrated in Figure 14-1 when the length of the charge distribution approaches zero. From Eqs. *14-43*, *14-50*, and *14-82*, we have

$$\mathbf{E} = -\frac{Q}{4\pi \epsilon_0 z'^2} \left(1 - \frac{u^2}{c^2} \right) \mathbf{k}. \tag{14-83}$$

When $u^2 \ll c^2$, this equation reduces to that for the electrostatic case. It will be observed that the correction term u^2/c^2 comes from $\partial \mathbf{A}/\partial t$, which opposes ∇V, and that $\mathbf{E} \longrightarrow 0$ when $u \longrightarrow c$.

It is interesting to note that, although V and $\mathbf{A}$ are the same as for a fixed charge and for a fixed element of current, respectively, $\mathbf{E}$ is different from that of a fixed charge. The reason for this is that $\partial \mathbf{A}/\partial t$ is not zero at the point of observation.

14.3.2. The H Vector for a Charge Moving with a Constant Velocity u. Point of Observation on the Trajectory. We now wish to calculate the magnetic field intensity

$$\mathbf{H} = \frac{1}{\mu_0} \nabla \times \mathbf{A} \tag{14-84}$$

at the origin. This is really simple. By symmetry, $\mathbf{H}$, if it exists, can only be oriented along the z-axis. From the fundamental definition of the curl, which is stated in Eq. *1-69*,

$$H = \frac{1}{\mu_0} \lim_{\rho \to 0} \frac{1}{\pi \rho^2} \oint A_\varphi \rho \, d\varphi, \tag{14-85}$$

where the line integral is evaluated around a small circle of radius ρ centered on the origin and normal to the z-axis. By symmetry, $\mathbf{A}$ has no φ component, and, at the origin, $\mathbf{H} = 0$.

14.3.3. E and H Vectors for a Moving Charge. General Case. The general case of a small charge Q moving with arbitrary velocity and acceleration is rather complex and is best treated by the methods of relativity. It will therefore not be discussed at length. It is found that*

* See, for example, J. A. Stratton, *Electromagnetic Theory* (McGraw-Hill, New York, 1941), page 475, or W. K. H. Panofsky and M. Phillips (Addison-Wesley, Cambridge, 1955), page 29.).

$$\mathbf{E} = \frac{Q}{4\pi\epsilon_0} \frac{1}{\left([r] - \frac{[\mathbf{r}]\cdot[\mathbf{u}]}{c}\right)^2} \left\{ \frac{[\mathbf{r}] - \frac{[r][\mathbf{u}]}{c}}{[r] - \frac{[\mathbf{r}]\cdot[\mathbf{u}]}{c}} \left(1 - \frac{[u]^2}{c^2}\right) \right.$$

$$\left. + \frac{1}{c^2}\left(\frac{[\mathbf{r}] - \frac{[r][\mathbf{u}]}{c}}{[r] - \frac{[\mathbf{r}]\cdot[\mathbf{u}]}{c}} [\mathbf{r}]\cdot[\dot{\mathbf{u}}] - [r][\dot{\mathbf{u}}]\right)\right\}, \qquad (14\text{-}86)$$

$$\mathbf{H} = \frac{Q}{4\pi} \frac{1}{\left([r] - \frac{[\mathbf{r}]\cdot[\mathbf{u}]}{c}\right)^2} \left\{ \frac{[\mathbf{u}]\times[\mathbf{r}]}{[r] - \frac{[\mathbf{r}]\cdot[\mathbf{u}]}{c}} \left(1 - \frac{[u]^2}{c^2}\right) \right.$$

$$\left. + \frac{1}{c}\left(\frac{([\mathbf{u}]\times[\mathbf{r}])([\dot{\mathbf{u}}]\cdot[\mathbf{r}])}{c\left([r] - \frac{[\mathbf{r}]\cdot[\mathbf{u}]}{c}\right)} + [\dot{\mathbf{u}}]\times[\mathbf{r}]\right)\right\}. \qquad (14\text{-}87)$$

The quantities $[\mathbf{r}]$ and $[\mathbf{u}]$ are illustrated in Figure 14-3.

Let us examine the above expressions for the case in which the velocity **u** of the charge Q is constant and much smaller than the velocity of light c. Then **E** reduces to

$$\mathbf{E} = \frac{Q}{4\pi\epsilon_0 r^2}\mathbf{r}_1 \qquad (u \ll c, \dot{u} = 0), \qquad (14\text{-}88)$$

which is Eq. *2-3*. We also have

$$\mathbf{H} = \frac{Q\mathbf{u}\times\mathbf{r}}{4\pi r^3} \qquad (u \ll c, \dot{u} = 0). \qquad (14\text{-}89)$$

This is to be compared with the magnetic induction **B** due to a short current element $I\,\mathbf{dl}$ flowing in a conducting wire, as found in Eq. *5-9:*

$$\mathbf{B} = \frac{\mu_0 I\,\mathbf{dl}\times\mathbf{r}_1}{4\pi r^2}. \qquad (14\text{-}90)$$

It will be seen that the two expressions agree if we assume that a charge Q moving with a velocity **u** is equivalent to an element of current $I\,\mathbf{dl}$.

For $u \ll c$, and $\dot{\mathbf{u}}$ along **u**,

$$\mathbf{E} = \frac{Q}{4\pi\epsilon_0 r^2}\left(\mathbf{i} + \frac{r\dot{u}}{c^2}\sin\theta\,\mathbf{j}\right), \qquad (14\text{-}91)$$

since

$$[\dot{\mathbf{u}}] = [\dot{u}](\cos[\theta]\,[\mathbf{i}] - \sin[\theta]\,[\mathbf{j}]). \qquad (14\text{-}92)$$

As usual, we use spherical polar coordinates with the origin at the position of the moving charge, as in Figure 14-4. We have not used brackets in Eq. *14-91* because, in this case, the position of the charge changes little in the time that the signal takes to travel the distance r. The first term is that given by Coulomb's law. The second is a radiation term which varies as $1/r$ and as $\sin \theta$, and which is along $\mathbf{j}$, as in the case of the electric field intensity for an electric dipole, Eq. *13-81*. Moreover, for a charge oscillating at a circular frequency ω, $\dot{u}$ is proportional to ω^2, and $\omega^2/c^2 = 1/\lambda^2$. This radiation term therefore agrees with that for the electric dipole.

It will be shown in Problem 14-3 that the Poynting vector $\mathbf{S} = \mathbf{E} \times \mathbf{H}$ is zero and that the radiated energy is therefore zero when the acceleration $\dot{u}$ is zero. *A moving charge therefore radiates energy only when it is accelerated.*

Upon examination of the various terms within the braces in Eqs. *14-86* and *14-87* for $\mathbf{E}$ and for $\mathbf{H}$, it will be observed that the radiation terms, that is, those which involve the acceleration $\dot{u}$, vary as $1/r$, whereas the others which involve only the velocity $\mathbf{u}$ vary as $1/r^2$.

14.3.4. The E and H Vectors for an Accelerated Charge Moving Along a Straight Line.
Let us consider the *radiation field*, that is, the part of the field

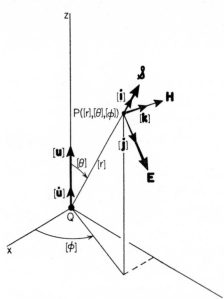

Figure 14-4. *A charge Q moves in a straight line with a velocity* [u] *at the time* $t - [r]/c$. *The field is observed at P* ([r], [θ], [φ]). *The angular distributions of* **E** *or of* **H** *are shown in Figure 14-5, for various values of the ratio* u/c.

that involves $\dot{u}$, for the case where $\dot{u}$ is along $\mathbf{u}$. The charge is then accelerated along a straight line. As usual, we choose moving spherical coordinates with the origin at the position of the charge and with the polar axis along the velocity $\mathbf{u}$, as in Figure 14-4. It is *not* assumed that $u \ll c$. Then

$$\mathbf{E}_{\text{rad}} = \frac{\mu_0 Q([\dot{u}] \cos [\theta] [\mathbf{i}] - [\dot{u}])}{4\pi[r] \left(1 - \dfrac{[u] \cos [\theta]}{c}\right)^3},$$

$$(14\text{-}93)$$

or, using Eq. *14-92*, we have

$$\mathbf{E}_{\text{rad}} = \frac{\mu_0 Q[\dot{u}] \sin [\theta]}{4\pi[r] \left(1 - \dfrac{[u] \cos [\theta]}{c}\right)^3} [\mathbf{j}],$$

$$(14\text{-}94)$$

$$\mathbf{H}_{\text{rad}} = \frac{Q[\dot{u}] \sin [\theta]}{4\pi c[r] \left(1 - \dfrac{[u] \cos [\theta]}{c}\right)^3} [\mathbf{k}].$$

$$(14\text{-}95)$$

The vectors $\mathbf{E}$ and $\mathbf{H}$ are shown in Figure 14-4. They are orthogonal, and

$$\frac{E}{H} = \left(\frac{\mu_0}{\epsilon_0}\right)^{1/2} = 377 \text{ ohms,} \qquad (14\text{-}96)$$

as for a plane wave in free space (Eq. *9-28*).

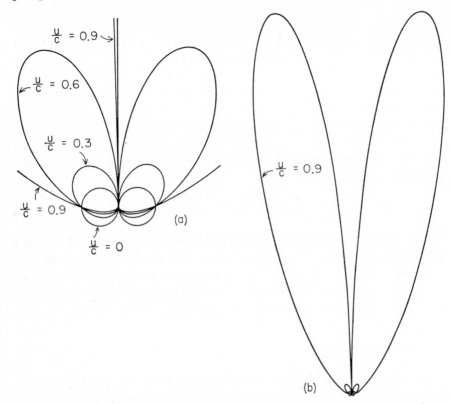

Figure 14-5. *Polar diagrams, on two different scales of* $\mathbf{E}_{rad}$ *or of* $\mathbf{H}_{rad}$ *for a charge accelerated in the direction of its velocity* **u**. *Part b is plotted on a scale fifteen times smaller than part a. The magnitude of* $\mathbf{E}_{rad}$ *or of* $\mathbf{H}_{rad}$ *calculated from Eqs. 14-94 or 14-95 is plotted here as a function of* $[\theta]$ *for various values of the ratio u/c. In both (a) and (b) the velocity and the acceleration point upward. For low velocities u, such as those of the electrons in a conductor, the radiation field is symmetrical about the equator* $[\theta] = \pi/2$. *For higher velocities, the field shifts in the forward direction. There is zero field both forward and backward along the trajectory.*

Figure 14-5 shows how the magnitude of **E** or of **H** depends on $[\theta]$ for various values of u/c. It will be observed that the electric field moves forward as the velocity increases. The *magnitude* of $\mathbf{E}_{rad}$ is proportional to the acceleration, whereas the *variation* of $\mathbf{E}_{rad}$ with the angle $[\theta]$ depends on the velocity. It must be remembered that the angular dependence we are concerned with here is that which is "seen" by a fixed observer with respect to which the charge has the velocity **u**.

The Poynting vector $\mathbf{S}$ is not zero, and the radiation field carries away energy in the radial direction: from Problem 14-3,

$$\mathbf{S} = \mathbf{E} \times \mathbf{H} = \mathbf{E}_{rad} \times \mathbf{H}_{rad}, \qquad (14\text{-}97)$$

and

$$S = \frac{\mu_0}{16\pi^2 c} \frac{Q^2 [\dot{u}]^2}{[r]^2} \frac{\sin^2 [\theta]}{\left(1 - \frac{[u] \cos [\theta]}{c}\right)^6} [\mathbf{i}] \qquad (\dot{u} \parallel u). \qquad (14\text{-}98)$$

This is again with respect to a system of coordinates with respect to which the charge Q has the velocity **u**.

It is interesting to compare this result with the value of **s** for an electric dipole, since in that case the acceleration $\dot{u}$ of the conduction electrons is along **u** if thermal agitation is neglected. We then have $u/c \ll 1$, and the above equation reduces to

$$S = \frac{\mu_0 Q^2 \dot{u}^2}{16\pi^2 c r^2} \sin^2 \theta \, \mathbf{i} \qquad (\dot{u} \parallel u, u \ll c). \qquad (14\text{-}99)$$

As in Eq. *14-91*, we have again omitted the brackets around r, θ, and **i** because the displacement $u(r/c)$ of the charge in the time r/c is negligible compared to r. Comparing this with Eq. *13-88*, we find that both expressions vary as $\sin^2 \theta / r^2$. For a charge vibrating with an angular frequency ω, $\dot{u}$ is proportional to ω^2, or to $1/\lambda^2$, and **s** varies as $1/\lambda^4$ in both cases.

14.4 Summary

The subject discussed in this chapter is the *electromagnetic field of a moving charge*. In the particular case of a charge moving with a constant velocity, in which the point of observation is on the trajectory, V and **A** are the same as for a fixed charge and for a fixed element of current, respectively. In the general case of a charge Q moving with a velocity **u**, we have the *Lienard-Wiechert* potentials

$$V = \frac{1}{4\pi\epsilon_0} \frac{Q}{[r] - \frac{[\mathbf{r}] \cdot [\mathbf{u}]}{c}} \qquad (14\text{-}34)$$

and

$$\mathbf{A} = \frac{\mu_0}{4\pi} \frac{Q[\mathbf{u}]}{[r] - \frac{[\mathbf{r}] \cdot [\mathbf{u}]}{c}}, \qquad (14\text{-}41)$$

where the vector **r** points *from* the charge *to* the point of observation.

The general expressions for **E** and for **H** are given in Eqs. *14-86* and *14-87*.

When the charge Q moves with a fixed velocity **u**, and for a point on the trajectory, the electric field intensity is given by the usual electrostatic formula for a fixed charge, multiplied by the factor $1 - (u/c)^2$, and $\mathbf{H} = 0$.

When the moving charge accelerates along a straight line, it radiates energy, and the Poynting vector is given by

$$S = \frac{\mu_0}{16\pi^2 c} \frac{Q^2 [\ddot{u}]^2}{[r]^2} \frac{\sin^2 [\theta]}{\left(1 - \dfrac{[u]}{c} \cos [\theta]\right)^6} [\mathbf{i}].$$ (14-98)

This agrees with the value of S for the radiation from a short electric dipole, in which case $u/c \ll 1$.

Problems

14-1. A point charge Q moves with a constant velocity u in the positive direction along the z-axis, and its position z' is given by ut. Calculate $\partial \mathbf{A}/\partial t$ at the origin in various ways.

14-2. Show that, in the general case, the field of a moving charge is such that

$$\mu_0 c \mathbf{H} = [\mathbf{r}_1] \times \mathbf{E},$$

with the result that the $\mathbf{E}$ and $\mathbf{H}$ vectors for a moving charge are always orthogonal.

14-3. Calculate the Poynting vector S for the general case of a moving charge. Show that the terms of $\mathbf{E}$ and $\mathbf{H}$ which do not involve the acceleration $\dot{u}$ do not contribute to the radiated energy.

14-4. A charge Q moves at a constant velocity $\mathbf{u}$ along the z-axis, and its position z' is given by ut. Show that the electric field intensity $\mathbf{E}$ and the magnetic field intensity $\mathbf{H}$ are given by

$$\mathbf{E} = \frac{Q}{4\pi\epsilon_0} \frac{\rho \mathbf{i} - (z' - z)\mathbf{k}}{\left\{(z' - z)^2 + \rho^2 \left(1 - \dfrac{u^2}{c^2}\right)\right\}^{3/2}} \left(1 - \frac{u^2}{c^2}\right)$$

and

$$\mathbf{H} = \frac{Qu}{4\pi} \frac{\rho \mathbf{j}}{\left\{(z' - z)^2 + \rho^2 \left(1 - \dfrac{u^2}{c^2}\right)\right\}^{3/2}} \left(1 - \frac{u^2}{c^2}\right)$$

at a fixed point (ρ, φ, z) in cylindrical coordinates (see Problem 8-10).

Draw a polar plot of E as a function of the angle θ of spherical polar coordinates for $u = 0$, $u = 0.707c$, $u = c$.

Sketch lines of force around the charge to show the general characteristics of the field for the above values of u.

14-5. An ion beam carries a charge of λ coulombs per meter of length at a constant velocity $\mathbf{u}$. Using the results of the preceding problem, show that

$$\mathbf{E} = \frac{\lambda}{2\pi\epsilon_0 \rho} \mathbf{i}$$

and that

$$\mathbf{H} = \frac{I}{2\pi\rho} \mathbf{j}$$

in cylindrical coordinates, ρ being the distance between the beam and the point of observation.

APPENDIX A

NOTATION

A.1. *Space, Time, Mechanics*

Element of length or distance	dl, ds, dr	Time	t
		Period	$T = 1/f$
Total length or distance	l, L, s, r	Frequency	$f = 1/T$
		Angular frequency	$\omega = 2\pi f$
Element of area	da	Velocity	$\mathbf{u}, \mathbf{v}$
Total area	S	Acceleration	$\mathbf{a} = \partial\mathbf{u}/\partial t$
Element of volume	$d\tau$	Angular velocity	$\boldsymbol{\omega}$
Total volume	τ	Angular accelera-	
Solid angle	Ω	tion	$\boldsymbol{\alpha} = \partial\boldsymbol{\omega}/\partial t$
Normal to a surface	$\mathbf{n}$	Mass	m
Wave length	λ	Density	ρ
Wave length in free space	λ_0	Generalized coordinate	q
Wave length of a guided wave	λ_g	Momentum	$\mathbf{p}$
		Moment of inertia	I
Radian length	$\lambda = \lambda/2\pi = 1/k_r$	Force	$\mathbf{F}$
Wave number	$k = k_r - jk_i$	Torque	$\mathbf{M}$
Attenuation		Pressure	p
constant	k_i	Energy	W
Attenuation		Potential energy	QV, E_p
distance	$\delta = 1/k_i$	Kinetic energy	T, E_k

A.2. *Electricity and Magnetism*

Quantity of electricity	Q	Linear charge density	ν, λ
Velocity of light	$c = 2.998 \times 10^8$ meters/second	Electrostatic potential, scalar potential	V
Volume charge density	ρ		
Surface charge density	σ	Induced Electromotance, Voltage	$\mathcal{V}$

Electric field intensity	**E**	Magnetic flux	Φ
Electric displacement	**D**	Permeability of vacuum	$\mu_0 = 4\pi \times 10^{-7}$ henry/meter
Permittivity of vacuum	$\epsilon_0 = 8.854 \times 10^{-12}$ farad/meter	Relative permeability	K_m
Dielectric coefficient	K_e	Permeability	$K_m\mu_0 = \mu = B/H$
Permittivity	$K_e\epsilon_0 = \epsilon = D/E$	Magnetic dipole moment/volume	**M**
Q of a medium	Q	Magnetic susceptibility	χ_m
Electric dipole moment	**p**	Magnetic dipole moment	**m**
Electric dipole moment/volume	**P**	Volume magnetic pole density	ρ_m
Molecular polarizability	α	Surface magnetic pole density	σ_m
Electric susceptibility	χ_e	Resistance	R
Electric quadrupole moment	q	Reactance	X
Electric current	I	Capacitance	C
Volume current density	**J**	Self-inductance	L
		Mutual inductance	M
Surface current density	λ	Impedance	$Z = R + jX$
Avogadro's number	$N_A = 6.023 \times 10^{23}$/mole	Conductance	$G = R/Z^2$
		Susceptance	$B = -X/Z^2$
Molecular weight	M	Admittance	$Y = G + jB = 1/Z$
Boltzmann constant	$k = 1.380 \times 10^{-23}$ joule/°K	Resistivity	ρ
		Conductivity	σ
Electronic charge	$e = 1.602 \times 10^{-19}$ coulomb	Poynting vector	**S**
		Vector potential	**A**
Magnetic induction	**B**	Scalar magnetic potential	V_m
Magnetic field intensity	**H**	Reluctance	R

A.3. Mathematical Symbols

Approximately equal to	$\approx$	Real part of z	Re z
Proportional to	$\propto$	Imaginary part of z	Im z^*
Factorial n	$n!$	Modulus of z	$|z|$
Exponential of x	e^x, $\exp(x)$	Arc tangent x	arc tan x
Decadic log of x	$\log x$	Complex conjugate of z	z^*
Natural log of x	$\ln x$	Vector	**E**

Gradient	∇	Unit vector along **r**	$\mathbf{r}_1$
Divergence	$\nabla\cdot$	Field point	(x, y, z)
Curl	$\nabla\times$	Source point	(x', y', z')
Laplacian	∇^2	Average	$\bar{\mathbf{E}}$
Unit vectors for all systems	$\mathbf{i}, \mathbf{j}, \mathbf{k}$		

APPENDIX B

VECTOR DEFINITIONS,

IDENTITIES,

AND THEOREMS

B.1. *Definitions*

B.1.1. RECTANGULAR COORDINATES

$$\nabla f = \mathbf{i}\frac{\partial f}{\partial x} + \mathbf{j}\frac{\partial f}{\partial y} + \mathbf{k}\frac{\partial f}{\partial z}$$

$$\nabla \cdot \mathbf{A} = \frac{\partial A_x}{\partial x} + \frac{\partial A_y}{\partial y} + \frac{\partial A_z}{\partial z}$$

$$\nabla \times \mathbf{A} = \mathbf{i}\left(\frac{\partial A_z}{\partial y} - \frac{\partial A_y}{\partial z}\right) + \mathbf{j}\left(\frac{\partial A_x}{\partial z} - \frac{\partial A_z}{\partial x}\right) + \mathbf{k}\left(\frac{\partial A_y}{\partial x} - \frac{\partial A_x}{\partial y}\right)$$

$$\nabla^2 f = \frac{\partial^2 f}{\partial x^2} + \frac{\partial^2 f}{\partial y^2} + \frac{\partial^2 f}{\partial z^2}$$

$$\nabla^2 \mathbf{A} = \mathbf{i}\,\nabla^2 A_x + \mathbf{j}\,\nabla^2 A_y + \mathbf{k}\,\nabla^2 A_z$$

B.1.2. CYLINDRICAL COORDINATES

$$\nabla f = \mathbf{i}\frac{\partial f}{\partial \rho} + \mathbf{j}\frac{1}{\rho}\frac{\partial f}{\partial \phi} + \mathbf{k}\frac{\partial f}{\partial z}$$

$$\nabla \cdot \mathbf{A} = \frac{1}{\rho}\frac{\partial}{\partial \rho}(\rho A_\rho) + \frac{1}{\rho}\frac{\partial A_\phi}{\partial \phi} + \frac{\partial A_z}{\partial z}$$

$$\nabla \times \mathbf{A} = \mathbf{i}\left(\frac{1}{\rho}\frac{\partial A_z}{\partial \phi} - \frac{\partial A_\phi}{\partial z}\right) + \mathbf{j}\left(\frac{\partial A_\rho}{\partial z} - \frac{\partial A_z}{\partial \rho}\right) + \mathbf{k}\frac{1}{\rho}\left(\frac{\partial}{\partial \rho}(\rho A_\phi) - \frac{\partial A_\rho}{\partial \phi}\right)$$

$$\nabla^2 f = \frac{1}{\rho}\frac{\partial}{\partial \rho}\left(\rho\frac{\partial f}{\partial \rho}\right) + \frac{1}{\rho^2}\frac{\partial^2 f}{\partial \phi^2} + \frac{\partial^2 f}{\partial z^2}$$

B.1.3. SPHERICAL COORDINATES

$$\nabla f = \mathbf{i}\frac{\partial f}{\partial r} + \mathbf{j}\frac{1}{r}\frac{\partial f}{\partial \theta} + \mathbf{k}\frac{1}{r \sin \theta}\frac{\partial f}{\partial \phi}$$

$$\nabla \cdot \mathbf{A} = \frac{1}{r^2}\frac{\partial}{\partial r}(r^2 A_r) + \frac{1}{r \sin \theta}\frac{\partial}{\partial \theta}(A_\theta \sin \theta) + \frac{1}{r \sin \theta}\frac{\partial A_\phi}{\partial \phi}$$

$$\nabla \times \mathbf{A} = \mathbf{i} \frac{1}{r \sin \theta} \left[\frac{\partial}{\partial \theta} (A_\phi \sin \theta) - \frac{\partial A_\theta}{\partial \phi} \right]$$

$$+ \mathbf{j} \frac{1}{r} \left[\frac{1}{\sin \theta} \frac{\partial A_r}{\partial \phi} - \frac{\partial (r A_\phi)}{\partial r} \right] + \mathbf{k} \frac{1}{r} \left[\frac{\partial (r A_\theta)}{\partial r} - \frac{\partial A_r}{\partial \theta} \right]$$

$$\nabla^2 f = \frac{1}{r^2} \frac{\partial}{\partial r} \left(r^2 \frac{\partial f}{\partial r} \right) + \frac{1}{r^2 \sin \theta} \frac{\partial}{\partial \theta} \left(\sin \theta \frac{\partial f}{\partial \theta} \right) + \frac{1}{r^2 \sin^2 \theta} \frac{\partial^2 f}{\partial \phi^2}$$

B.2. *Identities*

$\nabla \cdot (f\mathbf{A}) = f(\nabla \cdot \mathbf{A}) + \mathbf{A} \cdot \nabla f$

$\nabla' \left(\frac{1}{r} \right) = \frac{\mathbf{r}_1}{r^2}$, where $\nabla' \left(\frac{1}{r} \right)$ is calculated at the source point (x', y', z') and $\mathbf{r}_1$ is the unit vector from the source point (x', y', z') to the field point (x, y, z).

$\nabla \left(\frac{1}{r} \right) = -\frac{\mathbf{r}_1}{r^2}$ when the gradient is calculated at the field point, with the same unit vector.

$\nabla \times f\mathbf{A} = f(\nabla \times \mathbf{A}) - \mathbf{A} \times \nabla f$

$\nabla \cdot (\mathbf{A} \times \mathbf{B}) = \mathbf{B} \cdot (\nabla \times \mathbf{A}) - \mathbf{A} \cdot (\nabla \times \mathbf{B})$

$\nabla \times \nabla \times \mathbf{A} = \nabla(\nabla \cdot \mathbf{A}) - \nabla^2 \mathbf{A}$ (see Section 1.8.6).

$$(\mathbf{A} \cdot \nabla)\mathbf{B} = \mathbf{i} \left[A_x \frac{\partial B_x}{\partial x} + A_y \frac{\partial B_x}{\partial y} + A_z \frac{\partial B_x}{\partial z} \right] + \mathbf{j} \left[A_x \frac{\partial B_y}{\partial x} + A_y \frac{\partial B_y}{\partial y} + A_z \frac{\partial B_y}{\partial z} \right]$$

$$+ \mathbf{k} \left[A_x \frac{\partial B_z}{\partial x} + A_y \frac{\partial B_z}{\partial y} + A_z \frac{\partial B_z}{\partial z} \right]$$

B.3. *Theorems*

Divergence theorem: $\int_S \mathbf{A} \cdot \mathbf{da} = \int_\tau \nabla \cdot \mathbf{A} \, d\tau$,

where S is the surface which bounds the volume τ.

Stoke's theorem: $\int_C \mathbf{A} \cdot \mathbf{dl} = \int_S (\nabla \times \mathbf{A}) \cdot \mathbf{da}$,

where C is the closed curve which bounds the surface S.

$\int_\tau (\nabla \times \mathbf{A}) \, d\tau = \int_S \mathbf{A} \times \mathbf{da}$,

where S is the surface which bounds the volume τ.

APPENDIX C

CONVERSION TABLE

(c = 3 × 10⁸ meters/second)

Examples: One meter equals 100 centimeters. One volt equals 10^8 electromagnetic units of potential.

M.K.S. SYSTEM		C.G.S. SYSTEM	
		esu	emu
Length	meter	10^2 centimeters	10^2 centimeters
Mass	kilogram	10^3 grams	10^3 grams
Time	second	1 second	1 second
Force	newton	10^5 dynes	10^5 dynes
Energy	joule	10^7 ergs	10^7 ergs
Power	watt	10^7 ergs/second	10^7 ergs/second
Charge	coulomb	3×10^9	10^{-1}
Electric potential	volt	$1/300$	10^8
Electric field intensity	volt/meter	$1/(3 \times 10^4)$	10^6
Displacement	coulomb/meter²	$12\pi \times 10^5$	$4\pi \times 10^{-5}$
Displacement flux	coulomb	$12\pi \times 10^9$	$4\pi \times 10^{-1}$
Polarization	coulomb/meter²	3×10^5	10^{-5}
Current	ampere	3×10^9	10^{-1}
Conductivity	mho/meter	9×10^9	10^{-11}
Resistance	ohm	$1/(9 \times 10^{11})$	10^9
Capacitance	farad	9×10^{11}	10^{-9}
Magnetic pole strength	weber	$1/(12\pi \times 10^2)$	$10^8/4\pi$
Magnetic flux	weber	$1/300$	10^8 maxwells
Magnetic induction	weber/meter²	$1/(3 \times 10^6)$	10^4 gausses
Magnetic field intensity	ampere/meter	$12\pi \times 10^7$	$4\pi \times 10^{-3}$ oersted
Magnetomotance	ampere	$12\pi \times 10^9$	$4\pi/10$ gilberts
Magnetic polarization	ampere/meter	$1/(3 \times 10^{13})$	10^{-3}
Inductance	henry	$1/(9 \times 10^{11})$	10^9
Reluctance	ampere/weber	$36\pi \times 10^{11}$	$4\pi \times 10^{-9}$

APPENDIX D

THE COMPLEX

POTENTIAL

The complex potential provides, as we shall see, a powerful means for determining electrostatic fields. It is restricted, however, to two-dimensions, that is, to fields which are essentially constant in one direction. End-effects due to the finite length of the conductors in this particular direction are assumed to be negligible in the region considered. The method also assumes zero space charge density.

Similar methods of calculation are used in other fields of physics in the study of quantities which satisfy Laplace's equation. One important example is the field of hydrodynamics.

D.1. *Functions of the Complex Variable*

Let us first consider the complex variable

$$z = x + jy, \qquad (D\text{-}1)$$

where x and y are real numbers and where $j = (-1)^{1/2}$. This quantity can be represented by a point in the complex plane with x as abscissa and jy as ordinate, as in

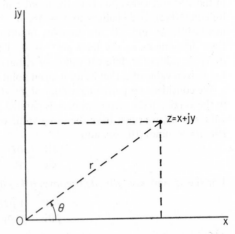

Figure D-1

Point $z = x + jy$ in the complex plane. The quantity r is called the modulus, and θ the argument, of the complex number z.

Figure D-1. This z must not be confused with the z-coordinate of Cartesian or cylindrical coordinates.

We can have functions $W(z)$ such as z^2, or $1/z$, or $\ln z$, and so on, and

$$W(z) = U(x, y) + jV(x, y) \tag{D-2}$$

with a real part U and an imaginary part jV, U and V being both *real* functions of x and of y. For example,

$$z^2 = (x + jy)^2 = (x^2 - y^2) + 2jxy, \tag{D-3}$$

in which

$$U = x^2 - y^2 \quad \text{and} \quad V = 2xy. \tag{D-4}$$

The function $W(z) = U + jV$ can be represented as a point on another complex plane with U as abscissa and jV as ordinate. We then speak of the z-plane and of the W-plane.

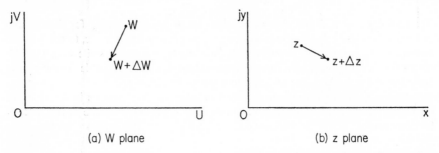

(a) W plane   (b) z plane

Figure D-2. *The function $W(z) = U(x, y) + jV(x, y)$ shown in the W-plane. When z changes to $z + \Delta z$, W changes to $W + \Delta W$, and the ratio $\Delta W/\Delta z$ is equal to dW/dz for $\Delta z \to 0$.*

We shall consider functions $W(z)$ such that the derivative dW/dz exists in the region considered. This condition leads to an important pair of equations. First, let us examine the meaning of the derivative dW/dz by considering Figure D-2. The point W in the W-plane corresponds to the point z in the z-plane, according to some specified function $W(z)$. If z changes to $z + \Delta z$, W changes similarly to $W + \Delta W$, where the increments Δz and ΔW are complex numbers. The derivative dW/dz is the ratio of these increments at the limit $\Delta z \longrightarrow 0$. The value of this derivative can take on different values for different values of z, but we wish to have a single value of dW/dz for a given value of z, that is, for a given point in the z-plane, *no matter how dz is chosen*.

We consider two particular values of dz: dx and $j\,dy$. In the first case, dz is parallel to the x-axis; in the second case, dz is parallel to the jy-axis. For both of these particular values of dz, we must have the same value of dW/dz. For the first case, the value of dW/dz becomes $\partial W/\partial x$, and

$$\frac{\partial W}{\partial x} = \frac{\partial U}{\partial x} + j\frac{\partial V}{\partial x}. \tag{D-5}$$

For the second case, dW/dz becomes $\partial W/j\,\partial y$, and

$$\frac{\partial W}{j\,\partial y} = \frac{1}{j}\frac{\partial U}{\partial y} + \frac{\partial V}{\partial y}. \tag{D-6}$$

These two expressions must be equal:

$$\frac{\partial U}{\partial x} + j\frac{\partial V}{\partial x} = \frac{1}{j}\frac{\partial U}{\partial y} + \frac{\partial V}{\partial y}. \tag{D-7}$$

Then

$$\frac{\partial U}{\partial x} = \frac{\partial V}{\partial v} \quad \text{and} \quad \frac{\partial U}{\partial y} = -\frac{\partial V}{\partial x}. \qquad (D\text{-}8)$$

These are the *Cauchy-Riemann equations*. The functions U and V are related to each other through these equations and are called *conjugate functions*.

A function $W(z)$ is said to be *analytic* if its four partial derivatives exist and are continuous throughout the region considered and, moreover, if they satisfy the Cauchy-Riemann equations.

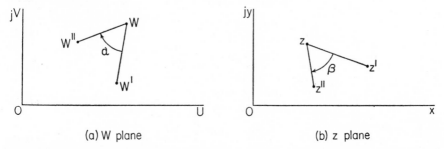

(a) W plane   (b) z plane

Figure D-3. *The three points W, W', and W" correspond, respectively, to z, z', and z". The angles α and β are equal when $z' \to z$ and $z'' \to z$, as long as dW/dz exists and is not zero.*

D.2. *Conformal Transformations*

Consider now a point z and two neighboring points z' and z'' in the z-plane. These three points correspond to three other points in the W-plane: the point W and the neighboring points W' and W'', as in Figure D-3. Since dW/dz is unique at the point z, then

$$\frac{dW}{dz} = \lim_{z' \to z} \frac{W' - W}{z' - z} = \lim_{z'' \to z} \frac{W'' - W}{z'' - z}. \qquad (D\text{-}9)$$

If $dW/dz \neq 0$, it can be written in the form $Ae^{i\phi}$. (The argument ϕ has no meaning if $dW/dz = 0$.) Then, at the limits $z' \longrightarrow z$ and $z'' \longrightarrow z$, considering only the arguments of the various complex quantities, we have

$$\arg(W' - W) = \arg(z' - z) + \phi, \qquad (D\text{-}10)$$
$$\arg(W'' - W) = \arg(z'' - z) + \phi, \qquad (D\text{-}11)$$
$$\arg(W' - W) - \arg(W'' - W) = \arg(z' - z) - \arg(z'' - z), \qquad (D\text{-}12)$$

or

$$\alpha = \beta, \qquad (D\text{-}13)$$

where the angles α and β are as in Figure D-3. This result does not apply to points where $dW/dz = 0$.

The angle between two infinitesimal line segments is therefore conserved in passing from the z- to the W-plane, as long as the derivative dW/dz exists and is not zero. For example, the two families of straight lines represented by $U = $ constant and $V = $ constant in the W-plane are clearly orthogonal. Then, the corresponding curves $U = $ constant and $V = $ constant in the z-plane are also orthogonal.

Since there is a one-to-one correspondence between the points in the z-plane and those in the W-plane, we can imagine the W-plane to be distorted into the z-plane according to the function $W(z)$. Then a geometrical figure in the W-plane is "mapped" into a corresponding figure in the z-plane, and inversely. This process is called a *conformal transformation*.

D.3. *The Function $W(z)$ as a Complex Potential*

We have

$$\frac{\partial W}{\partial x} = \frac{dW}{dz}\frac{\partial z}{\partial x} = \frac{dW}{dz}, \tag{D-14}$$

$$\frac{\partial^2 W}{\partial x^2} = \frac{d^2 W}{dz^2}, \tag{D-15}$$

$$\frac{\partial W}{\partial y} = \frac{dW}{dz}\frac{\partial z}{\partial y} = j\frac{dW}{dz}, \tag{D-16}$$

$$\frac{\partial^2 W}{\partial y^2} = -\frac{d^2 W}{dz^2}, \tag{D-17}$$

and

$$\frac{\partial^2 W}{\partial x^2} + \frac{\partial^2 W}{\partial y^2} = 0. \tag{D-18}$$

The function $W(z)$ is thus a solution of Laplace's equation in two dimensions. Separating real and imaginary quantities, we find that

$$\frac{\partial^2 U}{\partial x^2} + \frac{\partial^2 U}{\partial y^2} = 0 \quad \text{and} \quad \frac{\partial^2 V}{\partial x^2} + \frac{\partial^2 V}{\partial y^2} = 0. \tag{D-19}$$

Thus both U and V independently satisfy Laplace's equation, and either one can be set to be the electrostatic potential which also satisfies Laplace's equation, since we have assumed zero space charge density.

If the imaginary part of W is taken to be the electrostatic potential, then the equipotentials are given by $V =$ constant. Since the $U =$ constant curves are orthogonal to the equipotentials, as we have seen above, they therefore define the lines of force, from Section 2.3. The function V is then called the *potential function*, U is called the *stream function*, and W is called the *complex potential function*. It is shown in Problem D-2 that the electrostatic field intensity E is given by

$$E = \left|\frac{dW}{dz}\right| \tag{D-20}$$

at any point in the field.

A two-dimensional electrostatic field with zero space charge density is therefore completely determined once the complex potential function $W(z)$ is known.

It is essential to recall here the uniqueness theorem derived earlier in Section 4.2, according to which there is only one field configuration which satisfies given boundary conditions. Thus, if in one way or another we can find a satisfactory function $W(z)$, then that function is the proper one and the only one.

The determination of $W(z)$ is usually intuitive and empirical. However, much work has been done in this connection, and it is usually possible to determine the proper function for simple geometries.[*] One can usually arrive at $W(z)$ by using some function of the complex potential for some other known field.

---

[*] See, for example, E. Durand, *Electrostatique et magnétostatique.* (Masson et Cie, Paris, 1953) and E. Kober, *Dictionary of Conformal Representations* (Dover, New York, 1952).

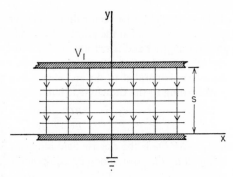

Figure D-4

A parallel-plate capacitor with its lower plate grounded and its upper plate at potential V_1. End effects are neglected. The horizontal lines are equipotentials $V = (V_1/s)y = $ constant; the vertical lines are lines of force $U = (V_1/s)x = $ constant.

As an illustration, let us consider the field inside an infinite parallel-plate capacitor as in Figure D-4. The equipotentials and the lines of force are given respectively by $y = $ constant and $x = $ constant.

Setting V to be the electrostatic potential,

$$V = \frac{V_1}{s} y. \tag{D-21}$$

This suggests that the function $W(z)$ must be

$$W(z) = U + jV = \frac{V_1}{s}(x + jy) = \frac{V_1}{s} z. \tag{D-22}$$

Thus,

$$U = \frac{V_1}{s} x. \tag{D-23}$$

We could also have determined the stream function U through the **Cauchy-Riemann** equations.

D.4. *The Stream Function*

We have seen above that the stream function is a constant along a line of force. We shall now see that it is quantitatively just as important as the potential function. We shall assume, as in Section D.3, that V is the potential function.

Figure D-5 shows three equipotentials and three lines of force in a portion of an

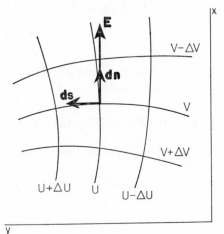

Figure D-5

A set of lines of force and a set of equipotentials in a portion of an electrostatic field. The elementary vectors **dn** *and* **ds** *are directed respectively, along the line of force and along the equipotential at the point considered. The vector* **dn** *points in the direction of* **E**, *and the vector* **ds** *points to the left when one looks along* **dn**. *For convenience, the axes are chosen to be parallel to these vectors as shown.*

electrostatic field. The vector **dn** is an element of length along the line of force normal to the equipotential at the point considered. The vector **ds** is an element of length along an equipotential and is oriented with respect to **dn** such that it points to the *left* when viewed along **dn**. For convenience, we choose our x- and jy-axes as shown, such that the x-axis is parallel to **dn** and the jy axis is parallel to **ds** at the point considered.

According to the Cauchy-Riemann equations,

$$\frac{\partial U}{\partial s} = \frac{\partial U}{\partial y} = -\frac{\partial V}{\partial x} = -\frac{\partial V}{\partial n}. \qquad (D\text{-}24)$$

Since $-\partial V/\partial n$ is the electric field intensity **E** at the point, the positive direction for **E** being along **dn**, then, along an equipotential,

$$dU = E\,ds. \qquad (D\text{-}25)$$

This relation is valid for any point in the field as long as V is chosen to be the potential function, and **E** and **ds** are oriented as in Figure D-5.

The stream function is thus related to $E\,ds$. This quantity $E\,ds$ is the flux of **E** crossing the equipotential in the direction of **dn** through an element of area on the equipotential surface which is ds wide and whose height, measured in the direction perpendicular to the paper, is the unit of length, namely, one meter. Integrating Eq. D-25 along an equipotential between the lines of force U_1 and U_2, we obtain

$$U_2 - U_1 = \int_{U_1}^{U_2} \frac{dU}{ds}\,ds = \int_{U_1}^{U_2} E\,ds. \qquad (D\text{-}26)$$

The line of force for which the stream function is zero is chosen arbitrarily, just as for the equipotential on which the potential is zero. Thus the charge density σ at the surface of a conductor is

$$\sigma = \epsilon_0 E = \epsilon_0 \frac{dU}{ds}, \qquad (D\text{-}27)$$

where the vector **ds** points toward the *left* when one looks toward the *outside* of the conductor into the field.

The total charge Q per unit length on a cylindrical conductor whose axis is perpendicular to the paper is obtained by integrating $\sigma\,ds$ around the periphery of the conductor in the direction of increasing ds:

$$Q = \oint \sigma\,ds = \epsilon_0 \oint dU. \qquad (D\text{-}28)$$

The stream function is thus useful for determining surface charge densities and total charges on conductors.

D.5. *The Parallel-plate Capacitor*

Let us return to the parallel-plate capacitor of Figure D-4, for which we found the complex potential function $W(z)$ in Eq. D-22. The charge density on the lower plate is obtained from Eq. D-22 with the vector **ds** pointing toward the *left* when one looks toward the outside of the conductor into the field:

$$\sigma_{\text{lower}} = \epsilon_0 \frac{dU}{ds} = -\epsilon_0 \frac{dU}{dx} = -\epsilon_0 \frac{V_1}{s}, \qquad (D\text{-}29)$$

Similarly, the charge density on the upper plate is found to be $+\epsilon_0(V_1/s)$. Both of these charge densities can be verified to be correct by using Gauss's law.

The capacitance C' per unit area is

$$C' = \frac{\sigma}{V_1} = \frac{\epsilon_0}{s},\qquad (D\text{-}30)$$

and

$$E = \left|\frac{dW}{dz}\right| = \frac{V_1}{s},\qquad (D\text{-}31)$$

as expected.

We have thus verified our method of calculation by applying it to a well-known field.

D.6. *The Cylindrical Capacitor*

In the case of the cylindrical capacitor, as in Figure D-6, the equipotentials are concentric circles, whereas the lines of force are radial straight lines.

We find empirically the following complex potential function, which is justified below:

$$W(z) = \frac{jV_1}{\ln\frac{r_2}{r_1}}\ln\frac{z}{r_1},\qquad (D\text{-}32)$$

or, writing

$$z = re^{j\theta},\qquad (D\text{-}33)$$

we obtain

$$W(z) = \frac{jV_1}{\ln\frac{r_2}{r_1}}\left(\ln\frac{r}{r_1} + j\theta\right),\qquad (D\text{-}34)$$

$$= -\frac{V_1}{\ln\frac{r_2}{r_1}}\theta + j\frac{V_1}{\ln\frac{r_2}{r_1}}\ln\frac{r}{r_1}.\qquad (D\text{-}35)$$

Thus

$$U = -\frac{V_1}{\ln\frac{r_2}{r_1}}\theta,\qquad (D\text{-}36)$$

and

$$V = \frac{V_1}{\ln\frac{r_2}{r_1}}\ln\frac{r}{r_1}.\qquad (D\text{-}37)$$

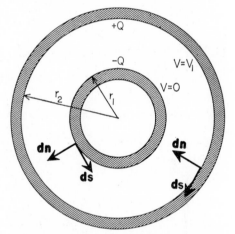

Figure D-6. *A section through a cylindrical capacitor of internal radii r_1 and r_2. The inner cylinder is grounded, and the outer one is at a potential V_1, the charges being, respectively, $-Q$ and $+Q$.*

The above expression for $W(z)$ is justified as follows: (a) the logarithm serves to give equipotentials and lines of force of the required form $r = $ constant and $\theta = $ constant when the real and imaginary parts of $W(z)$ are set equal to constants; (b) the factor j serves to make V the potential; (c) the ratio z/r_1 makes V equal to zero at $r = r_1$; (d) finally, the factor $V_1/\ln(r_2/r_1)$ serves to make the potential equal to V_1 at $r = r_2$.

Let us find the charge on the inner cylinder. To do this we must integrate the stream function U in the direction of ds or of increasing θ between $-\pi$ and $+\pi$, as in Figure D-6. Then

$$Q_{inner} = -\frac{2\pi\epsilon_0}{\ln\frac{r_2}{r_1}}V_1.\qquad (D\text{-}38)$$

The charge on the outer cylinder is found by integrating U in the direction of decreasing θ, and $Q_{outer} = -Q_{inner}$, as expected.

The capacitance C' per unit length normal to the paper is given by

$$C' = \left|\frac{Q}{V_1}\right| = \frac{2\pi\epsilon_0}{\ln\frac{r_2}{r_1}},\qquad (D\text{-}39)$$

which is correct, and E is also given correctly by

$$E = \left|\frac{dw}{dz}\right| = \left|\frac{V_1}{\ln\frac{r_2}{r_1}}\frac{1}{z}\right|,\qquad (D\text{-}40)$$

$$= \frac{V_1}{r\ln\frac{r_2}{r_1}}.\qquad (D\text{-}41)$$

D.7. *Field Due to Two Parallel Line Charges of Opposite Polarity*

As an example of the use of the complex potential for determining electrostatic fields, we consider the field due to two parallel line charges of Q coulombs/meter and of opposite polarity, as in Figure D-7 The line charges shown at $-a$ and at $+a$ are presumed to be infinitely long in the direction perpendicular to the paper.

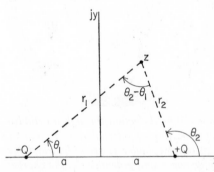

The potential V at any point due to this charge distribution can be found by integration, as in Problem 2-21:

$$V = \frac{Q}{2\pi\epsilon_0}\ln\frac{r_1}{r_2},\qquad (D\text{-}42)$$

where Q is the charge per unit length perpendicular to the paper, and r_1 and r_2 are as in Figure D-7. This equation shows that $V \longrightarrow +\infty$ at $r_2 = 0$, $V \longrightarrow -\infty$ at $r_1 = 0$, and $V = 0$ at $r_1 = r_2$, which is correct. Also, for a given value of r_1, V varies as the logarithm of r_2 and, similarly, for a given value of r_2, V varies as the logarithm of r_1, which is also correct.

Figure D-7. *Line charges of $-Q$ and $+Q$ coulombs/meter are situated, respectively, at $x = -a$ and $x = +a$.*

We can also rewrite V as follows:

$$V = \frac{Q}{2\pi\epsilon_0}\ln\left|\frac{z+a}{z-a}\right|.\qquad (D\text{-}43)$$

This suggests

$$W(z) = j\frac{Q}{2\pi\epsilon_0}\ln\frac{z+a}{z-a}, \qquad (D\text{-}44)$$

$$= j\frac{Q}{2\pi\epsilon_0}\ln\left(\left|\frac{z+a}{z-a}\right|\frac{e^{j\theta_1}}{e^{j\theta_2}}\right), \qquad (D\text{-}45)$$

$$= j\frac{Q}{2\pi\epsilon_0}\left[\ln\left|\frac{z+a}{z-a}\right| + j(\theta_1 - \theta_2)\right], \qquad (D\text{-}46)$$

and

$$U = \frac{Q}{2\pi\epsilon_0}(\theta_2 - \theta_1), \qquad (D\text{-}47)$$

$$V = \frac{Q}{2\pi\epsilon_0}\ln\left|\frac{z+a}{z-a}\right| = \frac{Q}{2\pi\epsilon_0}\ln\frac{r_1}{r_2}. \qquad (D\text{-}48)$$

The lines of force are given by the equation $\theta_2 - \theta_1 = $ constant. They are thus arcs of circles passing through the line charges and centered on the jy-axis, both above and below the x-axis.

The equipotential V is determined by the equation

$$\frac{r_1}{r_2} = \exp\left(2\pi\epsilon_0 V/Q\right). \qquad (D\text{-}49)$$

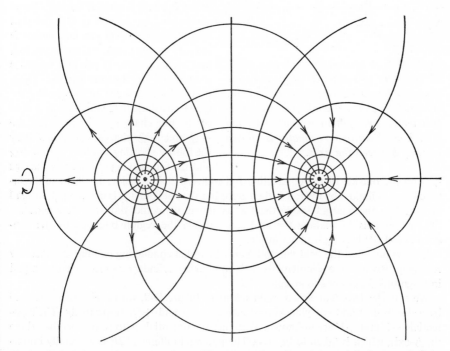

Figure D-8. *Lines of force (indicated by arrows) and equipotentials for two infinite line charges perpendicular to the paper. All the curves are circles. The equipotential surfaces are generated, as usual, by rotating the figure about the axis identified by the curved arrow.*

It is shown in Problem D-3 that this equipotential is a cylinder whose radius is $|a \operatorname{csch}(2\pi\epsilon_0 V/Q)|$ and whose axis is situated at $x = |a \coth 2\pi\epsilon_0 V/Q|$. For $V \longrightarrow +\infty$, the equipotential surface reduces to a line perpendicular to the paper and situated at $x = a$, as expected. Similarly, for $V \longrightarrow -\infty$, we have a line at $x = -a$.

The equipotentials and lines of force are shown in Figure D-8.

D.8. *Field Due to Two Parallel Conducting Circular Cylinders of Opposite Polarity*

The field investigated above was shown to have equipotentials in the form of circular cylinders whose axes are all parallel. We can place an *uncharged* conducting foil on any of these equipotentials without disturbing the field in any way. When we do this, charges migrate inside the conducting foil so as to cancel the electrostatic field within it, and charges of opposite polarity appear on the two surfaces. In this way, the field remains everywhere exactly as it was, except for the conducting region inside the foil, where the field is zero. If the line charge surrounded by the foil is $+Q$ per unit length, a charge $-Q$ per unit length is induced on the inside surface of the foil, and a charge of $+Q$ per unit length is induced on the outside surface. These induced charges are of course due to the electrostatic field and are due to *both* of the line charges. We can cancel the $+Q$ and $-Q$ charges surrounded by the foil by shorting the line charge $+Q$ and the foil, leaving us with a net charge

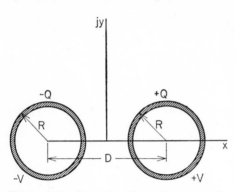

Figure D-9. *A section through two parallel cylinders of radius R whose axes are separated by a distance D and which carry charges −Q and +Q coulombs/meter, respectively. The potentials are −V and +V. The origin of coordinates is chosen midway between the axes.*

$+Q$ on the outside of the conducting foil and zero charge inside. The field in the internal region limited by the foil is then zero, but the field outside is unchanged. Instead of canceling the charges inside the foil as above, we could similarly have canceled the charges outside, making the field zero outside the region bounded by the conducting foil but leaving it intact inside.

We can now find the field due to a pair of parallel conducting circular cylinders by replacing two of the equipotentials with conducting cylinders carrying charges equal in magnitude but opposite in sign.

We consider two cylinders of radius R as in Figure D-9, with their axes separated by a distance D and carrying known charges $-Q$ and $+Q$, respectively. Their potentials $-V$ and $+V$ are unknown. These are the potentials with respect to that along the jy-axis, which is taken to be zero. The potential difference $2V$ is especially important, since it is required for the calculation of the capacitance per unit length of the system.

The function $W(z)$ for the pair of cylinders is the same as in Eq. *D-44*, except for the fact that now the quantity a is an unknown, such that

$$R = a \operatorname{csch}\left(\frac{2\pi\epsilon_0 V}{Q}\right), \qquad (D\text{-}50)$$

and

$$\frac{D}{2} = a \coth\left(\frac{2\pi\epsilon_0 V}{Q}\right). \qquad (D\text{-}51)$$

Since

$$\coth^2 x - \operatorname{csch}^2 x = 1, \qquad (D\text{-}52)$$

we have

$$a = \left[\left(\frac{D}{2}\right)^2 - R^2\right]^{1/2}. \qquad (D\text{-}53)$$

Substituting this value of a in Eq. *D-50* for R, recalling that the capacitance per meter $C' = Q/2V$, we find that

$$C' = \frac{\pi\epsilon_0}{\sinh^{-1}\left(\frac{D^2}{4R^2} - 1\right)^{1/2}}, \qquad (D\text{-}54)$$

$$= \frac{\pi\epsilon_0}{\cosh^{-1}(D/2R)}. \qquad (D\text{-}55)$$

It will be observed that the capacitance per meter C' depends only on the ratio D/R, and not on the actual dimensions, just as in the case of the cylindrical capacitor. When $D = 4R$, $C' = 21.2$ micromicrofarads/meter.

Problems

D-1. Two cylinders of length l and radius a have their axes parallel and separated by a distance D in a liquid with a dielectric coefficient K_e. A potential difference V is applied between the cylinders. Calculate the force of attraction for the case in which $l = 1.00$ meter, $a = 0.500$ centimeter, $D = 2.50$ centimeters, $K_e = 2.6$, and $V = 1.00 \times 10^4$ volts. Neglect end effects.

D-2. Show that the electric field intensity E for a two-dimensional field in the xy-plane is given by

$$E = \left|\frac{dW}{dz}\right|,$$

where W is the complex potential and $z = x + jy$.

D-3. Show that the equipotentials defined by Eq. *D-49* are circular cylinders given by

$$\left[x - a \coth\left(\frac{2\pi\epsilon_0 V}{Q}\right)\right]^2 + y^2 = a^2 \operatorname{csch}^2\left(\frac{2\pi\epsilon_0 V}{Q}\right).$$

D-4. Consider an unknown two-dimensional field due to two charged conductors A' and B' in the complex z'-plane, and a known two-dimensional field due to the charged conductors A and B in the z-plane. Points in the z'-plane are related to those in the z-plane according to the transformation $z' = z'(z)$, and the corresponding potentials are equal: $V_A = V_{A'}$ and $V_B = V_{B'}$.

Show that there is conservation of charge under this transformation and that there is, in consequence, conservation of capacitance.

APPENDIX E

INDUCED

ELECTROMOTANCE

IN MOVING SYSTEMS*

So as to explore further the meaning of Eq. *6-45,*

$$\mathbf{\nabla} \times \mathbf{E} = -\frac{\partial \mathbf{B}}{\partial t} + \mathbf{\nabla} \times (\mathbf{u} \times \mathbf{B}), \qquad (E\text{-}1)$$

in which the induced electric field intensity **E** is measured in one coordinate system and the magnetic induction **B** in another, let us consider the following experiments.

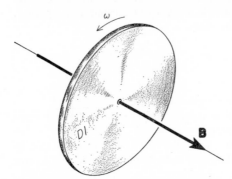

Figure E-1. *A circular, nonconducting, nonmagnetic disk rotating with angular velocity ω about an axis perpendicular to its plane and parallel to a uniform magnetic field* **B**.

Experiment 1

Figure E-1 shows a circular disk *D1* rotating with an angular velocity *ω* about an axis perpendicular to its plane and parallel to a uniform magnetic field **B**. The disk is assumed to be both nonconducting and nonmagnetic.

We now station two observers, one in the laboratory and one on the rotating disk, both equipped with a "curl-meter," a "B-meter," and a stop watch. The "curl-meter" consists of a small loop of wire capable of orientation in any direction and connected in series with a sensitive, infinite-impedance voltmeter. By definition, the component of $\mathbf{\nabla} \times \mathbf{E}$ normal to the plane containing the path of integration is

$$(\mathbf{\nabla} \times \mathbf{E})_n = \lim_{S \to 0} \frac{\oint \mathbf{E} \cdot d\mathbf{l}}{S}. \qquad (E\text{-}2)$$

The voltmeter reading divided by the area of the loop is thus the component of the curl in the direction of the normal to the loop, if the loop is small enough. The "B-meter" can be a cathode ray tube with the deflection of the electron beam on the tube face calibrated in webers/meter². The stop watch is used to measure the time rate

---

*This discussion closely parallels a published paper by D. R. Corson, *Am. J. Phys.*, **24,** 126 (1956).

of change of **B**. The observers know nothing about the magnetic field except what they measure with their own instruments.

The laboratory observer measures a uniform magnetic field: $\mathbf{B}_L = \mathbf{B}$. He determines its direction and magnitude by observing the deflection of his electron beam for at least two mutually perpendicular orientations. He also observes that, for each orientation, the beam deflection is time-independent, such that $\partial \mathbf{B}_L / \partial t = 0$. Furthermore, his "curl-meter" reads zero for all orientations, since there is no changing flux through the loop, and thus

$$\nabla \times \mathbf{E}_L = -\frac{\partial \mathbf{B}_L}{\partial t} = 0. \qquad (E\text{-}3)$$

When the disk observer points his electron beam in the plane of the disk, he always records the same deflection, no matter where he is on the disk. When he points it parallel to the axis of the disk, he always records zero deflection. He therefore concludes that the magnetic induction is uniform and perpendicular to his disk. His value $\mathbf{B}_{D1}$ is the same as that of the laboratory observer: $\mathbf{B}_{D1} = \mathbf{B}_L = \mathbf{B}$. The "curl-meter" on the disk sees only a constant flux, and

$$\nabla \times \mathbf{E}_{D1} = 0 \qquad (E\text{-}4)$$

everywhere on the disk. Thus, the disk observer finds

$$\nabla \times \mathbf{E}_{D1} = -\frac{\partial \mathbf{B}_{D1}}{\partial t} = 0. \qquad (E\text{-}5)$$

Now let us consider a second similar nonconducting and nonmagnetic disk $D2$ rotating with an angular velocity ω about an axis in the plane of the disk and perpendicular to the direction of **B**, as indicated in Figure E-2. An observer on this disk, if equipped with the same instruments as the other observers, will ascribe entirely different properties to the field.

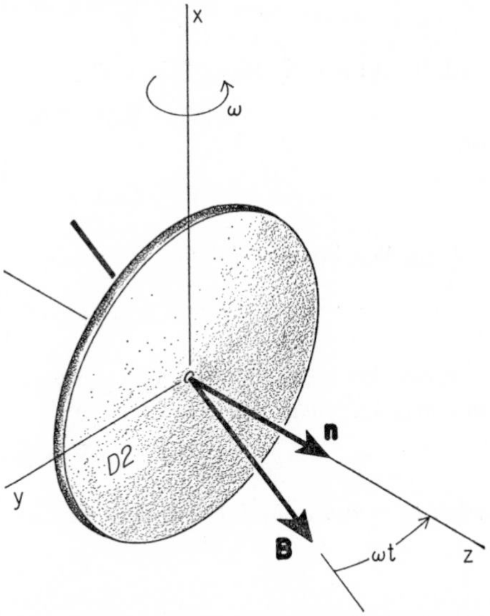

Let the observer on disk $D2$ establish a coordinate system with its z-axis perpendicular to the plane of the disk and its x-axis parallel to the axis of the rotation. When he points his electron beam in the z direction, the x-component of the beam deflection measures $(B_{D2})_y$, and the y-component measures $(B_{D2})_x$. He finds that

Figure E-2. *A nonconducting, nonmagnetic disk rotating with an angular velocity ω about an axis in the plane of the disk and perpendicular to the direction of a uniform magnetic field* **B**.

$$(B_{D2})_x = 0, \qquad (E\text{-}6)$$
$$(B_{D2})_y = B_0 \sin \omega t. \qquad (E\text{-}7)$$

When he points his beam in the y direction, the x-deflection measures $(B_{D2})_z$, and the z-deflection measures $(B_{D2})_x$:

$$(B_{D2})_x = 0, \qquad (E\text{-}8)$$
$$(B_{D2})_z = B_0 \cos \omega t. \qquad (E\text{-}9)$$

He finds these same fields no matter where he measures on his disk. He can describe the field he measures as a uniform field $\mathbf{B}_0$ rotating with angular velocity ω about his x-axis. If he were to compare notes with the laboratory observer, he would find that $\mathbf{B}_0 = \mathbf{B}_L = \mathbf{B}$.

What about his "curl-meter"? When the disk observer points it such that the axis of the loop is in the x-direction, there is no flux through the loop, and the reading is zero. Then

$$(\boldsymbol{\nabla} \times \mathbf{E}_{D2})_x = -\frac{\partial (B_{D2})_x}{\partial t} = 0. \qquad (E\text{-}10)$$

When he points the loop axis in the z direction, there is a changing flux through the loop, and

$$\left(\frac{d\Phi}{dt}\right)_{D2} = -BS\omega \sin \omega t, \qquad (E\text{-}11)$$

where S is the area of the loop. Then, for this orientation,

$$\oint \mathbf{E}_{D2} \cdot \mathbf{dl} = BS\omega \sin \omega t, \qquad (E\text{-}12)$$

and, from the definition of the curl,

$$(\boldsymbol{\nabla} \times \mathbf{E}_{D2})_z = B\omega \sin \omega t, \qquad (E\text{-}13)$$

or

$$(\boldsymbol{\nabla} \times \mathbf{E}_{D2})_z = -\frac{\partial (B_{D2})_z}{\partial t} = B\omega \sin \omega t. \qquad (E\text{-}14)$$

If the "curl-meter" reading is calculated for the y-component, we find that

$$(\boldsymbol{\nabla} \times \mathbf{E}_{D2})_y = -\frac{\partial (B_{D2})_y}{\partial t} = -B\omega \cos \omega t. \qquad (E\text{-}15)$$

From this experiment we can see that, *no matter how an observer may be moving in a magnetic field*,

$$\boldsymbol{\nabla} \times \mathbf{E} = -\frac{\partial \mathbf{B}}{\partial t} \qquad (E\text{-}16)$$

when he measures both E and B in the coordinate system in which he is at rest.

Experiment 2

Let us now suppose that each observer is given some conducting wire and is told to try to arrange it so as to induce an electromotance in a closed circuit at rest in his own coordinate system. For the laboratory observer,

$$\boldsymbol{\nabla} \times \mathbf{E}_L = -\frac{\partial \mathbf{B}_L}{\partial t} = 0 \qquad (E\text{-}17)$$

everywhere and, from Stokes's theorem, the induced electromotance

$$\oint \mathbf{E}_L \cdot \mathbf{dl} = 0 \qquad (E\text{-}18)$$

for any closed path.

The observer on disk $D1$ has the same experience, and if $D1$ is made of conducting material, there are no eddy currents induced in it.

Again the situation is different in *D2*. Let the conductor be a single loop around the rim of the disk, with a voltmeter connected in series. The voltmeter can either be on the disk or in a fixed position in the laboratory and connected to the loop by means of slip rings. The voltmeter is read both by the observer on the disk and by the laboratory observer. The former can calculate what the meter will read by invoking the Faraday law, since he knows $\partial \mathbf{B}_{D2}/\partial t$:

$$\oint \mathbf{E}_{D2} \cdot \mathbf{dl} = S \frac{\partial (B_{D2})_z}{\partial t}, \tag{E-19}$$

$$= B_0 S \omega \sin \omega t. \tag{E-20}$$

He can also calculate the electromotance from Stokes's theorem, since he has measured $\nabla \times \mathbf{E}_{D2}$ for every point on the disk:

$$\oint \mathbf{E}_{D2} \cdot \mathbf{dl} = \int_S (\nabla \times \mathbf{E}_{D2}) \cdot \mathbf{da}, \tag{E-21}$$

$$= B_0 S \omega \sin \omega t. \tag{E-22}$$

The two results are the same, of course, since

$$\nabla \times \mathbf{E}_{D2} = -\frac{\partial \mathbf{B}_{D2}}{\partial t}. \tag{E-23}$$

Now let us calculate what the laboratory observer thinks the meter on the disk will read according to the Faraday law. He says that $d\Phi/dt$ differs from zero because the circuit is rotating in a time-independent field, whereas the observer on the disk says that $d\Phi/dt$ differs from zero because his circuit is in a time-varying field. The laboratory man calculates $d\Phi/dt$ through the rotating loop and gets

$$\oint \mathbf{E}_{D2} \cdot \mathbf{dl} = B_L S \omega \sin \omega t, \tag{E-24}$$

where his B_L is the same as the B_0 measured by the rotating observer.

The laboratory observer can also calculate the electromotance using Equation *E-1*:

$$\nabla \times \mathbf{E}_{D2} = -\frac{\partial \mathbf{B}_L}{\partial t} + \nabla \times (\mathbf{u} \times \mathbf{B}_L). \tag{E-25}$$

He must use this complete expression, since the path around which he calculates the electromotance is moving in his coordinate system. Since

$$\frac{\partial \mathbf{B}_L}{\partial t} = 0, \tag{E-26}$$

the equation

$$\nabla \times \mathbf{E}_{D2} = \nabla \times (\mathbf{u} \times \mathbf{B}_L) \tag{E-27}$$

holds everywhere on the disk or, excluding terms of zero curl,

$$\mathbf{E}_{D2} = \mathbf{u} \times \mathbf{B}_L. \tag{E-28}$$

The laboratory observer then says that

$$\oint \mathbf{E}_{D2} \cdot \mathbf{dl} = \oint (\mathbf{u} \times \mathbf{B}_L) \cdot \mathbf{dl}. \tag{E-29}$$

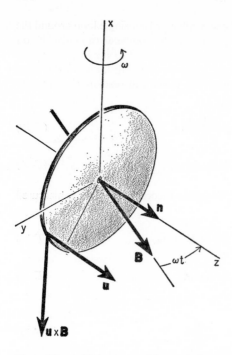

Figure E-3

The vector product $\mathbf{u} \times \mathbf{B}$ *on the rim of a disk rotating about an axis lying in its plane and perpendicular to a uniform magnetic field* $\mathbf{B}$. *The vector* $\mathbf{u}$ *is perpendicular to the plane of the disk.*

From Figure E-3, at an arbitrary point on the rim of the disk,

$$\mathbf{u} = \omega r \sin \theta, \tag{E-30}$$

and

$$|\mathbf{u} \times \mathbf{B}_L| = B_L r\omega \sin \theta \sin \omega t. \tag{E-31}$$

Thus

$$\oint (\mathbf{u} \times \mathbf{B}_L) \cdot \mathbf{dl} = \int_0^{2\pi} B r\omega \sin \theta \sin \omega t \cos\left(\frac{\pi}{2} - \theta\right) r\, d\theta, \tag{E-32}$$

$$= SB\omega \sin \omega t, \tag{E-33}$$

as with the Faraday law.

The laboratory observer and the *D2* observer therefore agree as to the voltmeter reading, but they disagree as to the reason for the induced electromotance. The laboratory observer says that the magnetic field is static but that the Lorentz force $(\mathbf{u} \times \mathbf{B})$ on the free charges in the moving conductor produces the electromotance. The disk *D2* observer, on the other hand, says that the conductor is at rest but that it is in a time-dependent magnetic field.

Experiment 3

As a final example, let us consider the *Faraday disk* or, as it is also called, the *homopolar generator*. Let us return to the disk *D1*. We place a conducting ring around its circumference and use a conducting axle. The axle and the ring are connected by a radial conducting wire attached rigidly to the disk, and the circuit is completed by brushes and a stationary wire with a voltmeter in series, as indicated in Figure E-4.

According to the laboratory observer, $\partial \mathbf{B}_L / \partial t$ is everywhere zero, and

$$\oint \mathbf{E} \cdot d\mathbf{l} = \oint (\mathbf{u} \times \mathbf{B}_L) \cdot d\mathbf{l}. \tag{E-34}$$

The part of the circuit that is stationary in the laboratory has $\mathbf{u} = 0$. On the rim and on the axle, $(\mathbf{u} \times \mathbf{B}_L)$ is everywhere perpendicular to the path of integration, thus there is no contribution to the integral. Along the radial conductor, the laboratory observer finds that

$$\oint \mathbf{E} \cdot d\mathbf{l} = \int_0^R r\omega B_L \, dr, \tag{E-35}$$

$$= \frac{R^2 \omega B}{2}. \tag{E-36}$$

With the Faraday law, it is important to specify carefully the surface through which the flux is to be calculated. It can be any surface bounded by the path of integration in the electromotance calculation. For convenience we may choose a surface lying in two planes, as in Figure E-4. The only part of this surface in which the flux differs from zero is the part that lies on the disk. The rate of change of flux through this part of the surface is readily calculated.

If the observer on the disk calculates the electromotance, he finds that $\partial \mathbf{B}_{D3} / \partial t$ is also everywhere zero and that the only place where $(\mathbf{u} \times \mathbf{B}_{D3})$ differs from zero is in the portion of the circuit external to his disk. He sees this part of the circuit rotating with respect to the disk with angular velocity ω. Again, since the only contribution to the electromotance is in the radial parts of the circuit, his calculation also gives

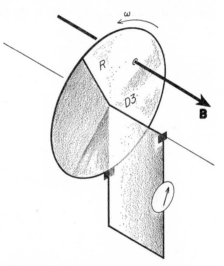

Figure E-4. *Homopolar generator.*

$$\oint \mathbf{E} \cdot d\mathbf{l} = \frac{R^2 \omega B}{2}. \tag{E-37}$$

The laboratory observer says there is an electromotance induced in the circuit because of the Lorentz force on the moving charges of the disk, and the disk observer says there is an electromotance because of the Lorentz force on the moving charges of the portion of the circuit external to the disk, but they always agree on the voltmeter reading.

If the *whole* disk is made of conducting material, the electromotance is calculated in exactly the same way. It makes no difference what integration path we choose from the axle to the rim, as long as the path is at rest relative to the disk. It is essential that this part of the path be at rest relative to the conductor, since the charges which experience the force resulting in the electromotance are, on the average, at rest with respect to the conductor. The electromotance is independent of the path in the conductor, since only the radial components of the path elements contribute to the integral of $(\mathbf{u} \times \mathbf{B}) \cdot d\mathbf{l}$.

The electromotance may also be calculated for the conducting disk from the Faraday law. Again we may choose any path in the moving conductor, as long as it is at rest relative to it. The result is the same as with the wire discussed above.

Our discussion is strictly valid only for large magnetic fields and small angular velocities, since centrifugal and Coriolis effects have been neglected. For practical laboratory purposes, however, this is not a limitation. The ratio of the Lorentz force to the centripetal force on an electron in a disk rotating with angular velocity ω in a magnetic field B is

$$\frac{F_L}{F_C} = \frac{e}{m}\frac{B}{\omega}. \tag{E-38}$$

For an angular velocity of 1800 revolutions/minute and a magnetic field of one weber/meter^2, this ratio is about 10^9. This complete separation of electrical and mechanical effects is a consequence of the large value of the ratio e/m for an electron.

APPENDIX F

THE EXPONENTIAL

NOTATION

The subject of this appendix is a mathematical technique for solving what is probably, from the point of view of the physicist, the most important class of differential equations.

The sine and cosine functions play a particularly important role in all of physics, mostly because of the relative ease with which they can be generated and measured by the ordinary types of instruments. They are also relatively easy to manipulate mathematically. All other periodic functions, such as square waves, for example, are vastly more complicated to use, both experimentally and mathematically.

The mathematical technique which we shall develop here is therefore widely used, despite the fact that it can apply only to functions of the form

$$x = x_0 \cos(\omega t + \theta), \qquad (F\text{-}1)$$

where x_0 is the *amplitude* of x, ω is the *angular frequency*, and t is the time. The quantity $(\omega t + \theta)$ is the *phase*, or *phase angle*, θ being the phase at $t = 0$. We shall limit our discussion to the cosine function, since the sine can be transformed to a cosine by an appropriate choice of θ. We shall assume that the origin of time is chosen such that $\theta = 0$.

The procedure for differentiating $\cos \omega t$, although elementary, is rather inconvenient: the cosine function is changed to a sine, the result is multiplied by ω, and the sign is changed. To find the second derivative, the sine is changed back to a cosine, and the result is again multiplied by ω, but this time without changing sign, and so on.

Differentiation can be simplified if it is kept in mind that

$$e^{j\omega t} = \cos \omega t + j \sin \omega t, \qquad (F\text{-}2)$$

where $j = \sqrt{-1}$. Then

$$x = x_0 \cos \omega t = \mathrm{Re}\, x_0 e^{j\omega t}, \qquad (F\text{-}3)$$

where Re is an operator which means "Real part of" whatever follows.

Let us calculate the first two derivatives:

$$\frac{dx}{dt} = \frac{d}{dt} \mathrm{Re}\, (x_0 e^{j\omega t}), \qquad (F\text{-}4)$$

$$= \mathrm{Re}\, (j\omega x_0 e^{j\omega t}), \qquad (F\text{-}5)$$

$$= -\omega x_0 \sin \omega t, \qquad (F\text{-}6)$$

$$\frac{d^2x}{dt^2} = \text{Re}\ \{(j\omega)^2 x_0 e^{j\omega t}\}, \tag{F-7}$$

$$= -\omega^2 x_0 \cos \omega t. \tag{F-8}$$

The results are, of course, the same as are obtained by the usual method.

We now adopt the following convention: *we shall express the quantities x, dx/dt, d^2x/dt^2, and so forth, as exponential functions without writing the Re operator, but with the tacit understanding that only the real part must be used.* Then $x = x_0 \cos \omega t$ will be written as

$$x = x_0 e^{j\omega t}, \tag{F-9}$$

and

$$\frac{dx}{dt} = j\omega x_0 e^{j\omega t} = j\omega x, \tag{F-10}$$

$$\frac{d^2x}{dt^2} = (j\omega)^2 x_0 e^{j\omega t} = (j\omega)^2 x, \tag{F-11}$$

. . . .

With this convention, *the operator d/dt can be replaced by the factor jω.* This simplification is so useful that the exponential notation is almost invariably used to represent sinusoidally varying quantities, whether they are mechanical, acoustical or electrical.

The coefficient before the exponential function can itself be complex. For example, $jx_0 e^{j\omega t}$ means

$$\text{Re}\ (jx_0 e^{j\omega t}) = -x_0 \sin \omega t \tag{F-12}$$

if x_0 is real. Since $j = e^{j\pi/2}$, one can also write that

$$\text{Re}\ (jx_0 e^{j\omega t}) = \text{Re}\ (x_0 e^{j(\omega t + \pi/2)}), \tag{F-13}$$

$$= x_0 \cos \left(\omega t + \frac{\pi}{2}\right), \tag{F-14}$$

$$= -x_0 \sin \omega t. \tag{F-15}$$

One common case is

$$(a + jb)e^{j\omega t} = \sqrt{a^2 + b^2} \exp \left\{ j\left(\omega t + \arctan \frac{b}{a}\right)\right\}, \tag{F-16}$$

where we have written

$$a + jb = \sqrt{a^2 + b^2} \exp \left\{ j \arctan \left(\frac{b}{a}\right)\right\} \tag{F-17}$$

in the usual manner on the assumption that a is positive in order that the angle chosen lies either in the first or fourth quadrant. Thus

$$\text{Re}\ (a + jb)e^{j\omega t} = \sqrt{a^2 + b^2} \cos \left(\omega t + \arctan \frac{b}{a}\right). \tag{F-18}$$

If a is not positive, one must be careful to use the proper angle in the exponent. For example, the argument of $(-1 + 2j)$ is $(\pi - \arctan 2)$, not $\arctan (-2)$.

Space-dependent functions can also be represented with the exponential notation. For example, in an electric field, the vector $\mathbf{E}$ is oriented in some direction in space. It can also be a function of the time, such that

$$\mathbf{E} = \mathbf{E}_0 \cos (\omega t + \theta), \tag{F-19}$$

where $\mathbf{E_0}$ is a vector whose magnitude is the maximum value of $\mathbf{E}$. We then write

$$\mathbf{E} = \mathbf{E_0}e^{j(\omega t+\theta)} \tag{F-20}$$

or

$$= \mathbf{E_0}e^{j\theta}e^{j\omega t}. \tag{F-21}$$

The coefficient of $e^{j\omega t}$ can thus be both a vector and a complex quantity, the former property having to do with the orientation of the quantity in space, whereas the second property is related to the phase angle in the time dependence.

The exponential notation is used as follows. The sine or cosine functions are expressed in the form $x_0e^{j(\omega t+\theta)}$, which is of course equal to $x_0\{\cos(\omega t + \theta) + j\sin(\omega t + \theta)\}$. We are concerned only with the real part, which is the first term; the second term can be considered as parasitic. Then, as long as the mathematical operations used are restricted to additions, subtractions, differentiations and integrations, the real and imaginary parts do not mix. *The technique is thus particularly useful for solving linear differential equations with constant coefficients.* Once the calculations are completed, the resulting expressions are often left in exponential form. However, if amplitudes and phases are required, the imaginary part is rejected, and the result is expressed again as a cosine function.

A note of *warning* is necessary here. The exponential technique is valid only for mathematical operations which do not mix the real and the imaginary parts. For example, for any two complex numbers A and B,

$$\text{Re}(A + B) = \text{Re}(A) + \text{Re}(B), \tag{F-22}$$

but

$$\text{Re}(A \times B) \neq \text{Re}(A) \times \text{Re}(B). \tag{F-23}$$

Whenever multiplications of $e^{j\omega t}$ terms are involved in the calculations, one must revert to the cosine functions and not use the exponential technique.

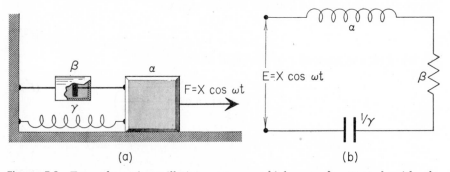

Figure F-1. *Examples of oscillating systems which can be treated with the exponential notation.*

Solving a Linear Differential Equation with Constant Coefficients, Using the Exponential Notation

As an illustration, let us consider the following differential equation, where all the terms are real:

$$\alpha\frac{\partial^2 x}{\partial t^2} + \beta\frac{\partial x}{\partial t} + \gamma x = X\cos\omega t. \tag{F-24}$$

This could be the differential equation describing the motion of a mass α under the influence of a force $X \cos \omega t$, a restoring force $-\gamma x$ proportional to the displacement x from equilibrium, and a damping force $-\beta\, \partial x/\partial t$ proportional to the velocity $\partial x/\partial t$, as in Figure F-1a: the product of the mass α and the acceleration $\partial^2 x/\partial t^2$ is equal to the sum of the applied forces.

It could also be the differential equation for the charge x on a capacitor whose capacitance is $1/\gamma$ in series with an inductance α and a resistance β, for an applied voltage $X \cos \omega t$, as in Figure F-1b: the applied voltage is equal to the sum of the voltages across α, β, and $1/\gamma$.

This equation can be solved, without using the exponential notation, as follows. We consider only the steady-state solution and neglect all transient effects obtained by setting the right-hand side equal to zero. There is, on the left, a sum of three terms involving the unknown function x, its first, and its second derivatives, with constant coefficients. Since the derivatives of the sine and cosine functions are themselves sine and cosine functions, it is plausible to try a function of the form

$$x = A \cos \omega t + B \sin \omega t. \qquad (F\text{-}25)$$

Substituting this expression for x in Eq. F-24, and setting the coefficient of $\cos \omega t$ on the left-hand side equal to X and that of $\sin \omega t$ equal to zero, one can determine the coefficients A and B. The sum $(A \cos \omega t + B \sin \omega t)$ is then put into the form $C \cos (\omega t + \theta)$, and the result is as follows:

$$x = \frac{X}{\sqrt{(\gamma - \alpha\omega^2)^2 + \beta^2\omega^2}} \cos\left(\omega t - \arctan \frac{\beta\omega}{\gamma - \alpha\omega^2}\right). \qquad (F\text{-}26)$$

We have assumed that $\gamma > \alpha\omega^2$ in writing out the arc tan term; otherwise this expression would not be correct, as noted above.

The procedure is much simpler with the exponential notation. Substituting $j\omega$ for the operator d/dt in Eq. F-24, we can write directly that

$$x = \frac{X e^{j\omega t}}{-\alpha\omega^2 + j\omega\beta + \gamma}. \qquad (F\text{-}27)$$

The amplitude and phase of x can be found easily:

$$x = \frac{X}{\sqrt{(\gamma - \alpha\omega^2)^2 + \beta^2\omega^2}} \frac{e^{j\omega t}}{\exp\left(j \arctan \dfrac{\beta\omega}{\gamma - \alpha\omega^2}\right)}, \qquad (F\text{-}28)$$

$$= \frac{X}{\sqrt{(\gamma - \alpha\omega^2)^2 + \beta^2\omega^2}} \left\{ \cos\left(\omega t - \arctan \frac{\beta\omega}{\gamma - \alpha\omega^2}\right) \right.$$

$$\left. + j \sin\left(\omega t - \arctan \frac{\beta\omega}{\gamma - \alpha\omega^2}\right) \right\}. \qquad (F\text{-}29)$$

If we reject the imaginary part, we obtain the same result as in Eq. F-26.

The value of dx/dt corresponding to the velocity in Figure F-1a and to the current in Figure F-1b can be calculated easily:

$$\frac{dx}{dt} = j\omega x = \frac{j\omega X e^{j\omega t}}{-\alpha\omega^2 + j\omega\beta + \gamma}, \qquad (F\text{-}30)$$

or, rationalizing and again rejecting the imaginary part, we obtain

$$\frac{dx}{dt} = \frac{X}{\sqrt{\left(\dfrac{\gamma}{\omega} - \alpha\omega\right)^2 + \beta^2}} \cos\left\{\omega t + \arctan \frac{(\gamma - \alpha\omega^2)}{\beta\omega}\right\}. \qquad (F\text{-}31)$$

APPENDIX G

WAVES

A wave involves the propagation of a disturbance of some sort in space. One can think, for example, of the waves formed when a stretched string is fixed at one end and moved rapidly in a vertical plane in some arbitrary way at the free end.

If we call $y(t)$ the vertical position of the moving end, then it turns out that the vertical position y at a distance z along the string is given by $y\{(t - (z/u)\}$, assuming no losses and a perfectly flexible string. The vertical position at z is thus given by the position at the moving end at a previous time $t - (z/u)$, the quantity z/u being the time required for the disturbance to travel through the distance z at the velocity u.

More generally, we can consider waves propagating in an extended region, such as acoustic waves in air or light waves in space. The quantity propagated can be either a scalar or a vector quantity. For example, in an acoustic wave, we can consider the propagation of pressure, which is a scalar. In an electromagnetic wave, we can consider the propagation of the electric field intensity vector $\mathbf{E}$ or of its components E_x, E_y, and E_z.

G.1. *Plane Sinusoidal Waves*

If a certain quantity α propagating with a velocity u is given at $z = 0$ by

$$\alpha = \alpha_0 \cos \omega t, \tag{G-1}$$

then, for any position z in the direction of propagation of the plane wave,

$$\alpha = \alpha_0 \cos \omega \left(t - \frac{z}{u} \right). \tag{G-2}$$

This expression describes an *unattenuated plane sinusoidal wave*, since the amplitude α_0 is constant, and since α depends on z but not on x or on y. The *wave fronts*, which are surfaces of constant phase at a given time, are thus perpendicular to the z-axis. The quantity α_0 is called the *amplitude* of the wave. For a given position z, we have a sinusoidal variation of α with time. For a given time t, we also have a sinusoidal variation with z, as in Figure *G-1*.

The *phase angle* shown between brackets is a constant; that is,

$$t - \frac{z}{u} = \text{constant} \tag{G-3}$$

for a point traveling with the velocity

$$\frac{dz}{dt} = u. \tag{G-4}$$

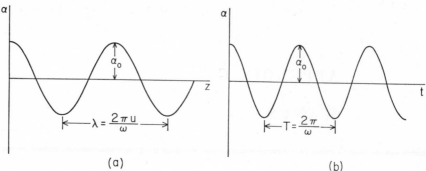

Figure G-1. *The quantity* $\alpha = \alpha_0 \cos (\omega t - kz)$ *as a function of z and as a function of t.*

The quantity u is called the *phase velocity* of the wave, since it is the velocity with which the phase $\omega \left(t - \dfrac{z}{u} \right)$ is propagated in space.

We often write

$$\alpha = \alpha_0 \cos (\omega t - kz), \qquad (G\text{-}5)$$

where

$$k = \frac{\omega}{u} \qquad (G\text{-}6)$$

is called the *wave number*. It is important to note that *this wave number is 2π times that used in optics.* For this reason, the quantity k is also called the *circular wave number*.

The *wave length* λ is the distance over which kz changes by 2π radians, as shown in Figure G-1a:

$$k\lambda = 2\pi. \qquad (G\text{-}7)$$

If we write

$$\frac{\lambda}{2\pi} = \lambdabar, \qquad (G\text{-}8)$$

where $\lambdabar$ is read as "lambda bar," we have

$$k = \frac{1}{\lambdabar}. \qquad (G\text{-}9)$$

The quantity $\lambdabar$ is called the *radian length*. It is the distance over which the phase of the wave changes by one radian; this is about $\lambda/6$, and is therefore considerably less than one-quarter wave length. It turns out that the quantity which appears in nearly all the calculations is $\lambdabar$, and not λ. We are already familiar with the fact that it is preferable to use the circular frequency ω instead of the frequency f. In both cases the intuitively simple quantity, namely, the wave length or the frequency, is not the one which is "natural" from a mathematical standpoint.

With the exponential notation, the wave traveling in the positive direction along the z-axis is written*

$$\alpha = \alpha_0 e^{j(\omega t - kz)}. \qquad (G\text{-}10)$$

* We shall use the notation of Eq. *G-10*. Notice, however, that one could equally well write

$$\alpha = \alpha_0 e^{-j(\omega t - kz)},$$

since the cosine is an even function. The latter notation is frequently used where it is convenient to omit the factor $e^{-j\omega t}$ for brevity. A wave traveling in the positive direction is then simply written

$$\alpha = \alpha_0' e^{kz}.$$

Similarly, a wave traveling in the negative direction along the z-axis is described by

$$\alpha = \alpha_0 e^{j(\omega t + kz)}. \qquad (G\text{-}11)$$

We shall have occasion to use plane sinusoidal waves traveling in some given direction specified by a unit vector $\mathbf{n}$. The wave fronts are then normal to $\mathbf{n}$, and such a wave is given by

$$\alpha = \alpha_0 \exp\left(j\{\omega t - k(\mathbf{n}\cdot\mathbf{r})\}\right), \quad (G\text{-}12)$$

as can be seen in Figure G-2. When $\mathbf{n}$ coincides with the unit vector in the z direction, $\mathbf{n}\cdot\mathbf{r} = z$.

If a plane wave traveling along the z-axis is attenuated, its amplitude decreases exponentially, and

$$\alpha = \alpha_0 \exp\left\{j(\omega t - k_r z) - k_i z\right\}. \quad (G\text{-}13)$$

It is now k_r which is related to the wave length:

$$k_r = \frac{1}{\lambda}, \qquad (G\text{-}14)$$

whereas the quantity k_i is such that the wave is reduced in amplitude by a factor of e in a distance

$$\delta = \frac{1}{k_i}. \qquad (G\text{-}15)$$

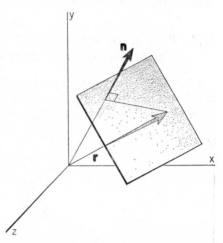

Figure G-2. *The plane shown is defined by* $\mathbf{n}\cdot\mathbf{r} = constant$, *the constant being the distance between the plane and the origin.*

The velocity u of the wave is

$$u = \frac{\omega}{k_r}. \qquad (G\text{-}16)$$

We can also rewrite Eq. *G-13* in the form

$$\alpha = \alpha_0 e^{j(\omega t - kz)}, \qquad (G\text{-}17)$$

where

$$k = k_r - jk_i. \qquad (G\text{-}18)$$

It is important to note the *negative sign* in the above expression.

The quantity k is still called the wave number in this general case. However, it is complex, its *imaginary* part corresponding to absorption. It will be observed that an attenuated wave traveling in the positive direction along the z-axis requires that the real part of k be a positive quantity and that the imaginary part be a negative quantity. Otherwise, the wave would grow exponentially in amplitude with increasing z. The quantities k_r and k_i in Eq. *G-18* are thus both positive quantities. In transmission line theory the quantity jk is written as γ, and is called the *propagation constant*.

The wave is attenuated by a factor of $1/e = 0.368$ in a distance $\delta = 1/k_i$. The quantity δ is called the *attenuation distance*, and k_i is called the *attenuation constant*.

An attenuated wave traveling in the negative direction along the z-axis is given similarly by

$$\alpha = \alpha_0 \exp\left\{j(\omega t + k_r z) + k_i z\right\}, \qquad (G\text{-}19)$$

$$= \alpha_0 \exp\left\{j(\omega t + kz)\right\}, \qquad (G\text{-}20)$$

where k_r and k_i are again positive quantities and where k is defined as above

We shall meet with cases in which $k_r = 0$. Then Eq. *G-13* becomes

$$\alpha = \alpha_0 e^{-k_i z} e^{j\omega t}. \tag{G-21}$$

The phase angle ωt is then independent of z, all points are in phase, there is no traveling wave, and the amplitude decreases exponentially with z.

G.2. Waves on a Stretched String. The Differential Equation for an Unattenuated Wave

It is interesting to consider at this point the simple case of transverse waves propagating along a stretched string. We assume small transverse displacements on a flexible string of mass ρ per unit length stretched with a tension F, as in Figure G-3.

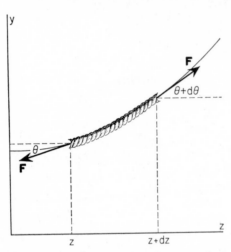

Figure G-3 shows an element of the string at some given time t. Both its displacement y and its angle θ are functions of both the position z along the string and the time t. We assume that there is no motion along the z-axis, in order that the stretching force F will be constant all along the string.

The element of mass $\rho \, dz$ takes on an acceleration $\dfrac{\partial^2 y}{\partial t^2}$ under the action of the forces F at either end, and

$$\rho \, dz \, \frac{\partial^2 y}{\partial t^2} = F\{\sin(\theta + d\theta) - \sin\theta\}, \tag{G-22}$$

$$= F \, d(\sin\theta), \tag{G-23}$$

$$= F \cos\theta \, d\theta. \tag{G-24}$$

Figure G-3. *Element of string stretched with a force* **F**. *The angles and the displacement from the z-axis are grossly exaggerated for clarity.*

Then

$$\cos\theta \, \frac{\partial\theta}{\partial z} = \frac{\rho}{F} \frac{\partial^2 y}{\partial t^2}. \tag{G-25}$$

We have written a partial derivative for θ, since the $d\theta$ found above was for a given time t. For waves of small amplitude, we can set $\cos\theta = 1$ and $\theta = \partial y/\partial z$, such that

$$\frac{\partial^2 y}{\partial z^2} = \frac{\rho}{F} \frac{\partial^2 y}{\partial t^2}. \tag{G-26}$$

We can verify that the above differential equation does correspond to a wave motion by substituting for y *any* function of $\{t - (z/u)\}$ or of $\{t + (z/u)\}$. We assume, of course, that the second partial derivatives exist. We find that the phase velocity u is given by

$$u = \left(\frac{F}{\rho}\right)^{1/2}. \tag{G-27}$$

This result is general, and an *un*attenuated wave traveling with a velocity u along the z-axis is described by the following differential equation:

$$\frac{\partial^2 \alpha}{\partial z^2} = \frac{1}{u^2} \frac{\partial^2 \alpha}{\partial t^2}. \qquad (G\text{-}28)$$

The differential equation for an attenuated wave will be discussed in Section G.5.

It will be observed that the above differential equation (*G-28*) is much more general than Eq. *G-10*. It does not involve the amplitude α_0, the angular frequency ω, or the wave number k, but only the velocity u. The differential equation therefore applies equally well to any wave form, periodic or not, and to any amplitude. Equation *G-28* is also independent of the sign of u, since it involves only u^2. It can therefore represent waves traveling in either direction along the z-axis.

For a sinusoidal wave,

$$\frac{\partial^2 \alpha}{\partial z^2} = -\frac{\omega^2}{u^2} \alpha = -k^2 \alpha, \qquad (G\text{-}29)$$

and

$$\left(\frac{\partial^2 \alpha}{\partial z^2} + k^2 \right) \alpha = 0. \qquad (G\text{-}30)$$

G.3. *Solution of the Differential Equation for an Unattenuated Wave by the Separation of Variables*

Equation *G-28* can be solved formally by the method of separation of variables (Section 4.5). We set

$$\alpha = T(t)\, Z(z), \qquad (G\text{-}31)$$

where T and Z are respectively functions of t and of z only. Substituting this value of α in Eq. *G-28* and dividing by TZ, we obtain

$$\frac{1}{Z}\frac{d^2 Z}{dz^2} = \frac{1}{u^2 T}\frac{d^2 T}{dt^2}. \qquad (G\text{-}32)$$

The term on the left is a function only of z, whereas that on the right is a function only of t. Then both sides of the equation can be equated to a separation constant $-k^2$

$$\frac{1}{Z}\frac{d^2 Z}{dz^2} = -k^2, \qquad (G\text{-}$$

$$\frac{1}{T}\frac{d^2 T}{dt^2} = -k^2 u^2, \qquad ($$

and

$$T = A e^{juk t} + B e^{-juk t},$$

$$Z = C e^{jkz} + D e^{-jkz}.$$

Then

$$\alpha = AC e^{jk(ut+z)} + BD e^{-jk(ut+z)} + AD e^{jk(ut-z)} + BC e^{-jk(ut-z)}. \quad \text{tially}$$

Now α is some physical quantity which must not increase or decrease entials with either z or t. This condition requires that k be a real number. Th then reduce to sine and cosine functions. .s, we can

Since the coefficients AC, BD, and so on, are as yet undetermined c set AC to be some complex number $(G\text{-}38)$

$$AC = G e^{i\phi},$$

where G and ϕ are real. Also, α must be a real quantity, and we r nave $(G\text{-}39)$

$$BD = G e^{-i\phi}$$

in order that the first two terms of Eq. *G-37* can add up to give a cosine function.
    Similarly, we can set

$$AD = Fe^{i\theta} \tag{G-40}$$

and

$$BC = Fe^{-i\theta}. \tag{G-41}$$

Finally, α can be written as follows:

$$\alpha = 2F \cos (kut - kz + \theta) + 2G \cos (kut + kz + \phi), \tag{G-42}$$

where the angles θ and ϕ are constant. Comparing this with Eq. *G-5*, we find that the above equation determines a pair of waves traveling in opposite directions with a common velocity u. The separation constant k is the wave number, and

$$ku = \omega = 2\pi f. \tag{G-43}$$

Since α is a function only of z and of t, the waves are planar, with wave fronts parallel to the xy-plane.

It will be observed that the formal solution which we arrived at by separating the variables z and t has led us to a very special class of waves; namely, sine waves. We did not find a general function of $\{t - (z/u)\}$. This is quite disturbing at first sight, since our formal solution is presumably general. There is no contradiction, however, for the following reason. Since our differential equation is linear, that is, since its terms are all of the first degree in α or its derivatives, the sum of any number of solutions is also a solution. Any type of periodic wave form encountered in practice can be expressed as a Fourier series of sines and cosines of the fundamental frequency and of its harmonics (Section 4.5). Even individual nonperiodic pulses can be analyzed in a somewhat similar manner by means of Fourier integrals.* Any wave form can thus be synthesized by combining terms of the form shown in Eq. *G-42* with appropriate amplitudes and wave numbers.

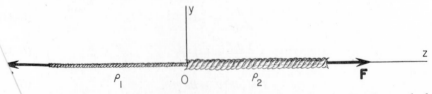

e G-4. *Two strings of densities ρ_1 and ρ_2 fixed together at 0 and stretched
    force* **F.**

G

*flection of a Wave on a Stretched String
    a Point where the Density Changes from ρ_1 to ρ_2*

    If tw
force *F*, as of different densities ρ_1 and ρ_2 are tied together and stretched with a
and partly gure G-4, a wave traveling along the first section will be partly reflected
    * See, for e mitted at the knot.
p. 287.   , J. Stratton, *Electromagnetic Theory* (McGraw-Hill, New York, 1941),

The wave velocities are respectively

$$u_1 = \left(\frac{F}{\rho_1}\right)^{1/2}$$

and

$$u_2 = \left(\frac{F}{\rho_2}\right)^{1/2},$$

(G-44)

and the corresponding wave numbers are

$$k_1 = \frac{\omega}{u_1} = \omega\left(\frac{\rho_1}{F}\right)^{1/2}$$

and

$$k_2 = \frac{\omega}{u_2} = \omega\left(\frac{\rho_2}{F}\right)^{1/2}.$$

(G-45)

Let us assume that a wave travels to the right along string 1. We shall call this the incident wave and set

$$y_i = y_{oi}e^{j(\omega t - k_1 z)},$$

(G-46)

y being the lateral displacement of the string and $z = 0$ being chosen at the knot For the wave transmitted to string 2, we have

$$y_t = y_{ot}e^{j(\omega t - k_2 z)}.$$

(G-47)

Finally, for the wave reflected back at the knot,

$$y_r = y_{or}e^{j(\omega t + k_1 z)}.$$

(G-48)

We assume, for simplicity, that there are no reflected waves formed at the supports.

In the above three expressions for y_i, y_t, and y_r, the amplitude y_{oi} of the incident wave can be assumed to be known. Thus we have two quantities to determine: y_{ot} and y_{or}.

It is possible to calculate the values of y_{ot} and y_{or} in terms of y_{oi}, ρ_1, and ρ_2 by considering the conditions of continuity which must be satisfied at the knot. First, there must, of course, be continuity of the displacement y: the value of y just to the left of the knot must be equal to its value just to the right. Then

$$y_i + y_r = y_t \qquad (z = 0),$$

or

$$y_{oi} + y_{or} = y_{ot}.$$

(G-49)

Second, there must be continuity of the slope of the string dy/dz. The reason for this is as follows. We have assumed implicitly that the knot was weightless. Thus the sum of the forces acting on it must be zero, and the two opposing tension forces F at that point must be along the same line. Then

$$-k_1 y_{oi} + k_1 y_{or} = -k_2 y_{ot}.$$

(G-50)

Solving these equations, we obtain

$$\frac{y_{or}}{y_{oi}} = \frac{k_1 - k_2}{k_1 + k_2} = \frac{\rho_1^{1/2} - \rho_2^{1/2}}{\rho_1^{1/2} + \rho_2^{1/2}},$$

(G-51)

$$\frac{y_{ot}}{y_{oi}} = \frac{2k_1}{k_1 + k_2} = \frac{2\rho_1^{1/2}}{\rho_1^{1/2} + \rho_2^{1/2}}.$$

(G-52)

Since the ratio y_{ot}/y_{oi} is always real and positive, the transmitted wave is always in phase with the incident wave. On the other hand, the ratio y_{or}/y_{oi} can be either positive or negative. The reflected wave is in phase with the incident wave if $\rho_1 > \rho_2$, and π radians out of phase if $\rho_1 < \rho_2$. If $\rho_1 = \rho_2$ there is no discontinuity, no reflected wave, and $y_{ot} = y_{oi}$.

G.5. *Waves on a Stretched String with Damping. The Differential Equation for an Attenuated Wave*

Let us return to the case of the stretched string of uniform density ρ. We assume now that the string is in a viscous medium that provides a damping force which is proportional to the velocity. The damping force on the element of string dz is then

$$dF_D = -b \, dz \, \frac{\partial y}{\partial t}, \qquad (G\text{-}53)$$

and, from Eq. *G-24*, we now have

$$\rho \, dz \, \frac{\partial^2 y}{\partial t^2} = F \cos \theta \, d\theta - b \, dz \, \frac{\partial y}{\partial t}, \qquad (G\text{-}54)$$

or

$$\frac{\partial^2 y}{\partial z^2} = \frac{\rho}{F} \frac{\partial^2 y}{\partial t^2} + \frac{b}{F} \frac{\partial y}{\partial t}. \qquad (G\text{-}55)$$

We can show that this is the differential equation for an attenuated wave by trying a solution of the form

$$y = y_o e^{j(\omega t - k'z)}. \qquad (G\text{-}56)$$

Substituting, we find that

$$k'^2 = \frac{\omega^2 \rho}{F} \left(1 - j \frac{b}{\omega \rho} \right), \qquad (G\text{-}57)$$

and the wave number k' is now obviously complex. The above differential equation is therefore that of an attenuated wave. This is to be expected, since it is identical to Eq. *G-26*, except for the addition of the second term on the right-hand side. This term corresponds to a damping force which dissipates energy.

Equation *G-55* can also be rewritten as

$$\frac{\partial^2 y}{\partial z^2} = -\frac{\omega^2 \rho}{F} \left(1 - j \frac{b}{\omega \rho} \right) y = -k'^2 y, \qquad (G\text{-}58)$$

or

$$\left(\frac{\partial^2}{\partial z^2} + k'^2 \right) y = 0 \qquad (G\text{-}59)$$

This equation is similar to Eq. *G-30*, except that the wave number k' is now complex. It represents a pair of attenuated waves traveling in opposite directions along the z-axis.

It will be observed from Eq. *G-57* that the differential equation is equally well satisfied by $+k'$ or by $-k'$, that is, by waves traveling in either direction along the z-axis.

We can find both k_r and k_i by recalling Eq. *G-18* and substituting

$$k' = k'_r - jk'_i \qquad (G\text{-}60)$$

In Eq. *G-57*, which gives

$$k'_r = \pm \omega \left(\frac{\rho}{2F} \right)^{1/2} \left\{ 1 \pm \left(1 + \frac{b^2}{\omega^2 \rho^2} \right)^{1/2} \right\}^{1/2} \qquad (G\text{-}61)$$

and

$$k_i' = \pm\omega \left(\frac{\rho}{2F}\right)^{1/2} \left\{-1 \pm \left(1 + \frac{b^2}{\omega^2\rho^2}\right)^{1/2}\right\}^{1/2}. \qquad (G\text{-}62)$$

Since, by definition, k_r and k_i are both positive and real (Section G.1), the $\pm$ signs must all be replaced by $+$ signs, and

$$k_r' = \omega \left(\frac{\rho}{2F}\right)^{1/2} \left\{1 + \left(1 + \frac{b^2}{\omega^2\rho^2}\right)^{1/2}\right\}^{1/2}, \qquad (G\text{-}63)$$

$$k_i' = \omega \left(\frac{\rho}{2F}\right)^{1/2} \left\{-1 + \left(1 + \frac{b^2}{\omega^2\rho^2}\right)^{1/2}\right\}^{1/2}. \qquad (G\text{-}64)$$

It will also be recalled from Section G.1 that the velocity of the wave is ω divided by the real part of the propagation constant. This reduces to $(F/\rho)^{1/2}$ when $b = 0$, as expected.

G.6. *Solution of the Differential Equation for an Attenuated Wave by the Separation of Variables*

The differential equation *G-55* which we found above is general, and any attenuated wave traveling along the z-axis is described by

$$\frac{\partial^2\alpha'}{\partial z^2} = g\frac{\partial^2\alpha'}{\partial t^2} + h\frac{\partial\alpha'}{\partial t}. \qquad (G\text{-}65)$$

We can solve this equation formally by the method of separation of variables, as in Section G.3. We set

$$\alpha' = T'(t)Z'(z), \qquad (G\text{-}66)$$

substitute in Eq. *G-65*, and divide by $T'Z'$. Then

$$\frac{1}{Z'}\frac{d^2Z'}{dz^2} = \frac{g}{T'}\frac{d^2T'}{dt^2} + \frac{h}{T'}\frac{dT'}{dt}, \qquad (G\text{-}67)$$

where the left-hand side is a function only of z, whereas the right-hand side is a function only of t. Then

$$\frac{1}{Z'}\frac{d^2Z'}{dz^2} = -k'^2, \qquad (G\text{-}68)$$

and

$$\frac{g}{T'}\frac{d^2T'}{dt^2} + \frac{h}{T'}\frac{dT'}{dt} = -k'^2. \qquad (G\text{-}69)$$

From the first of these equations,

$$Z' = C'e^{jk'z} + D'e^{-jk'z}, \qquad (G\text{-}70)$$

and k' is the wave number.

The second equation takes on a more familiar form when rewritten as

$$g\frac{d^2T'}{dt^2} + h\frac{dT'}{dt} + k'^2T' = 0. \qquad (G\text{-}71)$$

We can assume a sinusoidal wave without losing generality, as was noted in Section G.3, and set

$$T' = A'e^{j\omega t}. \qquad (G\text{-}72)$$

The quantity ω must be real in order that the amplitude of the wave can decrease only with z. Substituting in Eq. *G-71*, we find that

$$k'^2 = \omega^2 g \left(1 - j\frac{h}{\omega g} \right). \tag{G-73}$$

This result is identical to that which we found in Eq. *G-57*, the coefficients g and h of the general differential equation for an attenuated wave (Eq. *G-65*) being equal, respectively, to ρ/F and to b/F in the differential equation for an attenuated wave on a stretched string (Eq. *G-55*).

If we again set

$$k' = k_r' - jk_i', \tag{G-74}$$

we find that

$$k_r' = \omega \left(\frac{g}{2} \right)^{1/2} \left\{ 1 + \left(1 + \frac{h^2}{\omega^2 g^2} \right)^{1/2} \right\}^{1/2}, \tag{G-75}$$

$$k_i' = \omega \left(\frac{g}{2} \right)^{1/2} \left\{ -1 + \left(1 + \frac{h^2}{\omega^2 g^2} \right)^{1/2} \right\}^{1/2}, \tag{G-76}$$

as in Eqs. *G-61* and *G-62*, since $g = \rho/F$, and $h = b/F$.

Finally, from Eqs. *G-66*, *G-70*, and *G-72*, we have

$$\alpha' = A'C'e^{j(\omega t + k'z)} + A'D'e^{j(\omega t - k'z)}, \tag{G-77}$$

where $k' = k_r' - jk_i'$. The first term represents a plane wave traveling in the negative direction along the z-axis, whereas the second term represents a similar wave traveling in the positive direction.

In this general case, the wave velocity u is ω/k_r, which reduces to $(1/g)^{1/2}$ when $h = 0$. The wave is attenuated by a factor of e in a distance $\delta = 1/k_i$, which approaches infinity as h approaches zero.

These results are the same as those of the preceding section.

G.7. *Wave Propagation in Three Dimensions*

In the case of a wave propagating in space, the wave equation is similar to Eq. *G-65*, except that the second derivative with respect to z is replaced by the Laplacian

$$\nabla^2 \alpha = g\frac{\partial^2 \alpha}{\partial t^2} + h\frac{\partial \alpha}{\partial t}. \tag{G-78}$$

The coefficients g and h again determine the wave number as in Eqs. *G-75* and *G-76*. For sinusoidal waves,

$$\nabla^2 \alpha = (-g\omega^2 + j\omega h)\alpha, \tag{G-79}$$

or

$$\nabla^2 \alpha + k^2 \alpha = 0, \tag{G-80}$$

where k is the wave number. We have omitted the primes which were used previously to identify the attenuated wave.

If there is no attenuation, $h = 0$, $g = 1/u^2$, and

$$\nabla^2 \alpha = \frac{1}{u^2}\frac{\partial^2 \alpha}{\partial t^2} \tag{G-81}$$

for any waveform, u being the phase velocity.

G.8. *Wave Propagation of a Vector Quantity*

As yet, we have only considered waves in which the quantity which is propagated is a scalar. Vector quantities, such as an electric field intensity $\mathbf{E}$, for example, can also propagate as a wave, and then, for a plane wave propagating in the positive direction of the z-axis,

$$\mathbf{E} = \mathbf{E}_o e^{j(\omega t - kz)}. \tag{G-82}$$

Since $\mathbf{E}_o$ is a vector, we may write that

$$\mathbf{E} = (E_{ox}\mathbf{i} + E_{oy}\mathbf{j} + E_{oz}\mathbf{k})e^{j(\omega t - kz)}, \tag{G-83}$$

where E_{ox}, E_{oy}, and E_{oz} are the components of $\mathbf{E}_o$. These components may conceivably depend on x and on y, but they do *not* depend on z, because a plane sinusoidal wave is characterized by the dependence on t and on z, which is shown in the exponential function.

INDEX

549